MOLECULAR LUMINESCENCE

An International Conference

E. C. LIM
Wayne State University

W. A. BENJAMIN, INC.

New York 1969 Amsterdam

MOLECULAR LUMINESCENCE

An International Conference

Library of Congress Catalog Card Number 68-59232
Manufactured in the United States of America
12345Q32109

*The manuscript was put into production on November 11, 1968;
this volume was published on February 1, 1969*

**W. A. BENJAMIN, INC.
New York, New York 10016**

ORGANIZING COMMITTEE

A. C. Albrecht, Cornell University, Ithaca, N.Y.
F. Dörr, Technische Hochschule, Munich, Germany
M. A. El-Sayed, University of California, Los Angeles, California
Th. Förster, Technische Hochschule, Stuttgart, Germany
R. M. Hochstrasser, University of Pennsylvania, Philadelphia, Pennsylvania
Y. Kanda, Kyushu University, Fukuoka, Japan
E. C. Lim, Loyola University, Chicago, Illinois
D. S. McClure, Princeton University, Princeton, New Jersey
S. P. McGlynn, Louisiana State University, Baton Rouge, Louisiana
G. W. Robinson, California Institute of Technology, Pasadena, California
I. G. Ross, Australian National University, Canberra A.C.T., Australia
A. Weller, Max-Planck-Institut für Spektroskopie, Göttingen, Germany

CHAIRMAN OF SCIENTIFIC SESSIONS

L. Augenstein, Michigan State University, East Lansing, Michigan
E. A. Chandross, Bell Telephone Laboratories, Murray Hill, New Jersey
G. A. Crosby, Washington State University, Pullman, Washington
M. A. El-Sayed, University of California, Los Angeles, California
L. Goodman, Rutgers University, New Brunswick, New Jersey
R. M. Hochstrasser, University of Pennsylvania, Philadelphia, Pennsylvania
Y. Kanda, Kyushu University, Fukuoka, Japan
R. A. Keller, National Bureau of Standards, Washington, D.C.
R. E. Kellogg, E. I. du Pont de Nemours & Co., Wilmington, Delaware
S. P. McGlynn, Louisiana State University, Baton Rouge, Louisiana
S. Nagakura, University of Tokyo, Tokyo, Japan
I. G. Ross, Australian National University, Canberra A.C.T., Australia
B. Stevens, University of South Florida, Tampa, Florida
A. Weller, Max-Planck-Institut für Spektroskopie, Göttingen, Germany
M. W. Windsor, TRW Systems, Redondo Beach, California

CONFERENCE SECRETARIES

Doris McCutchen
Anne Mariella

A Note from the Publisher

This volume was printed directly from a typescript prepared by the author, who takes full responsibility for its content and appearance. The Publisher has not performed his usual functions of reviewing, editing, typesetting, and proofreading the material prior to publication.

The Publisher fully endorses this informal and quick method of publishing lecture notes at a moderate price, and he wishes to thank the author for preparing the material for publication.

PREFACE

The International Conference on Molecular Luminescence was held at Loyola University (Chicago) during August 20-23, 1968. The conference consisted of 64 contributed papers, devoted to various areas of current interest in luminescence and radiationless transitions in molecular systems. All but four of these papers are incorporated in the proceedings.

The basic financial support for the conference was provided by Loyola University, with additional contributions from American Instrument Company and Eastman Kodak Company.

The advice and encouragement of members of the organizing committee and the valuable service of the chairmen of scientific sessions are very gratefully acknowledged.

Thanks are due to Dr. and Mrs. Raymond Mariella, Messrs. John Borgard, Paul Frakes, Richard Maday, Peter Vaccarella, and Mrs. Peggy Skinner, all of Loyola University, for their various assistance during the conference.

Thanks are also due to members of my research group, Messrs. Charles Lazzara, Raymond Li, John Stanislaus, Mrs. Raymond Li, Drs. Asish Chandra and Yoshiya Kanda for their help prior to, during, and subsequent to the conference, and graduate students in the chemistry department, Messrs. Mark Meister, Lee Nylander, and John Vanderberg, for their help during the conference.

Finally, I wish to thank the conference secretaries, Misses Doris McCutchen and Anne Mariella, for attending to the numerous details of the conference. Miss Mariella's service in the preparation of the proceedings has been indispensable.

Chicago, Illinois
November 1968

E. C. Lim
Conference Chairman
and Editor

TABLE OF CONTENTS

EFFECTS OF HIGH PRESSURES ON THE PHOSPHORESCENCE OF AROMATIC HYDROCARBONS AT 77°K*

Henry W. Offen and David E. Hein

Department of Chemistry
University of California
Santa Barbara, California 93106

INTRODUCTION

The combination of optical spectroscopy and high pressure technology has recently gained attention in the study of molecular interactions. Drickamer[1] is credited with extending our knowledge of the electronic properties of solids to ultrahigh pressures. This achievement in high-pressure research was possible through his novel design of an optical cell.[2] We have recently adapted his basic design for spectroscopic studies at liquid nitrogen temperatures.[3] From the viewpoint of molecular electronic spectroscopy there are obvious advantages in low temperature studies. For example, the present pressure work on phosphorescence in EPA

---

*This work was supported in part by the U. S. Office of Naval Research.

solutions would not have commenced without low-temperature capabilities.

The role of the environment in modifying electronic structure and processes may be dominant and specific or very weak. The problem of environmental effects continues to be of interest because quantitative information is frequently elusive, yet an understanding of environmental influences is prerequisite for the application of many theoretical models in electronic spectroscopy, be these explanations for quasiline spectra in frozen paraffins or radiationless transitions from electronically excited molecules. We anticipate that the pressure parameter is a major candidate for elucidating intermolecular interactions in the 0-40 kbar interval. By orientation, the compression energy per atom in this pressure range, as estimated from the isothermal equation of state, is less than 80 cm^{-1} which is appreciable in comparison to the cohesive energy in molecular crystals or solutions, but sufficiently small compared to intramolecular energies of organic solute molecules. Hence, we may treat the intermolecular forces at high pressures as perturbations of the electronic structure of the solute, particularly when excited states of the solvent are much higher than for the solute under study. The difference in interaction energy between two electronic states and the appropriate solvent cage generally determines the influence of compression on optical spectra and lifetimes.

This work illustrates the influence of high pressures on phosphorescence spectra and triplet lifetimes of aromatic molecules. Such studies have been carried out in boric acid glass[4] and in polymer matrices[5-8] at room temperature. Since the environment in plastics at 298°K is ill-defined and unknown processes may contribute to the observed effects, it is desirable to make pressure measurements in EPA rigid glass, which is a common solvent in molecular electronic spectroscopy. The results communicated here for three naphthalene compounds, illustrating isotopic and heavy-atom substitution, do not contradict general conclusions drawn from studies in degassed polymer matrices at 298°K.[7,8]

EXPERIMENTAL

The high pressure optical cell and pressure calibration has been described.[9] Radiation from a PEK 100 w Hg lamp passes through water and Corning no. 7-54 and no. 0-53 filters and falls on the cylindrical sample chamber consisting of sodium chloride. The phosphorescence spectra are observed at right angles after passing through out-of-phase choppers, driven by paired synchros.[10] The optical system consists of a Jarrell-Ash 0.5 m spectrometer and a 1P21 photomultiplier tube. For triplet lifetimes the photomultiplier detector was exposed to the total phosphorescence intensity in the absence of the excitation beam. The dynamic intensity changes were displayed on the Tektronix Model 561A oscilloscope and photographed.

The compounds naphthalene (Aldrich, zone-refined) and naphthalene-d_8 (Merck, Sharpe and Dohme) were used as purchased. 2-bromonaphthalene (Eastman Kodak) was recrystallized from ethanol and twice sublimed. Solutions ($\sim 5 \times 10^{-3}$ M) of EPA (Matheson, Coleman and Bell) and solute were bubbled with N_2 gas prior to filling the sample chamber of the optical cell. The rigid glass at 77°K changed its transmittance of visible and ultraviolet light considerably at high pressures so that quantitative information on phosphorescence intensities was not obtained. The spectra are slowly scanned in the sequence 0 kbar (before <u>any</u> pressure application), 10, 20, 30 and 0 kbar. Lifetime measurements were made at 5 kbar intervals. Since the steel disks stretched appreciably above 30 kbar, only one pressure cycle could be applied when 40 kbar measurements of triplet lifetimes were made.

PHOSPHORESCENCE SPECTRA

The 1 atm and 30 kbar phosphorescence spectra of naphthalene-d_8 and 2-bromonaphthalene in EPA at 77°K are illustrated in Figs. (1) and (2). The pressure response of $C_{10}D_8$ and $C_{10}H_8$ is identical as far as phosphorescence spectral effects are concerned in this rigid matrix. The raw data taken from the spectrograms of $C_{10}H_8$ and $C_{10}D_8$ at different pressures is presented graphically in Fig. (3). First of all, a monotonic band red shift, similar for both molecules, is induced by high pressures. The red shift of 225 $\pm$ 25 cm^{-1} at 30 kbar corresponds to a 7.5 cm^{-1}/kbar decrease in the triplet-singlet energy gap. The spectral shift of the phosphorescence of 2-bromonaphthalene is uncertain, because the rich vibronic structure[11] at 1 atm is transformed into broad symmetrically-shaped bands by matrix compression (Fig. (2)). The position of the center of gravity of the first group of satellite bands near 484 nm remains unaffected by increasing pressures. The 1 atm 0-0 band of $C_{10}H_7Br$ is located 270 cm^{-1} below that of $C_{10}D_8$ which is indicative of stronger electrostatic interactions between solvent and polar solute. An undesirable feature is irreversible modifications in the solute spectra after the sample pressure is released. The changes in the spectra are in the same direction as those produced by matrix compression. This is indicated in Fig. (3) by the entry of two points at atmospheric pressure. Thus the bands are found 20-50 cm^{-1} lower in energy after one pressure cycle. This is presumably due to microscopic structural changes in the rigid glass, although experimental factors such as residual pressure due to friction may also contribute to the observed effects.

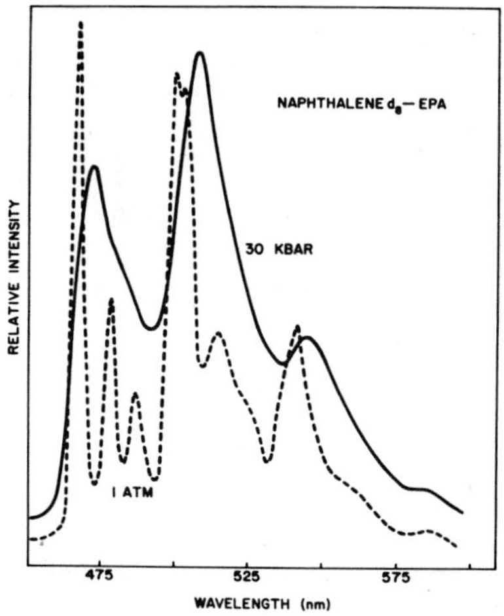

Figure 1 Phosphorescence spectra of naphthalene-d_8 in EPA at 77°K. The slitwidths are 400μ and 220μ for the 1 atm and 30 kbar spectra respectively.

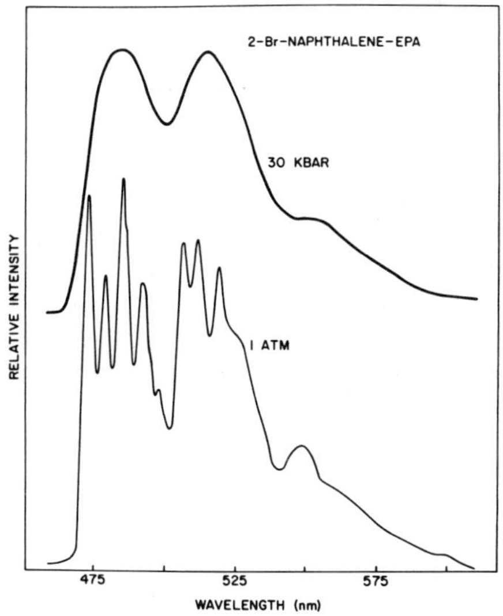

Figure 2 Phosphorescence spectra of 2-bromonaphthalene in EPA at 77°K. The slitwidths are 400μ and 150μ for the 1 atm and 30 kbar spectra, respectively.

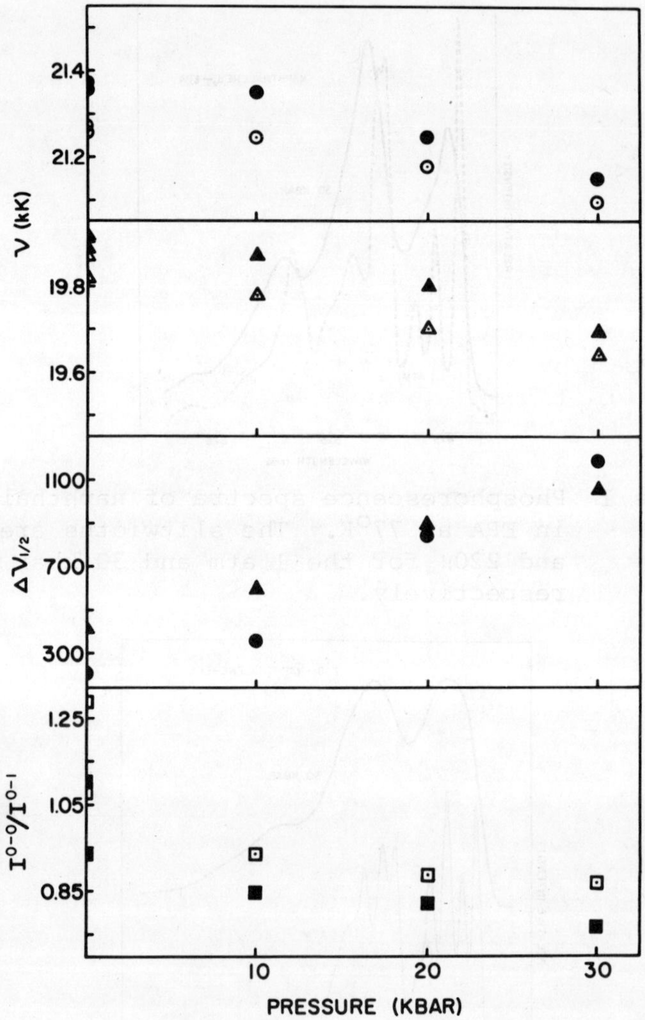

Figure 3 Phosphorescence band location (1000 cm^{-1}), bandwidth (cm^{-1}) and peak intensity ratios as a function of pressure. The compounds $C_{10}H_8$ and $C_{10}D_8$ are identified by open and solid symbols, respectively. The circles refer to the 0-0 band and the triangles to the 0-1 band. Square symbols are used for the intensity ratios of the 0-0 band relative to the 0-1 band.

In contrast to the small pressure-induced red shift, the bandwidth $\Delta\nu_{\frac{1}{2}}$ is greatly influenced by pressure. Figs. (1) and (2) demonstrate that compression enhances the background continuum and has a "smearing-out" effect on vibronic structure. The 30 kbar spectra of all three compounds show two major peaks separated by about 1400 cm^{-1} which probably corresponds to a totally symmetric C-C stretch vibration of the molecule.[12] The experimentally observed increase in the width at half-height is shown in Fig. (3) for $C_{10}D_8$ (identical for $C_{10}H_8$). The bands remaining at 30 kbar are conveniently labeled as the 0-0 and 0-1 bands, where the latter band refers to the assumed excitation of one quantum of the 1400 cm^{-1} skeleton breathing motion. The three-fold increase in $\Delta\nu_{\frac{1}{2}}$ in the 0-30 kbar interval results in spectra which are similar to those observed at 1 atm in degassed plastic media. Pressure broadening leads to similar bandwidths at 30 kbar but to an asymmetric band shape for $C_{10}H_8$ and $C_{10}D_8$ in contrast to a symmetric band shape for the bromo-substituted naphthalene. Irreversible pressure effects yield bands which are 10-20% broader after one compression to 30 kbar. Another sensitive index of microscopic matrix changes is the relative peak heights of the 0-0 and 0-1 bands, plotted as ratios in Fig. (3). Band broadening and possible intensity redistribution have considerably reduced the 0-0 band intensity after one pressure cycle. It should be remembered that the pressure data graphed in Fig. (3) are necessarily qualitative in nature.

Two factors may contribute to band broadening. One explanation considers a distribution of sites, each with different solute-solvent interactions. The fact that triplet decays remain exponential within 4% but change under pressure suggests that the spread in environmental interactions is rather narrow, unless the factors responsible for bandwidth and lifetime are very different. The other hypothesis invokes identical but strongly pressure-dependent and anisotropic force fields at each site. The triplet state, equilibrated in its solvent cage, may have a slightly different geometry than in the ground state so that the emission process would be very sensitive to environmentally-induced distortions and cause simultaneous excitation of low-frequency vibrations in the ground state of the solute molecule. As the size of the solvent shell is reduced by matrix compression vibrational coupling with "lattice phonons" and intramolecular vibrations in the solvent molecules becomes more probable and contributes to the background continuum in the spectra. Though the exact causes of band broadening are unknown, these experiments define the magnitude of the pressure effects in a polar glass.

TRIPLET DECAY

While the pressure-induced spectral effects are very similar for the three naphthalene compounds, this is not true for the kinetics of triplet depopulation at high pressures. The first observation is that the measured phosphorescence lifetimes τ_p remain exponential and shorten under increasing pressures. This is consistent with previous measurements at room temperature in polymer matrices.[5,7,8] Secondly, the quantity ln τ_p demonstrates a reasonably linear dependence on pressure, as illustrated in Fig. (4) for $C_{10}D_8$ and $C_{10}H_7Br$. Although the graph illustrates the results for only one pressure cycle, the same slope (within 20%) is found in repetitive pressure cycles up to 30 kbar. Thirdly, the longer the initial (1 atm) lifetimes $\tau_p(0)$ the faster the electronic relaxation under matrix compression. Finally, irreversible matrix effects after compression are observed in the phosphorescence lifetimes. The original lifetime, which shortens for $C_{10}D_8$ about 10% after one pressure cycle but then remains unaffected by

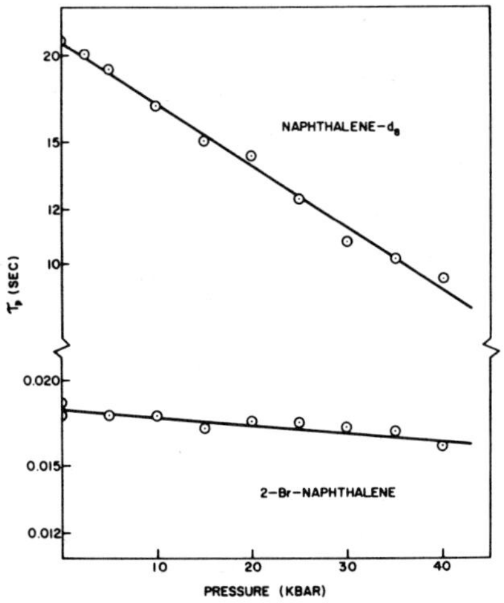

Figure 4 Phosphorescence lifetimes τ_p of naphthalene-d_8 and 2-bromonaphthalene in EPA at 77°K as a function of increasing pressure in one pressure cycle.

TABLE I: Phosphorescence Lifetimes (sec) and Activation Volumes at 77°K

	$\tau_p(0)$ [a]	$\tau_p(30)$ [b]	$-\Delta V$ [c]
Naphthalene-d_8	20.5	10.5	0.22
Naphthalene	2.48	1.75	0.10
2-Bromonaphthalene	0.018	0.016	0.03

[a] Phosphorescence lifetimes at 1 atm before pressure treatment.
[b] Phosphorescence lifetimes at 30 kbar.
[c] Units of $Å^3$/molecule.

further pressure treatment, is restored by melting the EPA glass and subsequent refreezing. Although the triplet decay is exponential over two lifetimes within 4%, the measured lifetime at a given isobar may on occasion differ by as much as 15% from one run to another. These matrix relaxation effects contribute to the uncertainties in lifetime measurements, but they are not sufficient to distract from the different trends in the pressure effects on these three related compounds.

It is customary in kinetic processes to treat macroscopic pressure phenomena in terms of activation volumes $\Delta V^{\dagger}$.[13,14,15] The expression for triplet decay in this terminology is

$$d\ln\tau_p/dP = \Delta V^{\dagger}/RT \quad (1)$$

where P is the pressure, T is the temperature, and R is the ideal gas constant. The use of this equation does not necessarily imply the existence or nature of an "activated transition state," instead we prefer to consider Eq. (1) as a convenient expression for comparing the relative sensitivity of various solute molecules to matrix compression. It is seen from Table I that the "activation volumes" differ considerably for the three related compounds. The $\Delta V^{\dagger}$ values are negative and show that the rate of triplet decay is enhanced at 30 kbar by 10-50%, depending upon the substituents on the naphthalene ring.

The order of magnitude of the density or volume effect on lifetimes of electronically excited molecules may be predicted within the context of this macroscopic description. Eq. (1) can be written in terms of the isothermal compressibility ρ to read

$$\Delta V^{*} = -RT\rho d\ln\tau_p/d\ln V \quad (2)$$

It has been found convenient to account for medium effects in radiative transition rates in terms of the refractive index n.[16] If the same "correction" factor n^2 is assumed for radiationless transitions, then $\tau_p \alpha n^{-2}$, and Eq. (2) becomes

$$\Delta V^{\dagger} = RT\rho\, d\ln n^2/d\ln V. \quad (3)$$

If the thermodynamic properties of EPA rigid glass were known at 77°K, the applicability of this equation could be more closely checked. The pressure dependence of the dielectric constant ε of liquid ethanol has been measured to give $d\ln\varepsilon/d\ln V = -1$.[14,17] If the same relation were true at optical frequencies ($\varepsilon = n^2$) and in frozen EPA solvent, then $d\ln n^2/d\ln V = -1$. This latter relation predicts $\tau_p \alpha V$, i.e. the fractional change in volume and lifetime are equal. Bridgman[18] has measured the compressibilities of the liquid solvents isopentane, ether and ethanol to be, respectively, 17, 12 and 10 $Mbar^{-1}$ (1 $Mbar^{-1} = 10^{-6}$ bar^{-1}) near 6 kbar. If we assume that the frozen solvent mixture at 77°K has a compressibility one-half as large as the least compressible component, then Eq. (3) predicts $\Delta V^{\dagger} = -0.05$ Å^3/molecule at liquid nitrogen temperatures.

Bulk properties such as compressibilities and refractive index can predict order of magnitude effects but cannot explain the significant differences in $\Delta V^{\dagger}$ among the three compounds listed in Table I. Such explanations must be sought on the molecular level. For example, a simple n^2 dependence of radiationless rates would not be expected to be applicable to deuterated naphthalene, where factors other than electronic matrix elements are important in determining the rate of electronic relaxation. It is reasonable to assume that solute aggregation, intermolecular energy transfer, triplet-triplet absorption, and other reversible photochemical processes are absent under the present experimental conditions. Therefore $\tau_p^{-1} = k_p + k'_p$ and only intramolecular radiative (k_p)

and radiationless (k'_p) intersystem crossing transitions can be influenced by matrix compression. Unfortunately there remain uncertainties about the relative and absolute magnitude of k_p and k'_p, but the probable situation at 77°K is that k_p is equal for $C_{10}H_8$ and $C_{10}D_8$[19] and that $k_p \geq k'_p$ in $C_{10}D_8$ and $k_p < k'_p$ in $C_{10}H_8$. The great difference in k'_p of isotopically substituted aromatic hydrocarbons is mainly attributed to the Franck-Condon factor F.[20,21] On the basis of this assumption and the results in Table I it is concluded that the vibrational overlap F is enhanced by at least 50% in deuterated naphthalene. The smaller "pressure catalysis" of bromonaphthalene is probably related to the 100-fold increase in spin-orbit coupling, which makes the intramolecular processes less sensitive to environmental changes.

These experiments on three naphthalene compounds in EPA have demonstrated that (1) the triplet energy is lowered by ∿1% under 30 kbar matrix compression; (2) the vibronic band structure in phosphorescence spectra is merged into broad bands under pressure, independent of isotopic and heavy-atom substitution; and (3) pressure selectively enhances electronic relaxation by 10-50% at 30 kbar. The magnitude of the pressure effects which has been established for this class of compounds should serve as useful tests for molecular theories involving environmental interactions and electronic relaxation. Further work on temperature and pressure effects of other types of molecules and matrices may modify or further clarify the present attitudes.

REFERENCES

1. For example: H. G. Drickamer, Solid State Physics 17, 1 (1965).
2. R. A. Fitch, T. E Slykhouse, and H. G. Drickamer, J. Opt. Soc. Am. 47, 1015 (1957).
3. H. W. Offen, R. L. Tanquary and K. F. Sterrett, J. Appl. Phys. 38, 5245 (1967).
4. D. W. Gregg and H. G. Drickamer, J. Chem. Phys. 35, 1780 (1961).
5. H. W. Offen and B. A. Baldwin, J. Chem. Phys. 44, 3642 (1966).
6. M. F. Nicol, J. Chem. Phys. 45, 4753 (1966).
7. B. A. Baldwin and H W. Offen, J. Chem. Phys. 46, 4509 (1967).
8. B. A. Baldwin and H. W. Offen, J. Chem. Phys. 48, 000 (1968).
9. H. W. Offen, R. L. Tanquary and K. F Sterrett, J. Appl. Phys. 38, 5245 (1967).
10. B. A. Baldwin and H. W. Offen, Rev. Sci. Instr. 38, 1164 (1967).
11. T. Pavlopoulos and M. A. El-Sayed, J. Chem. Phys. 41, 1082 (1964).
12. D. S. McClure, J. Chem. Phys. 19, 670 (1951).
13. E. Whalley, Ann. Rev. Phys. Chem. 18, 205 (1967).
14. E. Whalley, Advances in High Pressure Research, R. S. Bradley, Ed. (Academic Press, New York, 1966), Vol. I.
15. R. W. Keyes, in Progress in Very High Pressure Research, F. B. Bundy, W. R. Hibbard, Jr. and H. M. Strong, Eds. (Wiley and Sons, New York, 1961).
16. S. J. Strickler and R. A. Berg, J. Chem. Phys. 37, 814 (1962).
17. I. S. Jacobs and A. W. Lawson, J. Chem. Phys. 20 1164 (1952).
18. P. W. Bridgman, Proc. Am. Acad. Arts Sci. 66, 185 (1931); ibid. 49, 3 (1913); Proc. Phys. Soc. (London), 41, 341 (1929).

19. E. C. Lim and J. D. Laposa, J. Chem. Phys. 41, 3257 (1964); M. S. de Groot and J. H. van der Waals, Molecular Phys. 4, 189 (1961).
20. W. Siebrand and D. F. Williams, J. Chem. Phys. 46, 403 (1967).
21. W. Siebrand, J. Chem. Phys. 47, 2411 (1967); ibid. 46, 440 (1967).

TEMPERATURE EFFECTS ON THE PHOSPHORESCENCE OF AROMATIC HYDROCARBONS IN PLASTICS

Peter F. Jones and Seymour Siegel

Aerospace Corporation
El Segundo
California

Recently we observed that the effect of temperature on the lifetime τ of deuterated naphthalene was considerably smaller than previously reported[1] and that the magnitude of the effect was dependent upon the conditions of sample preparation. Because of the theoretical significance of the nature of the effect of temperature on intramolecular decay processes, we undertook a study to determine the limiting values of the phosphorescence lifetimes at room temperature of several aromatic hydrocarbons and their perdeuterated analogs using poly(methyl methacrylate) as a rigid solvent matrix. In addition, we measured the temperature variations in the phosphorescence spectra and the product of the quantum yield for intersystem crossing Φ_{isc} and the rate constant for radiative decay of the triplet state k_r.

These studies included benzophenone, naphthalene, phenanthrene, biphenyl, pyrene, and the perdeuterated analogs of the last four molecules. Phosphorescence spectra were recorded at room temperature and $77^{\circ}K$ and were corrected for instrumental response. All measurements of the temperature dependence of phosphorescence intensities were corrected for the structural changes in the spectra. For all of the molecules the phosphorescence spectra sharpen and shift to the blue ~ 150 to $200\ cm^{-1}$ upon cooling.

For thoroughly degassed samples and in the absence of photochemical reactions, the phosphorescence lifetimes of those molecules whose lowest triplet states are π,π^* type decrease by only 13 to 37 per cent upon warming from 4° to $300^{\circ}K$. Stern-Volmer plots for oxygen quenching of the phosphorescence verify that residual oxygen is not responsible for the observed temperature effects. Even after the oxygen is removed the lifetimes gradually increase to the limiting values with thermal annealing <u>in vacuo</u>. The latter results substantiate that variations in the solvent cage can modify the rate of decay of a solute triplet state. The temperature variations in τ are somewhat larger for the perprotonated molecules than for their perdeuterated analogs, which suggests that changes in the rate constant for non-radiative decay k_{nr} are responsible for the temperature dependence of τ.

Variations in the product of k_r and Φ_{isc} were evaluated by simultaneous measurements of temperature variations of the phosphorescence intensity I and the triplet state lifetime. Of the molecules studied, only pyrene $-h_{10}$ and pyrene $-d_{10}$ exhibit a temperature variation in $(k_r\Phi_{isc})$ larger than experimental uncertainty ($\pm$ 20%). For pyrene $-h_{10}$ and pyrene $-d_{10}$, $(k_r\Phi_{isc})_{300^{\circ}K}/(k_r\Phi_{isc})_{77^{\circ}K} = 2.8 \pm 0.2$ and 4.7 ± 0.3, respectively. For pyrene $-d_{10}$, temperature variations in k_r and Φ_{isc} were evaluated separately by simultaneous measurements of I, τ, and the intensity of the EPR signal E. Relative changes in E/τ give the temperature dependence of Φ_{isc}, and relative changes in I/E give the temperature dependence of k_r. From the EPR experiments we find $(k_r)300^oK/(k_r)77^oK = 0.9 \pm 0.2$ and $(\Phi_{isc})300^oK/(\Phi_{isc})77^oK = 4.9 \pm 0.9$. Thus, the large temperature variation in $(k_r\Phi_{isc})$ for pyrene is entirely due to temperature variations in Φ_{isc}. These results agree with the observations of others[2,3] that there is a thermally activated process for intersystem crossing in pyrene.

Making use of our measurements[4] of the temperature dependence of the fluorescence lifetimes of pyrene $-h_{10}$ and pyrene $-d_{10}$, we find that at room temperature there are two different routes for intersystem crossing from the lowest excited singlet state S_1 to the lowest triplet state T_o. In addition to a thermally activated transition from S_1 to the first excited triplet state T_1 intersystem crossing occurs directly from S_1 to T_o. At 77^oK only the direct transition $T_o \leftarrow S_1$ occurs. We also find that the rate constant for the $T_o \leftarrow S_1$ transition exhibits a deuterium effect (factor of ~ 2.4) similar to that observed for the $S_o \leftarrow T_o$ nonradiative transition.

Although we cannot completely exclude the possibility that the rate constants for both radiative and non-radiative decay vary with temperature, we find that our results are consistent with an analysis that assumes that only the non-radiative rate constant is temperature-dependent. Expressing the temperature dependence of τ as

$$\frac{\tau(77^oK)}{\tau\ (T)} = 1 + A(1 - \Phi_p)\exp(-\Delta E/kT) \qquad (1)$$

where $\Phi_p = k_r/(k_r + k_{nr})$ at 77^oK, we estimate an activation energy of $\Delta E = 500 \pm 200\ cm^{-1}$ for the thermally activated nonradiative decay mode of the lowest π,π^* triplet states.

Temperature effects on the phosphorescence of benzophenone differ in many ways from those on the π,π^* phosphorescences. Upon warming from 77° to 300°K, the phosphorescence lifetime decreases by approximately a factor of three, while the intensity decreases by a factor of ten. Since Φ_{isc} is independent of temperature,[5,6] k_r must be decreasing[7] by a factor of 3.3. Based upon the reported quantum yield of benzophenone phosphorescence at 77°K(0.74)[8,9] we find that k_{nr} increases by approximately a factor of ten[7] over this temperature range. From our results alone it is not possible to evaluate the relative importance of bimolecular photochemical reactions and intramolecular decay in determining the temperature dependence of k_{nr} for benzophenone. The fact that the temperature variation in k_r observed for benzophenone is larger than that observed for the aromatic hydrocarbons may be related to the n,π^* character of the benzophenone triplet state; however, Ladner and Becker[10] have reported similar effects for the decay of the π,π^* ground triplet state of p-phenylbenzophenone. At first thought it might seem surprising that k_r should decrease (rather than increase) with increasing temperature, however, these results can be rationalized in terms of the rigid low-temperature matrix affecting the benzophenone molecular symmetry. Although it is generally assumed that k_r is independent of temperature, we know of no convincing evidence for this assumption. On the contrary, it is well documented[11,12] that the spin-forbidden triplet-singlet radiative transition is extremely sensitive to subtle perturbations.

REFERENCES

1. R. E. Kellogg and R. P. Schwenker, J. Chem. Phys. 41, 2860 (1964).
2. B. Stevens, M. F. Thomaz, and J. Jones, J. Chem. Phys. 46, 405 (1967).
3. J. B. Birks and T. A. King, Proc. Roy. Soc. 291A, 244 (1966).
4. P. F. Jones and S. Siegel, submitted to Chem. Phys. Letters.
5. A. A. Lamola and G. S. Hammond, J. Chem. Phys., 43, 2129 (1965).
6. R. Borkman and D. R. Kearns, Chem. Commun., 14, 446 (1966).
7. Melhuish, Trans. Far. Soc. 62, 3384 (1966), has obtained similar results for benzophenone in PMM by a slightly different method.
8. E. H. Gilmore, G. E. Gibson, and D. S. McClure, J. Chem. Phys. 20, 829 (1952); ibid., 23, 399 (1955).
9. V. L. Ermolaev, Usp. Fiz. Nauk, 80, 3 (1963); English translation, Soviet Phys.-Usp. 17, 333 (1963).
10. S. J. Ladner and R. S. Becker, J. Chem. Phys. 43, 3344 (1965).
11. M. A. El-Sayed, Accounts Chem. Res. 1, 8 (1968).
12. G. W. Robinson, J. Chem. Phys. 46, 572 (1967).

ENVIRONMENTAL EFFECTS ON PHOSPHORESCENT LIFETIMES

G. F. Hatch, M. D. Erlitz and G. C. Nieman

Department of Chemistry
University of Rochester
Rochester, New York 14627

INTRODUCTION

Both radiative and non-radiative processes contribute to the decay of the lowest triplet state of aromatic molecules. If the possibility of perturbations due to heavy atoms or paramagnetic species (e.g., oxygen) is excluded, the radiative probabilities are relatively independent of environment and even of molecular species. The situation with regard to non-radiative transitions is less easily defined since both intramolecular and intermolecular pathways may contribute to the decay processes.

This paper deals with environmental effects on non-radiative transitions which are primarily intramolecular in nature. These transitions are commonly believed to arise from a breakdown of the Born-Oppenheimer approximation and the resultant coupling of the triplet state with vibrational levels in the ground singlet state.[1-3] The role of the solvent in such a picture is to add to the quasicontinuum of states needed to satisfy energy resonance conditions. The solvent also acts as an energy sink for the rapid vibrational relaxation which occurs after the rate limiting transition from the initial state. The effects of the environment on such transitions are expected to be small. In particular, only small temperature effects are expected and these should only become pronounced above room temperature.[2]

Experimentally, careful attention must be given to the possibility of intermolecular non-radiative transitions. When the solvent has thermally accessible triplet levels energy transfer may occur via the host to impurity quenching sites or to other triplets with which annihilation takes place.[4-6] These effects are particularly pronounced in the phosphorescence of "pure" crystals where the observed emission usually comes from shallow impurity traps.[7] Non-radiative transitions may also result from a direct interaction with impurities or other triplets which may be present in the solvent. This is also the case in viscous solutions, such as glycerol, in which temperature effects on the first-order decay rate are believed to be primarily due to the diffusion of oxygen.[8]

When intermolecular decay routes have been eliminated, phosphorescent lifetimes have usually been found to be independent of other environmental changes. For example, naphthalene, which is probably the most thoroughly studied of all aromatic compounds, shows only small lifetime variations (in most cases less than 20%) as a function of solvent if heavy atom solvents are excluded.[9] Also, in plastic matrices the phosphorescent lifetime of naphthalene is found to decrease by a factor of about 2 in going from 77°K to room temperature.[10] In going to higher temperatures a large decrease in lifetime is observed but this is believed to arise from the diffusion of impurities. Naphthalene dissolved in durene shows a temperature dependent lifetime,[11] but it has been suggested that this is due to energy transfer[12] and/or impurity levels associated with durene.[2]

Benzene has been cited as an anomalous case which shows large environmental effects. The initial evidence for this claim is the observation by Robinson[13] of longer lifetimes for benzene in argon and in methane at 4.2°K than were observed by McClure[14] in EPA at 77°K. Although Robinson initially explained these observations in terms of the absence of low frequency solvent vibrations, it has since been thought that these data represent evidence for a large temperature effect.[2] Temperature effects have also been reported by de Groot and van der Waals.[15] They observed a decrease in the ESR signal decay times in going from 20°K to 77°K for perdeuterobenzene and for perdeuterotoluene in a glassy matrix of cyclohexane and decalin.

The work reported here is an initial study of some benzene derivatives in a variety of crystalline matrices as a function of temperature. Large temperature effects are observed for most systems in addition to large solvent effects. Both the temperature and the solvent effects are strongly dependent on the solute species and its deuteration.

EXPERIMENTAL

Solutions for these studies were approximately 0.1% by weight ($\sim 10^{-2}$ M). Most of the solutions were prepared by mixing the appropriate amounts of the solvent and solute vapors in a greaseless vacuum system followed by condensing the mixtures into quartz sample cells ($\sim$0.2 mm thick) which were sealed off. Eastman Kodak spectrograde cyclohexane and the isotopic benzenes were stored over a liquid sodium-potassium alloy in the same vacuum system. This treatment served to remove most traces of impurities, especially oxygen. Borazine and its derivatives were prepared in our laboratory in solvent-free reactions.[16]

By controlling the rate of cooling of the cyclohexane samples, either of the two low temperature phases could be produced essentially free of the other phase.[17] The low temperature stable (monoclinic) phase was used most often because of its relative ease of preparation and the greater transparency of the crystals. The pure metastable (cubic) phase could be prepared only by cooling thin samples at a rate faster than that provided by direct immersion into liquid nitrogen at 77°K, and even then several attempts were often necessary before an adequate crystal could be prepared.

Phosphorescence decay curves were obtained from photographs of oscilloscope traces of the output of a 1P28 photomultiplier. Values of the decay rate, k, were obtained by applying a least square fit to 21 points measured from each photograph covering an intensity drop of a factor of 10-30. Most of the decays were quite exponential when a monochromator with a bandwidth of 5 cm^{-1} was used. Glass filters with a bandwidth as large as 5000 cm^{-1} sometimes gave slightly distorted curves, especially in the visible spectral regions, but the calculated k's were essentially independent of bandwidth. Those cases where non-exponential decays were observed will be discussed below. The measured rates were found to be independent of the exciting light intensity, the solute concentration (below 1%), and the temperature and light exposure history of the sample. The steady-state phosphorescence intensity was somewhat a function of the sample history with solutes such as toluene.

RESULTS

BENZENES. An Arrhenius plot of the observed rate constant for phosphorescent decay, k, is given in Figure 1 for C_6H_6 and C_6D_6 dissolved in

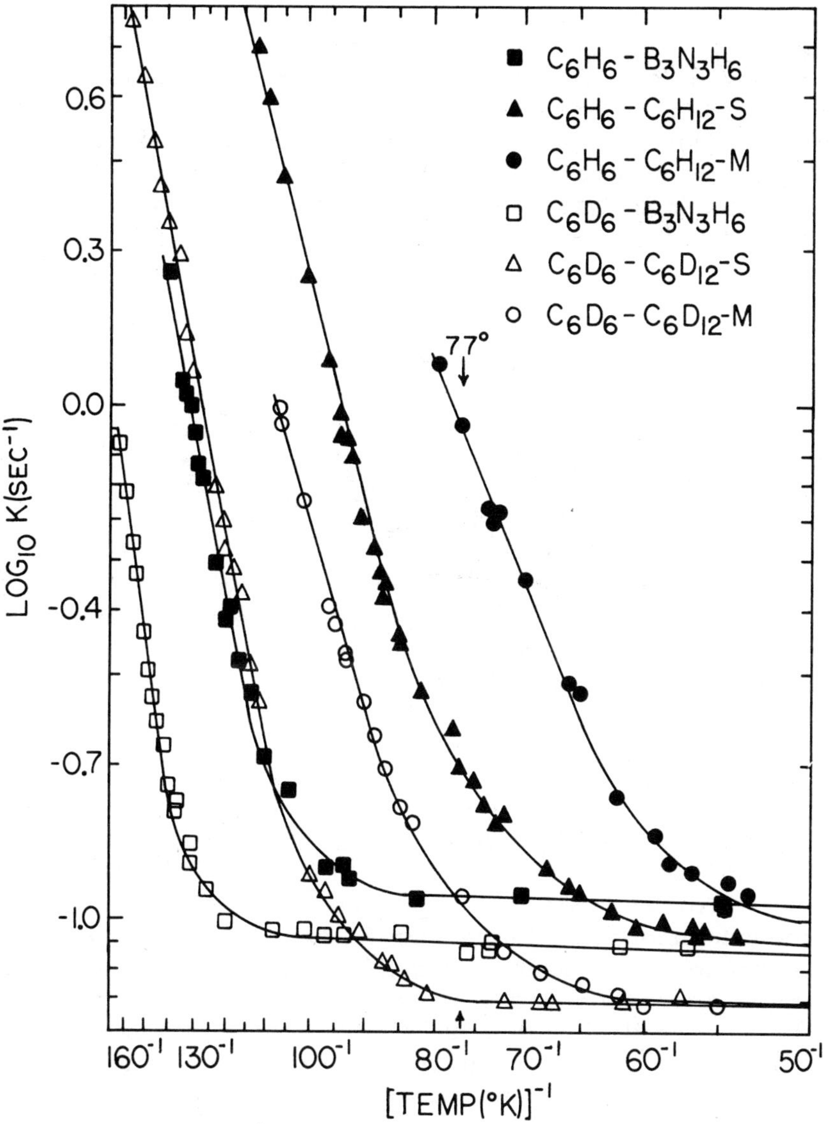

Figure 1 Logarithm of the observed phosphorescent decay rate vs the reciprocal temperature for benzene. $B_3N_3H_6$ is borazine; C_6H_{12}-S and C_6H_{12}-M are respectively the stable and metastable phases of cyclohexane; and $k = 1/\tau_{obs}$.

borazine and the stable (S) and metastable (M) phases of cyclohexane. The following should be noted.

(1) For a given solvent the perdeuterobenzene lifetime (reciprocal of the observed decay rate constant) is greater than the perprotobenzene lifetime as expected, but the ratio of these lifetimes is a function of both solvent and temperature.

(2) In many cases the lifetime at 77°K is not representative of the low temperature value.

(3) The lifetime at low temperature in cyclohexane is longer than that in borazine but is nearly independent of the crystal phase of cyclohexane.

(4) The approximate temperature at which the lifetime begins to shorten noticeably (the onset temperature) for a given solute increases in the order: metastable cyclohexane, stable cyclohexane, borazine. The onset temperature is also a strong function of the solute, increasing with the degree of deuteration of benzene.

(5) The slope of the temperature dependent portion of the lifetime curve is steeper for curves which have a higher onset temperature.

There is also a very slight shift to higher temperatures of the onset temperature upon deuteration of the solvent.

For the benzenes the steady state phosphorescence intensity decreases as the temperature increases in a manner which closely parallels the increase in the decay rate. This indicates that the observed changes are in the non-radiative transition rate rather than in the radiative rate. A temperature dependent broadening of the spectral lines is also observed, but this occurs in different temperature regions from the lifetime changes.

The rate data are fitted using a least square percentage deviation criterion to an equation of the form:

$$k = k^{o} + A\exp(-E_a/T) \tag{1}$$

Here both the activation energy, E_a, and the limiting rate, k^o, are adjustable parameters; T is the absolute temperature. Although Eq. (1) gives a good fit (standard deviation ∿5%) to the data there are definite and systematic deviations from this form. These fits always indicate limiting rates which are too large because the observed curves change more slowly in the onset temperature region than a curve of the form of Eq. (1) would. This is probably due to the inadequacy of using a single temperature-independent activation energy.

Least square fits were also made using a fixed value of k^o chosen from the low temperature data. Figure (2) is an Arrhenius plot of $k-k^o$ for several isotopic isomers of benzene each dissolved in the stable phase of cyclohexane. Note that the points deviate from the predicted straight line especially in the low temperature region referred to above. This low temperature deviation is greater for the more protonated species. In going to higher temperatures the experimental curvature is less pronounced, but still evident, indicating that the activation energy is temperature dependent. The sharp upward rate change near the temperature of the cyclohexane phase change (186°K) should also be noticed.

Figure (2) indicates that the decay constant of C_6D_5H lies very nearly half way between those of C_6D_6 and C_6H_6. This is also true of the low temperature limiting rate which shows that for benzene, at least, the deuterium effect is not a linear function of the number of detueriums.[18]

Table I gives the activation energies, E_a, and frequency factors, A, found for representative systems. Typical values are respectively 700 cm^{-1} and 10^4 sec^{-1}. Notice that there are significant increases in the activation energies upon solute deuteration and changes with solvent which parallel

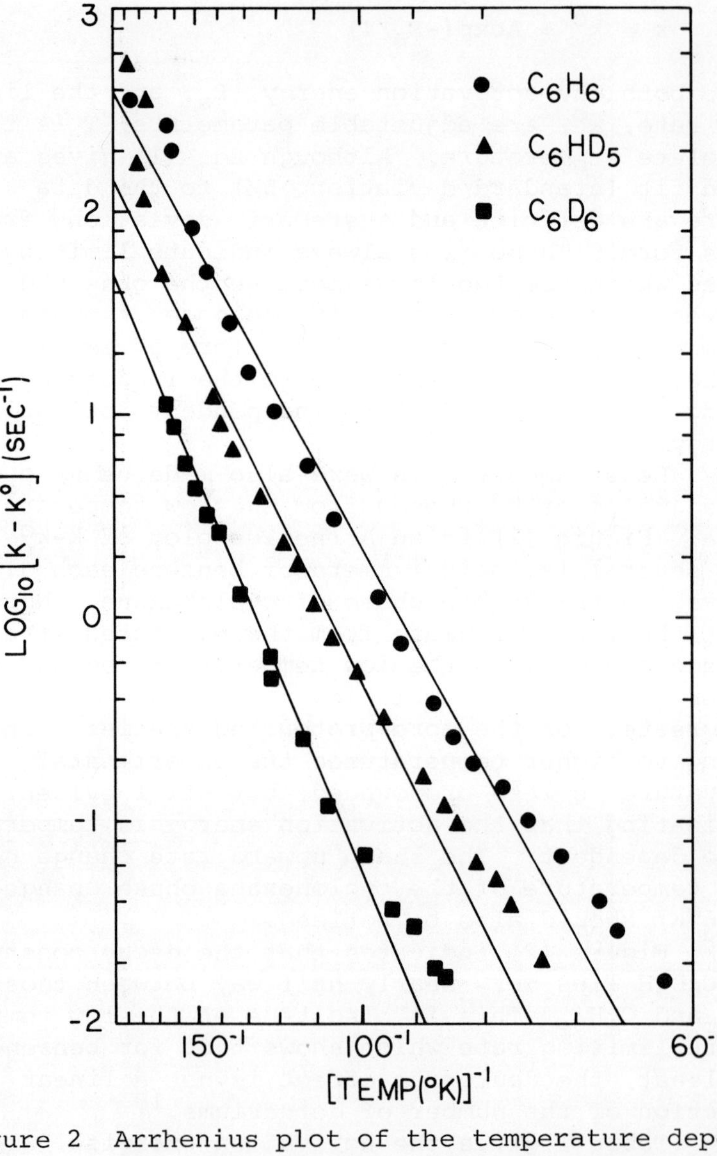

Figure 2 Arrhenius plot of the temperature dependent portion of the phosphorescent decay rate for a variety of benzenes in the stable phase of cyclohexane. The limiting rate, k^o, was chosen from the low temperature data.

TABLE I: Benzene Phosphorescence Parameters;[a] Temperature and Solvent Effects

Solute	Solvent					
	C_6H_{12}-S		C_6H_{12}-M		$B_3N_3H_6$	
	E_a	A	E_a	A	E_a	A
C_6H_6	570	4.6×10^3	480	6.7×10^3	1000	6.8×10^4
C_6H_5D	560	6.3×10^3			970	2.4×10^4
C_6HD_5	720	1.8×10^4			1280	1.4×10^5
C_6D_6	790	9.8×10^3	670	1.0×10^4	1400	2.0×10^5
C_6D_6[c]	860	1.6×10^4	640	5.6×10^3		

[a] From a least square fit to $k = k^o + A\exp(E_a/T)$.

[b] C_6H_{12}-S, C_6H_{12}-M, and $B_3N_3H_6$ represent respectively the stable and metastable phases of cyclohexane and borazine. The activation energy, E_a, is in cm^{-1} ($\pm$ 50 cm^{-1}) and the pre-exponential factor, A, is in sec^{-1} ($\pm$ 50%).

[c] Perdeuterocyclohexane solvent.

the behavior of the onset temperature. Presumably the frequency factors after correction for small degeneracy factors represent the transition rate from some thermally accessible state located E_a above the zero-point triplet state.

Table II lists the phosphorescent lifetimes for C_6H_6 and C_6D_6 in various solvents near 4.2°K. The large differences between the low molecular weight solvents, argon and methane, and the more typical solvents cyclohexane and borazine are quite evident. In both the latter solvents the lifetimes have changed only very slightly from their values of 50°K. Not all of these changes are in the non-radiative rate as is evidenced by the observed solvent dependency of the spectra. For example, the 0,0 band is much stronger relative to the vibronic bands for C_6H_6 in borazine than it is if cyclohexane or C_6D_6 is the solvent. However, most of the lifetime differences would appear to be in the non-radiative rate since the relative 0,0 intensities do not always parallel the lifetime changes.

RESULTS

METHYLBENZENES AND OTHER COMPOUNDS. Our work on the methylbenzenes has just begun so any conclusions should be judged as tentative. De Groot, Hasselmann, and van der Waals[19] have studied the ESR spectrum of mesitylene (1,3,5-trimethylbenzene) dissolved in B-trimethylborazine and found the signal to be very temperature dependent in the temperature range of 77-150°K. They tentatively interpret their findings on the basis of two energy levels separated by 280 cm^{-1} which result from a dynamical Jahn-Teller distortion of mesitylene. The phosphorescent lifetime of mesitylene in B-trimethylborazine is temperature independent below 130°K. Above this temperature the lifetime decreases in a fashion similar to benzene. The

TABLE II: Benzene Phosphorescent Lifetimes; Solvent Dependence at 4.2°K

Solvent	C_6H_6 (τ-sec)	C_6D_6 (τ-sec)
Cyclohexane[a]	11.8	15.3
Borazine	10.2	12.5
C_6D_6	9.5	
Argon[b]	16.	26.
Methane[b]	16.	22.
EPA[c] (77°)	8.5	13.0

[a] Essentially identical results are obtained with both the stable and metastable phases and with perdeuterocyclohexane.
[b] Ref. 13.
[c] A. H. Kalantar (private communication). Ref. 14 gives 7.0 sec for C_6H_6.

activation energy is 1820 cm^{-1} although the decays are not exponential at the higher temperatures. Nevertheless, phosphorescence can still be observed ($\tau \sim 1$ msec) at room temperature even though the melting point of the solvent is near 40°C.

Both mesitylene and toluene dissolved in cyclohexane have triplet lifetimes which are non-exponential and temperature dependent around 77°K. However, there is evidence for radical formation in these systems[20] and the steady-state intensity changes are much larger than the lifetime changes. Nevertheless the lifetimes and non-exponential character of the decays are independent of the exciting light intensity and of any temperature cycling, i.e., returning to a given temperature yields the same decay independent of the previous sample history.

Perdeuterotoluene (a natural impurity) in C_6D_6 and perprototoluene in C_6H_6 have also been studied in the vicinity of 10°K and above. Here the decays are exponential and the observed temperature effects are likely related to thermal depopulation of the toluene traps (depth ~ 700 cm^{-1}). The interesting point is that the phosphorescent lifetimes at 10°K of perdeuterotoluene and perprototoluene are respectively 6.4 sec and 5.9 sec. Thus, in this case, the deuterium effect is almost non-existent in sharp contrast to the usual behavior.

Naphthalene in cyclohexane shows a phosphorescent lifetime which is temperature dependent above 100°K; whereas in trans-decalin no such dependence is found even up to within 10°K of the melting point ($\sim$240°K). In decalin, however, there is a 100-fold decrease in the steady-state emission intensity upon raising the temperature from 50°K to 200°K.

According to de Groot and van der Waals[15] triptycene shows a negative temperature effect, i.e., the lifetime goes from 5.0 to 12.0 sec on changing from 20 to 77°K. Our finding for triptycene in cyclohexane is that the 5.1 sec lifetime at 60°K decreases only to 4.9 sec at 180°K but decreases suddenly to about 1.5 sec upon going through the phase transition. The steady-state intensity is also temperature independent below the phase change but drops by a factor of approximately 100 at this point; a factor much larger than the corresponding lifetime change.

DISCUSSION

An entirely satisfactory explanation of these observations is not readily apparent. In all likelihood a number of different mechanisms are operative in the different experiments. Nevertheless a number of proposals can be eliminated.

Careful attention has been given to the elimination of intermolecular effects. In view of the small activation energies, the large trap depths, and the direction of the deuterium effect for the benzenes in cyclohexane thermal depopulation to the solute singlet state or to solvent triplet states followed by quenching is highly unlikely. Direct interaction with impurities or with other triplets should depend on the exciting light intensity, give non-exponential decays, and be nearly independent of solute deuteration; all of which are in disagreement with the benzene data. Diffusion of solvent impurities, such as oxygen, should give quenching nearly independent of solute deuteration which is again clearly not the observation.

Since the data are not consistent with an intermolecular mechanism, a primarily intramolecular mechanism must be sought. The observation that the one totally symmetric CH stretching mode of C_6D_5H is half as effective as the six CH modes of C_6H_6 in reducing the benzene phosphorescent lifetime suggests that only certain CH modes are effective. It might be proposed that the continuum of final vibrational states in the singlet manifold has superimposed on it a number of discrete levels to which intersystem crossing is very efficient. However, the deuterium and solvent effects on the activation energies and on the triplet state energies do not seem to be consistent with this interpretation.

The solvent effects may well be related to the size of the cavity in which the solute fits. Unfortunately the relevant x-ray data are not available; even the crystal structures are not known with certainty.[21] Such effects may also account for the temperature dependence of the activation energies. The solvent effects may also be related to the phonon field,[22] but the activation energies seem much too large.

The magnitude of the activation energies for benzene suggest the involvement of skeletal vibrations. The change in intersystem crossing rate with initial vibronic state is commonly proposed as the mechanism for a temperature effect.[2] However, it is hard to reconcile the observed large pre-exponential factors ($\sim 10^4$ sec^{-1}) with such an interpretation, even when the pure electronic transition is forbidden as with benzene. In addition, the activation energies should be only slightly smaller for C_6D_6 than for C_6H_6. Experimentally a large deuterium effect in the opposite direction is observed.

The increase in the activation energy with deuterium substitution is consistent with the intermediate state being another electronic state rather than a vibrational state. The Jahn-Teller states discussed by Siebrand[2] and others[20] are possible candidates. Our experiments with the isotope splittings resulting from a non-hexagonal benzene triplet indicate considerable solvent involvement, even to the extent of changing the geometry of the most stable configuration.[23,24] However, the lack of a lifetime change in the temperature range where large ESR changes are detected for mesitylene in

B-trimethylborazine hardly seems consistent with this interpretation.

Isomerization or chemical reactions have been proposed as an explanation for the drop in Fluorescence and triplet yields upon short wavelength excitation of benzene and toluene in the gas phase.[25,26] The difficulty here is with the very small quantum yields for formation of products other than the original compound. Nevertheless, at energies high above the ground electronic state vibrational displacements will be large and the distinction between an excited state of benzene and an excited state of dewar benzene, for example, may be rather academic. Thus a tunneling through potential barriers (or even potential crossing) reminiscent of predissociation might be proposed.[27] The potential surfaces would be expected to be rather sensitive to solvent perturbations and a dissociative reaction would also relax spin conservation rules thus increasing the rate. Chemical reactions, such as radical formation followed by recombination with a trapped hydrogen atom, seem to be rather attractive proposals for the methylbenzenes. Incidentally, extrapolation of our benzene data to room temperature yield triplet lifetimes of the order of 10^{-4} sec. This is not too much larger than the 2.6×10^{-5} sec value measured in the gas phase.[28]

One further observation is that the higher the temperature at which the triplet lifetime begins to shorten the higher the activation energy. This seems to be true regardless of the solute-solvent combination, including the data for naphthalene in durene and in plastics at high temperatures. This result is expected if the pre-exponential factors are constant for all systems. It is also perhaps interesting (but without theoretical justification) that a plot of $\log(k-k^{o})$ verses T instead of 1/T yields a surprisingly good fit to the rate data for <u>all</u> of the benzene-solvent combinations. Even the data for naphthalene in durene differ in slope by a factor of less than two from the benzene data, whereas the activation energies differ by a factor of over five.

In conclusion, the large temperature and solvent effects reported here are not explained by the current theories of radiationless transitions. The situation is complicated by the fact that the solvent and temperature effects seem to be interrelated and hard to separate from one another. More experiments must be performed before an adequate explanation can be proposed.

REFERENCES

1. G. W. Robinson and R. P. Frosch, J. Chem. Phys., 38, 1187 (1963); G. W. Robinson, ibid., 47, 1967 (1967).
2. W. Siebrand, ibid., 47, 2411 (1967).
3. M. Bixon and J. Jortner, ibid., 48, 715 (1968).
4. G. F. Hatch and G. C. Nieman, ibid., 48 (in press); H. Sternlicht, G. C. Nieman, and G. W. Robinson, ibid., 38, 1326 (1963).
5. T. Azumi and S. P. McGlynn, ibid., 39, 1186 (1963); T. N. Misra and S. P. McGlynn, ibid., 44, 3816 (1966).
6. N. Hirota, ibid., 43, 3354 (1965); N. Hirota and C. A. Hutchison, Jr., ibid., 42, 2869 (1965).
7. B. A. Piatnitskii, Doklady Akad. Nauk S. S. S. R., 68, 281, 483 (1949).
8. R. Livingston and W. R. Ware, J. Chem. Phys., 39, 2593 (1963).
9. F. R. Lipsett and G. Macpherson, Can. J. Phys., 44, 1485 (1966).
10. R. E. Kellogg and R. P. Schwenker, J. Chem. Phys., 41, 2860 (1964).
11. S. G. Hadley, H. E. Rast, Jr., and R. A. Keller, ibid., 39, 705 (1963).
12. M. Kinoshita, K. Stolzle, and S. P. McGlynn, ibid., 48, 1191 (1968).
13. M. R. Wright, R. P. Frosch, and G. W. Robinson, ibid., 33, 934 (1960).
14. D. S. McClure, J. Chem. Phys., 17, 905 (1949).
15. M. S. de Groot and J. H. van der Waals, Mol. Phys., 6, 545 (1963).
16. G. W. Schaeffer, R. Schaeffer, and H. I. Schlesinger, J. Amer. Chem. Soc., 73, 1612 (1951).
17. J. D. Spangler and N. G. Kilmer, J. Chem. Phys., 48, 698 (1968).
18. S. H. Lin and R. Bersohn, ibid., 48, 2732 (1968).
19. M. S. de Groot, I. A. M. Hesselmann, and J. H. van der Waals, Mol. Phys., 10, 91 (1965); J. H. van der Waals, A. M. D. Berghuis, and

M. S. de Groot, ibid., 13, 301 (1967).
20. P. M. Johnson and A. C. Albrecht, J. Chem. Phys. 48, 851 (1968).
21. J. D. Spangler and H. Sponer, Spectrochim. Acta, 19, 169 (1963).
22. M. Gouterman, J. Chem. Phys. 36, 2846 (1962).
23. G. C. Nieman and D. S. Tinti, ibid. 46, 1432 (1967).
24. M. S. de Groot, I. A. M. Hesselmann and J. H. van der Waals, Mol. Phys. 13, 583 (1967).
25. C. L. Braun, S. Kato, and S. Lipsky, J. Chem. Phys. 39, 1645 (1963).
26. W. A. Noyes, Jr., D. Phillips, J. Lemaire, and C. S. Burton, Advances in Photochemistry (Interscience, New York, 1967), p. 621.
27. G. R. Hunt, E. F. McCoy, and I. G. Ross, Australian J. Chem. 15, 591 (1962).
28. C. S. Parmenter and B. L. Ring, J. Chem. Phys. 46, 1998 (1967).

FLUORESCENCE AND PHOSPHORESCENCE OF AROMATIC HYDROCARBONS IN POLY(METHYLMETHACRYLATE) AS A FUNCTION OF TEMPERATURE

John L. Kropp and William R. Dawson

Chemical Sciences Department
TRW Systems
One Space Park, Redondo Beach, California

INTRODUCTION

Much of the work done on fluorescence and phosphorescence has been done in liquid solutions or in rigid glasses at 77°K. As the temperature of a liquid solution is varied, the environment about the molecule changes and much of the change in absorption spectra, fluorescence yields and fluorescence lifetimes in solution can be related to the changes in solvent viscosity. A matrix that changes little with temperature will enable one to study the molecular properties themselves without changing environmental influence. Poly-(methylmethacrylate) PMM offers such an environment. This is well known and PMM has been used as

*Supported by the Office of Naval Research, under Contract N00014-67-C0327.

a matrix in many studies.

We have studied the effects of variation of temperature upon fluorescence and phosphorescence yields, Φ_F and Φ_P, and lifetimes, τ_F and τ_P. This has enabled us to calculate the radiative lifetime of fluorescence and also to learn more about the processes that are important in temperature-sensitive deactivation of the singlet and the triplet state. At the same time, measurements of the efficiency of triplet formation Φ_T as a function of temperature have been made for some of the compounds studied. This enables us to calculate the radiative rate of depopulation of the triplet also.

Most of the molecules studied have weak, long wavelength absorption bands that are α in character (Clar notation). These molecules usually have relatively low fluorescence yields at room temperature; molecules with intense, long wavelength absorption, such as perylene, often have high fluorescence yields at room temperature resulting in smaller temperature dependence than compounds with lowest α bands.

The basic energy level diagram for an aromatic hydrocarbon is shown in Figure 1. The various decay processes from S_1 and from T_1 are shown; k_1 is the rate constant for radiative decay of S_1; k_2 nonradiative decay from S_1 directly to ground; k_3 is the rate constant for intersystem crossing from S_1 to T_1. Similarly, k_4 and k_5 are the rate constants for radiative and non-radiative decay, respectively, from T_1 to S_o.

These rate constants can be expressed in relation to the measured parameters

$$k_1 = \Phi_F \tau_F^{-1};\ k_2 = (1 - \Phi_F - \Phi_T)\tau_F^{-1}$$

$$k_3 = \Phi_T \tau_F^{-1};\ k_4 = \Phi_P \Phi_T^{-1} \tau_P^{-1}$$

$$k_5 = (1 - \Phi_P \Phi_T^{-1})\tau_P^{-1}$$

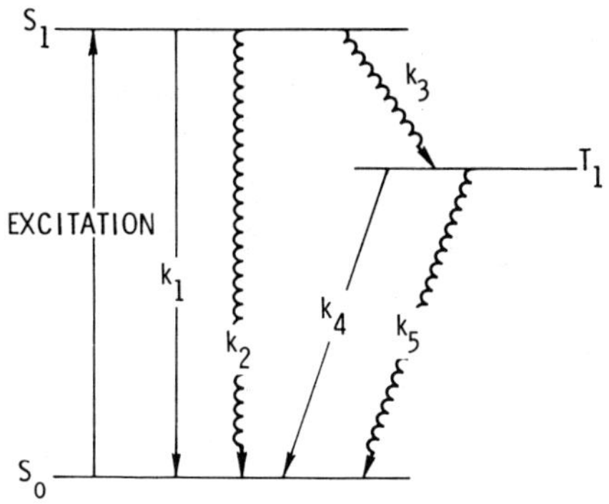

Figure 1 Energy level diagram for an aromatic molecule.

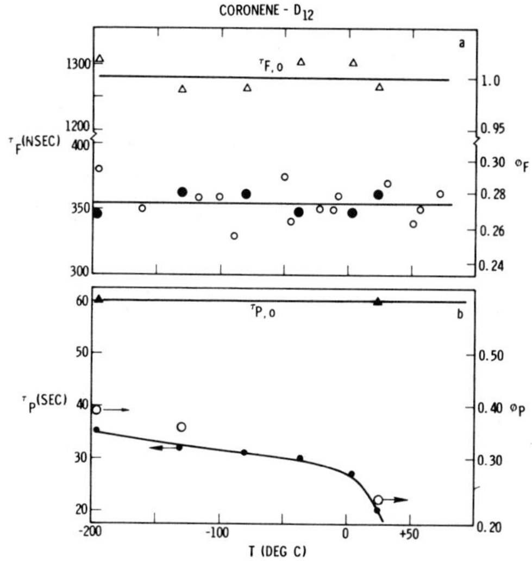

Figure 2 Variation of luminescence lifetime and yields with temperature for coronene-d_{12} in PMM. (a) Fluorescence lifetime (τ_F) ○ left hand ordinate, fluorescence yields (Φ_F) ● right hand ordinate, radiative lifetime ($\tau_{F,o}$) △ left hand ordinate. (b) Phosphorescence lifetimes (τ_p) ● left hand ordinate, phosphorescence yields (Φ_p) ○ right hand ordinate, radiative lifetime of phosphorescence ($\tau_{p,o}$) ▲.

The experimental details involved in determining Φ_F, Φ_P, Φ_T, τ_F, and τ_P are described elsewhere.[1]

RESULTS

The fluorescence yields and lifetimes have been obtained for coronene, coronene-d_{12}, benzcoronene, the dibenzanthracenes, 1,12-benzperylene, pyrene-h_{10} and pyrene-d_{10}. The results for coronenes and benzcoronene[1b] and pyrenes[2] are reported in detail elsewhere. In addition, phosphorescence yields and lifetimes are available for many of these compounds as a function of temperature. Triplet yields have been determined also for coronene, coronene-d_{12} and benzcoronene.

Phosphorescence yields and lifetimes always vary with temperature.[3] The temperature dependence of fluorescence yields and lifetimes we have determined fall into three classes; (1) no temperature dependence of yield or lifetime; (2) yield and lifetime both decrease with increasing temperature in the same proportion; and (3) the lifetime shows a greater decrease with increasing temperature than does the fluorescence yield. We have not observed any case where the fluorescence yield decreases more rapidly with increasing temperature than does the lifetime.

Coronene-h_{12} and coronene-d_{12} show no change in fluorescence lifetime or yield with temperature. The data for coronene-d_{12} are shown in Figure 2. However, most of the molecules studied showed corresponding changes in τ_F and Φ_F with increasing temperature. 1,2-benzcoronene, pyrene-h_{10}, pyrene-d_{10}, 1,2;5,6-dibenzanthracene, and 1,2;7,8-dibenzanthracene all show this effect. Typical data are presented for pyrene-d_{10} in Figure 3, and for 1,2;7,8-dibenzanthracene in Figure 4. Finally, Figure 5, shows data for 1,2;3,4-dibenzanthracene. For this compound the values of Φ_F are far more temperature sensitive

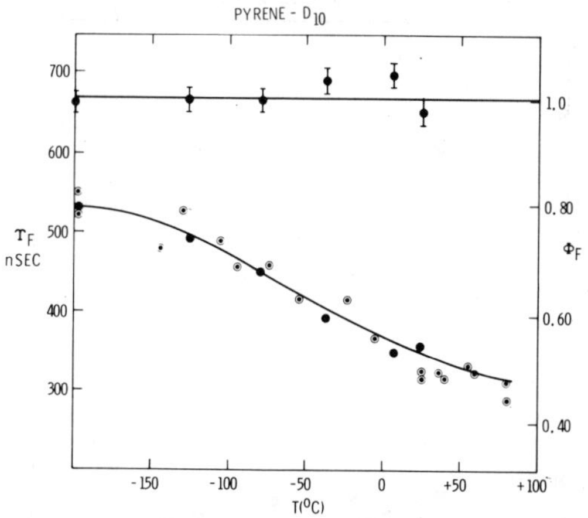

Figure 3 Variation of fluorescence lifetime ◉, fluorescence yield ●, and radiative lifetime ⌶, with temperature for pyrene-d_{10} in PMM. (Left hand ordinate is lifetime, right hand fluorescence yield).

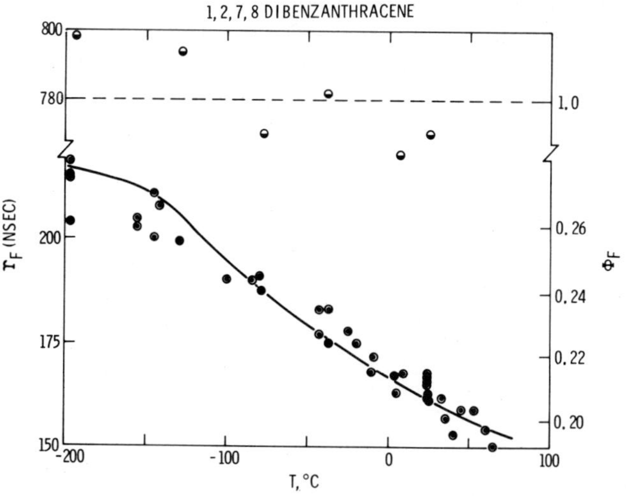

Figure 4 Variation of fluorescence lifetime ◉, fluorescence yield ●, and radiative lifetime ⊖, with temperature for 1,2:7,8 dibenzanthracene in PMM. (Left hand ordinate is lifetime, right hand ordinate is fluorescence yield).

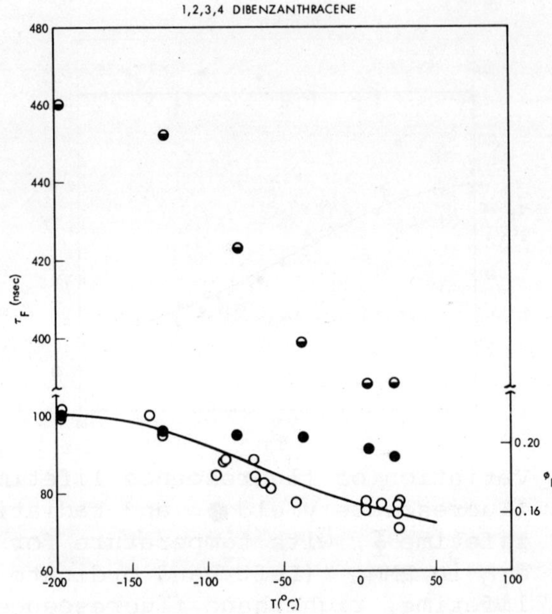

Figure 5 Variation of fluorescence lifetime ○; fluorescence yield ● and radiative lifetime ◓ with temperature of 1,2;3,4 dibenzanthracene in PMM.

TABLE II: Rate Constants for Depopulation of S_1 and T_1 in Coronene and Benzocoronene

Process (sec^{-1})	Coronene-h_{12} 77^oK	Coronene-h_{12} 296^oK	Coronene-d_{12} 77^oK	Coronene-d_{12} 296^oK	Benzocoronene 77^oK	Benzocoronene 296^oK
k_1	8.4×10^5	8.4×10^5	7.8×10^5	7.8×10^5	9.0×10^5	9.6×10^5
k_2	1.6×10^5	2.8×10^5	1.4×10^5	1.7×10^5	a	2.6×10^5
k_3	2.1×10^6	2.0×10^6	1.0×10^6	1.0×10^6	1.5×10^6	1.7×10^6
k_4	0.017	0.018	0.017	0.017	0.025	0.025
k_5	0.086	0.141	0.012	0.033	0.21	0.32

a Since $\Phi_F + \Phi_T > 1$, k_2 is considered to be zero.

many molecules.[5] The data here show that for the molecules studied, the radiative lifetime ($\tau_{F,o} = k_1^{-1}$) is independent of temperature. Data for the coronenes, pyrenes, 1,2;7,8 dibenzanthracene, 1,2;5,6 dibenzanthracene and 1,2 benzcoronene are all constant to within 5% from -196°C to 50°C. This constancy is expected for most aromatic hydrocarbons on the basis of the relative constancy of abosrption with temperature. The two surprising cases are 1,12 benzperylene and 1,2;3,4 dibenzanthracene where the radiative lifetime decreases with increasing temperature. The variation of τ_F with temperature for these compounds is similar to that for other compounds studied. Thus ΔE is the same as it is for compounds for which $\tau_{F,o}$ is constant. The value of Φ_F, however, decreases more slowly than τ_F for these compounds as the temperature is raised. In fact, for 1,12 benzperylene the value of Φ_F <u>increases</u> from 0.36 at -196°C to 0.40 at +75°C.[1b] The reason for this effect is not apparent at the present time.

In both of the compounds where this anomalous effect is noted, the α(or ^1L_b) band is longest in wavelength, but the p(or ^1L_a) band is unusually close (about 1100 cm^{-1} to the blue). The other compounds have a shift of 3000 (cm^{-1}) between these bands. What effect these bands may have upon the weaker ^1L_b band is not immediately apparent. Also, determination of whether the radiative lifetime is really changing or whether there is emission from the ^1L_a level, as well as the ^1L_b level, must await further data.

Values of the radiative lifetime of phosphorescence, $\tau_{P,o}$ or k_4^{-1}, have been determined accurately only for coronene-h_{12}, coronene-d_{12}, and benzcoronene. These values show that $\tau_{P,o}$ is independent of temperature for these compounds. The values of k_4 for coronene and benzcoronene differ about 33% from each other and both values are considerably lower than the value of 0.033 chosen by Siebrand[6] as a common radiative lifetime for all triplets. The less precise results with the dibenzanthracenes indicate that each molecule will have a different value of $\tau_{P,o}(k_4^{-1})$ and thus it is better to treat k_4 individually for each molecule in any theoretical treatment.

Finally, in passing, we note that $\tau_{F,o}$ is the same within 10% for coronene and coronene-d_{12} and for pyrene-h_{10} and pyrene-d_{10} (Table II). The values of $\tau_{P,o}$ for coronene-h_{12} and for coronene-d_{12} are equal. Equal values for radiative lifetimes for protonated and deuterated analogs have long been assumed in calculations and these values merely confirm such assumptions.

TEMPERATURE DEPENDENCE OF τ_F. The dependence of lifetime and intensity upon temperature can be used to test theories of radiationless transitions. Robinson and Frosch,[7] Siebrand[6] and Lin[8] all suggest that there may be but a small temperature dependence for radiationless deactivation. In most cases[3,4] the phosphorescence lifetime vs. temperature has been studied in PMM. In these cases the major contribution to radiationless energy loss is due to C-H vibrations. However, it is important to note that even in the completely deuterated coronene at -196°C, radiationless deactivation of the triplet still occurs (cf. Table II).

The fluorescence lifetimes of all of the molecules studied, except coronene-h_{12} and coronene-d_{12}, show a decrease as the temperature is raised. Since, in most cases, the radiative lifetime remains constant, the decrease in fluorescence lifetime corresponds to an increased rate for radiationless loss of energy. This increase can be either in the intersystem crossing from S_1 to T_1, or in the direct transition from S_1 to S_o. We believe that the following results suggest that the latter process accounts for the observed lifetime decay.

(1) The triplet yield for 1,2 benzcoronene measured at -196°C and 23°C has decreased the same amount as Φ_F and τ_F, thus indicating a corresponding decrease in Φ_T.

(2) The activation energies of all of the lifetime changes are small and are close to the same value (e.e, 250-500 cm^{-1}). If the thermal activation is due to $S_1 - T_1$ enhancement, then we expect ΔE to vary over a wider range and dependent on the energy of the first triplet excited state above S_1.

The activation energies are similar to those observed from the decrease of phosphorescence lifetime with increasing temperature (500 cm^{-1} - 800 cm^{-1}).[3,4] This suggests that there may be common features in the mechanisms of singlet and triplet deactivation, k_2 and k_5.

We can correlate the process responsible for the quenching either with the molecule itself, or by some interaction with the host. Quenching by diffusion as the temperature is raised would quench singlets and triplets in proportion to their lifetimes. Thus, if a singlet state is quenched even slightly the triplet phosphorescence would be completely eliminated. This is not the case, however.

Of all of those treating radiationless transitions, Lin[8b] is the only one to give an explicit equation relating to the temperature dependence of radiationless transitions. However, Jortner[9] and Dexter and Fowler[10] have similar theories. This equation is

$$1/\tau - 1/\tau_o = a/\tau_o e^{-\theta/T} \quad (2)$$

In this equation τ_o is the lifetime at T = 0°K. However, lifetimes of both fluorescence and phosphorescence are almost constant below 150°K, thus we used the values of τ_F and τ_P at 77°K as τ_o; a and θ are constants related to the vibrational levels responsible for quenching. In this form the equation is the same as our experimental Equation (1). If we take our A and multiply it by our τ_o we obtain Lin's a factor. This is done in the last column of Table I. This factor varies slightly as the value of τ_o^{-1} and k_1 vary. What is particularly interesting is that if one performs this operation on phosphorescence data, a varies from 5-30, or a varies by a factor of only 10 between singlets and triplets.

Thus even though the values of A determined for singlet and triplet deactivation with temperature differ by 10^6 sec^{-1}, the values of a are quite similar. Based on Lin's theory we conclude that the temperature dependent deactivation of S_1 is a process that is similar to temperature dependent deactivation of T_1 in a rigid matrix; and, that both involve the direct radiationless conversion to the ground state by processes involving low frequency vibrations. This process involving increased radiationless deactivation from higher vibrational levels, is predicted in the theories of Bixon and Jortner[9] and Dexter and Fowler,[10] as well as Lin. Such a mechanism contrasts to deactivation via C-H vibrations that has a low rate constant and is generally only operative in triplet deactivation.

REFERENCES

1. a) W. R. Dawson, J. Opt. Soc. Am., 58, 222 (1968).
   b) W. R. Dawson and J. L. Kropp (to be published).
2. W. R. Dawson, M. W. Windsor, J. L. Kropp (to be published).
3. R. Kellogg and W. Schwenker, J. Chem. Phys. 41, 2860 (1964).
4. J. L. Kropp and W. R. Dawson, J. Phys. Chem. 71, 4499 (1967).
5. Cf. W. R. Ware and B. A. Baldwin, J. Chem. Phys., 40, 1703 (1964).
6. W. Siebrand, J. Chem. Phys., 47, 2411 (1967).
7. G. W. Robinson and R. P. Frosch, J. Chem. Phys., 38, 1187 (1963).
8. a) S. H. Lin, J. Chem. Phys., 44, 3759 (1966).
   b) S. H. Lin and R. Bersohn, J. Chem. Phys. 48, 2732 (1968).
9. a) J. Jortner and R. S. Berry, J. Chem. Phys. 48, 2757 (1968).
   b) M. Bixon and J. Jortner, J. Chem. Phys. 48, 715 (1968).
10. D. L. Dexter and W. B. Fowler, J. Chem. Phys. 47, 1379 (1968).

PRESSURE DEPENDENCE OF THE FLUORESCENCE SPECTRUM OF BENZENE

L. M. Logan, Ilze Buduls, and I. G. Ross

Chemistry Department
School of General Studies
Australian National University
Canberra, A.C.T.

The objects of this study were (1) to measure the overall rate of vibrational energy loss by an excited molecule in collision with other neutral molecules; (2) to discern as far as possible the pathways, through the manifold of vibrational states, by which energy is lost; and (3) to measure the dependence of the quantum yield of fluorescence upon the vibrational energy content.

The molecules studied were benzene and benzene-d_6, continuously excited by the 2537 Å line of a low pressure Hg lamp operated at 30°C, which was also the temperature of the experiments. The apparatus was tolerably similar to that of Kistiakowsky and Parmenter,[1] of which this work may be regarded as an extension in a particular direction. The measurements made were of the fluorescence spectra of benzene at 0.12 torr, both alone and in the presence of foreign gases at pressures up to 500 torr. Spectra were recorded photographically and photoelectrically.

With 2537 Å irradiation, benzene is excited to a vibrational level (or, rather, levels[2]) having an excess of vibrational energy (above the zero point level of the $^1B_{2u}$ state) of approximately 1700 cm^{-1}, which is the same as the mean vibrational energy at 440°K. The molecules must thus lose energy upon interacting with the heat bath. With benzene-d_6 the vibrational state reached on excitation is again not definite, but the vibrational energy excess is probably less, at about 1200 cm^{-1}. In view of triplet yield measurements[3] in which the 2537 Å excitation appears to produce anomalous results compared with those obtained at other wavelengths, it may be remarked here that there is no qualitative difference in the results we obtain in experiments with benzene-d_0 and benzene-d_6, beyond what might be expected from the difference in vibrational energy immediately after absorption.

As is well known,[4,5] increasing the pressure in an experiment of this kind suppresses the sharp "resonance" spectrum (sharp, because rotational profiles are not developed) and replaces it eventually by an "equilibrated" fluorescence in which only the lower vibrational levels are populated and rotational band structure is evident. A curious feature[4] of this change of character is that, as the pressure is increased and resonance lines die out, the equilibrated spectrum appears (on photographic plates at least) to arise, like Aphrodite from the sea, fully developed and properly proportioned. Of the intermediate vibrational levels, which should presumably be populated after say one collision, there is no obvious sign. This result we confirmed in an extensive series of spectra, taken on a Hilger large quartz spectrograph, with several different foreign gases as well as with pure benzene itself at different pressures. In particular, not a single resolved band, not being part of the resonance fluorescence, is present in the partly equilibrated emission which is not there also at the highest pressures used.

The reason for this is apparent in photoelectric spectra, namely, at low to intermediate pressures of foreign gases the total intensity of the structured emission drops by more than 50%, and is replaced by an intense continuum which then attenuates again as the pressure is further raised. From this we conclude that our objective (2), admittedly an ambitious one, is not attainable in benzene, but that one can see parts of the process, namely the initial step and the rate of completion.

We now define these observable steps more precisely.

The intensity of the resonance spectrum was monitored via the same lines as Kistiakowsky and Parmenter used, namely a strong "doublet" at 2617 Å. The equilibrated spectrum is rather badly overlaid by the resonance emission, and the part of it most suitable for measurement is the band group based on a parent band named[6] B_0^0. Band B_0^0 originates from the zero point level of the upper state. Near it are strong sequence bands B_0^1 and B_0^2 originating from the one- and two-quantum levels of the 237 cm^{-1} (upper state) e_{2u} vibration. Some other weaker sequence bands lie among or near these three but their intensities could not be satisfactorily measured at the resolution used in the photographic work (the monochromator was that of a Uvispek spectrophotometer). By measuring the intensities of bands B_0^0, B_0^1, B_0^2, and correcting for the differences in their intrinsic intensities (obtained in absorption) we were thus able to measure the populations of the zero point level and of the levels 0 + 237 and 0 + 2 x 237. For convenience these levels will be referred to as B_0, B_1, B_2 respectively.

The measurable processes are then as follows. Process A is the departure, due to collisions from the initial levels responsible for the 2617 Å resonance doublet into any of the manifold of vibrational states below, or not far above, this initial level. There are many of these, e.g., in benzene-d_0 about 430, not counting degeneracies, in the energy range 0 to 2000 cm^{-1}. Because the nonresonance spectrum after a few collisions is mostly diffuse, there is no single destination state; rather, as might be expected, many states are reached and step A is the totality of all such processes. After some more collisions molecules begin to work their way down through the stack of vibrational levels we call process B.

The rate of process A thus measures the probability that some energy, however small, is lost (or gained) as the result of one collision. The rate of process B, on the other hand, is a measure of the average amount of energy lost per collision. These two quantities are quite different. One might envisage that one kind of colliding molecule might remove a little energy often, and another a large amount of energy, but less frequently. The first would then show out favorably in process A, and the second in process B.

Process A is a simple bimolecular one, and its rate can be calculated from Stern-Volmer plots of the intensity of the resonance doublet as a function of pressure. Process B is more complex and there is no ready means of analysing the data. In particular, Wilson, Noble and Lee[7] have shown, from computer experiments, that two extreme models for vibrational quenching lead to growth curves for the populations of states B_0, B_1, B_2 which are qualitatively depressingly similar. In their "strong" collisional model all downward quantum jumps, due to collisions, are equally probable; the probability of upward jumps is determined by microscopic reversibility. In their "weak" model, applied to the uniform stack of vibrational levels of a multidimensional harmonic oscillator, only one-quantum jumps are permitted; all are equally probable. Every molecule which reaches the zero point level must thus have resided for a while in every intermediate level. The only qualitative difference between the observations expected from the two models is that at the time when the lowest levels are beginning to fill, the weak collision model permits a temporary population inversion among the low states, whereas their populations are never inverted in the strong model. Such inversions among the levels B_0, B_1, B_2 are in fact just detectable in our results and so the weak model is favored for approximate calculations. Meanwhile, <u>relative</u> efficiencies for process B for different foreign gases can be fairly accurately determined from the circumstance that plots of the populations of B_0, B_1, B_2 against log (pressure) are all sigmoid curves of very similar shape. The pressures for equivalent extents of equilibration thus stand in a nearly constant ratio throughout the entire equilibration process, for all foreign gases.

Intuitively, the results are most readily interpretable when expressed in terms, not of pressure, but of collision numbers. In calculating these we used gas kinetic radii for the quenching gases, and for excited benzene the gas kinetic radius increased by 0.03 Å to allow for the enlarged ring. There is, of course, the obvious objection that the intermolecular potential associated with an electronic molecule is likely to be of longer range, and the effective radius may vary with the foreign gas. Meanwhile, in conventional collision number terms our results may be summarized as follows.

For Process A (removal of <u>some</u> energy) collision numbers range from 37 for the least efficient gas (helium) to 5 for isopentane. Within this range relative efficiencies stand in the order He $\sim$ H_2 $<$ D_2 $<$ Ar $\sim$ N_2 $<$ CO_2 $\sim$ Kr $<$ cyclohexane $\sim CHF_3$ $<$ O_2(quenches) $<$ H_2O $<$ ether $<$ isopentane.

For process B (average amount of energy removed per collision) the relative efficiencies span a wider range of 1 (helium) to 37 (ether) and are in the order He $\sim$ Ar $\sim$ Kr < N_2 < D_2 $\sim$ H_2 << CHF_3 < CO_2 << H_2O $\sim$ cyclohexane < isopentane < ether.

For benzene-d_6 we can at present report only two results, for N_2 and CO_2. For Process A (which, however, takes place from a lower level) the efficiencies of both gases are decreased slightly (10%). For Process B the ratio of efficiencies (CO_2:N_2) declines from 3.9 (benzene-d_0) to 2.9 (benzene-d_6). This decrease is perhaps to be expected since there is less energy, in total, to lose.

The average amounts of energy lost per collision can be roughly estimated by noticing that in weak collision models[6] the population of the lowest level reaches 50% of its equilibrium value at a dimensionless parameter Π which is rather insensitive to the actual details of the energy level pattern. Π here is defined as the product of the probability, per collision, of a one-quantum downward jump times the mean lifetime of the excited state. We take for Π the value 3, obtained from the diagrams in Ref. 7. From the values of the pressure at half-height of the B_0 growth curve the average energy lost per collision takes values ranging from 3 cm^{-1} for the inert gases to 110 cm^{-1} for ether. Other gases fall in between, in the order listed for Process B above. These estimates we feel to be uncertain to within a factor of 2.

In all these calculations it was assumed that the lifetime of the excited state is a constant throughout the degradation process. Donovan and Duncan's[8] figure of 5.9×10^{-7} sec was used. However, it is known that the quantum yield of fluorescence does depend on the vibrational energy excess[1,9] and the figure used (an extrapolated value to zero pressure, obtained with radiofrequency excitation) will no doubt eventually be revised. A simple revision of the lifetime would merely rescale the collision numbers quoted for process A, and the mean energies given in the interpretation of process B. A changing lifetime with pressure, if less than say 50%, would also mildly modify the process B figures.

The evidence for lifetime variation which most closely relates to the present work is that of Kistiakowsky and Parmenter, who found a 40% decrease in integrated emission intensity when the pressure of the cyclohexane, as foreign gas, was increased from 0 to 15 torr. This decline, interpreted as a decrease in lifetime, runs closely parallel to the decay of the state reached at initial excitation (i.e. of the resonance spectrum) and they assumed that it was complete when vibrational equilibration was complete. Our measurements of process B, however, show that the matter is not as simple as this. Thermalization of benzene is much harder to achieve than has been supposed. Cyclohexane does not in fact quite do so, even at 50 mm, which is as close to its saturated vapor pressure as we can reach with our gas mixing techniques. N_2 does not do so even at 550 torr. The only cases, in fact, in which we did achieve excited benzene which was fully in vibrational equilibrium were with isopentane and with benzene itself (though we offer no figure for the latter: benzene is undoubtedly highly efficient, as is seen in photographic experiments, but its measurement quantitatively requires a special strategy). With N_2 as foreign gas the decline in quantum yield roughly follows the decay of the resonance spectrum, and is complete (again a 40% decrease) at 25 torr. Yet at this pressure the population of the low levels B_0, B_1, B_2 has barely begun and most of the molecules, when they emit, are still resident in high vibrational levels. For benzene-d_6 and N_2 the observations are the same except only that the fall in quantum yield is now only 20%. For these results we have no explanation.

We conclude with some remarks on rotational equilibration, for the study of which our photoelectric system has insufficient resolution. The process can however be traced in photographic plates and particularly in a clear band D_0^0. In this band two peaks of unequal intensity are seen with 30 torr of Ar; at 125 torr they have reversed their intensities; and at 500 torr the initially strong peak has all but disappeared. At the same pressure vibrational equilibration has just passed the half way point. We conclude that with argon as colliding gas rotational equilibration is more rapid than vibrational equilibration by a modest factor of say 4.

DISCUSSION

In the context of studies of vibrational energy exchange this work stands in a rather lonely position between conventional ultrasonic work, usually performed on smaller molecules, less highly excited, and leading for the most part to a single relaxation time, and the work of Neporent[11,12,13] and others on the pressure dependence of much larger molecules with structureless spectra. In analysing these diffuse emissions, energy redistribution within the molecule is assumed to be rapid, so that the molecule is assigned a definite vibrational temperature and the effect of the foreign gas on this temperature is then followed, e.g., from the position of the emission maximum. In benzene no such rapid energy redistribution occurs; our measurements of the B processes show clearly that the molecules cannot be characterized by a temperature until they have reached equilibrium with their surroundings. The estimates obtained for the energy transferred per collision, in benzene, are nonetheless within reach of those deduced from the experiments with larger molecules. Thus, for 3-dimethylamino-6-aminophthalimide,[13] excited with a nominal energy excess of 700 cm^{-1}, the energy loss per collision ranges from 6 to 51 cm^{-1} between He and isopentane. However, these figures are greatly increased when the energy excess is increased; our experiments do not yet offer evidence on this last feature.

The results we obtain may also be relevant to the rate of energy loss in solution. This is normally, but on no real evidence, assumed to be instantaneous. We are struck by the relatively small increase in overall efficiency, in our process B, in going from monoatomic gases to large flexible molecules such as isopentane which is surely, in Robinson's evocative phrase, a molecular mattress. Suppose we adopt a cage model of a liquid hydrocarbon solvent, in which an electronically excited solvent molecule effectively interacts with its surroundings via collisions with solvent neighbors at a frequency somewhat less than intramolecular vibration frequencies: at 10^{12} sec^{-1} say. Then assuming each collision removes 100 cm^{-1} of energy, as our results suggest, the time required for thermalization in representative situations would not be negligible in experiments performed on a picosecond time scale, and indeed direct evidence for this has been found in such experiments.[14]

REFERENCES

1. G. B. Kistiakowsky and C. S. Parmenter, J. Chem. Phys. 42, 2942 (1965).
2. C. S. Parmenter, private communication.
3. W. A. Noyes and D. A. Harter, J. Chem. Phys. 46, 674 (1967).
4. B. R. Cuthbertson and G. B. Kistiakowsky, J. Chem. Phys. 4, 9 (1936).
5. C. K. Ingold and C. L. Wilson, J. Chem. Soc. 955 (1936).
6. F. M. Garforth and C. K. Ingold, J. Chem. Soc. 427, 440 (1948).
7. D. J. Wilson, B. Noble and B. Lee, J. Chem. Phys. 34, 1392 (1961).
8. D. P. Craig, J. Chem. Soc. 2146 (1950).
9. J. W. Donovan and A. B. F. Duncan, J. Chem. Phys. 35, 1389 (1961).
10. J. A. Poole, J. Phys. Chem. 69, 1343 (1965).
11. B. S. Neporent, Zh. Fiz. Khim. 24, 1219 (1950).
12. M. Boudart and J. T. Dubois, J. Chem. Phys. 23, 233 (1955).
13. S. O. Mirumyants and B. S. Neporent, Opt. Spectry. U.S.S.R. 8, 414 (1960).
14. P. M. Rentzepis, Paper presented at the Fourth Molecular Crystal Symposium, Enschede, 1968.

TEMPERATURE AND SOLVENT EFFECTS ON THE FLUORESCENCE SPECTRUM OF 2,2'-BINAPHTHYL

Donald L. Horrocks

Chemistry Division
Argonne National Laboratory
Argonne, Illinois 60439

INTRODUCTION

In a study of the processes which determine the fluorescence of a solute in a solvent many techniques need to be employed. In this investigation the effects of temperature, concentration, excitation energy and type of solvent upon the fluorescence spectrum and efficiency of 2,2'-binaphthyl were studied.

The fluorescence spectrum of 2,2'-binaphthyl shows two major peaks at 355 mμ and 375 mμ. It has been shown that some solvents (aromatics and alcohols) enhance the emission from the higher energy level, 355 mμ. Other solvents (alicyclic and aliphatic) show a decrease in the 355 mμ band relative to the lower energy band, 375 mμ. The temperature and wavelength of excitation radiation produce changes in the relative amounts of fluorescence from these two energy levels for 2,2'-

binaphthyl in the alicyclic and aliphatic type solvents but show little or no effect for 2,2'-binaphthyl in the alcohol type solvents. A decrease in temperature or an increase in energy of excitation radiation (from 310 mμ to 260 mμ) increased the yield of the 355 mμ peak relative to the 375 mμ peak for 2,2'-binaphthyl in the alicyclic and aliphatic type solvents.

It is generally concluded[1] that molecules dissolved in cyclohexane show sharper vibrational structure than in alcohols and aromatics. However, in this work sharper structure was obtained with aromatic and alcohol type solvents. Since the 2,2'-binaphthyl has the same bridge structure between the two naphthyl groups as is present in bi-phenyl, there is a small steric hindrance to rotation about the bridging bond due to an overlap of the hydrogen atoms in the ortho positions. This might be the explanation for the temperature effect. Also the aromatic and alcohol type solvents may interact with the excited species in such a way as to hinder this freedom of rotation.

EXPERIMENTAL

COMPOUNDS. The compounds 1,1'-binaphthyl and 2,2'-binaphthyl were specially purified by dissolution, column elution and re-crystallization (at reduced temperature).[2] Three different sources of 2,2'-binaphthyl were purified in this manner and no differences in behavior were observed. Also, two sources of zone refined 2,2'-binaphthyl were used and the same properties were measured. All solvents used in this work were of spectroscopic grade.

SAMPLES. All samples were prepared by weighing the solute and solvent (flushed with argon to remove air) into a thin-walled (0.5 mm thick) quartz tubes (5 mm I.D.). The total sample volume was

0.25 ml for all of this investigation. The samples were prepared free of dissolved gases by the freeze, pump and thaw technique on a vacuum line. The samples were permanently sealed by flame to prevent evaporation or redissolution of gases, especially oxygen.

SCINTILLATION MEASUREMENTS. The relative scintillation efficiencies of the samples were measured by the Compton edge technique.[3] The scintillation measurements were made for the fast electrons produced by the Compton scattering of the 662 keV gamma rays from a ^{137}Cs source. The equipment used for measurement of the relative scintillation efficiencies has been described previously.[4]

FLUORESCENCE MEASUREMENTS. The fluorescence spectra were measured with the Aminco-Bowman Spectrophotometer (American Instruments Co.) with the Corrected Spectra attachment. The spectra were obtained by the front surface excitation-observation technique which helps reduce the probability of distortions of the spectra by self-absorption at high solute concentrations. Also to prevent scattering of the excitation beam into the analyzer monochromator the samples were placed at a slight angle so as not to be perpendicular to the excitation beam.

Fluorescence spectra were measured at different temperatures by equilibrating the sample in a constant temperature bath and then quickly placing it in the spectrophotometer for measurement. In all cases the spectra were repeated several times to be sure of the temperature effect.

RESULTS

CONCENTRATION EFFECT. The relative scintillation (fast electron excitation) and relative fluorescence (uv radiation excitation) efficiencies as a function of the concentration of solute in toluene were measured for the compounds 1,1'-binaphthyl (1,1'-BN) and 2,2'-binaphthyl (2,2'-BN). The results are shown in Figure 1. Both of these compounds have the same molecular composition differing only in their geometrical arrangement;

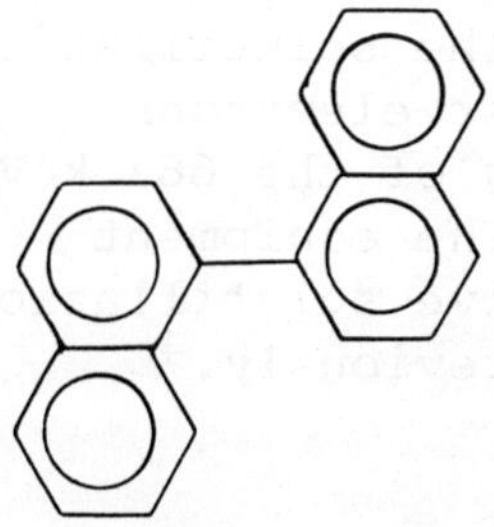

1,1'-binaphthyl

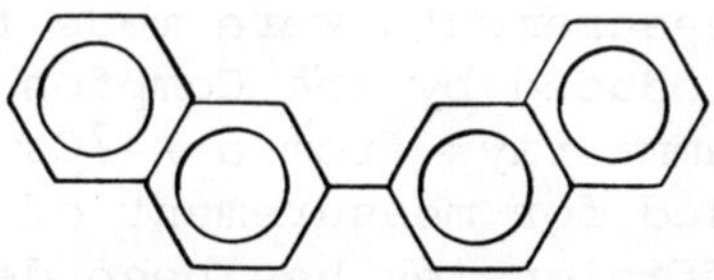

2,2'-binaphthyl

The 1,1'-BN can not obtain a co-planar configuration because of steric hinderance between the two naphthyl groups. However, 2,2'-BN can have a co-planar configuration with both naphthyl groups in the same plane.

From previous studies[5,6,7] it has been demonstrated that one requirement for the self-quenching process is the ability of the whole chromophore of the solute to obtain a co-planar configuration. In this work this theory was demonstrated by the lack of self-quenching for 1,1'-BN and the presence of self-quenching for 2,2'-BN. Figure 1 shows that the two different modes of excitation, fast electron and uv radiation, lead to the same concentration dependency in toluene solutions.

Figure 2 shows the fluorescence spectra for uv radiation excitation (310 mμ) as a function of the concentration of 1,1'-BN and 2,2'-BN in

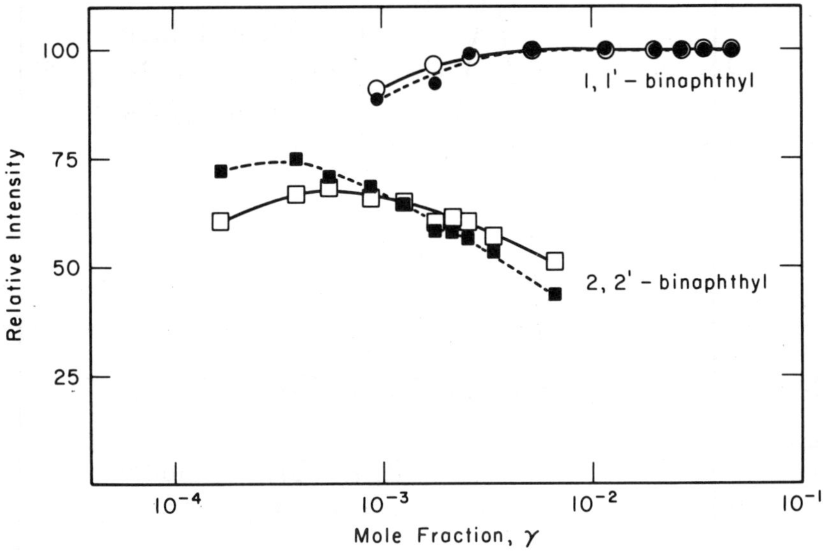

Figure 1 Relative scintillation (fast electron excitation) and fluorescence (uv radiation excitation) yields normalized to 100 for the maximum yield of 1,1'-binaphthyl as a function of the concentration of 1,1'-binaphthyl and 2,2'-binaphthyl in toluene. The mole fraction, γ, is $n_2/(n_1 + n_2)$ where n_1 and n_2 are the moles of solvent and solute, respectively.

——— fast electron excitation

----- uv radiation excitation

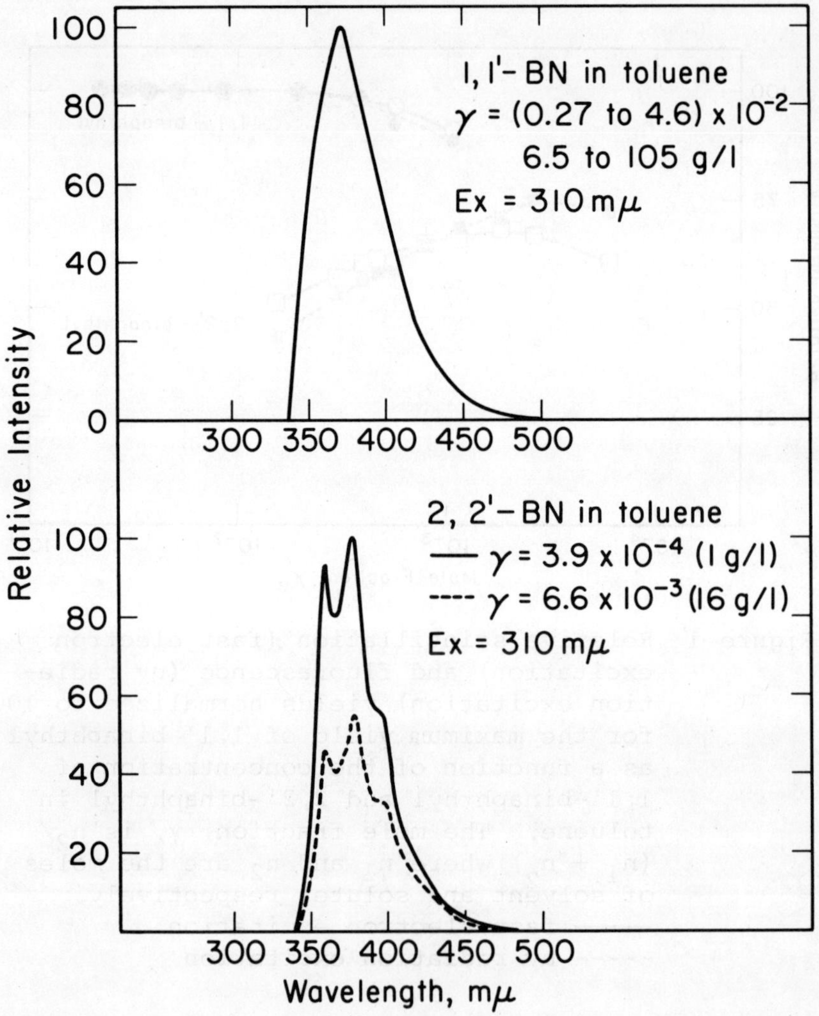

Figure 2 Concentration effect upon the fluorescence spectra of 1,1'-binaphthyl and 2,2'-binaphthyl in toluene. Spectra are normalized to relative intensity of 100 for the maximum of the fluorescence intensity.

toluene. In both cases the spectral distribution of the spectrum was not altered by concentration changes. This indicates that no excimers were formed over the concentration ranges studied. Over a wide concentration range (6 to 105 g/l) the relative fluorescence yield of 1,1'-BN was unchanged. At lower concentrations there was a decrease in the relative fluorescence yield, but no change in the spectral distribution, which was probably due to low geometry of the uv excitation beam and the solute molecules.

Figure 1 shows that there is a peak in the relative fluorescence yield of 2,2'-BN in toluene at about 1 g/l with decreases at lower and higher concentrations. The drop at lower concentrations is again probably a geometry effect. At the higher concentrations there is an increasing amount of self-quenching.

EXCITATION ENERGY EFFECT. The energy of the uv radiation which excited 2,2'-binaphthyl had an effect upon the relative amounts of the two major peaks in the fluorescence spectrum. For a given solvent an increase in energy from 310 mμ to 260 mμ produced an increase in the relative amount of the higher energy band of fluorescence, 355 mu. The effect was much greater for the alicyclic and aliphatic type solvents such as cyclohexane and n-hexane. Figure 3 shows the fluorescence spectrum of 2,2'-BN in cyclohexane at room temperature excited with 310 mμ and 260 mμ radiation. Listed in Table I are the ratios of the intensities of the two peaks for excitation with 310 mμ and 260 mμ radiation. Because of the strong absorption of 260 mμ radiation by aromatic solvents such as toluene it was not possible to make a comparison with toluene as the solvent.

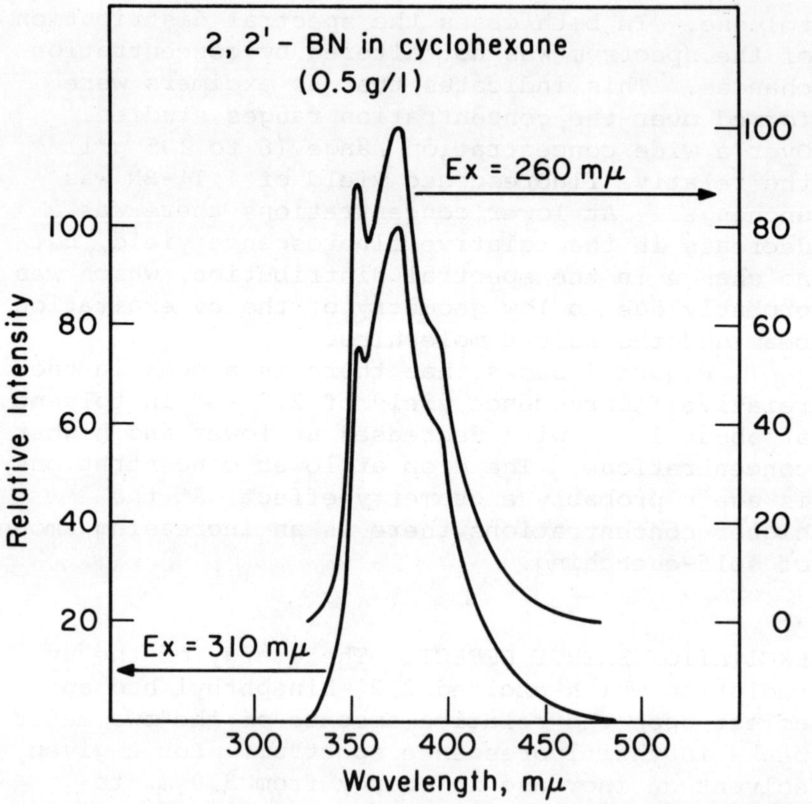

Figure 3 Effect of excitation energy upon the fluorescence spectrum of 2,2'-binaphthyl in cyclohexane. Energy of uv excitation radiation (Ex) was 310 mμ and 260 mμ.

TABLE I: Relative Intensity of Selected Parts of the Fluorescence Spectrum

Solvent	Temperature °C	I_{355}/I_{375} Ex = 310 mμ	I_{355}/I_{375} Ex = 260 mμ	I_{valley}/I_{375} Ex = 310 mμ	I_{valley}/I_{375} Ex = 260 mμ
Toluene	100	.90		.82	
	24	.90		.78	
	0	.90		.76	
	-78	.90		.68	
Ethanol	100	.92	.94	.82	.82
	24	.92	.94	.79	.79
	0	.92	---	.74	
	-78	.92	.94	.66	.66
Cyclohexane	100	a	.84	a	.81
	24	.75	.87	.72	.78
	4	.75	.88	.71	.77
n-hexane	100	a	.81	a	.79
	24	.77	.86	.72	.77
	0	---	.87	---	.75
	-78	.79	.93	.64	.69

[a] There was no valley at all, only a shoulder. I_{355}, I_{375}, and I_{valley} are the intensities of the 355 mμ peak, the 375 mμ peak and the valley between these two peaks, respectively. Ex is the excitation radiation.

SOLVENT EFFECT. The choice of solvent had very little effect upon the wavelength of the fluorescence spectrum of 2,2'-BN. Table II lists the solvents studied and the wavelengths of the two major peaks and the low energy shoulder of the fluorescence spectra. The solvents are divided into two groups. There is a small red shift from the alicyclic and aliphatic types to the aromatic and alcohol types.

In general it has been the practice to use a solvent such as cyclohexane to provide a better resolved fluorescence spectrum. However, in this work it was observed that the alicyclic and aliphatic type solvents gave poorer resolution of the fluorescence bands than did the aromatic and alcohol type solvents. Table I also lists the ratio of the intensities of the two peaks for different solvents. The relative intensity of these two peaks was dependent upon the type of solvent employed. The relative intensity of the 355 mμ peak was considerably less for the alicyclic and aliphatic type solvents provided the temperature was not lowered too much (as will be discussed in the next section).

TEMPERATURE EFFECT. Table I gives results of the study of the effect of temperature on the relative intensity of the two major peaks of the fluorescence spectrum and the depth of the valley between them (the degree of resolution). Figures 4 and 5 show the effect of temperature upon the fluorescence spectra of 2,2'-BN in ethanol and n-hexane, respectively. In all cases a decrease in temperature produced a deepening of the valley and even lead to the resolution of a peak from the shoulder at 395 mμ at -78°C.

The effect of temperature upon the relative intensity of the two peaks was dependent upon the type of solvent. The aromatic and alcohol type solvents showed no change in the relative

TABLE II: Solvent Effect on the Fluorescence Spectrum

Solvents with peaks at 355, 375, and (395) mμ	Solvents with peaks at 357, 377, and (397) mμ
n-hexane	toluene
n-pentane	benzene
cyclohexane	ethanol
cyclopentane	1-hexanol
paraffin oil	
methyl-cyclohexane	
cyclohexane	
1,5-hexadiene	

(395) and (397) indicate shoulders in the spectra which are resolved as peaks only at temperatures as low as -78°C.

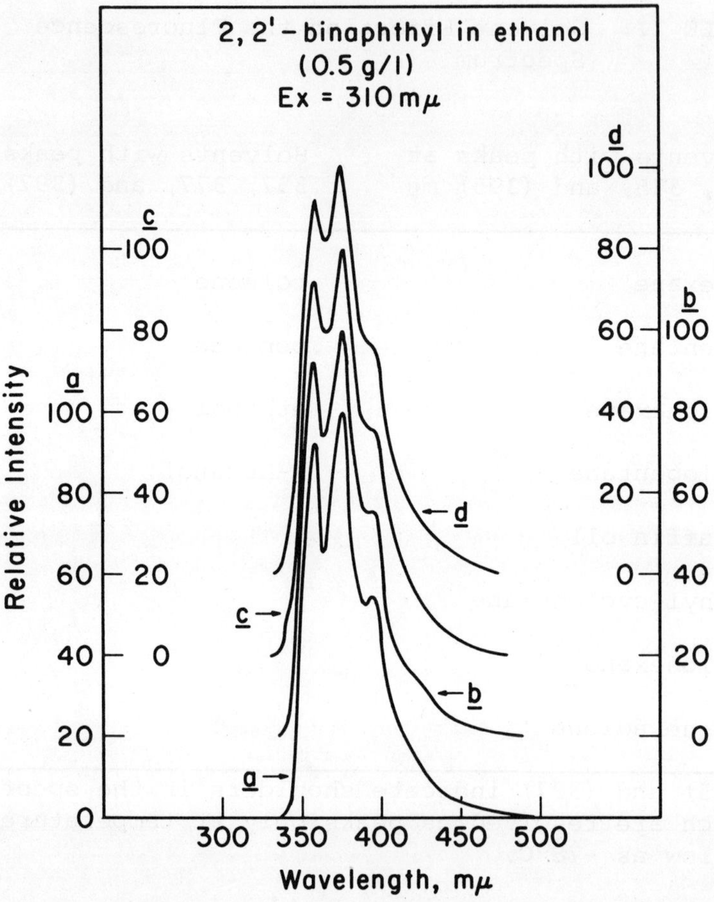

Figure 4 Effect of temperature upon the fluorescence spectrum of 2,2'-binaphthyl in ethanol at 0.5 g/l and Ex of 310 mμ. (a) -78°C (b) 0°C (c) 24°C and (d)100°C.

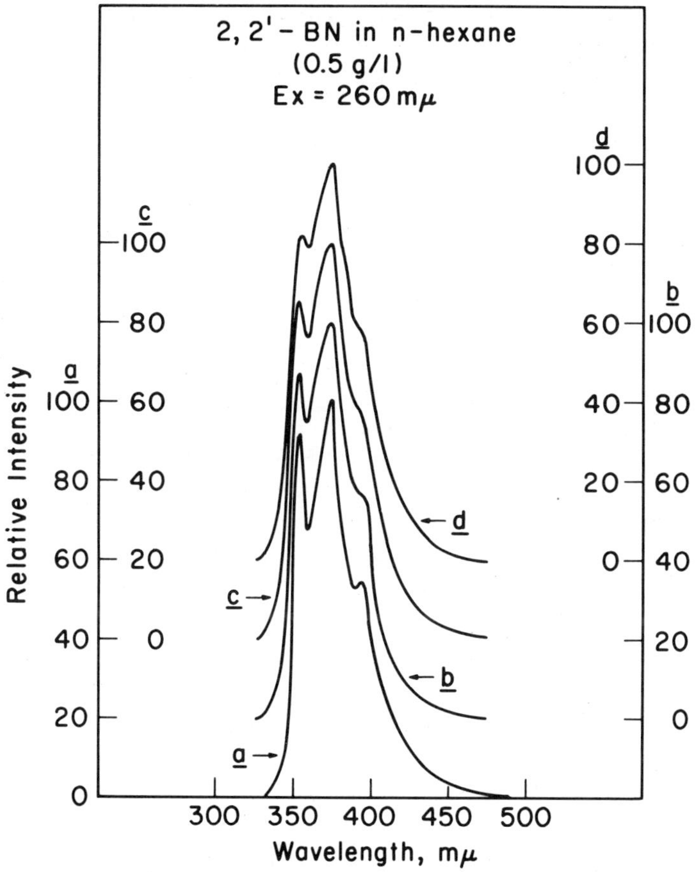

Figure 5 Effect of temperature upon the fluorescence spectrum of 2,2'-binaphthyl in n-hexane at 0.5 g/l and Ex of 260 mμ. (a) -78°C, (b) 0°C, (c) 24°C, and (d) 100°C.

intensities as a function of the temperature between 100°C and -78°C. In the alicyclic and aliphatic type solvents a decrease in the temperature increased the relative amount of the 355 mμ intensity.

DISCUSSION OF RESULTS

Three main points were concluded from the results of this investigation;

(1) With alicyclic and aliphatic type solvents the intensity of the 355 mμ peak is dependent upon the energy of the excitation radiation and the temperature.

(2) With aromatic and alcohol type solvents the intensity of the 355 mμ peak is independent of the temperature and only slightly dependent upon the energy of the excitation radiation.

(3) The resolution of the peaks of the spectrum is improved by decreasing the temperature.

The bridging bond in 2,2'-BN is the same as in bi-phenyl but there are two configurations which are possible;

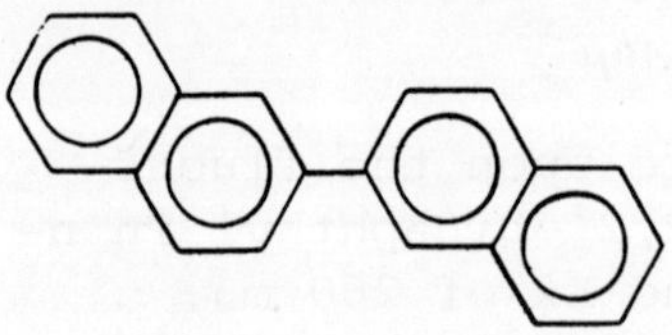

(1)

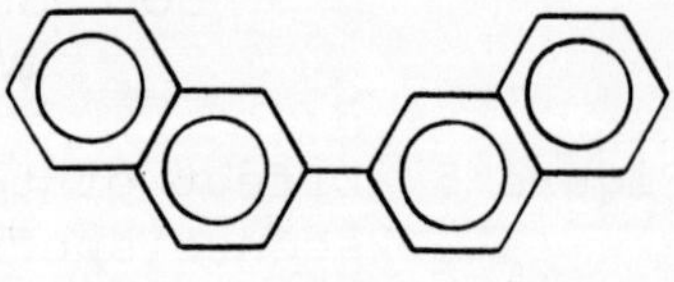

(2)

It is possible that one of these configurations may be more probable than the other. In the solvents such as cyclohexane and n-hexane the conversion from the less favorable form to the more favorable form may be unhindered. However, lowering the temperature may reduce the probability of this intraconversion. Also certain solvents such as the aromatics and alcohols may also hinder the intraconversion. The increased energy of excitation may promote the lower energy form into the higher energy form. Each of these factors could lead to an increased emission from the higher energy level.

The improved resolution between the peaks in the fluorescence with reduced temperature can also be explained as the result of less intraconversion between the two states. This could be the result of longer lifetimes of the different forms and emission with less overlap of energy.

The lack of self-quenching of 1,1'-BN and presence of self-quenching of 2,2'-BN with increasing concentration confirms the requirement of a co-planar chromophore for self-quenching. These results also could be concluded to show that in the excited state the 2,2'-BN has a planar chromophore. If the freedom of rotation is responsible for the differences in the intensity of the 355 mμ peak, there should be less self-quenching in solvents such as cyclohexane. Unfortunately the solubility limit of 2,2'-BN in cyclohexane is too low to permit this type of a study. Methyl substituted 2,2'-BN should have an increased solubility[2] and could aid in this type of study provided the methyl groups were substituted in other than the ortho position where they would destroy the co-planar chromophore.

REFERENCES

1. I. B. Berlman, Handbook of Fluorescence Spectra of Aromatic Molecules (Academic Press, New York, 1965), p. 32.
2. H. O. Wirth, F. U. Herrmann, G. Herrmann and W. Kern, Organic Scintillators, D. L. Horrocks, Ed. (Gordon and Breach, New York, 1968), p. 321.
3. D. L. Horrocks, Nature 202, 78 (1964).
4. D. L. Horrocks, Nucl. Instr. Meth. 27, 253 (1964); ibid. 30, 157 (1964).
5. D. L. Horrocks and H. O. Wirth, Organic Scintillators, D. L. Horrocks, Ed. (Gordon and Breach, New York, 1968), p. 375.
6. D. L. Horrocks and H. O. Wirth, J. Chem. Phys. (in press, 1968).
7. D. L. Horrocks, J. Chem. Phys. (in press, 1968).

ZEEMAN EFFECT OF PHOSPHORESCENCE

Tohru Azumi

Institute for Solid State Physics
University of Tokyo
Roppongi, Minato-ku, Tokyo, Japan

I. INTRODUCTION

Phosphorescence of organic molecules was interpreted by Terenin[1] and by Lewis and Kasha[2] to be the multiplicity forbidden emission; namely, for majority of organic molecules where the ground state is singlet the Jablonski's "phosphorescent state"[3] was identified as the triplet state. Since then, considerable efforts have been devoted to date to substantiate the mechanism suggested by these authors. It is at present the usual notion that the triplet nature of the phosphorescent state is fairly well established. However, it seems not unworthy to recall these efforts and to judge how much the usually accepted notion is founded.

Probably, the most direct works reported so far along this line are the measurements of paramagnetic susceptibility[4] in earlier days and the recent ESR measurements of the excited triplet state.[5] These works have revealed that the triplet state is produced by irradiation of solid solution of organic molecules by ultraviolet light and that it decays in a manner nearly identical to phosphorescence. The triplet state is considered simultaneously the phosphorescent state because of the approximate identity of the decay mode. Other evidence which shows the forbiddeness of the phosphorescence comes from the heavy-atom effect, both intramolecular and intermolecular. McClure[6] found that the introduction of heavy atoms such as halogen and sulfur to hydrocarbon molecules decreases the phosphorescence lifetime considerably, and that this lifetime decrease is quantitatively explained by the increase of spin-orbit coupling in the presence of heavy atoms. The decrease of the phosphorescence lifetime in the heavy atom containing solvents is also interpreted by McGlynn[7] in a similar manner.

As is seen in the two examples cited above, the phosphorescence lifetime data have frequently been presented as evidence supporting the identity of the phosphorescent state to the triplet state. However, conclusions based on lifetime data are not unique, and can not be served as a conclusive evidence. For, it is not certain whether the phosphorescent state is simultaneously the triplet state itself or is a certain kinetically rate-limiting state or species produced via the triplet state. In view of the long lifetime of the triplet state and its potency to photochemical reactions this suspicion does not seem too unrealistic. A pertinent example is delayed thermal fluorescence,[8] or alpha-phosphorescence[9] in the widely used, but somewhat misleading, terminology. This emission consists of thermal excitation to the singlet excited state followed by fluorescence emission; its lifetime is identical to that of the phosphorescence; however, as is well known, the emission starts out actually from the singlet state and not from the triplet state.

As described above many experiments carried out to date do not necessarily present conclusive evidence of the triplet nature of the phosphorescence. One might suppose that a Zeeman splitting of the phosphorescence would provide the most unambiguous verification of the triplet nature of the phosphorescent state. This experiment was already suggested by Weisman and Lipkin[10] in 1942; however, no attempts have been reported to date. The lack of such attempts is probably due to the difficulties in observing the phosphorescence spectrum sharp enough to resolve the Zeeman splitting.

In this paper are presented our efforts in this uncultivated field. Having succeeded observing Zeeman splitting for pyrazine, we analyze the phosphorescence intensities for the Zeeman split components. These analyses will provide us fertile information on the triplet subcomponents and on the manner in which the spin-forbidden emission processes acquire intensity.

II. ZEEMAN SPLITTING

We have succeeded observing the Zeeman splitting for the phosphorescence of pyrazine crystal.[11] The effect of the magnetic field is shown in Fig. 1. Here the upper portion is the emission under zero magnetic field. The four emission lines are, from left to right, 26106, 26096, 26090, and 26066 cm^{-1}. The group of these four lines are repeatedly found in progressions of 606, 759, 953, 1012, and 1254 cm^{-1}. In view of the agreement of these progressions with the Raman frequency,[12] the four lines shown in Fig. 1 are interpreted to be due to pyrazine.[13] Application of the magnetic field of 15400 gauss broadens the emission lines considerably as is shown in the lower portion of Fig. 1. Microphotometer tracings of the plate are shown in Fig. 2. It is now clear

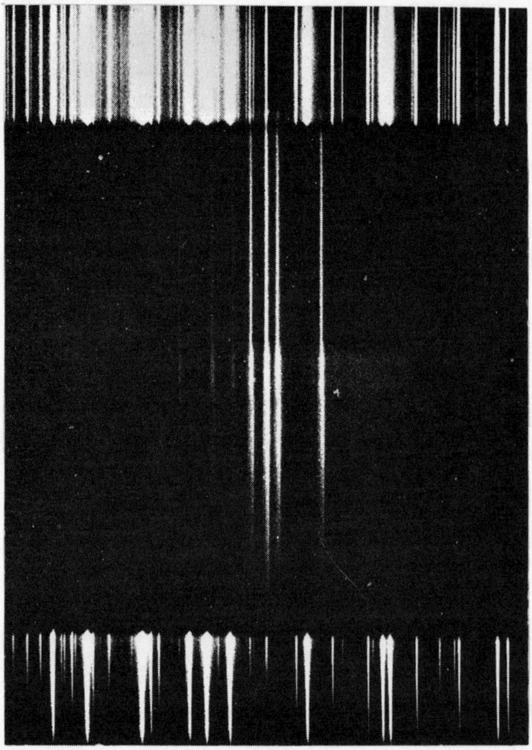

Figure 1 Zeeman effect of the phosphorescence of pyrazine crystals.

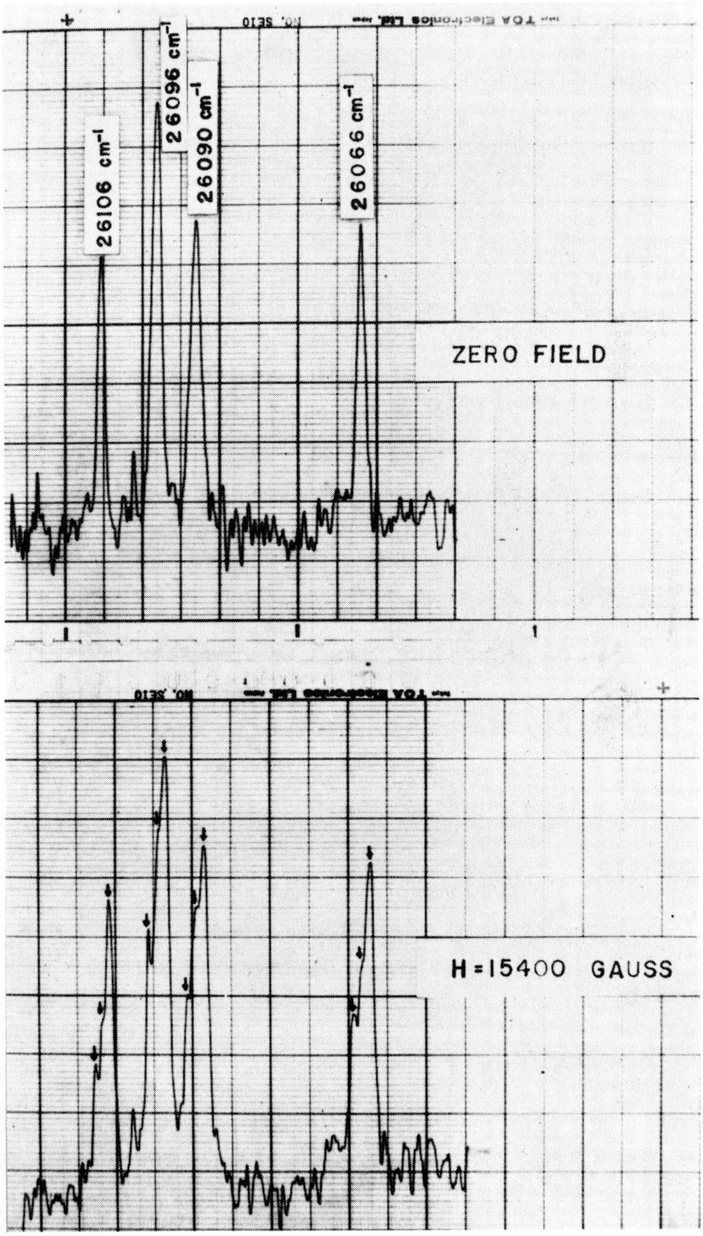

Figure 2 Microphotometer tracings of the plate shown in Figure 1.

that each line splits into three subcomponents, the lower energy component being the most intense. The separation between two nearest subcomponents is approximately 1.4 cm^{-1} for all lines.

The observed splitting of 1.4 cm^{-1} in the triplet state is just what one expects for the free spin. This observation is contrast to the statement of Douglas[14] that the Zeeman splitting of the singlet to triplet absorption of pyrazine vapor is small compared with the splitting of the free spin. Further, this observation may also indicate that the zero field splitting parameters D and E are negligible at this magnetic field.

III. PHOSPHORESCENCE INTENSITIES

Let the lowest triplet state be produced by an excitation of an electron from a molecular orbital ψ_a to a molecular orbital ψ_b. We choose the following zeroth order triplet eigenfunctions.

$$|T_x\rangle = 2^{-\frac{1}{2}}(|\overline{\psi}_a\overline{\psi}_b| - |\psi_a\psi_b|)$$

$$|T_y\rangle = 2^{-\frac{1}{2}}(|\overline{\psi}_a\overline{\psi}_b| + |\psi_a\psi_b|) \qquad (1)$$

$$|T_z\rangle = 2^{-\frac{1}{2}}(|\psi_a\overline{\psi}_b| + |\overline{\psi}_a\psi_b|)$$

The Hamiltonian for Zeeman effect is represented by

$$H = g\beta H(\ell S_x + mS_y + nS_z) \qquad (2)$$

where ℓ, m, and n are direction cosines of molecular axes, x, y, and z, respectively, with the field direction. Further, the zero field splitting parameters D and E are neglected. When magnetic field is applied, triplet wavefunctions $|T_1\rangle$, $|T_0\rangle$, and $|T_{-1}\rangle$ are now represented in terms of (1) as

$$\begin{bmatrix} |T_1\rangle \\ \\ |T_0\rangle \\ \\ |T_{-1}\rangle \end{bmatrix} = \begin{bmatrix} \sqrt{\dfrac{1-\ell^2}{2}} & \dfrac{n+i\ell m}{\sqrt{2(1-\ell^2)}} & \dfrac{-(n\ell+im)}{\sqrt{2(1-\ell^2)}} \\ \\ \ell & im & n \\ \\ \sqrt{\dfrac{1-\ell^2}{2}} & \dfrac{n-i\ell m}{\sqrt{2(1-\ell^2)}} & \dfrac{-(n\ell-im)}{\sqrt{2(1-\ell^2)}} \end{bmatrix} \begin{bmatrix} |T_x\rangle \\ \\ |T_y\rangle \\ \\ |T_z\rangle \end{bmatrix} \quad (3)$$

The spin-orbit interaction which makes spin-forbidden triplet-singlet transitions allowed is approximated as

$$H_{so} = \sum_i \xi_i \ell_i s_i \quad (4)$$

where two electron operators are neglected. Then, the phosphorescence intensities from the three subcomponents, $|T_1\rangle$, $|T_0\rangle$, and $|T_{-1}\rangle$, which are denoted by I_1, I_0, and I_{-1}, are easily obtained as

$$\begin{bmatrix} I_1/g_1 \\ \\ I_0/g_0 \\ \\ I_{-1}/g_{-1} \end{bmatrix} = c \begin{bmatrix} \dfrac{1-\ell^2}{2} & \dfrac{1-m^2}{2} & \dfrac{1-n^2}{2} \\ \\ \ell^2 & m^2 & n^2 \\ \\ \dfrac{1-\ell^2}{2} & \dfrac{1-m^2}{2} & \dfrac{1-n^2}{2} \end{bmatrix} \begin{bmatrix} u_x \\ \\ u_y \\ \\ u_z \end{bmatrix} \quad (6)$$

where c is a proportionality constant, g's represent the Boltzmann populations of the respective components, and further, u_x, u_y, and u_z represent the contribution to intensity from ℓ_x, ℓ_y, and ℓ_z, in spin-orbit coupling (4). This relationship may be verified using an oriented sample; this is the subject we are presently attempting to work. In the following, intensity relationship is derived for the pyrazine solution in which solutes are randomly oriented. The manner of derivation is not described here since it is similar to that adapted by Albrecht[15] in developing the theory of photoselection.

We consider the experimental arrangement shown schematically in Fig. 3. Namely, excitation is effected with the unpolarized light incident along b axis onto ac face. The magnetic field is applied along c axis. The emitted phosphorescence may be viewed along b axis or along c axis. These two types of observations are denoted as straight view and side view, respectively. We assume that at a given wavelength absorption takes place in x, y, and z axes of the molecule with the fraction of r_x, r_y, and r_z, respectively. Similarly, we assume that at a given wavelength the phosphorescence is polarized along x, y, and z axes with the fraction of q_x, q_y, and q_z, respectively.

Rather tedious integration procedures yield the results in Table I for the two different observations.

For 0,0 band of pyrazine phosphorescence, group theoretical consideration predicts $u_y = 1$ and $q_z = 1$. Polarization observed by Krishna and Goodman[16] is in agreement with this prediction. (The molecular axes are defined as recommended by Mulliken. Namely, z axis lies in the molecular plane in the N-N axis and x axis is normal to the molecular plane.) We consider two different wavelength regions of excitation, one for $^1B_{2u}(\pi,\pi^*)$ state (at 37839 cm^{-1}) and the other for $^1B_{3u}(n,\pi^*)$ state (at 30776 cm^{-1}). Namely, for the former, $r_y = 1$ and for the latter $r_x = 1$. Then, for $^1B_{2u}(\pi,\pi^*)$ excitation,

$$I_1:I_0:I_{-1} = 13g_1:16g_0:13g_{-1} \tag{9}$$

Similarly for $^1B_{3u}(n,\pi^*)$ excitation,

$$I_1:I_0:I_{-1} = 8g_1:5g_0:8g_{-1} \tag{10}$$

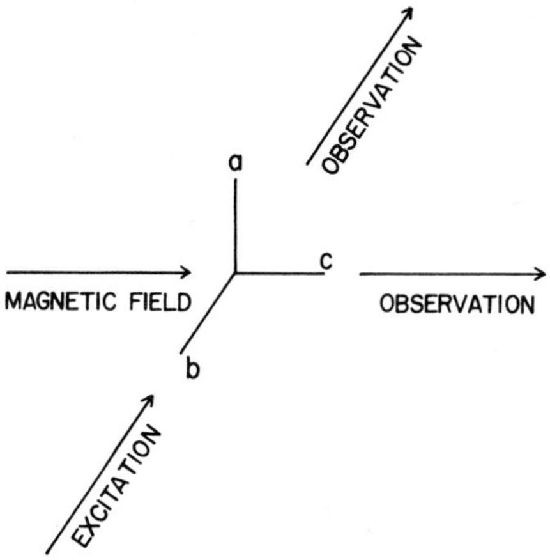

Figure 3 Experimental arrangement.

	$^1B_{2u}(\pi,\pi^*)$ EXCITATION		$^1B_{3u}(n,\pi^*)$ EXCITATION	
	VERTICAL EXCITATION	HORIZONTAL EXCITATION	VERTICAL EXCITATION	HORIZONTAL EXCITATION
	H=0 H≠0	H=0 H≠0	H=0 H≠0	H=0 H≠0
A/g	14 5 4 5	28 5 18 5	14 4 6 4	28 11 6 11
B/g	28 11 6 11	28 5 18 5	28 6 16 6	28 11 6 11
C/g	28 12 4 12	14 4 6 4	28 11 6 11	14 6 2 6
P (STRAIGHT VIEW)	$\frac{-1}{3}$ $\frac{-7}{17}$ 0 $\frac{-7}{17}$	$\frac{1}{3}$ $\frac{1}{9}$ $\frac{1}{2}$ $\frac{1}{9}$	$\frac{-1}{3}$ $\frac{-7}{15}$ 0 $\frac{-7}{15}$	$\frac{1}{3}$ $\frac{5}{17}$ $\frac{1}{2}$ $\frac{5}{17}$
P (SIDE VIEW)	$\frac{-1}{3}$ $\frac{-3}{8}$ $\frac{-1}{5}$ $\frac{-3}{8}$	0 0 0 0	$\frac{-1}{3}$ $\frac{-1}{5}$ $\frac{-5}{11}$ $\frac{-1}{5}$	0 0 0 0

Figure 4 Predicted phosphorescence intensities and polarizations for pyrazine phosphorescence under different modes of excitation (see the text).

If these ratios are calculated with the Boltzmann distribution at 4.2°K for three substates that are 1.4 cm^{-1} apart successively,

$$I_1:I_0:I_{-1} = 1.0:0.76:0.38 \quad (11)$$

for $^1B_{2u}(\pi,\pi^*)$ excitation

and

$$I_1:I_0:I_{-1} = 1.0:0.39:0.38 \quad (12)$$

for $^1B_{3u}(n,\pi^*)$ excitation

Now our experimental results shown in Fig. 2 are for polycrystalline sample. We shall first assume that in our polycrystalline sample, the molecules are randomly oriented. While admitting that this is a crude approximation, we shall compare the results expressed in (11) and (12) with those of Fig. 2. It is then seen that the intensity relationship is more in conformity with the $^1B_{2u}(\pi,\pi^*)$ excitation, which is exactly what we expect from our experimental conditions.

The above treatments may be extended to the cases where both excitation and observation are carried out with polarized light. General equations, which are similar in form to Eqs. (9) and (10) but are considerably more complex, are available. However, because of their complexity, these equations are not reproduced here. We merely present in Fig. 4, as a specific example, the prediction for pyrazine phosphorescence. In Fig. 4 are shown predicted phosphorescence intensities polarized either along a, b, or c axis (these are denoted by A, B, C, respectively) under the four different modes of excitation.

The length of the vertical lines and the numbers specified indicate the phosphorescence intensities divided by the population of the upper level. It is immediately seen how zero field intensities are split up into three subcomponents under the presence of magnetic field. Shown also in Fig. 4 are the values of polarization, P,

$$P = \frac{I_{\parallel} - I_{\perp}}{I_{\parallel} + I_{\perp}}$$

for straight view and for side view.

It is clear from Fig. 4 that the phosphorescence intensity distributions along the three triplet subcomponents vary to a great deal according to the manner of excitation and observation. In this viewpoint, we suggest that the polarization measurements under the magnetic field be carried out; these experiments will give us valuable information on the magnetic subcomponents of the triplet state.

TABLE I

(1) Straight view (observation along b axis)

$$I_0 = g_0 \tilde{r}\left\{u_x\begin{bmatrix}24 & 16 & 16\\16 & 16 & 10\\16 & 10 & 16\end{bmatrix} + u_y\begin{bmatrix}16 & 16 & 10\\16 & 24 & 16\\10 & 16 & 16\end{bmatrix} + u_z\begin{bmatrix}16 & 10 & 16\\10 & 16 & 16\\16 & 16 & 24\end{bmatrix}\right\}\tilde{q}$$

$$I_{\pm 1} = g_{\pm 1}\tilde{r}\left\{u_x\begin{bmatrix}16 & 13 & 13\\13 & 20 & 16\\13 & 16 & 20\end{bmatrix} + u_y\begin{bmatrix}20 & 13 & 16\\13 & 16 & 13\\16 & 13 & 20\end{bmatrix} + u_z\begin{bmatrix}20 & 16 & 13\\16 & 20 & 13\\13 & 13 & 16\end{bmatrix}\right\}\tilde{q} \qquad (7)$$

(2) Side view (observation along c axis)

$$I_0 = g_0 \tilde{r}\left\{u_x\begin{bmatrix}9 & 24 & 23\\10 & 15 & 17\\9 & 17 & 16\end{bmatrix} + u_y\begin{bmatrix}17 & 8 & 17\\22 & 11 & 23\\17 & 9 & 16\end{bmatrix} + u_z\begin{bmatrix}16 & 17 & 9\\17 & 16 & 9\\23 & 23 & 10\end{bmatrix}\right\}\tilde{q}$$

$$I_{\pm 1} = g_{\pm 1}\tilde{r}\left\{u_x\begin{bmatrix}16.5 & 12.5 & 13\\19.5 & 13.5 & 16\\20 & 16 & 13\end{bmatrix} + u_y\begin{bmatrix}12.5 & 20.5 & 16\\13.5 & 15.5 & 13\\16 & 20 & 13\end{bmatrix} + u_z\begin{bmatrix}13 & 16 & 20\\16 & 13 & 20\\13 & 13 & 16\end{bmatrix}\right\}\tilde{q} \qquad (8)$$

Where $\tilde{r} = \begin{bmatrix}r_x & r_y & r_z\end{bmatrix}$ and $\tilde{q} = \begin{bmatrix}q_x\\q_y\\q_z\end{bmatrix}$

TABLE I: (Continued)

Hence of course

$$\tilde{r}\begin{bmatrix} c_{11} & c_{12} & c_{13} \\ c_{21} & c_{22} & c_{23} \\ c_{31} & c_{32} & c_{33} \end{bmatrix}\tilde{q} =$$

$$\begin{aligned} & c_{11}r_xq_x + c_{12}r_xq_y + c_{13}r_xq_z \\ & + c_{21}r_yq_x + c_{22}r_yq_y + c_{23}r_yq_z \\ & + c_{31}r_zq_x + c_{32}r_zq_y + c_{33}r_zq_z \end{aligned}$$

REFERENCES

1. A. Terenin, Acta Physicochem. USSR, 18, 210 (1943).
2. G. N. Lewis and M. Kasha, J. Am. Chem. Soc. 66, 2100 (1944).
3. A. Jablonski, Z. Physik 94, 38 (1935).
4. G. N. Lewis and M. Calvin, J. Am. Chem. Soc. 67, 1232 (1945).
5. C. A. Hutchison and B. W. Mangum, J. Chem. Phys. 29, 952 (1958); J. H. van der Waals and M. S. de Groot, Mol. Phys. 2, 333 (1959); W. A. Yager, E. Wasserman, and K. M. R. Cramer, J. Chem. Phys. 37, 1148 (1962).
6. D. S. McClure, J. Chem. Phys. 17, 905 (1949).
7. S. P. McGlynn, M. R. Reynolds, G. W. Daigre and N. Christodouleas, J. Chem. Phys. 66, 2499 (1962); S. P. McGlynn, J. Daigre, and F. J. Smith, J. Chem. Phys. 40, 507 (1964).
8. S. P. McGlynn, T. Azumi, and M. Kinoshita, The Molecular Spectroscopy of the Triplet State, (Prentice Hall, 1968).
9. G. N. Lewis, D. Lipkin and T. T. Magel, J. Am. Chem. Soc. 63, 3005 (1941).
10. S. I. Weisman and D. Lipkin, J. Am. Chem. Soc. 64, 1916 (1942).
11. T. Azumi, Y. Udagawa, M. Ito and S. Nagakura, J. Chem. Phys. 47, 4850 (1967).
12. M. Ito and T. Shigeoka, J. Chem. Phys. 44, 1001 (1966).
13. These lines, however, do not coincide with the onset of the singlet to triplet absorption. Detailed examination of the spectra have revealed that these emission lines are due to some crystal defects of pyrazine. T. Azumi, Y. Nakano, and M. Ito (to be published).
14. A. E. Douglas, Disc. Faraday Soc. 35, 235 (1963).
15. A. C. Albrecht, J. Mol. Spectroscopy 6, 84 (1961).
16. V. G. Krishna and L. Goodman, J. Chem. Phys. 36, 2217 (1961).

POLARIZATION OF ELECTRONIC TRANSITIONS OF AROMATIC HYDROCARBONS

J. B. Gallivan and J. S. Brinen

Central Research Division
American Cyanamid Company
Stamford, Connecticut 06904

INTRODUCTION

The experimental verification of the assignment of electronic states involved in electronic emission and absorption processes has been significantly enhanced by the use of polarized light and method of photoselection.[1] This technique has been successfully applied to fluorescence and phosphorescence measurements,[2-5] to ESR-optical studies,[6,7] and in at least one instance[8] to triplet-triplet absorption measurements.

In this communication we report polarization measurements on both the spin-allowed ($S_1 \rightarrow S_o$ and $T \rightarrow T'$) and spin-forbidden ($T_1 \rightarrow S_o$) transitions of phenanthrene (h_{10} and d_{10}), chrysene and picene. These compounds were chosen because they form a simple series of aromatic hydrocarbons of known geometry and symmetry, and each exhibits well characterized luminescence and singlet-singlet absorption as well as strong triplet-triplet absorption spectra. Polarization measurements for some of the transitions of interest in these systems have been reported[2,9,10] but various experimental differences make quantitative comparisons impossible.

Albrecht[1,3] has stressed the value of coordinating fluorescence and phosphorescence studies and this detailed study, which also includes T → T' polarization results, permits group theoretical assignments of five electronically excited states for each molecule. Particular emphasis is placed on the pure electronic component (0-0 band) of the transitions involved. Variations in the polarization of vibronic bands within a given transition, differences in detail between the light and heavy phenanthrene and the vibronic interactions which account for these variations will be considered in a subsequent publication.

EXPERIMENTAL

The instrumentation used for the polarized luminescence and low temperature singlet-singlet absorption measurements has been described elsewhere.[11] A 1000 Watt Xenon Arc has been added as an excitation source for luminescence measurements. This source proved to be especially valuable for selective excitation into isolated vibronic bands of the different transitions in the near UV for the molecules examined. The low temperature absorption spectra were run at several different dilutions so that transitions having very different extinction coefficients could be observed at convenient optical densities.

The techniques and instrumentation used for triplet-triplet (T - T) absorption measurements have also been outlined previously.[12,13] To measure polarized T - T absorption spectra, one polarizer was placed between the UV source used for excitation and the sample, while the second was placed between the tungsten source used to monitor the T - T absorption and the sample. As in the case of the polarized luminescence, four separate measurements were made to obtain each data point. These four corresponded to parallel and perpendicular settings of the analyzer with respect to the polarizer set at first 0° (perpendicular to the lab axis) and then 90° (parallel to the lab axis). All polarization data were treated according to the equation derived in reference 11.

The sources of the chemicals used in this study and comments concerning their purity were given by Brinen.[13] For the phenanthrenes, 3-methylpentane (3MP) was used as the solvent, while 2-methyltetrahydrofuran (MTHF) proved to be a better solvent for the chrysenes and picene. Both of these solvents were purified by methods described previously.[14]

SPECTROSCOPIC MEASUREMENTS

Singlet-singlet absorption spectra of the molecules under investigation were measured at $77^{o}K$ in dilute solutions of organic glasses. These measurements served to define clearly the wavelength regions of the three lowest excited singlet states and permitted careful selection of excitation wavelengths for the luminescence measurements as required by the method of photoselection. The polarization of the fluorescence and phosphorescence was studied for excitation into the three different excited singlet states using a 1000 Watt Xenon Arc as an excitation source. Such careful excitation could not be achieved for the triplet-triplet polarization studies for which a 250 W Hg arc was employed. However, wherever possible, unique excitation into a single electronic transition was employed.

Although the emphasis in this study is placed on the polarization behavior of the 0-0 band of the transition under investigation, the relatively sharp emission spectra of these molecules permitted detailed vibronic polarization measurements. In determining the polarization of the vibrational bands the observed intensities were used with no attempt to resolve overlapping bands. Similarly, the high triplet-triplet extinction coefficients of these molecules[13] enabled polarization measurements to be performed on more than one vibronic band in the T-T' spectrum. The poor solubility of picene made these latter measurements too uncertain on bands other than the pure electronic band.

RESULTS AND DISCUSSION

The relevant data are presented in Figures 1-3 and Tables I-III for phenanthrene, chrysene and picene in that order. Because of the similarity between phenanthrene h_{10} and d_{10}, only the spectra of the latter are shown, while pertinent polarization data for both are given in Table I.

PHENANTHRENE (h_{10} and d_{10}). On the basis of absorption measurements on single crystals of phenanthrene, McClure[15,16] determined that the ^1L_b transition is short axis polarized, while the ^1L_a is long axis polarized. Ganguly and Choudhury[17] have shown that the fluorescence of the single crystal is also short axis polarized and several workers[2,4] have demonstrated this using the photoselection technique. Our results (Figure 1 and Table I) on the fluorescence 0-0 band show positive polarization with ^1L_b excitation in agreement with the previously published works. The observed negative polarization with ^1L_a excitation (Tables I, II) is also consistent with previous work. The strong negative polarization observed for 253 mμ excitation shows that this transition‡ is long axis polarized which agrees well with theoretical predictions.[18,19,20]

The 0-0 band of the phosphorescence is negatively polarized relative to all three absorption

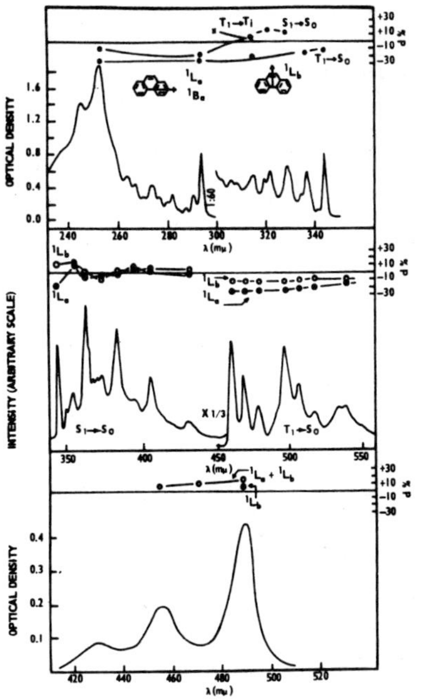

Figure 1 (a) Top-Singlet-singlet absorption spectrum of phenanthrene-d_{10} in 3MP at 77°K, showing the three lowest energy transitions and their polarizations. Above the spectrum the percent polarization of the fluorescence ($S_1 \rightarrow S_o$), phosphorescence ($T_1 \rightarrow S_o$) and triplet-triplet ($T_1 \rightarrow T_i$) absorption is shown for excitation at the wavelengths indicated.

(b) Middle-Fluorescence ($S_1 \rightarrow S_o$) and phosphorescence ($T_1 \rightarrow S_o$) spectra of $C_{14}D_{10}$ in 3MP at 77°K. Above the spectra the percent polarization is shown for the various vibrational bands of each transition for ^1L_b (330 mμ) and ^1L_a (294 mμ) excitation.

(c) Bottom-Triplet-triplet absorption spectrum of $C_{14}D_{10}$ in 3MP at 77°K. Above the spectrum the percent polarization at the indicated wavelengths is given for ^1L_b and mixed ^1L_a + ^1L_b excitation.

TABLE I: Polarization of the Electronic Transitions of Phenanthrene (h_{10} and d_{10})

Excitation Transition	Excitation Wavelength (mμ)	Percent Polarization: Fluorescence h_{10}	Fluorescence d_{10}	Phosphorescence h_{10}	Phosphorescence d_{10}	T-T Absorption h_{10}	T-T Absorption d_{10}
^1L_b	346[a]	-	-	-16.5	-11.5	-	-
	330	+10.0	+14.0	-20.5	-15.0	-	-
	315	+ 8.0	+ 8.0	-15.0	-22.0	- 5.0	+ 6.0
^1L_a	294	-19.5	-17.0	-28.5	-25.0	+21.0	+16.0
^1B_a	253	-14.5	- 2.0	-27.0	-24.5	-	-

[a] Fluorescence measurements could not be made at this excitation wavelength because of serious overlap of fluorescence and scattered exciting light.

bands. This is consistent with all previous determinations of phosphorescence polarization of aromatic hydroaarbons, where out-of-plane polarization predominates.[21] The out-of-plane polarization of the phosphorescence of aromatic hydrocarbons appears to be a general phenomenon[21] and reflects efficient spin-orbit coupling of the lowest triplet state with out-of-plane polarized π,σ^* and σ,π^* singlet states. The theoretical basis for this relatively efficient coupling and the very inefficient spin-orbit coupling between the π,π^* triplet state and the various π,π^* singlet states has been considered by McClure.[23] For both $C_{14}H_{10}$ and $C_{14}D_{10}$ the phosphorescence polarization is considerably more negative for ^1L_a and ^1B_b excitation than for ^1L_b excitation. This indicates that most (>2/3) of the in-plane contribution to the phosphorescence polarization is short-axis polarized.

A major difference in polarization behavior is observed in the T→T' measurements. The polarization of the most intense absorption band for $C_{14}D_{10}$ is positive (+16%) with respect to excitation which excites both ^1L_a and ^1L_b. Interposing a pyrex filter, completely eliminates direct ^1L_a excitation, lowers the observed optical density by a factor of three and reduces the observed polarization to +6%. For $C_{14}H_{10}$, $(^1L_a + {}^1L_b)$ excitation generated very weak T-T' absorption, and a much greater relative error than the mixed $^1L_a + {}^1L_b$ excitation, there is little doubt that for $C_{14}H_{10}$ a change in the sign of the polarization is observed.

---

‡We refer to this transition as the ^1B_a in accordance with the designations in reference 19. In references 18 and 20 the third electronic transition although long axis polarized is referred to a ^1B_b, an inconsistency in nomenclature as Ham and Ruedenberg emphasize.

The relatively strong positive polarization with respect to mixed excitation, which generates triplets primarily via ^1L_a excitation, demonstrates that the T-T' absorption is polarized parallel to this transition and is thus long-axis polarized. This is in agreement with previously reported experimental[8] and theoretical work.[24] Furthermore, the close agreement with theoretically calculated energies and oscillator strengths (with a scaling factor of ∿1/6 as discussed by Brinen[13]), clearly indicates that the upper triplet is a π, π* state. The very weak polarization obtained with ^1L_b excitation (primarily 313 mμ) is attributed to vibronic coupling between the ^1L_b and ^1L_a states. Further evidence of this coupling is seen in the fluorescence and phosphorescence polarization excitation spectra. The positive (+17%) polarization of the 0-0 band of fluorescence for 330 mμ excitation is reduced to +3% at 313 mμ. Similarly the phosphorescence becomes more negatively polarized as the excitation progresses to shorter wavelengths within the ^1L_b spectrum. The observations of the decrease in the T-T' polarization (0-0 band) with 313 mμ excitation relative to mixed ^1L_a and ^1L_b excitation is thus in agreement with luminescence polarization and with vibronic coupling in the ^1L_b spectrum with ^1L_a (or perhaps ^1B_a).

CHRYSENE. Simple benzo substitution on phenanthrene to give chrysene produces significant changes in the S-S absorption spectrum. The ^1L_b system is shifted to longer wavelength and a clean separation of the three lowest electronic transitions in the singlet manifold is observed. This permits relatively clean excitation for the photoselection experiments. The polarization results and excitation wavelengths are given in Figure 2 and Table II.

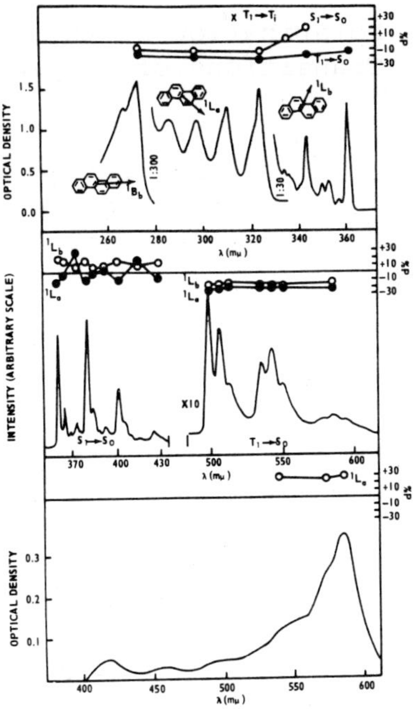

Figure 2 (a) Top: Singlet-singlet absorption of chrysene in 3MP at 77°K, showing the three lowest energy transitions and their polarizations. Above the spectrum the percent polarization of the fluorescence ($S_1 \rightarrow S_o$), phosphorescence ($T_1 \rightarrow S_o$) and triplet-triplet ($T_1 \rightarrow T_i$) absorption is shown for excitation at the wavelengths indicated.
(b) Middle: Fluorescence ($S_1 \rightarrow S_o$) and phosphorescence ($T_1 \rightarrow S_o$) spectra of $C_{18}H_{12}$ in 3MP at 77°K. Above the spectra the percent polarization is shown for the various vibrational bands of each transition for ^1L_b (344 mμ) and ^1L_a (322 mμ) excitation.
(c) Bottom: Triplet-triplet absorption spectrum of $C_{18}H_{12}$ in 3MP at 77°K. Above the spectrum the percent polarization at the indicated wavelengths is given for ^1L_a excitation.

TABLE II: Polarization of the Electronic Transitions of Chrysene

Excitation		Percent Polarization		
Transition	Wavelength (mμ)	Fluorescence	Phosphorescence	T-T Absorption
^1L_b	362*	-	-13.5	
	344	+18.5	-19.0	
	333	+ 2.5		
^1L_a	322	-14.0	-24.0	+27
^1B_b	273		-19.0	
	267	- 9.0		

* Fluorescence measurements could not be made at this excitation wavelength because of serious overlap of fluorescence and scattered exciting light.

The principal features of the polarization results for chrysene are similar to those of the phenanthrenes. The fluorescence is positively polarized with respect to the ^1L_b excitation, negatively polarized with ^1L_a excitation and less negatively polarized with ^1B_b excitation. Since chrysene has C_{2h} symmetry, the transition axes are not as immediately evident as they are in phenanthrene or picene (both C_{2v}). Ham and Ruedenberg[19] as well as Skancke[20] have predicted the polarization axes using the Free Electron Model and LCAO-MO calculations respectively. Because the latter treatment doesn't predict the polarization of the "forbidden" ^1L_b transition, we shall consider the free electron treatment. According to Ham and Ruedenberg the ^1L_b axis is at $+95^o$ to the axis which goes through the center of symmetry and is perpendicular to the bond containing that center. The ^1L_a and ^1B_b bands are respectively -12° and $+35^o$ to the same axis. Thus the ^1L_b is only 5° from the "short axis" while the ^1L_a is 107° and the ^1B_b $\sim 60^o$ relative to the ^1L_b. The less negative polarization observed with ^1B_b excitation is consistent with the above theoretical predictions of smaller angular separation between the ^1B_b and ^1L_b than between ^1L_a and ^1L_b.

The fluorescence polarization (0-0 band) becomes increasingly less positive as the excitation is moved to shorter wavelengths within the ^1L_b absorption band system. This again implies considerable vibronic coupling within the singlet manifold with either ^1L_a or ^1B_b. The severe alternation of vibronic polarization in the fluorescence spectrum parallels the reported results of Dörr and Gropper.[10]

The phosphorescence (0-0 band) demonstrates primarily out-of-plane polarized emission as negative polarization is observed throughout the excitation region. Since the results for ^1L_b and ^1B_b excitation are identical it is difficult to establish the direction of the in-plane contribution to the phosphorescence.

The T-T' absorption spectrum shows strong positive (+27%) polarization with respect to excitation in the ^1L_a region. Insufficient triplet population with ^1L_b excitation prohibited measurements of optical densities on excitation into this transition.

Because of the desirability of obtaining the polarization of the T-T' band with respect to clean ^1L_b excitation an effort was made to observe this phenomenon for deuterated chrysene. For $C_{18}D_{12}$ sufficient triplets were formed under 365 mμ excitation and a polarization of -10% was determined. Thus the T-T' absorption is polarized parallel to the ^1L_a transition, which agrees with El-Sayed's determination.[8] Because the transition axes are not mutually perpendicular in chrysene, the detailed comparison between the light and heavy compounds, as was carried out for phenanthrene, was not attempted.

PICENE. Picene has the same symmetry (C_{2v}) and the same transition axes as phenanthrene, and the principal polarization features of the transitions studied (Figure 3 and Table III) are also very similar. The fluorescence is positively polarized relative to ^1L_b excitation, and negatively polarized relative to ^1L_a and ^1B_a excitation. The absorption spectrum clearly shows that clean excitation into three S-S' transitions is possible. The results confirm that the fluorescence state is ^1L_b and are in substantial agreement with recently published work.[9]

The phosphorescence is negatively polarized relative to excitation into all three absorption bands and as was the case with the other compounds this reflects primarily out-of-plane polarization.

The intense T-T' band shows strong positive (+27%) polarization with respect to excitation into the ^1L_a band. Poor solubility prevented measurements with ^1L_b excitation even though the extinc-

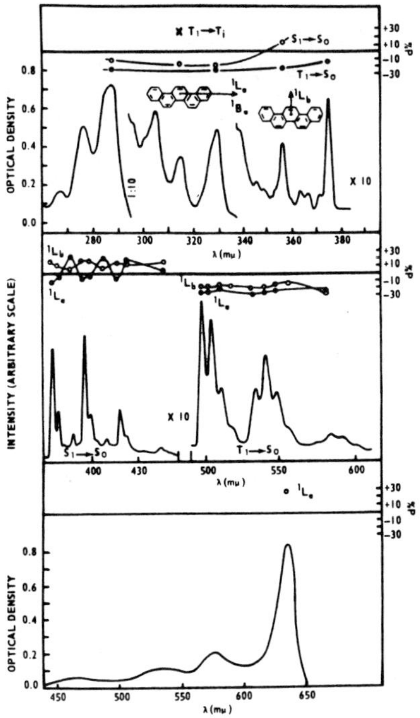

Figure 3 (a) Top: Singlet-singlet absorption spectrum of picene in 3MP at 77°K, showing the three lowest energy transitions and their polarizations. Above the spectrum the percent polarization of the fluorescence ($S_1 \rightarrow S_o$), phosphorescence ($T_1 \rightarrow S_o$) and triplet-triplet ($T_1 \rightarrow T_i$) absorption is shown for excitation at the wavelengths indicated.
(b) Middle: Fluorescence ($S_1 \rightarrow S_o$) and phosphorescence ($T_1 \rightarrow S_o$) spectra of $C_{22}H_{14}$ in 3MP at 77°K. Above the spectra the percent polarization is shown for the various vibrational bands of each transition for ^1L_b (355 mμ) and ^1L_a (325 mμ) excitation.
(c) Bottom: Triplet-triplet absorption spectrum of $C_{22}H_{14}$ in 3MP at 77°K. Above the spectrum the percent polarization at the indicated wavelengths is given for ^1L_a excitation.

TABLE III: Polarization of the Electronic Transitions of Picene

Excitation		Percent Polarization		
Transition	Wavelength (mμ)	Fluorescence	Phosphorescence	T-T Absorption
^1L_b	376*		-14.0	
	355	+11.0	-23.0	
^1L_a	325		-26.0	+27
	313	-16.0		
^1B_a	287	-11.0	-23.0	
	267	- 4.0	-25.5	

* Fluorescence measurements could not be made at this excitation wavelength because of serious overlap of fluorescence and scattered exciting light.

tion coefficient for the T-T' absorption is nearly twice that of phenanthrene and chrysene.[13] Optical density measurements on the other vibronic bands in the system were too weak to obtain reliable polarization values. This is the first reported measurement of the T-T' polarization of picene and the strong polarization shows clearly the T-T' absorption is long axis (^1L_a) polarized in agreement with theoretical predictions.[24]

ASSIGNMENT OF ELECTRONIC STATES. Making use of the rather limited number of experimental determinations[15-17] and the more extensive theoretical considerations[18-20] of the absolute polarization of the S-S' absorption transitions, we can state that the first three excited singlet states of phenanthrene and picene correspond to the ^1L_b, ^1L_a and ^1B_a states. (Platt nomenclature). The group theoretical designations of these states are $^1A_1$, $^1B_2$ and $^1B_2$ respectively (using the axial system of Orloff[25]) with the transition to the $^1A_1$ state characterized by in-plane short axis polarization and those to the $^1B_2$ states by in-plane long axis polarization. The lowest triplet state shows much more negative phosphorescence polarization when excited into the ^1L_a band than when excited into the ^1L_a band. As pointed out by Azumi and McGlynn[2] group theoretical considerations of spin-orbit mixing of singlet and triplet states involving first order vibrational coupling require that the phosphorescent state be ^3L_a ($^3B_2$ in our axial system, $^3B_1$ in McGlynn's) in nature. The allowed T-T absorption transition which is in-plane long axis polarized requires that the upper triplet state have A_1 symmetry. A more specific assignment of the upper triplet state is not possible on the basis of these results.

In chrysene the assignments have to be based on the theoretical predictions of the polarization of the ground state absorption transitions. Using Ham and Ruedenberg's assignments the three lowest excited singlet states are ^1L_b, ^1L_a and ^1B_b (all ^1B_u states), the lowest triplet is ^3L_a (^3B_u) while the upper triplet must have A_g symmetry.

SUMMARY

The spectroscopic properties of the aromatic hydrocarbons phenanthrene, chrysene and picene are such that they present a near ideal series for a comprehensive polarization study of the electronic transitions. Both luminescence phenomena are intense and display significant vibrational detail; the absorption from the metastable triplet is strong and in the visible region; while the ground state absorption is well defined and accessible for selective excitation. Condensed ring hydrocarbons of this type present no special geometrical problems, so that to a good approximation they can be considered planar in all of the electronic states involved. The C_{2v} symmetry of the phenanthrenes and picene is especially desirable since the in-plane polarization axes are mutually perpendicular and along the symmetry axes. In chrysene (C_{2h} symmetry) the in-plane transition axes are not mutually perpendicular, so that a quantitative analysis of the polarization data is not easily attained.

The results reported here illustrate that the similarities in polarization of the transitions studied are far more striking than the differences. For all four of the compounds studied the pure electronic component of the fluorescence is primarily in-plane short axis polarized; the phosphorescence largely out-of-plane polarized and the triplet-triplet absorption principally in-plane long axis polarized. Numerical differences in the polarization of these bands are apparent as are the differences in the vibronic bands within each transition. Such differences are also evident when the results of light and heavy phenanthrene are examined (Table I). In this paper we have chosen to emphasize the similarities in the pure electronic component of the transitions studied and will cover the differences in detail in another paper following a rigorous analysis of the vibrational bands of these transitions.

ACKNOWLEDGEMENT

The authors would like to thank J. G. Koren for running the low temperature singlet-singlet absorption spectra.

REFERENCES

1. A. C. Albrecht, J. Mol. Spectry. 6, 84 (1961).
2. T. Azumi and S. P. McGlynn, J. Chem. Phys. 37, 2413 (1963).
3. A. H. Kalantar and A. C. Albrecht, Ber. Bunsenges. Physik. Chem. 68, 361 (1964).
4. H. Zimmerman and N. Z. Joop, Electrochem. Ber. Bunsenges. Physil, Chem. 65, 66 (1961).
5. M. A. El-Sayed, J. Opt. Soc. Am. 53, 797 (1963).
6. S. Seigel and H. S. Judeikis, J. Phys. Chem. 70, 2205 (1966).
7. J. M. Lhoste, A. H. Haug and M. Ptak, J. Chem. Phys. 44, 648 (1966).
8. M. A. El-Sayed and T. Pavlopoulos, J. Chem. Phys. 39, 834 (1963).
9. R. Kiessling, G. Hohlneicher and F. Dörr, Z. Naturforshg. 22a, 1097 (1967).
10. F. Dörr and H. Gropper, Ber. Bunsenges. Physik. Chem. 67, 193 (1963).
11. J. B. Gallivan, J. S. Brinen and J. G. Koren, J. Mol. Spectry. 26, 24 (1968).
12. J. S. Brinen and W. G. Hodgson, J. Chem. Phys. 47, 2946 (1967).
13. J. S. Brinen, J. Chem. Phys. (in press).
14. J. B. Gallivan and W. H. Hamill, J. Chem. Phys. 44, 1279 (1966).
15. D. S. McClure, J. Chem. Phys. 25, 481 (1956).
16. D. S. McClure, J. Chem. Phys. 22, 1256 (1954).
17. S. C. Ganguly and N. K. Choudhury, J. Chem. Phys. 21, 554 (1953).
18. J. R. Platt, J. Chem. Phys. 17, 484 (1949).
19. N. S. Ham and K. Ruedenberg, J. Chem. Phys. 25, 13 (1956).
20. P. N. Skancke, Acta Chimica Scandinavica 19, 401 (1965).
21. S. K. Lower and M. A. El-Sayed, Chem. Rev. 66, 199 (1966).
22. M. A. El-Sayed, Nature 197, 481 (1963).
23. D. S. McClure, J. Chem. Phys. 20, 682 (1952).
24. M. K. Orloff, J. Chem. Phys. 47, 235 (1967).

VIBRONIC SPIN-ORBIT INTERACTIONS IN AROMATIC CARBONYL COMPOUNDS. I. ON THE ASSIGNMENT OF THE LOWEST TRIPLET STATE IN AROMATIC CARBONYL COMPOUNDS

E. C. Lim,* Y. Kanda,** and J. Stanislaus***

Department of Chemistry
Loyola University
Chicago, Illinois

Possible correlation between the nature of the lowest triplet state and photoreactivity of aromatic carbonyl compounds stimulated considerable amount of work relating to the assignment of the lowest triplet state in these molecules.[1,2,3] Most of the work to date has utilized the criteria of phosphorescence lifetime and/or phosphorescence excitation method to distinguish between n,π* and π,π* triplet states, and has led to the π,π* assignment for all the sbustituted acetophenones thus far studied (in ethanolic glass)[1,2] and for

*Address after November 1, 1968: Department of Chemistry, Wayne State University, Detroit, Michigan 48202.
**NSF Senior Foreign Scientist Fellow. Permanent address: Department of Chemistry, Faculty of Science, Kyushu University, Fukuoka, Japan.
***A part of thesis work.

acetophenone itself in ethylene glycol-water (EGW) matrix.[3]

The purpose of this paper is to show that polarization of phosphorescence is more consistent with the n,π* assignment than with the π,π* assignment for the lowest triplet states of many of these compounds, and to rationalize, within the framework of n,π* triplet state, the increase in phosphorescence lifetime and the decrease in photoreactivity by conjugating substituents and by hydrogen bonding solvents.

For ^{3}n,π* state of aryl ketones and aldehydes, the dominant spin-orbit coupling has been shown[4,5] to be the first-order mechanism involving ^1L_a state, and the 0,0 band of phosphorescence is predominantly in-plane (long-axis, in particular) polarized. For the emitting ^{3}π,π* state of heteroaromatic or aromatic carbonyl compounds, on the other hand, the in-plane polarized intensity is expected to appear through vibronic spin-orbit coupling involving n,π* states as intermediate states,[3,6] and the 0,0 band is expected to be largely out-of-plane polarized. The polarization of phosphorescence therefore provides a strong criterion for characterizing the lowest triplet state of these molecules. In Fig. 1 we present, by way of illustration the phosphorescence spectra and polarization characteristics of p-methyl, p-methoxy, and p-hydroxyacetophenones. It is clear that the 0,0 band of the emission is polarized nearly parallel to ^1L_a excitation for p-methylacetophenone in EPA glass, but it is nearly perpendicular to the same for p-hydroxyacetophenone in EPA glass. Furthermore, phosphorescence of p-hydroxyacetophenone exhibits an abrupt change in polarization outside the 0,0 band, consistent with the vibronic spin-orbit coupling mechanism. The lowest triplet state is therefore ^{3}n,π* for p-methylacetophenone and ^{3}π,π* for p-hydroxyacetophenone. The polarization of the 0,0 band of p-methoxyacetophenone is neither very positive nor

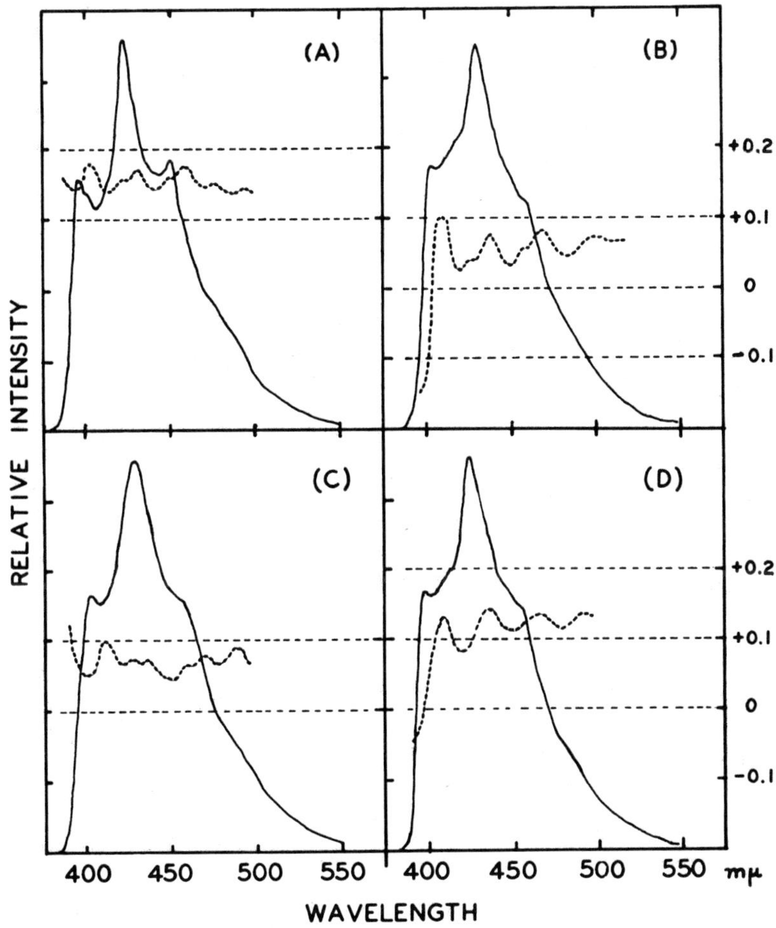

Figure 1 Phosphorescence spectra (solid curves) and polarization (broken curves) of substituted acetophenones in rigid glass at 77°K as obtained by excitation into ^1L_a band. (A) p-methylacetophenone in EPA; (B) p-hydroxyacetophenone in EPA; (C) p-methoxyacetophenone in 3MP; (D) p-methoxyacetophenone in EPA.

very negative when excited by ^1L_a band, and this suggests that the lowest triplet state of this molecule has considerably mixed character. Comparison of the polarization data with those of p-methyl and p-hydroxyacetophenone, nevertheless, indicates that the lowest triplet state of p-methoxyacetophenone is most probably n,π^* in 3-methylpentane (3MP) glass and probably π,π^* in EPA glass. Similar studies lead to $^3n,\pi^*$ assignment for the lowest triplet state of acetophenone, p-chloroacetophenone, and p-methylacetophenone in EPA glass, and for the lowest triplet state of all common, benzaldehyde derivatives (in EPA glass) except p-hydroxy and p-methoxybenzaldehyde.[7]

Assuming that the above conclusion based on the polarization data is correct, it is necessary to advance possible reasons for the increase in the phosphorescence lifetime when an electron donating substituent is introduced in the benzene ring of aryl ketones or aldehydes. The increase in lifetime is considerable and they amount, for example, to a factor of about twenty for methyl substitution. The ^1L_a state, which provides dipole allowed character to $^3n,\pi^*$ state through spin-orbit coupling, possesses considerable charge-transfer (CT) character.[8] The wave function for the ^1L_a state can be written as $\psi(^1L_a) = a\pi,\pi^* + b\pi_{Bz}a_\pi$, where $\pi_{Bz}a_\pi$ represents CT configuration arising from the transfer of an electron from the bonding π orbital of the benzene ring, π_{Bz}, to an antibonding orbital of the carbonyl group, a_π. Substitution of an electron donating group in the benzene ring has an effect of increasing the CT character of the ^1L_a state (as well as the ground state). Since there is no overlap between the non-bonding orbital of the carbonyl oxygen atom and the π_{Bz} orbital, the CT configuration $\pi_{Bz}a_\pi$ does not contribute to the spin-orbit interaction matrix elements $\langle ^1L_a|H_{so}|^3n,\pi^*\rangle$ and the increase in the CT character of the ^1L_a state should lead to the decrease in spin-orbit coupling. Furthermore, contamination of the ground state by CT configuration is expected to decrease the matrix elements $\langle {}^1\pi,\pi^* | H_{so} | {}^3n,\pi^* \rangle$ through the decrease of the π electron charge density on the oxygen atom. The increase in phosphorescence lifetime by an electron donating substituent can therefore be rationalized qualitatively without invoking the change in the emitting state from ${}^3n,\pi^*$ to ${}^3\pi,\pi^*$ state.

The decrease in photoreactivity by conjugating substituents[2,9] and by hydrogen bonding solvents[10] and the occurrence of heavy atom[1] and oxygen[11] effects on singlet-triplet ($S_o \rightarrow T_1$) absorption can also be explained within the framework of n,π^* lowest triplet state, if the vibronic coupling between ${}^3n,\pi^*$ state and higher-lying, but nearly degenerate, ${}^3\pi,\pi^*$ state is considered. The vibronic coupling between ${}^3n,\pi^*$ and ${}^3\pi,\pi^*$ states, whose occurrence can be verified through the solvent dependence of polarization and lifetime of phosphorescence,[12] is considerably greater in hydroxyl solvents than in hydrocarbon solvents, and in substituted acetophenone and benzaldehyde than in unsubstituted compounds due to the closer proximity of ${}^3n,\pi^*$ and ${}^3\pi,\pi^*$ states. The enhanced ${}^3\pi,\pi^*$ character in ${}^3n,\pi^*$ state can not only lead to the reduced photoreactivity, but it can also lead to the oxygen and heavy atom effect on singlet-triplet absorption, provided that the oscillator strength of the $S_o \rightarrow {}^3n,\pi^*$ transition is small. Thus, while oxygen and heavy atom-containing solvents may have negligible effects on the $S_o \rightarrow {}^3n,\pi^*$ absorption of acetophenone and benzaldehydes, they may have considerable effect on the $S_o \rightarrow {}^3n,\pi^*$ absorptions of substituted compounds.

Finally, the large increase in the lifetime by hydroxyl solvents[13] and by intramolecular hydrogen bonding[14] is also believed to be consistent with the ${}^3n,\pi^*$ lowest triplet state since the hydrogen bonding is expected to decrease matrix elements $\langle {}^1\pi,\pi^* | H_{so} | {}^3n,\pi^* \rangle$ due to the decreased non-bonding charge density on the oxygen atom.

The above results and considerations indicate that some of the aromatic ketones (p-methylacetophenone in EPA glass, for example) whose lowest triplet states have previously been assigned to the $^3\pi,\pi^*$ states may possess $^3n,\pi^*$ lowest triplet states. This conclusion is supported by the observation that p-methylacetophenone in EPA glass and p-methoxyacetophenone in 3MP glass exhibit polarization of phosphorescence which is strikingly similar to the polarization of phosphorescence of acetophenone in EPA glass (for which $^3n,\pi^*$ assignment of the lowest triplet state is almost certainly correct). Furthermore, the frequencies of vibrational progression in phosphorescence spectra of p-methylacetophenone in EPA glass and p-methoxyacetophenone in 3MP glass are closer to carbonyl stretching mode characteristic of $\pi^* \rightarrow n$ transition than to the ring stretching mode frequently appearing in $\pi^* \rightarrow \pi$ transition.

Although we consider the assignment based on the polarization data to be strong, we do not regard it to be conclusive. It is possible (although unlikely) that the polarization data leading to the $^3n,\pi^*$ assignment is the result of the direct spin-orbit coupling between $^3\pi,\pi^*$ (if it is indeed the lowest triplet state) and $^1\pi,\pi^*$ states, which occur as the consequence of the breakdown of the Born-Oppenheimer approximation. Breakdown of the Born-Oppenheimer approximation is not unexpected for these molecules in which there is a strong vibronic interaction between very close-lying $^3n,\pi^*$ and $^3\pi,\pi^*$ states. In addition, the second band (presumably of singlet-triplet character) observed by Kearns,[1] Yang,[2] and their coworkers in the phosphorescence excitation spectra of p-methyl and p-methoxyacetophenones is difficult to explain if the present conclusion is indeed correct. It is obvious that further, and more critical, studies are needed to resolve this inconsistency relating to the assignment of the lowest triplet states in aromatic ketones.

ACKNOWLEDGEMENT

This work was supported by the Army Research Office (Durham).

REFERENCES

1. D. R. Kearns and W. A. Case, J. Am. Chem. Soc. 88, 5087 (1966).
2. N. C. Yang, D. S. McClure, S. L. Murov, J. J. Houser, and R. Dusenbery, J. Am. Chem. Soc. 89, 5466 (1967).
3. A. A. Lamola, J. Chem. Phys. 47, 4810 (1967).
4. V. G. Krishna, J. Mol. Spectry. 13, 296 (1964).
5. R. Shimada and L. Goodman, J. Chem. Phys. 43, 2027 (1965).
6. E. C. Lim and J. M. H. Yu, J. Chem. Phys. 45, 4742 (1966); 47, 3270 (1967); E. C. Lim, Ber. Bunsenges, Physik. Chem. 72, 273 (1968).
7. The conclusions regarding the lowest triplet states of substituted benzaldehydes are the same as those of H. Baba and T. Takemura (to be published).
8. S. Nagakura and J. Tanaka, J. Chem. Phys. 22, 236 (1954).
9. See, for example, J. N. Pitts, Jr., H. W. Johnson, Jr., and T. Kuwana, J. Phys. Chem. 66, 2456 (1962).
10. R. D. Rauh and P. A. Leermakers, J. Am. Chem. Soc. 90, 2246 (1968).
11. D. A. Warwick and C. H. J. Wells, Spectrochim. Acta 24A, 589 (1968).
12. E. C. Lim, Y. Kanda, and J. Stanislaus (to be published).
13. For p-methylacetophenone, for example, the mean lifetimes of phosphorescence at 77°K are ca. 0.03 sec and 0.07 sec in 3MP and EPA matrices, respectively.
14. E. J. O'Connell, Jr., J. Chem. Phys. 47, 5453 (1967).

HEAVY-ATOM EFFECT ON THE T-S TRANSITION OF QUINOXALINE

Yoshio Murakami, Ryoichi Shimada and Yoshiya Kanda

Department of Chemistry
Faculty of Science
Kyushu University
Fukuoka, Japan

INTRODUCTION

The phosphorescence spectrum of quinoxaline has been studied by several investigators[1,2,3] and it was ascribed to a $^3L_a \rightarrow {}^1A_1$ transition. This conclusion was reached from experimental evidences such as the value of the electronic energy, phosphorescence lifetime, and spectral structure as well as the similarity of the electronic structure of quinoxaline to that of naphthalene.

We studied the heavy atom effect on the triplet-singlet transition of quinoxaline through substitution with chlorine and bromine atoms at 2 and 3 positions. The spin-orbit coupling mechanism will be discussed.

EXPERIMENTAL

Quinoxaline was synthesized from o-phenylenediamine and glyoxalsodium bisulfite, and the sample was purified by repeated distilling under reduced pressure just before the measurements. 2,3-dihalogenated quinoxalines (2,3-dichloro- and 2,3-dibromoquinoxaline) were prepared by heating the corresponding phosphorus oxyhalide ($POCl_3$ and $POBr_3$) with 2,3-dihydroxyquinoxaline, which was easily produced from o-phenylenediamine, oxalic acid dihydrate and hydrochloric acid. These halogen derivatives were purified by recrystallization from ethyl alcohol four times. Solvents such as methylcyclohexane and isopentane were purified by the ordinary method.

The ultraviolet and visible absorption spectra of these compounds were studied at room temperature with a Hitachi spectrophotometer, type EPS-2. The infrared spectra were studied with a Hitachi-Perkin-Elmer 125 infrared spectrophotometer for the 400-4000 cm^{-1} region using KBr disks, and a Hitachi EPI-LO2 for the 200-400 cm^{-1} using Nujol. The Raman spectra were observed photographically with a double prism spectrograph. The phosphorescence spectra were studied in methylcyclohexane at 4.2^{o}K and 77°K using a Hilger E2 spectrograph. For quinoxaline the phosphorescence was also observed in the crystal at 4.2^{o}K. The degree of polarization for the excitation and phosphorescence were obtained by the usual method in a mixed solvent of methylcyclohexane and isopentane (4:1 in volume ratio). The optical arrangement used for measurement is shown systematically in Fig. 1.

RESULTS

QUINOXALINE. The absorption and phosphorescence spectra and the polarization curves for the

Optical System for Measurment of Polarization

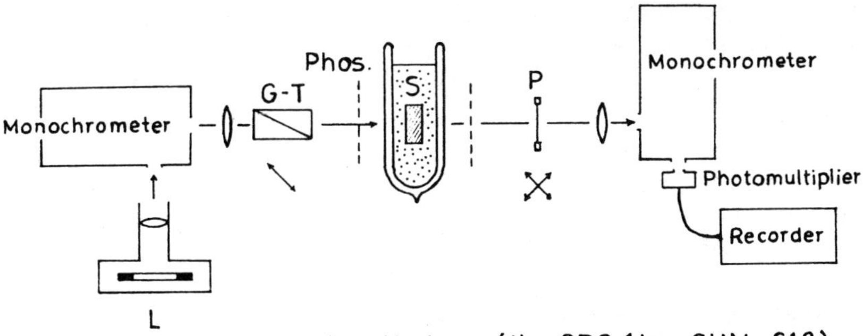

L : Hg lamp (the ORC 1kw, CHM-612)
G-T : Glan-Thompson prism
S : Sample
Phos.: Phosphoroscope
P : Ultraviolet sheet polaroid

Figure 1

S-T Transition in Quinoxaline

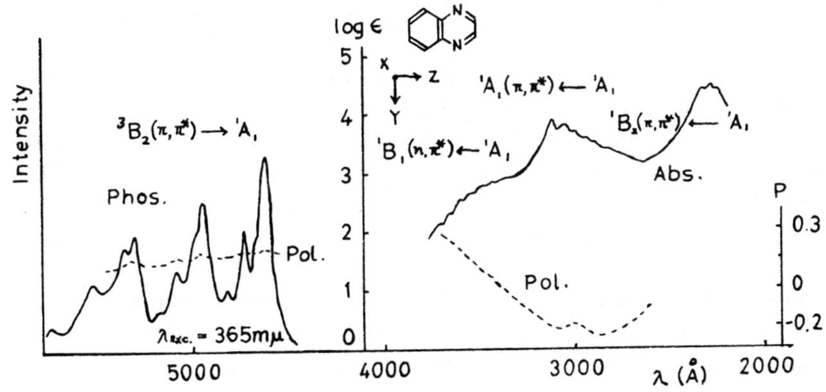

Figure 2

excitation and phosphorescence of quinoxaline were studied for comparison with those of the 2,3-dihalogenated quinoxalines. Results are shown in Fig. 2.

The degree of polarization of the 0-0 bands of the phosphorescence spectrum is positive with respect to the n,π^* excitation and negative with respect to the π,π^* excitation. This suggests that the lowest triplet state of this molecule should be of π,π^* character. By analogy with the molecular geometry of naphthalene, the state is assigned to $^3B_2(\pi,\pi^*)$.

The phosphorescence lifetime was 0.3 sec in methylcyclohexane at 77°K. This value is much smaller than that of naphthalene and this indicates that the $^3B_2(\pi,\pi^*)$ state couples strongly with the $^1B_1(n,\pi^*)$ state which is located very closely to the $^3B_2(\pi,\pi^*)$ state. Another possibility is that the lowest triplet state be a $^3A_1(\pi,\pi^*)$ state. However, this is not important since matrix elements of the type $\langle ^1B_1(n,\pi^*)|H_{SO}|^3A_1(\pi,\pi^*)\rangle$ are almost equal to zero. These arguments are in agreement with those by El-Sayed.[3]

The phosphorescence spectra of quinoxaline observed in methylcyclohexane at 4.2°K and 77°K and in the crystal at 4.2°K are given in Fig. 3. The vibrational structure of the crystal phosphorescence spectrum is exactly the same as that of the phosphorescence observed in methylcyclohexane except that the whole spectrum shifts by about 400 cm^{-1} toward longer wavelengths. This may indicate that the crystal phosphorescence is not due to an impurity but most possibly to a physical trap in the crystal lattice.

The shortest wavelength band was taken as the 0-0 band and most of the vibrational bands were assigned to totally symmetric vibrations. The polarization measurement of the crystal phosphorescence was made photographically with a Wollaston prism. The crystal sample was oriented

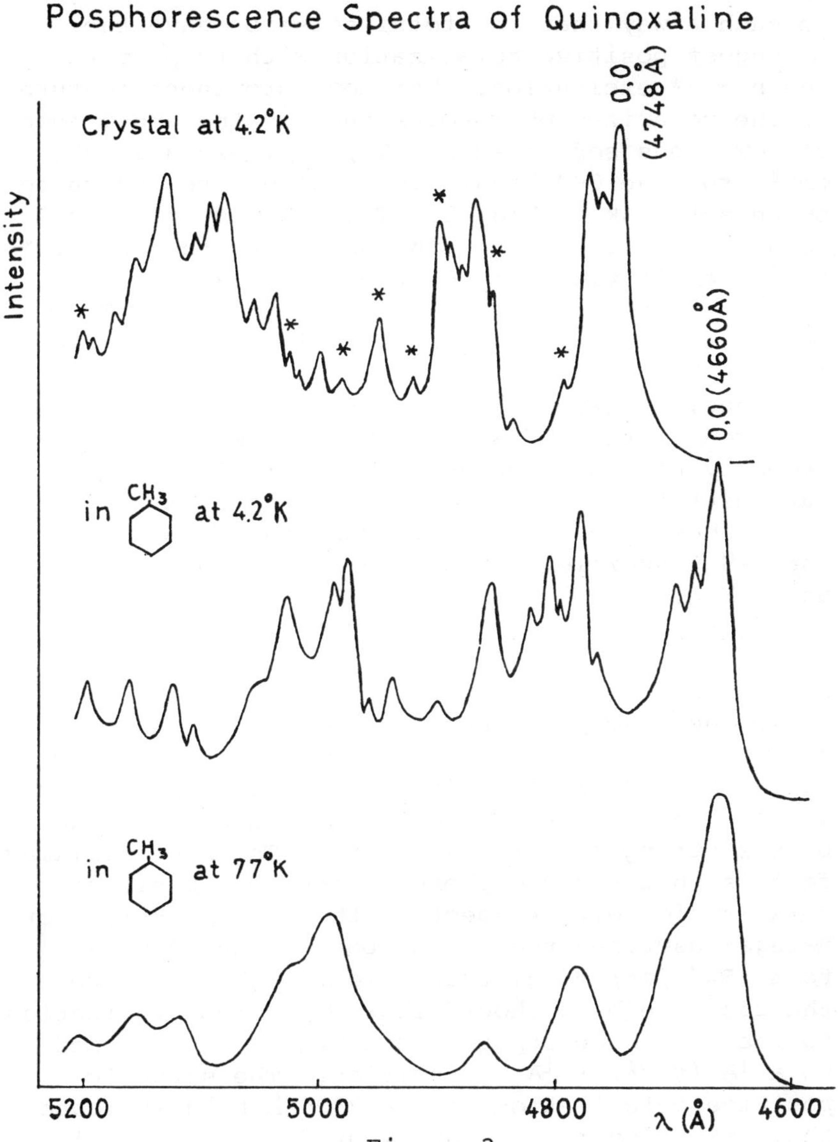
Posphorescence Spectra of Quinoxaline
Crystal at 4.2°K
0,0 (4748Å)
0,0 (4660Å)
in CH3 at 4.2°K
in CH3 at 77°K
Intensity
5200
5000
4800
4600
λ (Å)

Figure 3

in such a way that the total emission gave the strongest positive polarization with respect to the $n \rightarrow \pi^*$ excitation. The most prominent feature of the polarized phosphorescence is the appearance of new bands separated by 197, 463, 629 and 858 cm^{-1} from the 0-0 band. These bands are indicated by an asterisk in Fig. 3. They showed strongly negative polarization with respect to the $^1B_1(n,\pi^*) \leftarrow {}^1A_1$ excitation and positive polarization with respect to the $^1A_1(\pi,\pi^*) \leftarrow {}^1A_1$ excitation. Frequencies of these bands were assigned to out-of-plane vibrations of b_1 species because the same frequencies, except for the 197 cm^{-1} band, were observed in the infrared. The 197 cm^{-1} band was probably not seen because of the limitation of our instrument.

Thus, the spin-orbit coupling scheme for the T-S transition in quinoxaline can be written as in Fig. 7.

2,3-DICHLORO- AND 2,3-DIBROMOQUINOXALINE. Fig. 4 shows the absorption spectra and the excitation polarization spectra relative to the phosphorescence maxima of 2,3-dichloro- and 2,3-dibromoquinoxalines. The $n \rightarrow \pi^*$ bands shift to the blue and are hidden by the strong $\pi \rightarrow \pi^*$ absorption. The most striking fact is that the phosphorescence shows positive polarization with respect to the $\pi \rightarrow \pi^*$ excitation. Mataga[2] ascribed the strong band around 2300 Å to a $^1B_2(\pi,\pi^*) \leftarrow {}^1A_1$ transition, but if this were the case the band should show opposite polarization to the 3500 Å absorption band which was assigned to a $^1A_1(\pi,\pi^*) \leftarrow {}^1A_1$ transition. The strongly positive polarization of the 2300 Å band indicates that this band must be attributed to a $^1A_1(\pi,\pi^*) \leftarrow {}^1A_1$ transition and the band due to a $^1B_2(\pi,\pi^*) \leftarrow {}^1A_1$ transition is presumed to be located around 3000 Å where the polarization seems to be minimized.

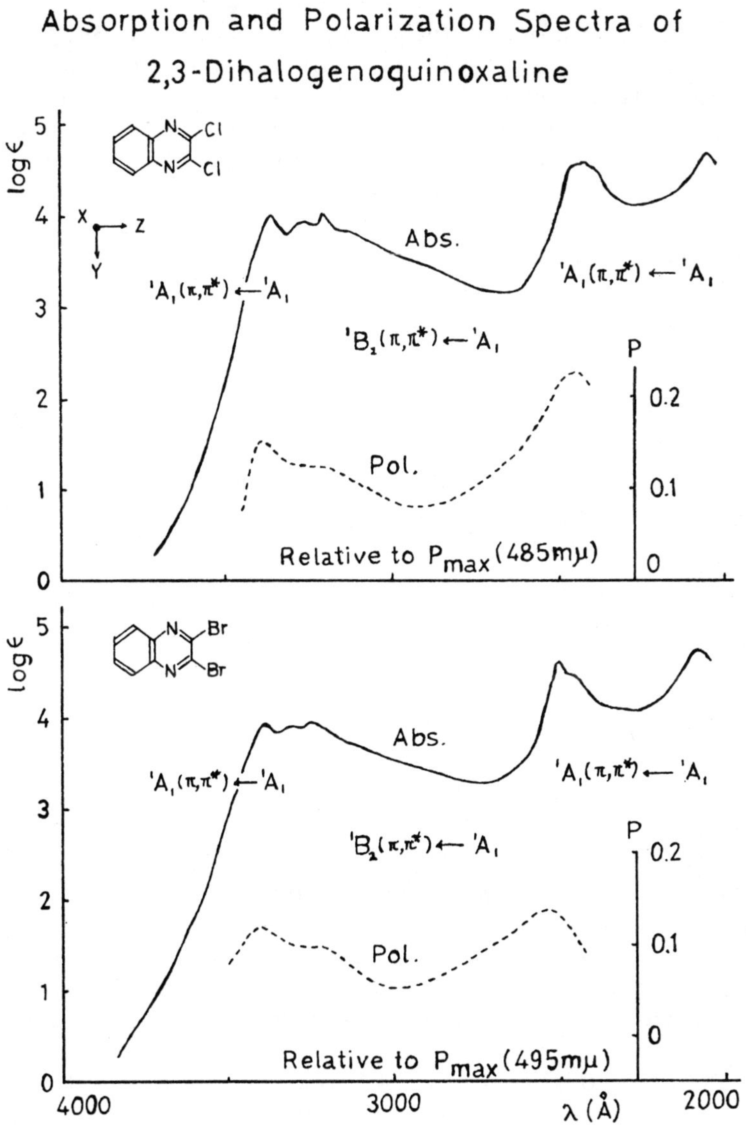

Absorption and Polarization Spectra of
2,3-Dihalogenoquinoxaline
log ε
Abs.
Pol.
Relative to Pmax(485mμ)
Relative to Pmax(495mμ)
P
λ (Å)
4000
3000
2000

Figure 4

The phosphorescence lifetimes of 2,3-dichloro- and 2,3-dibromoquinoxalines measured in methylcyclohexane at 77°K were 0.37 and 0.034 sec, respectively. It should be noted that bromo substitution shortens the lifetimes about one tenth that of quinoxaline.

The phosphorescence spectrum of 2,3-dichloroquinoxaline observed in methylcyclohexane at 4.2°K and 77°K is shown in Fig. 5. The phosphorescence polarization spectrum measured relative to the $^1A_1(\pi,\pi^*) \leftarrow {}^1A_1$ excitation is also included in this figure. The shortest wavelength band, which has rather strong intensity, was taken as the 0-0 band and the vibrational analysis was carried out. No vibrational data has been reported for these compounds so far. Vibrational frequencies used in the analysis were obtained from the infrared and Raman spectra studied by us.

It should be pointed out that the 0-0 band has a minimum degree of polarization although overall polarization is positive. Bands separated by 255 and 870 cm^{-1} from the 0-0 band, which are very strong in intensity and give strongly positive polarization, were attributed to a_2 and b_1 vibrations, respectively, because a frequency of 870 cm^{-1} was observed in the infrared very strongly while one at 255 cm^{-1} was not. The remaining rather weak bands were assigned to totally symmetric vibrations. Vibrational structure is essentially the same as that of quinoxaline except for the a_1 bands which decrease considerably in intensity. A detailed analysis is given in Fig. 5.

Fig. 6 shows the phosphorescence spectrum of 2,3-dibromoquinoxaline observed in methylcyclohexane at 4.2°K and 77°K and the phosphorescence polarization spectrum measured relative to the $^1A_1(\pi,\pi^*) \leftarrow {}^1A_1$ excitation. The vibrational structure of the phosphorescence spectrum is the same as that of 2,3-dichloroquinoxaline, and an a_2 band of 255 cm^{-1} and b_1 band of 855 cm^{-1}

Phosphorescence and Polarization Spectra
of 2,3-Dichloroquinoxaline

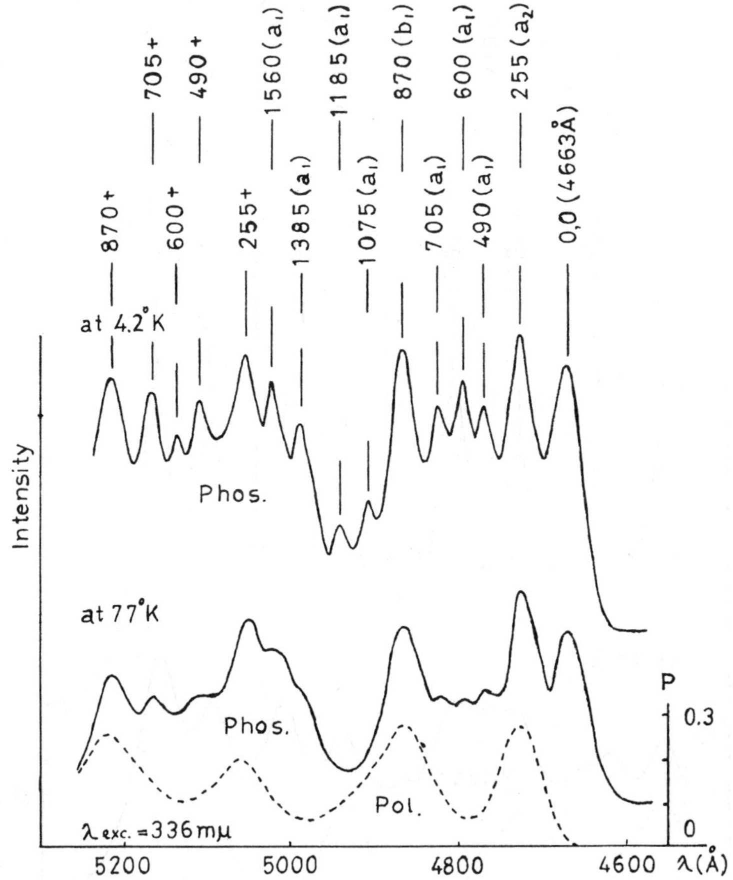

Figure 5

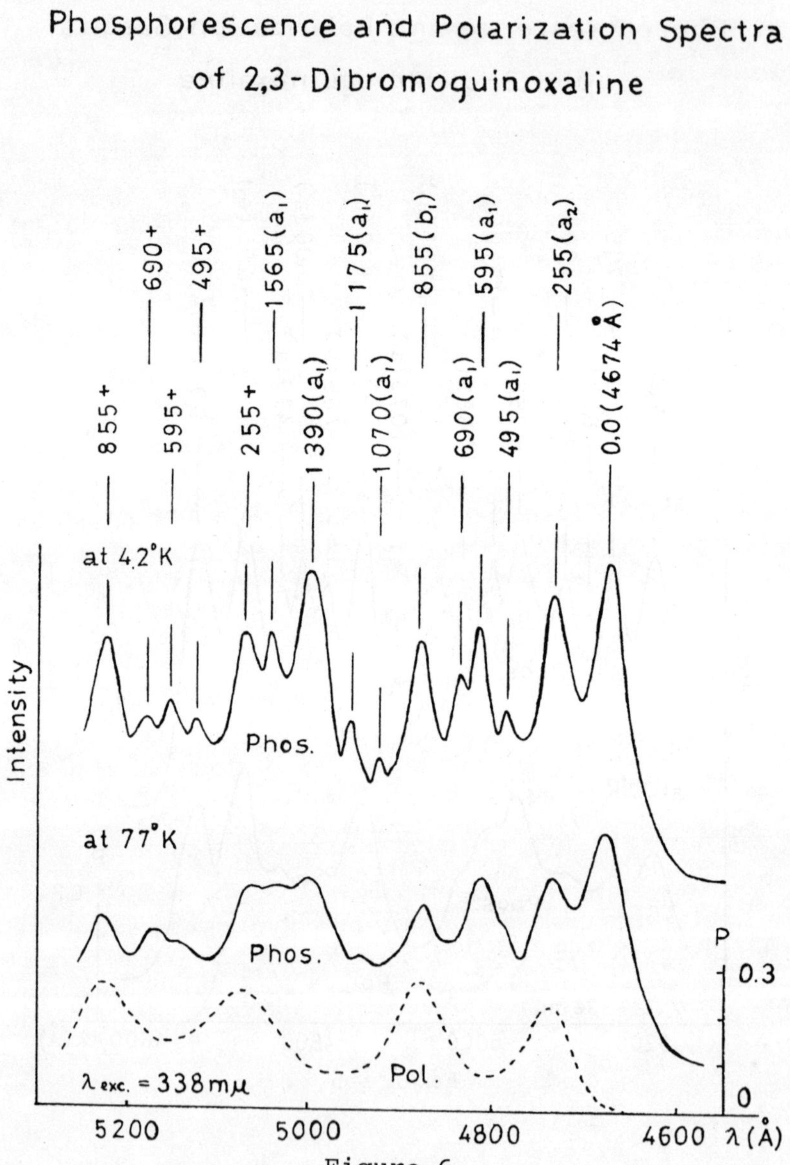
Phosphorescence and Polarization Spectra
of 2,3-Dibromoquinoxaline
855+
690+
595+
495+
255+
1565(a1)
1390(a1)
1175(a1)
1070(a1)
855(b1)
690(a1)
595(a1)
495(a1)
255(a2)
0,0(4674 Å)
at 4.2°K
Intensity
Phos.
at 77°K
Phos.
Pol.
λ exc. = 338mμ
P
0.3
0
5200
5000
4800
4600
λ(Å)

Figure 6

were found in the spectrum. The vibronic bands should have a positive degree of polarization while the ordinary bands should have a negative one. However, the ordinary bands appear positive, less positive than the vibronic bands, and the overall phosphorescence polarization spectra of the 2,3-dihalogenated quinoxalines appear positive in the whole region. This may be due to the presence of some unresolved b_1 bands in the spectra.

The spin-orbit coupling scheme for the T-S transition in 2,3-dihalogenated quinoxalines is concluded as follows: For the totally symmetric bands including the 0-0 band, the coupling mechanism should be the same as quinoxaline, that is,

$$^1B_1(n,\pi^*) \xleftrightarrow{\text{s.o.}} {}^3B_2(\pi,\pi^*)$$

The fact that the a_2 and b_1 bands show positive polarization with respect to the $^1A_1(\pi,\pi^*) \leftarrow {}^1A_1$ excitation indicates that the coupling mechanism for these bands should be shown as in Fig. 8.

DISCUSSION

Spin-orbit coupling consideration for the T-S transition in quinoxaline suggests that the matrix elements such as

$$\langle {}^1A_2(n,\pi^*)|L_y|{}^3B_2(\pi,\pi^*)\rangle$$

and

$$\langle {}^1A_1(\pi,\pi^*)|L_y|{}^3B_1(n,\pi^*)\rangle$$

are not important because of their vanishingly small values, where L denotes the orbital part of the spin-orbit interaction operator. This is consistent with the experimental result that no

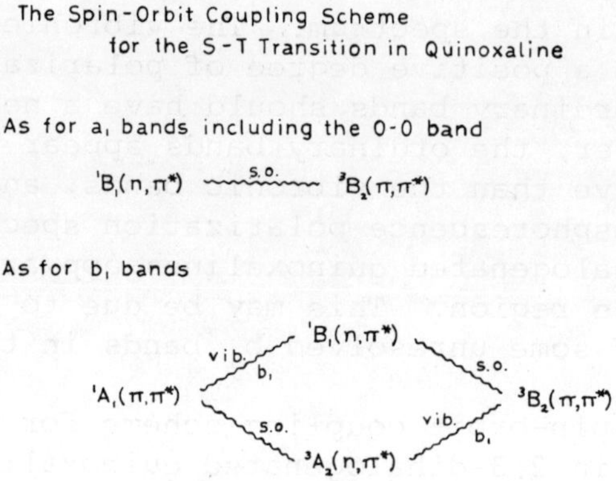

Figure 7

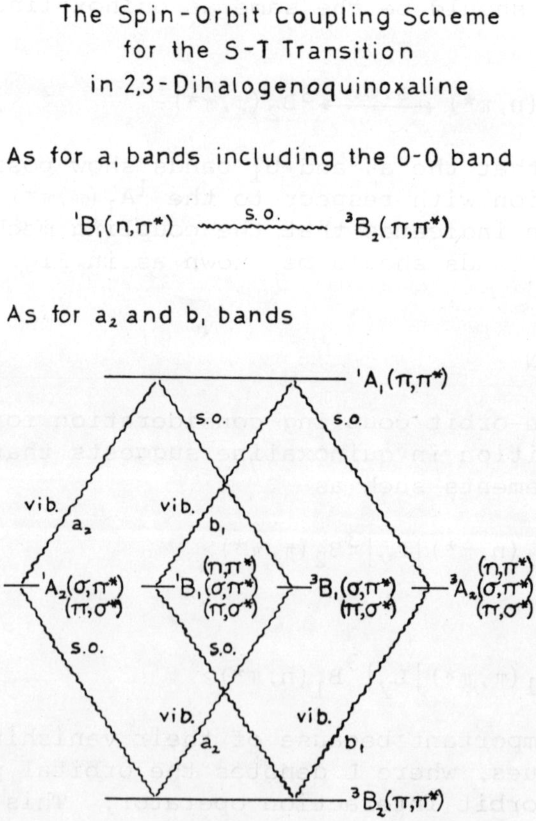

Figure 8

a_2 vibration was found in the phosphorescence spectrum. Theory also suggests that the first-order spin-orbit perturbation

$$\langle {}^1B_1(n,\pi^*)|L_z|{}^3B_2(\pi,\pi^*)\rangle$$

is much larger than the second-order spin-orbit vibronic perturbation

$$\langle {}^1A_1(\pi,\pi^*)|V_{b_1}|{}^1B_1(n,\pi^*)\rangle$$
$$\langle {}^1B_1(n,\pi^*)|L_z|{}^3B_2(\pi,\pi^*)\rangle$$

which indicates that the b_1 vibration should appear very weakly in the spectrum compared with the a_1 vibration in agreement with the experiment.

The following basic question immediately arises; "Why does the phosphorescence of 2,3-dihalogenated quinoxaline give positive polarization with respect to the ${}^1A_1(\pi,\pi^*) \leftarrow {}^1A_1$ excitation contrary to the case of quinoxaline?" Since the change from quinoxaline to 2,3-dihalogenated-quinoxaline alters the σ bond between carbon and halogen atoms, the σ_X bond is expected to be the key which solves the above question. The p_X orbital of the halogen atom mix with the π-orbital which is delocalized over the naphthalene skeleton. These considerations provide the T-S transition in 2,3-dihalogenated quinoxalines with new paths,

$$^1B_1(\sigma_X,\pi^*) \xleftrightarrow{\text{s.o.}} {}^3B_2(\pi,\pi^*)^*$$

and

*A ${}^1B_1(\pi,\sigma_X^*)$ state should also be considered, but this was abbreviated for simplicity. The reader should keep in mind that the symbol (σ,π^*) denotes both states, that is the (σ,π^*) and (π,σ^*) states.

$$^1A_2(\sigma_X,\pi^*) \xleftrightarrow{\text{s.o.}} {}^3B_2(\pi,\pi^*)$$

in addition to the original path

$$^1B_1(n,\pi^*) \xleftrightarrow{\text{s.o.}} {}^3B_2(\pi,\pi^*).$$

It should be noted that the matrix element

$$<{}^1A_2(\sigma,\pi^*)|L_y|{}^3B_2(\pi,\pi^*)>$$

has non-vanishing value in the case of 2,3-dihalogenated compounds due to the direction of the σ_X bond. It may readily be expected that in the bromo-compound the value of

$$<{}^1B_1(\sigma_X,\pi^*)|L_z|{}^3B_2(\pi,\pi^*)>$$

overcomes the value of

$$<{}^1B_1(n,\pi^*)|L_z|{}^3B_2(\pi,\pi^*)>$$

due to the heavy-atom contribution to the one center integral on the bromine atom. The remarkably short lifetime of the 2,3-dibromoquinoxaline phosphorescence may be due to this reason.

The $^1A_2(\sigma_X,\pi^*) \leftarrow {}^1A_1$ transition does not contribute to the intensification of the T-S transition to the first-order because this transition is prohibited. A weak $^1B_1(\sigma_X,\pi^*) \leftarrow {}^1A_1$ and a forbidden $^1A_2(\sigma_X,\pi^*) \leftarrow {}^1A_1$ transition can be perturbed by a strong $^1A_1(\pi,\pi^*$ or $\sigma,\sigma^*) \leftarrow {}^1A_1$ transition through b_1 and a_2 vibrations. The experimental fact that these vibrations were observed as strong bands in the phosphorescence spectra of 2,3-dihalogenated quinoxaline definitely indicates that the T-S transitions in these compounds are perturbed by $^1A_1 \leftarrow {}^1A_1$ transition to the second-order through b_1 and a_2 vibrations.

FURTHER WORK

El-Sayed found[4] in his study of 2,3-dihalogenated naphthalenes that both $^1A_1(\pi,\pi^*)$ and $^1B_2(\pi,\pi^*)$ states can perturb the lowest $^3B_2(\pi,\pi^*)$ state to the contrary of our results. The explanation of the reason why a $^1B_2(\pi,\pi^*)$ state does not contribute to the perturbation of the $^3B_2(\pi,\pi^*)$ states of 2,3-dihalogenated quinoxalines is puzzling. We must also make clear the reason why $^1B_1(n,\pi^*$ or $\sigma,\pi^*)$ and $^1A_2(\sigma,\pi^*)$ states are perturbed quite strongly by a $^1A_1(\pi,\pi^*$ or $\sigma,\sigma^*)$ state and why the characters of $^1B_1 \leftarrow {}^1A_1$ and $^1A_2 \leftarrow {}^1A_1$ transitions are governed by $^1A_1 \leftarrow {}^1A_1$ transitions in halogenated compounds.

REFERENCES

1. R. C. Hirt, F. T. King and J. C. Cavagnol, J. Chem. Phys. 25, 574 (1956).
2. N. Mataga, Busseiron Kenkyu, second band 3, 678 (1958).
3. M. A. El-Sayed and R. G. Brewer, J. Chem. Phys. 39, 1623 (1963).
4. M. A. El-Sayed, J. Chem. Phys. 43, 2864 (1965).

EXCIPLEX STUDIES III. RADIATIVE AND NON-RADIATIVE RELAXATION OF THE FLUORESCENCE STATE OF INDOLE AND METHYL DERIVATIVES OF INDOLE*

Michael S. Walker,** Thomas W. Bednar*** and Rufus Lumry

Laboratory for Biophysical Chemistry
Department of Chemistry
University of Minnesota
Minneapolis, Minnesota 55455

INTRODUCTION

In the absence of bimolecular quenching processes relaxation of the fluorescent state of an aromatic fluor may occur by :

	Process		
emission	$^1A^* \rightarrow {}^1A + h\nu$	k_F	(1)
internal conversion	$^1A^* \rightarrow {}^1A$	$k_{I.C.}$	(2)
intersystem crossing	$^1A^* \rightarrow {}^3A$	$k_{I.S.}$	(3)
or by quasi-chemical process	$^1A^* \rightarrow A$	k_i	(4)

*This is paper No. 45 from the Laboratory for Biophysical Chemistry. Please request reprints by this number.
**Present address: Research Laboratories, Xerox Corporation, Rochester, New York.
***Present address: Department of Biology, Marquette University, Milwaukee, Wisconsin.

In which case the fluorescence lifetime τ_M is given by

$$(\tau_M)^{-1} = k_M = k_F + k_{I.C.} + k_{I.S.} + \sum_i k_i \quad (5)$$

and the quantum yield of fluorescence Q_M by

$$Q_M = k_F/k_M = \tau_M/\tau_F \quad (6)$$

Of both experimental and theoretical significance are the effects of intermolecular interaction on the relaxation processes (1) to (4); this paper will concern itself only with the effects on these processes of hydrogen isotope in solvent, temperature and methyl substitution in indole solutes. Bowen and coworkers[1,2] have studied the effect of solvent on the quantum yield of fluorescence of several naphthylamine and anthracene derivatives. Their results showed that quantum yields could be represented by two processes, one dependent and the other independent of temperature. Bennett and McCartin[3] later concluded that for 9-methyl and 9,10-dichloroanthracene, the temperature dependence of the quantum yield (and τ_M) reflected intersystem crossing to a virtually degenerate triplet state. Recently, Horrocks et al.[4] have reported a solvent dependent singlet to triplet yield for 9-phenyl anthracene, while Eastman and Rosa[5] have correlated the solvent dependent radiationless relaxation of adenine in alcohol glasses with the cohesion and rigidity of the solvent.

Further, Nikitina et al.[6] have reported changes in the radiative lifetime of certain polyenes on going from aliphatic to aromatic solvents which they attributed to solute-solvent interaction, and changes in electronic structure of the pyrene-N,N-dimethyl aniline complex caused by interaction with polar solvents have been reported by Mataga et al.[7]

The present authors[8] have discussed the polar solvent-induced Stokes shift and loss in vibrational structure in the fluorescence spectra of indole derivatives, with no corresponding shift in the absorption spectra, in terms of both specific and non-specific excited-state solute-solvent interaction. In water indole, 1-methylindole and the other methyl derivatives of indole discussed in this paper form stable stoiciometric complexes with solvent in their singlet excited states. This paper is a consideration of the fluorescence quenching behavior of these complexes, called exciplexes.

EXPERIMENTAL

Indole, 2-methylindole and 5-methylindole were recrystallized from petroleum ether or methanol at low temperatures in the dark. 1-methyl, 3-methyl and 1,2,3-trimethyl derivatives, supplied by W. E. Noland (University of Minnesota) and 1,3-dimethylindole, supplied by R. L. Hinman (Union Carbide Company) were vacuum distilled.

Water (H_2O) was distilled while heavy water (D_2O) was Bio-Rad 99.8%.

Ultraviolet absorption and fluorescence spectra were recorded on a Cary 15 spectrophotometer and a spectrofluorimeter[8] respectively. Fluorescence quantum yields were measured by the method of Parker and Rees,[9] using quinine bisulphate in 0.1 N H_2SO_4 as the standard with a quantum yield of 0.55.[10] Solute concentrations were 10^{-5} M and excitation wavelength 280 nm.

Fluorescence lifetimes were measured using a phase modulated fluorometer described elsewhere.[11] A Schoeffel quartz monochromator (Model O.P.M. 30) was used in excitation, excitation wavelength 280 nm (half band width 5 nm). Narrow or wide band optical filters were used in emission. Quartz optics were used throughout the instrument and

R.C.A. C7268 photomultiplier tubes used as detectors. The sample cells were 1 cm x 0.5 cm quartz and enclosed in a thermostatted assembly, temperatures were measured with a copper constantan thermocouple. Samples, solute concentration 5×10^{-5} M to 5×10^{-4} M, were subjected to a minimum of four freeze-pump-thaw cycles at a pressure of 10^{-6} mm Hg and the cells sealed off.

RESULTS

Fluorescence lifetime, τ_M, and quantum yield, Q_M, values of indole and several methyl derivatives were measured as a function of temperature in H_2O, similar measurements were made for indole and 1-methylindole in D_2O. The lifetimes, yields and fluorescence wavelengths, for these compounds measured at 20°C in water are given in Table 1.

Measurements of τ_M and Q_M for indole and 1-methylindole in heavy water reflect a solvent deuterium isotope effect on these quantities with no change in the spectral distribution. The ratios

$$\tau_M(D_2O)/\tau_M(H_2O) = Q_M(D_2O)/Q_M(H_2O) \text{ of } 1.40$$

for indole and 1.02 for 1-methylindole at 20°C are in good agreement with the values of $Q_M(D_2O)/Q_M(H_2O)$ reported by Stryer[12] for these systems at the same temperature. However, at 50°C these ratios are 1.73 and 1.29 respectively. The temperature dependence of $\tau_M(D_2O)/\tau_M(H_2O)$ for indole and 1-methylindole is shown in Fig. 1 insert.

RADIATIVE LIFETIME τ_F. Radiative lifetimes of indole and 1-methylindole in water calculated from lifetime and yield values using Eq. (6) show

TABLE 1

Compound	Solvent	τ_M (nsec)	Q_M	$\tau_F = \tau_M/Q_M$ (nsec)	Fluorescence Wavelength* (nm)
Indole	H_2O	4.1	0.45	9.1	344
Indole	D_2O	5.7	0.63	9.0	344
1-Methylindole	H_2O	8.5	0.62	13.7	347
1-Methylindole	D_2O	8.7	0.63	13.8	347
2-Methylindole	H_2O	2.0	0.36	5.6	350
3-Methylindole	H_2O	9.1	0.52	17.5	362
5-Methylindole	H_2O	2.7	0.35	7.7	344
1,3-Dimethylindole	H_2O	15.6	0.73	21.3	371
1,2,3-Trimethylindole	H_2O	8.2	0.46	17.8	382

*Wavelengths are for fluorescence maxima.

no solvent isotope effect and increase on methyl substitution in the order 2-methyl < 5-methyl < indole < 1-methyl < 3-methyl < 1,2,3-trimethyl < 1,3-dimethyl. In cyclohexane as solvent τ_F(indole) < τ_F(1-methylindole).[13] While quantum yields for the other derivatives in cyclohexane were not measured, τ_M values were found to increase in the order 3-methyl < 1,3-dimethyl < 2-methyl < 1-methyl < indole < 5-methyl.[13] Further, an examination of the absorption spectra of these compounds in cyclohexane showed an approximate correlation between $\tau_M(H_2O)/\tau_M$(cyclohexane) and $\varepsilon_{max}(^1A - {}^1L_b)/\varepsilon_{max}(^1A - {}^1L_a)$. Transition moments $|M|$ were, therefore, calculated for both the $^1A - {}^1L_a$ and $^1A - {}^1L_b$ transitions in absorption using the formula (7)[14]

$$|M|_{CAL} = \left[0.302\ hcn \int \varepsilon d\nu_a / 8N\pi^3 e^2 \nu_a\right]^{\frac{1}{2}} \qquad (7)$$

and from radiative lifetimes using the approximate formula (8)

$$|M|_{OBS} = \left[3hk_F / 64\pi^4 \nu_e^3 e^2 n\right]^{\frac{1}{2}} \qquad (8)$$

where n is the solvent refractive index, $\int \frac{\varepsilon d\nu}{\nu}$ is the integral over the entire absorption band, ν_e is the frequency of maximum emission and $k_F = \tau_F^{-1}$. Calculation of transition moments from the absorption spectra necessitated separation of the ^1L_a and ^1L_b bands which overlap strongly for indole and its derivatives. Separation of these bands was carried out by assuming a mirror image relationship between the long wavelength edge (^1L_b band) in absorption and the fluorescence spectrum measured in cyclohexane and reflecting the emission spectrum about the 0'-0" transition, onto the absorption spectrum. Areas under both bands could be estimated in this way. Absorption spectra measured in water were not used since there is some loss in vibrational structure in this solvent and a consequent greater difficulty in separating the bands. Solvent shifts of the absorption bands are small and have a negligible effect on band areas relative to the errors of our method of band separation. Transition moments calculated from Eqs. (7) and (8) are given in Table 2.

TEMPERATURE DEPENDENCE OF τ_M. It was observed that both τ_M and Q_M for indole and its derivatives when measured in H_2O and D_2O are highly temperature dependent, but showed little temperature dependence in non-aqueous solvents such as methanol, dimethylsulphoxide or cyclohexane.[13] The variation of τ_M with temperature for indole and 1-methylindole in light and heavy water is shown in Fig. 1. Also shown are τ_M values for indole measured in methanol. Gally and Edelman have also reported a strong temperature dependence of Q_M for tryptophan in water.[15]

The temperature dependence of τ_M was analyzed with the assumption that $(\tau_M)^{-1} = k_M$ could be expressed in terms of a temperature-independent term k' and a single temperature-dependent term k(T), i.e.,

$$(\tau_M)^{-1} = k_M = k' + k(T) \tag{9}$$

with

$$k(T) = A\exp(-E_M/RT) = \frac{kT}{h}\exp(-\Delta H^{\ddagger}/RT)\exp(\Delta S^{\ddagger}/R) \tag{10}$$

In Eq. (10) the transmission coefficient has been set equal to unity. The validity of the assumption of a single temperature-dependent term is established by the accuracy with which the data conform to the requirement of the following analysis: Differentiating equation (9) w.r.t. 1/T gives

TABLE 2: Transition Moments

Compound	$\|M\|_{cal}$ $^1A - {}^1L_a$ Debye	$\|M\|_{cal}$ $^1A - {}^1L_b$ Debye	$\|M\|_{OBS}$ (Water) Debye	$\|M\|_{OBS}$ (Cyclohexane) Debye
Indole	2.63	2.08	3.28	2.22
1-Methylindole	2.21	2.45	2.69	3.21
2-Methylindole	2.87	2.49	4.30	-
3-Methylindole	2.27	2.56	2.54	-
5-Methylindole	2.82	1.90	3.56	-
1,2-Dimethylindole	2.67	2.67	2.39	-
1,2,3-Trimethylindole	-	-	2.73	-

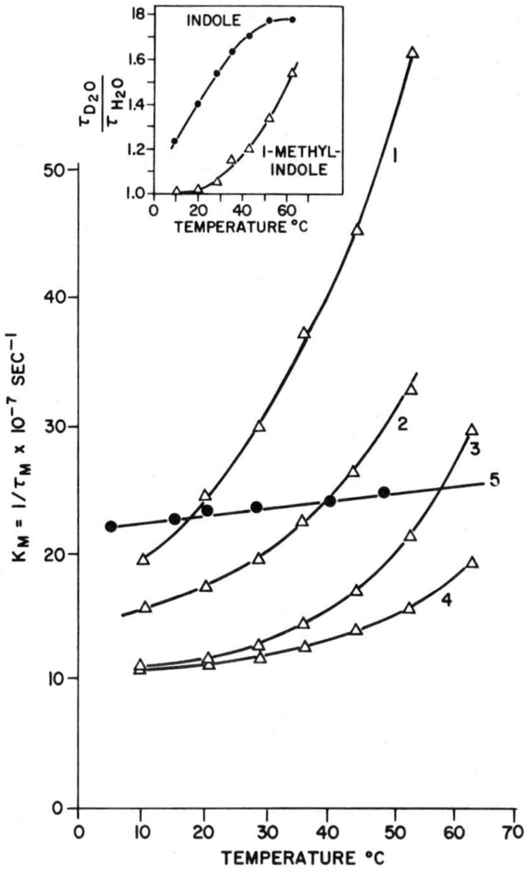

Figure 1 Temperature dependence of the fluorescence lifetimes, τ_M, of indole and 1-methylindole.
Curve 1; indole in H_2O.
Curve 2; indole in D_2O.
Curve 3; 1-methylindole in H_2O.
Curve 4; 1-methylindole in D_2O.
Curve 5; indole in methanol.
Insert: Temperature dependence of the ratio $\tau_M(D_2O)/\tau_M(H_2O)$ for indole and 1-methylindole.

$$-\left[dk_M/d(1/T)\right] = +\frac{AE_M}{R}\exp(-E_M/RT) \qquad (11)$$

and

$$\log\left[-dk_M/d(1/T)\right] = \log(AE_M/R)-E_M/2.3RT \qquad (12)$$

When the data were graphically analyzed according to Eq. (12) $\log\left[-dk_M/d(1/T)\right]$ vs $(1/T)$ plots were linear in all cases. Values of $(-dk_M)/d(1/T)$ were taken from plots of k_M against $1/T$.

Values of A and E_M are given in Table 3, values of k' were calculated by difference, i.e., $k' = k_M - k(T)$ and are also given in Table 3. The curves drawn through the data in Fig. 1 are in accordance with Eq. (9) and are in good agreement with the experimental data.

DISCUSSION

Gladchenko et al.[16] have reported a value of 4.1 nsec for the lifetime of indole in water which is in agreement with the value at 20°C reported here. Chen et al.[17] have reported a value of 2.7 nsec for indole in water at 23°C containing THAM-chloride buffer, which may be compared with the value of 3.7 nsec at the same temperature interpolated from Fig. 1 (curve 1). The somewhat lower value of τ_M in buffered solution may reflect quenching by buffer ions, but there are indications[18] that the fluorescence yield of indole compounds can vary with excitation wavelength. The yield of 0.45 for indole in water (20°C) is in agreement with values reported by Weber[19] and White.[20] However, the value of 0.55 for the quantum yield of quinine bisulphate, used here as a standard, has recently been questioned.[21,22] Any error in this value will result in comparable errors in the quantum yield and radiative lifetime

TABLE 3: Fluorescence Decay Parameters for Indole Derivatives in Water

Compound	Solvent	$k_F = (\tau_F)^{-1}$ x 10^7 sec^{-1}	k' x 10^7 sec^{-1}	A sec^{-1}	E_M kcal/mole
Indole	H_2O	11.0	13.9	2.05 x 10^{14}	8.5
Indole	D_2O	11.0	14.0	1.65 x 10^{15}	10.4
1-Methylindole	H_2O	7.3	10.6	6.15 x 10^{16}	13.1
1-Methylindole	D_2O	7.2	10.7	1.65 x 10^{15}	11.2
2-Methylindole	H_2O	18.0	20.0	8.20 x 10^{16}	11.5
3-Methylindole	H_2O	5.7	6.8	7.80 x 10^{16}	12.5
5-Methylindole	H_2O	13.0	15.0	3.30 x 10^{15}	9.7
1,3-Dimethyl-indole	H_2O	4.7	4.7	3.45 x 10^{14}	9.8
1,2,3-Trimeth-ylindole	H_2O	5.6	7.5	2.05 x 10^{17}	13.0

values reported here, but the relative values of these quantities and subsequent arguments presented in this paper will remain unchanged.

The observation of a solvent isotope effect on the lifetime of 1-methylindole at temperatures greater than 20° (Fig. 1) and the similar temperature dependence of k(T) for both 1-unsubstituted and 1-substituted indoles in water excludes proton-loss from the ring nitrogen as being responsible for the non-radiative processes. Protonation of this nitrogen in the excited state is very unlikely since studies of the pH dependence of quenching of indole and 1-methylindole in the alkaline pH region show that this atom becomes considerably more acidic on excitation. Furthermore, the non-radiative processes are not found to be pH dependent in the neutral pH region in which our experiments were carried out. Thus the arguments of Stryer[12] that changes in protonation in the excited state are responsible for the non-radiative processes of a variety of aromatic molecules are not applicable to indole, 1-methylindole, nor presumably to other methyl-substituted indoles we have studied. It is also noteworthy that k' is independent of solvent isotope for indole and 1-methylindole. Since $k' > k_F$, there is at least one temperature independent radiationless process (Table 3).

Förster and Rokos[23] have excluded proton-transfer as being responsible for the solvent isotope effect on the fluorescence yield of N-alkylated aromatic amines. They suggest that solute-solvent interaction is directly responsible for internal conversion in these molecules. Bowen and Seamen[1] have noted a relationship between the fluorescence shift and fluorescence quantum yield for several analogous amines in polar solvents, which Förster and Rokos[23] regard as evidence for a direct relation between the mechanism responsible for the red shift and that responsible for the quantum-yield change. A similar correlation has been reported by Viktorova[24] for several organic fluors in both single and bicomponent solvents, the quantum yield passing through a maximum value with an increasing Stokes shift in the emission. The author[24] explained this phenomenon in terms of discrete centers in mixed solutions corresponding to molecules of the fluor associated with different numbers of solvent molecules.

A comparison of our results with those of other authors must be delayed until the radiationless process with rate constant k(T) can be identified, possibilities being intersystem crossing, internal conversion, or electron transfer to solvent. The last possibility is strongly suggested by the finding of Grossweiner and Joschek[25] that solvated electrons are produced on irradiation of indole and since we have shown that there is a single temperature-dependent non-radiative process for indole. (See Postscript). However, the reports by Horrocks et al.[4] and by Bennett and McCartin[3] of temperature-dependent intersystem crossing to a triplet state lying at the same level or higher than the first excited singlet state show that this process also cannot be ruled out. The lowest triplet state of indole lies some 22,200 cm^{-1} above the ground state (measured in non-polar solvent glass) but details of the higher triplet states are not yet available. Such a process could explain even the remarkably large activation energies we have observed, but it is very difficult to see how such a process could have associated with it a real or apparent entropy of activation as large as 19 e.u./mole. It is generally accepted that internal conversion is not important for relaxation of the fluorescence state of aromatic molecules where the separation of the first excited and ground states is large.[26] It is possible in the case of indole compounds that strong coupling between the excited state and the solvent favors internal conversion but in this case it is difficult to account for the large activation enthalpies.

The large activation enthalpies and entropies for the k(T) process are most easily reconciled with a "chemical" quenching process involving solvent. The ejection of electrons into solvent is perhaps the most attractive possibility since our results appear to exclude changes in protonation of the indole compounds. The solvent isotope effect thus may be a consequence of differences in the solvation state of electrons in D_2O and H_2O. However, it should be remembered that the fluorescing species are exciplexes formed between indole and one or two solvent molecules and may show a hydrogen isotope effect as a result of intrinsically different properties of the H and D forms of these complexes. In the next paper in this series it will be shown that the temperature-dependent non-radiative process manifests a unique pattern of compensation of activation enthalpy by activation entropy which is characteristic of water as a solvent.

While the transition moments calculated from emission and absorption data using Eq. (7) and (8) can only be regarded as approximate, they do reflect a correlation between the moments for the ^1A - ^1L_a transition in absorption and the emission process in water, while in cyclohexane the expected correlation between emission and ^1A - ^1L_b absorption moments is observed. These correlations suggest that the state responsible for emission in non-polar solvents is the ^1L_b state while in polar solvents inversion of the ^1L_a and ^1L_b states occurs on equilibrium (exciplex formation) prior to emission. Bobrovich et al.[27] have measured the absorption and fluorescence-polarization spectrum of indole in polar and non-polar solvents and conclude that in polar solvents (glycerol) emission occurs from the ^1L_a state while in non-polar solvents (paraffin) emission occurs from the ^1L_b state with a contribution at longer wavelengths due to emission from the ^1L_a level (it may be pointed out that paraffins are notorious for the presence of polar impurities and the long wavelength contribution may be a result of indole association with such impurities). Zimmerman[28] has reported similar measurements, but his results are complicated by the use of alcohol at low temperature to interpret the emission in polar solvents since the emission for indole in polar glasses reverts, at least partially, to the non-complexed indole emission pattern observed in non-polar solvents.

An inversion of the energies of the ^1L_a and ^1L_b states which manifests itself almost entirely as a lowering of the ^1L_a state on exciplex formation is consistent with the expected sensitivity of the state with the transverse transition-moment vector in a molecule such as indole to solvent polarity since the excitation from the ^1A state to this state is very similar in sensitivity to that observed with naphthalene compounds substituted with polar groups in the α position. Solvent perturbations of the indole nitrogen atom are thus expected to have considerably larger effects on the energy of the ^1L_a state than on the energy of the ^1L_b state with longitudinally polarized transition moment (See Ref. 29 for example). However, the stability of indole exciplexes has been found[8] to be comparable to that of such excimers as that formed by one excited and one unexcited benzene molecule. It is now generally believed,[30] though probably not established,[31] that the stability of the benzene excimer requires the participation of charge-transfer states ($C_6H_6^+$ + $C_6H_6^-$, etc.) by configurational interaction. If this is also the case for the exciplex formed between indole and water molecules (Indole$^+$ + H_2O^-) one might expect the ^1L_a and ^1L_b states of pure indole to lose their indentity in the exciplex. This does not appear to be the case and suggests that the charge-transfer states are not important in exciplex formation with indole compounds. If so, since a variety of evidence already cited excludes the possibility of unusually strong bonding between excited indole and polar solvent molecules through hydrogen bonding to the ring nitrogen, either unusually strong hydrogen bonding between some carbon atom of the aromatic nucleus and the solvent molecules is responsible for exciplex stability or there is some other strong interaction between excited-state indole and small polar molecules, possibly through second moments, but perhaps involving higher moments of the charge distributions. It is obvious that there is much to learn about this recently discovered type of excited state complex.[32,33,34] In this connection it is interesting to note that although the ground-state indole complex with polar solvent corresponding to the stable exciplex has a repulsive wave function, the situation in carbazole is such that the complex has an attractive wave function in both singlet-excited and ground states.[35]

ACKNOWLEDGEMENTS

This work was supported by the Atomic Energy Commission through Contracts AT(11-1)794 and AT(11-1) 894.

POSTSCRIPT

T. Hopkins and R. Lumry find large yields of solvated electrons using an H_2O-scavenger method. Preliminary temperature data with 1-Me-indole conform to the predictions of this paper. To be published.

REFERENCES

1. E. J. Bowen and D. Seaman. Luminescence of Organic and Inorganic Materials. H. P. Kallman and G. M. Spruch, Eds. (John Wiley and Sons, Inc., New York, 1962), pp. 153-160.
2. E. J. Bowen and J. Sahu, J. Phys. Chem., 63, 4 (1959).
3. R. G. Bennett and P. J. McCartin, J. Chem. Phys., 44, 1969 (1966).
4. A. R. Horrocks, T. Medinger and F. Wilkinson, Photochem. Photobiol., 6, 21 (1967).
5. J. W. Eastman and E. J. Rosa, Photo. Photobiol., 7, 189 (1968).
6. A. N. Nikitina, G. S. Ter-Sarkisyan, B. M. Mikhailov and L. E. Minchenkova, Optics and Spec., 14, 347 (1963).
7. N. Mataga, T. Okada and N. Yamamoto, Chem. Phy. Lett., 1, 119 (1967).
8. M S. Walker, T. W. Bednar and R. Lumry, J. Chem. Phys., 45, 3455 (1966); ibid., 47, 1020 (1967).
9. C. A. Parker and W. T. Rees, Analyst 85, 587 (1960).
10. W. H. Melhuish, N. Z. J. Sci. Tech., 37, 142 (1955).
11. A. Muller, R. Lumry and H. Kokubun, Rev. Sci. Inst., 36, 1214 (1965).
12. L. Stryer, J. Am. Chem. Soc., 88, 5708 (1966).
13. M. S. Walker, T. W. Bednar and R. Lumry. Paper presented at the Livingston Symp. on Photochemistry. Minneapolis, U.S.A. (May, 1967). Also M. S. Walker and T. W. Bednar unpublished results.
14. H. H. Jaffe and M. Orchin, Theory and Application of Ultraviolet Spectroscopy (John Wiley and Sons, Inc., New York, 1962), p. 115.
15. J. A. Gally and G. M. Edelman, Biopolymers Symp., 1, 367 (1964).
16. L. F. Gladchenko, M. Y. Kostko, L. G. Pikulik and A. N. Sevchenko, Dokl. Akad. Nauk.

Belorussk., SSR 9, 647 (1965).
17. R. F. Chen, G. G. Vurek and N. Alexander, Science, 156, 949 (1967).
18. S. Georghiou, C. Tollefson and R. Lumry (unpublished observations, 1968).
19. G. Weber, T. Faraday Soc., 53, 646 (1957).
20. A. E. White, Dissertation, Sheffield, England (1960).
21. R. F. Chen, Analytical Biochem., 19, 374 (1967).
22. R. Rusakovicz and A. C. Testa, J. Phys. Chem., 72, 793 (1968).
23. Th. Förster and K. Rokos, Chem. Phys. Lett., 1, 279 (1967).
24. E. N. Viktorova, Optics and Spec., 22, 206 (1967).
25. L. I. Grossweiner and H. I. Joschek, Advan. Chem. Ser., 50, 279 (1965).
26. J. D. Laposa, E. C. Lim and R. E. Kellogg, J. Chem. Phys., 42, 3025 (1965).
27. V. P. Bobrovich, G. S. Kembrovskii and N. I. Mavenko, Dolk. Akad. Nauk. Beloruss., SSR 10, 936 (1966).
28. H. Zimmerman, Z. Electrochem., 65, 61 (1961); 64, 1215 (1960).
29. H. H. Jaffee and M. Orchin, Theory and Application of Ultraviolet Spectroscopy (John Wiley and Sons, Inc., New York, 1962), pp. 303-316.
30. B. N. Srinivasan, J. V. Russell and S. P. McGlynn, J. Chem. Phys., 48, 1967 (1968).
31. J. B. Birks, Chem. Physics Letters 1, 304 (1967).
32. J. B. Birks, Nature, 214, 1187 (1967).
33. N. Mataga, T. Okada, and K. Ezumi, Mol. Phys., 10, 203 (1966).
34. H. Beens, H. Knible and A. Weller, J. Chem. Phys., 47, 1183 (1967).
35. M. S. Walker, T. Bednar and R. Lumry (to be published).

HEAVY-ATOM EFFECTS IN THE EXTERNAL QUENCHING OF MOLECULAR PYRENE FLUORESCENCE IN SOLUTION

M. F. Thomaz* and B. Stevens**

Department of Chemistry
Sheffield University
Sheffield, England

INTRODUCTION

The reduction in molecular fluorescence yield γ_{FM} of a dissolved aromatic hydrocarbon A with increase in solute concentration (self-quenching) may be explained quantitatively in terms of processes 1-8 of the following kinetic scheme:

*NATO Pre-doctoral Fellow. On leave of absence from Commissao de Estudos de Energia Nuclear, Lisbon, Portugal.
**Present Address: Department of Chemistry, University of South Florida, Tampa, Florida 33620

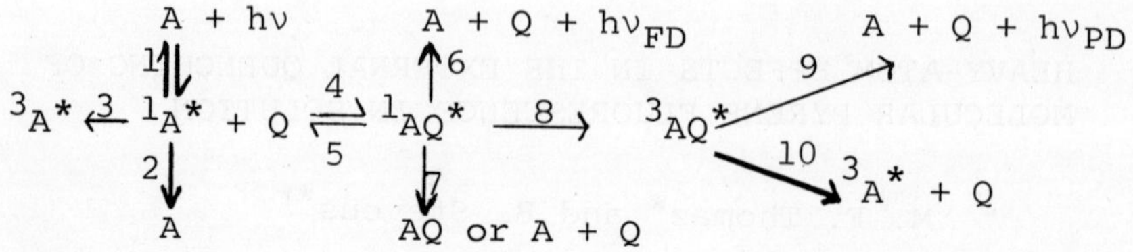

where Q ≡ A, AQ is the photodimer A_2 formed by the higher linear polyacenes and certain derivatives[1,2] and the asterisk denotes electronic excitation; if γ^o_{FM} and τ^o_{FM} $(= 1/[k_1 + k_2 + k_3])$ represent the molecular fluorescence yield and singlet state lifetime at infinite dilution the appropriate equation is

$$\frac{\gamma^o_{FM}}{\gamma_{FM}} = 1 + k_4[Q]\tau^o_{FM}\left(\frac{k_6 + k_7 + k_8}{k_5 + k_6 + k_7 + k_8}\right)$$

$$= 1 + k_Q\tau^o_{FM}[Q] \qquad (1)$$

The intermediate complex (excimer) $^1AQ^* \equiv {}^1A_2^*$ was first observed in emission (process 6) as a broad structureless band, red-shifted by ~6000 cm^{-1} from the 0'-0" molecular fluorescence band, by Förster and Kasper[3] for solutions of pyrene in benzene and subsequently reported for a number of other aromatic hydrocarbons and their derivatives;[4,5] both the excimer binding energy (~10 kcal/mole) and the repulsion energy of the unexcited molecules in the excimer configuration contribute to the observed red-shift of the fluorescence spectrum.[6]

Since process 5 is associated with an activation energy equal to the excimer binding energy in solution, an increase in temperature leads to a reduction in both the excimer fluorescence yield and in the self-quenching rate constant $k_A(\equiv k_Q)$ which may be considerably less than the diffusion-limited value $k_4 = k_d$ at room temperature according to the photostationary expression

$$k_A = k_4(k_6 + k_7 + k_8)/(k_5 + k_6 + k_7 + k_8) \quad (2)$$

and approaches zero for those solutes (naphthalene and phenanthrene) in which the excimer binding energy is small.[7] Theoretical considerations of this binding energy have shown that configuration interaction between charge resonance and exciton states is essential to account for the observed values;[8] the independence of the excimer band maximum on dielectric constant of the solvent confirms the absence of a resultant dipole moment.[9]

Hoytink et al.[10] have recently observed excimer phosphorescence (process 9) in concentrated cooled ethanolic solutions of naphthalene and phenanthrene, while Medinger and Wilkinson[11] have shown that process 8 followed by 10 is necessary to account for the concentration dependence of the molecular triplet yield of pyrene in ethanol at ambient temperatures.

A similar kinetic scheme can account for the quenching of molecular fluorescence in solution by a second quenching species $Q \neq A$. The key observation is again that of the long-wave structureless emission from the excited complex $^1AQ^*$ (process 6) reported by Leonhardt and Weller[12] and by Mataga, Okada and Ezumi[13] for the quenching of aromatic hydrocarbons by aniline and N-alkyl anilines; these authors recognised the similarity in behavior to the excimer system and interpreted their observations in terms of processes 1-8. Dissociation of the complex $^1AQ^*$ (process 5) with an activation-energy of ~10kcal/mole is responsible[14] for a negative temperature coefficient of the measured rate constant k_Q for dimethylaniline quenching of perylene in benzene and provides a qualitative explanation of the increase in k_Q for amine quenching of acridine fluorescence with a reduction in the ionisation potential of the quencher[15] and concomitant stabilisation of the charge transfer complex A^-Q^+. This direction of electron transfer has been confirmed by Weller and coworkers who observed the transient absorption spectrum of both the hydrocarbon radical anion (of perylene) and the quencher radical cation (of diethylaniline) in acetonitrile,[16] and who correlated the stability of the complex with diethylaniline, as the red-shift of its emission spectrum, with the reduction potential (electron affinity) of the hydrocarbon.[17]

As in the excimer scheme (Q ≡ A) the measured quenching rate constant given by equation (2) reflects the competition between complex dissociation (process 5) and complex relaxation processes 6, 7 and 8. Hammond and coworkers[18] conclude that fluorescence quenching by conjugated dienes populates the aromatic hydrocarbon ground state directly (process 7) with little or no chemical reaction, while the maleic anhydride quenching of anthracene fluorescence is accompanied by formation of the adduct AQ.[19] Evidence for process 8 is at present based on the observation of complex phosphorescence (process 9) in donor-acceptor systems which however exhibit C-T absorption bands,[20] and on the increased production of hydrocarbon triplet states by heavy-atom quenchers [21] which could result from dissociation of the complex triplet state $^3AQ^*$ (process 10) formed by enhanced intersystem crossing in the complex (process 8). This sequence of events would require that the measured fluorescence quenching rate constant k_Q, as expressed by equation (2), will depend both on the extent of spin-orbit coupling in the complex, <u>and</u> on its stability towards dissociation as determined by the donor-acceptor properties of the quenching partners; it is with the verification of these aspects of the overall quenching scheme that this contribution is directed. Pyrene was chosen as the fluor since its relatively long fluorescence lifetime allows the observation of significant quenching by relatively inefficient quenchers, and the use of benzene as solvent minimises the possibility of separation of the charge transfer complex components observed in high dielectric constant media.[16]

EXPERIMENTAL

The concentration of pyrene (Koch-Light RRI 5262) in benzene (Hopkins and Williams analar grade) was maintained at 10^{-5} to avoid effects due to photo-association (self-quenching) exhibited by this solute. The quenching reagents listed in Table 1, of the highest commercially-available purity were subjected to fractional distillation, passage through an activated alumina column or multiple recrystallization, and stored in a refrigerator until required. Each solution was purged with O_2-free nitrogen prior to measurement of the fluorescence decay constant (by pulsed-flash fluorimetry)[22] or to recording the emission spectrum (on the Aminco-Keirs spectrophotofluorimeter).

RESULTS AND DISCUSSION

Table 1 lists the values obtained for the quenching rate constants k_Q from relative intensity measurements according to equation (1) with τ^o_{FM} = 465 ± 15 nsec in benzene at 20 ± 2°C. In all cases the relative fluorescence yield exhibited a linear dependence on quencher concentration and no change in emission spectrum was observed at the highest concentrations of quenching species employed.

Column 3 of Table 1 lists values of k_Q estimated from the quencher concentration dependence of measured fluorescence decay constant $1/\tau_{FM}$ using the relationship

$$1/\tau_{FM} = 1/\tau^o_{FM} + k_Q [Q] \qquad (3)$$

TABLE 1: Rate Constants k_Q from Quenching of Pyrene Molecular Fluorescence (10^{-5} M in benzene) at 20 ± 2°C

Q	$k_Q(M^{-1}\ sec^{-1})^a$	$k_Q(M^{-1}\ sec^{-1})^b$	$\log(k_Q/n^2\zeta^2)^c$	$-E_{\frac{1}{2}}^d$ (volts)
C_6H_5Cl	7×10^4	1.6×10^5	-0.87	2.58[e]
$p\text{-}C_6H_4Cl_2$	2.1×10^5		-0.80	2.49
C_2HCl_3	1.1×10^6		-0.46	2.14
C_2Cl_4	1.9×10^6		-0.46	1.88
$CHCl_3$	3.7×10^6	8.8×10^6	0.08	1.67
CCl_4	2.3×10^8	2.5×10^8	1.62	0.78
C_2Cl_6	1.2×10^8	5.4×10^8	0.99	0.62
C_6Cl_6	1.6×10^9	3.4×10^9	2.12	1.44
C_2H_5Br	$1.8_4 \times 10^9$		-0.52	2.08
$n\text{-}C_3H_7Br$	$2.4_6 \times 10^9$	4.5×10^6	-0.39	2.20[f]
$i\text{-}C_3H_7Br$	1.6×10^6		-0.56	2.26[f]
$n\text{-}C_4H_9Br$	1.9×10^6		-0.52	2.27
$n\text{-}C_8H_{17}Br$	2.4×10^6		-0.41	2.38
CH_2Br_2	7.0×10^6		-0.54	1.48
C_6H_5Br	3.2×10^6	5×10^6	-0.28	2.32
$o\text{-}C_6H_4Br_2$	1.6×10^7		-0.20	1.83[e]
$p\text{-}C_6H_4Br_2$	1.3×10^7	2.6×10^7	-0.26	2.10
$1,2,4,5\text{-}C_6H_2Br_2$	4.0×10^8	6.6×10^8	0.61	1.45
C_6Br_6	3.2×10^9	9.9×10^9	1.16	0.75
$CHBr_3$	2.0×10^9	3.2×10^9	1.56	0.64
CBr_4	7.0×10^9	1.2×10^{10}	1.85	0.30
CH_3I	5.6×10^7		0.34	1.63
C_2H_5I	5.8×10^7	1.0×10^8	0.35	1.67
$n\text{-}C_4H_9I$	3.4×10^7		0.13	2.27[e]
C_6H_5I	9.8×10^7	1.4×10^8	0.58	1.62
$o\text{-}C_6H_4I_2$	1.6×10^9		0.60	1.23[e]
$p\text{-}C_6H_4I_2$	2.6×10^9		0.81	1.46[e]
CH_2I_2	4.2×10^9		1.01	1.12
CHI_3	1.5×10^{10}	1.7×10^{10}	1.82	0.49

a From equation (1).
b From equation (3).
c With ζ in units of cm^{-1}.
d Solvent 75% dioxan-water.[30]
e Reference 31.
f Solvent dimethylformamide.[32]

the decay of pyrene molecular fluorescence being exponential over a period of at least $3\tau_{FM}$ in each case examined. It is unlikely that time-dependent diffusional effects are responsible for the difference in k_Q values computed from equations (2) and (3) which at present is unexplained; however, a comparison of the data in columns 2 and 3 provides a strong indication that static quenching, due to complex formation in the ground state, does not contribute to the observed quenching effect.

The absence of complex fluorescence supports the findings of Wilkinson et al.[21] that heavy atom quenching produces exclusively the hydrocarbon triplet state, in which case ($k_8 >> k_6 + k_7$) equation (2) reduces to

$$k_Q \simeq k_4 k_8 / k_5 \quad (4)$$

for those systems in which the measured quenching rate constant is appreciably less than the expected diffusion-limited encounter constant k_4. The complex dissociation frequency k_5 may in turn be related to its dissociation energy E_5 by an equation of the form

$$k_5 = A_5 \exp(-E_5/RT) \quad (5)$$

where A_5 is a constant and E_5 is expressed, for a purely charge transfer interaction, in terms of the ionisation potential I_D and electron affinity E_A of the donor and acceptor components respectively, and the coulomb attraction energy $C(r)$ at the equilibrium donor-acceptor separation, r, i.e.

$$-E_5 = I_D - E_A - C(r) \quad (6)$$

By analogy with the internal effect of heavy atoms on the molecular intersystem crossing probability the rate constant of process 8 should be related to the matrix element of the spin orbit perturbation operator between the singlet and triplet states of the complex. Thus following treatments of the internal heavy atom effect by McClure[23] and of the combined internal and external effects of heavy atoms on the phosphorescence decay constant by McGlynn et al.,[24] k_8 is expressed in terms of the atomic spin-orbit coupling parameters ζ as

$$k_8 \simeq A_8(\sum_i \zeta_i)^2 \qquad (7)$$

where A_8 is related to the energy separation of the combining states $^1AQ^*$ and $^3AQ^*$ assumed constant. In this approximation equations (4)-(7) provide the relationship

$$\ln k_Q/(\sum_i \zeta_i)^2 \sim \text{constant} + (E_A - I_D)/RT \qquad (8)$$

for a series of complexes with a common rate of formation (k_4), activation entropy for dissociation (A_5), interionic separation (r) and energy separation of the combining states (A_8). The absence of any correlation between $\ln k_Q/(\sum_i \zeta_i)^2$, computed from the ζ values for the halogens given by McClure,[23] and the ionization potentials of the halobenzenes as measured by electron impact[25] indicates that these quenching species do not act as electron donors.

Electron affinities are not available for the majority of quenchers listed in Table 1. However, on the basis of simple calculations of σ and π orbital energies of haloalkanes and conjugated halides (LCAO MO neglecting overlap and electronic interaction), Fukui et al.[26] conclude that the lowest vacant orbitals are σ^*, particularly as the number and atomic weight of the halogen atoms increases, and that the electron affinities correlate with polarographic half-wave reduction potentials $E_{1/2}$ if it is assumed that electron transfer to σ^* is the potential-determining step. Use of the relationship

$$E_A = \underline{a}E_{1/2} + \underline{b}$$

where $\underline{a}$ and $\underline{b}$ are constants for the series, allows equation (8) to be written in the form

$$\log_{10}(k_Q/\underline{n}^2\zeta^2) \sim \text{constant} + \underline{a}E_{1/2}/2.303\ RT \quad (9)$$

for a given (fluorescent) donor and variable (quenching) acceptor containing $\underline{n}$ identical halogen atoms. The appropriate data are summarised in columns 4 and 5 of Table 1 and plotted in accordance with equation (9) in Figure 1 where the least squares representation (except for C_6Cl_6) of the data line given by

$$\log(k_Q/\underline{n}^2\zeta^2)[M^{-1}sec^{-1}(cm^{-1})^{-2}] = 2.14$$

$$+ 1.15\ E_{1/2}\ \text{(volts)}$$

at 20°C, provides the value $\underline{a}$ = 0.07; this is of the order computed by Fukui et al.[26] for the chlorobenzenes (0.14) and halomethanes (0.2).

In view of the approximations involved, the neglect of exciton state contribution to the complex stabilization energy (which may be significant for Q = C_6Cl_6) and the use of half-wave potentials (measured in a different solvent) which may not describe reversible reduction of the quenching species,[27] this treatment should be regarded as indicating a trend rather than establishing a correlation of quenching rate constants with spin-orbit coupling parameters and electron-acceptor properties of the quenching species. However the trend supports a direction of electron transfer which is the reverse of that established by Weller and coworkers for charge transfer complexes of aromatic hydrocarbons and amines in the excited state; in terms of the simple MO scheme[28] this requires that the ionization potential of the quencher exceeds that

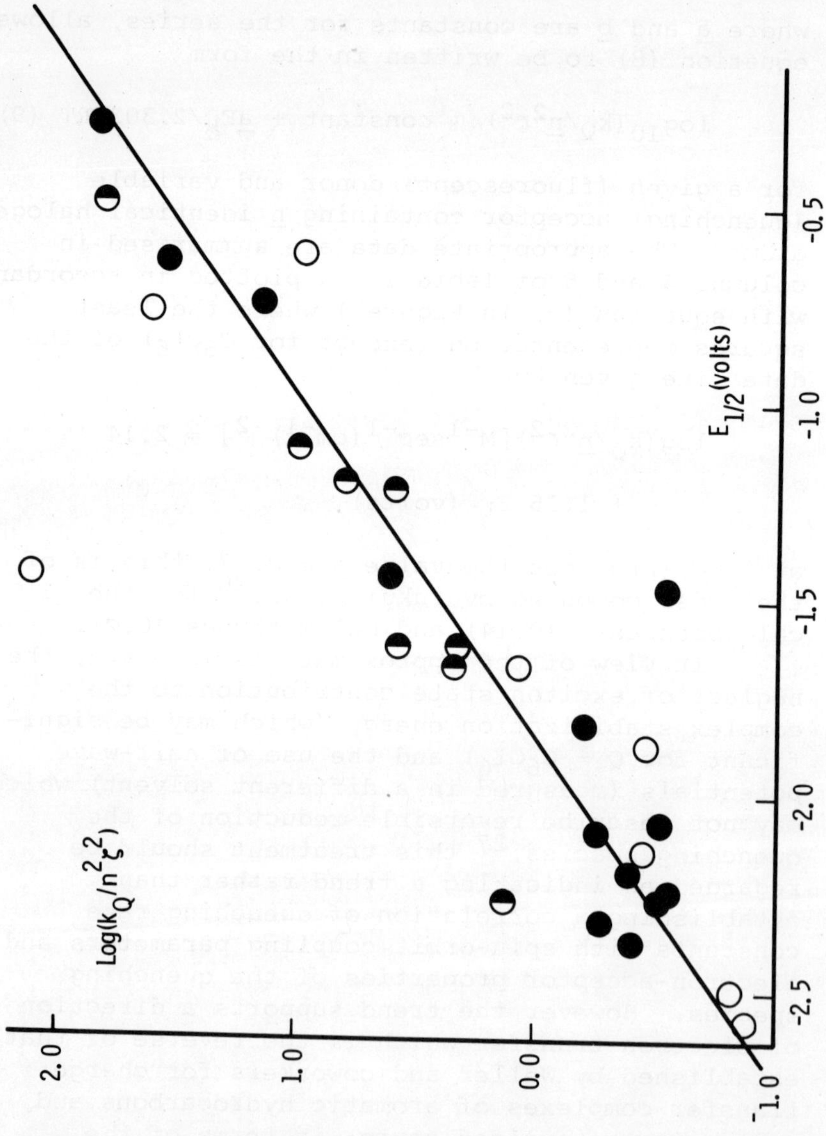

Figure 1 Plot of data in Table 1 according to Equation (9), for chlorine ○, bromine ● and iodine ◐ containing quenching species.

(7.58 volts)[29] of pyrene and that the lowest vacant (σ^*) orbital of the quencher lies below that (π^*) of the aromatic hydrocarbon and also below π^* of unsaturated quenchers as suggested by Fukui and collaborators.

The authors are grateful to Professor G. J. Hoytink for enlightening discussions, to the Science Research Council of Great Britain for the purchase of the Aminco-Keirs SPF and pulsed-flash fluorimeter components, and to NATO for the award of a fellowship to M.F.T.

REFERENCES

1. E. J. Bowen and D. W. Tanner, Trans. Faraday Soc., 51, 475 (1955).
2. J. B. Birks, J. H. Appleyard and R. Pope, Photochem. Photobiol. 2, 493 (1963).
3. Th. Förster and K. Kasper, Z. Elektrochem., 59, 977 (1955).
4. J. B. Birks and L. G. Christophorou, Nature (London), 194, 442 (1962); 197, 1064 (1963); Proc. Roy Soc., A277, 571 (1964).
5. T. V. Ivanova, G. A. Mokeeva and B. Y. Sveshnikov, Optics and Spectroscopy, 12, 325 (1962).
6. B. Stevens and M. I. Ban, Trans. Faraday Soc., 60, 1515 (1964).
7. B. Stevens and J. T. Dubois, Trans. Faraday Soc., 62, 1525 (1966).
8. e.g. T. Azumi and S. P. McGlynn, J. Chem. Phys., 41, 3131 (1964); T. Azumi, A. T. Armstrong and S. P. McGlynn, ibid. 41, 3839 (1964).
9. H. Beens, H. Knibbe and A. Weller, J. Chem. Phys., 47, 1183 (1967).
10. J. Langelaar, R. P. H. Rettschnick, A. M. F. Lamboy and G. J. Hoytink, Chem. Phys. Letters, 1, 609 (1968).
11. T. Medinger and F. Wilkinson, Trans. Faraday Soc., 62, 1785 (1966).
12. H. Leonhardt and A. Weller, Ber. Bunsenges. Physik. Chem., 67, 791 (1963).
13. N. Mataga, T. Okada and K. Ezumi, Mol. Phys., 10, 203 (1966).
14. W. R. Ware and H. P. Richter, presentation to 153rd ACS National Meeting, Miami Beach, Florida, April 1967.
15. A. Weller, Progress in Reaction Kinetics, G. Porter, Ed. (Pergamon Press, Oxford, 1961), Vol. I, p. 189.
16. H. Knibbe, D. Rehm and A. Weller, Ber. Bunsenges. Physik. Chem., 72, (1968).

17. H. Knibbe, D. Rehm and A. Weller, Z. Physik. Chem. N. F. 56, 95 (1967).
18. L. M. Stephenson, D. G. Whitten, G. F. Vesley and G. S. Hammond, J. Amer. Chem. Soc. 88, 3665 (1966).
19. J. P. Simons, Trans. Faraday Soc. 56, 391 (1960).
20. S. Iwata, J. Tanaka and S. Nagakura, The Triplet State, A. B. Zahlan, Ed. (Cambridge University Press, 1967), p. 433.
21. T. Medinger and F. Wilkinson, Trans. Faraday Soc. 61, 620 (1965).
22. cf. J. B. Birks and I. H. Munro, Progress in Reaction Kinetics, G. Porter, Ed. (Pergamon, Oxford, 1967), IV, 239.
23. D. S. McClure, J. Chem. Phys. 17, 905 (1949).
24. S. P. McGlynn, M. J. Reynolds, G. W. Daigre and N. D. Christodouleas, J. Phys. Chem. 66, 2499 (1962).
25. R. D. Hickling (private communication of data prior to publication which is gratefully acknowledged.
26. K. Fukui, K. Morokuma, H. Kato and T. Yonezawa, Bull. Chem. Soc. (Japan) 36, 217 (1963).
27. cf. comments by T. Berzins and P. Delahay, J. Amer. Chem. Soc. 75, 5716 (1953).
28. A. Weller, Fast Reactions and Primary Processes in Chemical Kinetics, S. Claesson, Ed. (Interscience) p. 413.
29. F. A. Matsen, J. Chem. Phys. 24, 602 (1956).
30. M. von Strackelberg and W. Stracke, Z. Elektrochem. 58, 118 (1949).
31. L. Meites, Polarographic Techniques (Interscience, 1965), Second Edition.
32. F. L. Lambert and K. Kobayashi, J. Amer. Chem. Soc. 82, 5324 (1960).

RELATIVE YIELD OF LUMINESCENCE OF QUENCHED VISCOUS SOLUTIONS

J. Hevesi

Institute of Experimental Physics
Attila József University
Szeged, Hungary

The quenching of luminescence of solutions by foreign substances was studied by many authors.[4-6,13,15,17,18] On the basis of the simplifying assumptions used by the authors the expressions giving the connection between the relative yield of luminescence F/F_0 and the quencher concentration c may be divided into two groups.[8] In the first group of these quenching theories[5,13,18] the influence of the mutual diffusion between the excited and the quencher molecules on the quenching efficiency was neglected; consequently relatively simple relations were given, containing only one or two arbitrary parameters to be fitted to the experimental data. The applicability of one of these above-mentioned quenching theories, elaborated by Jabłoński,[13] was studied[8] for viscous solutions of fluorescein quenched by KI. The results showed that in the case of viscous solutions the change of the relative yield of luminescence is described only approximately by Jabłoński's relation, since the mutual diffusion of the interacting molecules was neglected in its derivation. This suggested that for a general applicability, i.e. to describe the dependence of the relative yield of luminescence F/F_o on the quencher concentration c, on the viscosity η_ν and the temperature T of the solution and on the mean lifetime τ of the excited molecules, Jabłoński's relation should be modified.

A modification of this equation was suggested in Ref. 10 by taking into consideration the mutual diffusion of the interacting molecules and the influence of the temperature and viscosity of the solution on it. The aim of the present work is to obtain a modified form of Jabłoński's relation and to test its applicability and validity to the quenching of luminescence of viscous solutions by foreign quenchers. The correlation between the relative yield of luminescence and the lifetime of the excited molecules measured by phase-method will also be discussed.

In the study of the quenching mechanism of luminescence, Jabłoński[13] made several simplifying assumptions. One of them was the non-consideration of the mutual diffusion of the interacting molecules. He suggested that for a simplified model of the luminescent center, consisting of an excited molecule with an active sphere in which quenchers may be present, the relative yield of luminescence of solutions as a function of the quencher concentration should be given by the following expression

$$\frac{F}{F_o} = \frac{1 - \exp(-\nu)}{\nu} \qquad (1)$$

where F_o is the yield of the luminescence of unquenched solution, F is that of the quenched one, $\nu = n \times v$ is the mean value of the number of quencher molecules in the active spheres of volume $v\ cm^3$ at the concentration $n\ cm^{-3}$ of the quenchers. This relation contains only one arbitrary parameter to be fitted to the experimental data, viz. the volume $v = \nu/n$ of the active sphere.

In viscous quenched solutions the change in the relative yield of luminescence with variation in the quencher concentration is described approximately by relation (1). It is, however, not applicable when at a constant quencher concentration the temperature T and the viscosity η_ν of the solution or the mean lifetime τ of the excited molecule are changed. This deviation, at a given quencher concentration, can be only explained by assuming a corresponding change of the volume v of the active sphere with variation in any one of the above-mentioned quantities. The validity of this assumption was experimentally proved in Refs. 8 and 9.

The necessary modification of Jabloński's relation can easily be obtained in the following manner. Owing to the mutual diffusion of the interacting molecules the volume v of the active sphere should depend on the temperature and viscosity of the system. We have therefore to modify Jabłoński's quenching theory by taking into consideration the process of the diffusion. It is well-known that the Brownian motion of the molecules in solutions is proportional to the square root of the mutual diffusion coefficient D and of the time t, i.e. $\sqrt{D \times t}$. Thus, if the above-mentioned expansion of the volume of the active sphere may be due to the influence of the mutual diffusion a relation should exist between v and $\sqrt{D \times t}$. Our earlier results[8,9] suggested that this relation should be linear with a good approximation. According to the theory of the dynamic quenching of luminescence for viscous solutions[4] the volume v of the active sphere may be regarded as consisting of the following parts (Fig. 1): Around the excited molecule with radius ζ being an effective sphere

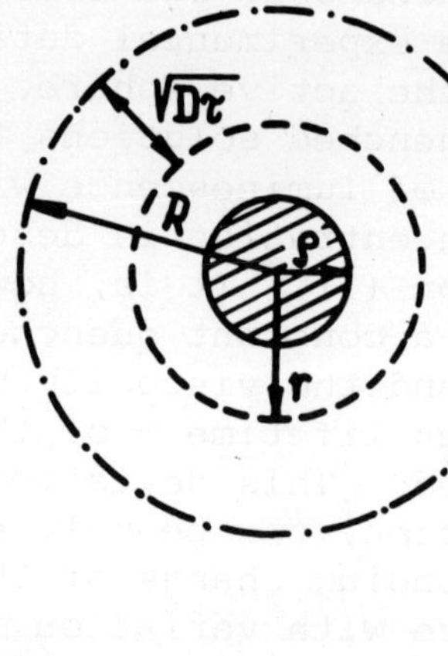

Figure 1

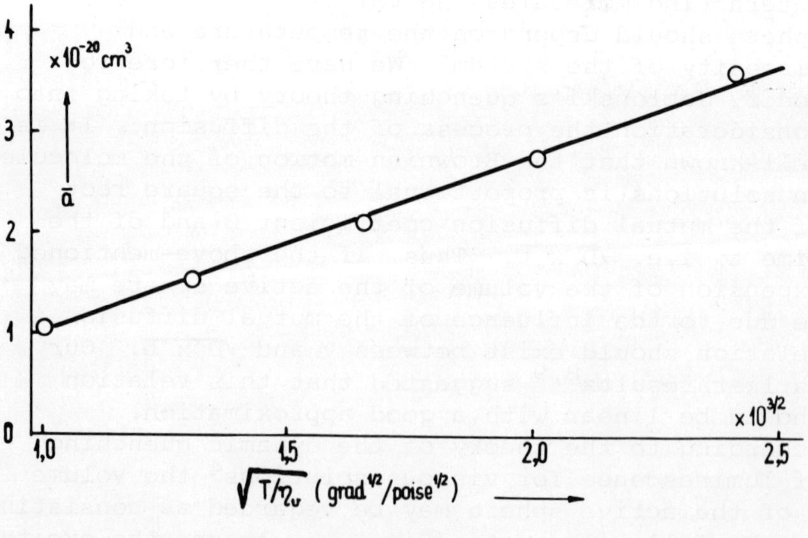

Figure 2

with constant radius r independent of the diffusion and a spherical shell of radius $\sqrt{D \times \tau}$ around the effective sphere (in the cases of the excited molecules the time of the motion is τ) which is to be ascribed to the diffusion. It can be seen from Fig. 1 that

$$R = r + \sqrt{D \times \tau} \quad (2)$$

and the volume of the active sphere (= volume of the effective sphere + volume of the spherical shell) is

$$v = (4\pi/3)\left[(r + \sqrt{D \times \tau})^3 - \zeta^3\right] \quad (3)$$

Neglecting the values of $(\sqrt{D \times \tau})^3$ and $(4\pi rD\tau)$ in Equation (3) we get

$$v \approx (4\pi/3)(r^3 - \zeta^3) + 4\pi r^2\sqrt{D \times \tau} \quad (4)$$

As the first part of the right side of equation (4) is independent of D we can write

$$v \approx A' + B'\sqrt{D \times \tau} \quad (5)$$

where $A' = (4\pi/3)(r^3 - \zeta^3)$ and $B' = 4\pi r^2$. Substituting for the well-known value of D into (5) and reducing the constants independent of T and η_ν we have

$$v \approx A' + m'\sqrt{(T/\eta_\nu) \times \tau} \quad (6)$$

where $m' = B'\sqrt{(k/6\pi)(1/\zeta' + 1/\zeta)}$ in which k is Boltzmann's constant, ζ' and ζ are the radius of the quencher and of the luminescent molecules, respectively. As it was expected relation (6) gave a linear connection between v and the square root of the temperature and viscosity of the solution and the lifetime τ of the excited molecule. (It is to be noted here that this relation and the above considerations connected with it are valid only in the case of a relatively large viscosity of the solution, because the volume of the spherical shell can be regarded as proportional to $\sqrt{D \times \tau}$ which is small in comparison with the radius of the effective sphere).

Re-writing the Jabłoński's relation (1) we get

$$\frac{F}{F_o} = \frac{1 - \exp(-ac)}{ac} \tag{7}$$

where c is the quencher concentration in mM, a is an empirical constant adherent to volume v of the effective sphere by $a = 6.02 \times 10^{20} \times v$, because $\nu = n \times v$ and $n = 6.02 \times 10^{20} \times c$ in relation (1). The value of a can be determined experimentally by (7). Substituting the value of v into (6) we have

$$a = A + m\sqrt{(T/\eta_\nu) \times \tau} \tag{8}$$

Using Eqs. (7) and (8) we obtain the modified form of Jabłoński's relation

$$\frac{F}{F_o} = \frac{1 - \exp\left[-(m\sqrt{(T/\eta_\nu) \times \tau} + A) \times c\right]}{\left[(m\sqrt{(T/\eta_\nu) \times \tau} + A) \times c\right]}, \tag{9}$$

which also contains only one arbitrary parameter A. It can be seen that the modified relation (9) at very high viscosity of the solution ($\eta_\nu \to \infty$), where $D \approx 0$, agrees with the original Jabłoński's relation (1).

The assumption that at a given quencher concentration the volume v of the active sphere changes by variation in any one of the above-mentioned quantities (T, η_ν and τ) was proved in Ref. (8) and (9). It was also shown there that the relation between v and $\sqrt{D \times \tau}$ is linear with a good approximation corresponding to relation (6). As a further justification of the validity of the linear relation (6) and consequently of (8) we plotted the values of a x 10^{-20} cm^3 versus $\sqrt{(T/\eta_\nu)}$ calculated from (7) for the luminescence of viscous solutions of fluorescein quenched by KI (Fig. 2). F/F_o was measured at 436 nm wavelength of excitation. It can be seen from Fig. 2 that the linearity is well fulfilled in the temperature and viscosity range examined. This proves that the expansion of the volume v of the active sphere is really due to the mutual diffusion of the interacting molecules.

In order to check the validity of relation (9), quenching of the luminescence of fluorescein by KI and KBr, and of trypaflavine by Rhodamine B and of Rhodamine B by KI was studied at different temperatures. The experimental details are given in Talbe I. The solvent used was a mixture of glycerin (60%) and water. The glycerin was purified to spectroscopical purity by repeated vacuum distillation. (It is to be noted that in the solutions of the second series series No. 2 of Table I , the glycerin concentration was changed between 0 and 85 volume %).

The absorption and the luminescence spectra of the solutions were determined by the method described in Ref. 8. The determination of the relative yield of luminescence was carried out according to the method given in Ref. 14. For the study of the effect of temperature, the cuvette, containing the solution, was placed in a thermostatically controlled compartment of the equipment. The temperature of the solutions was determined by a thermistor (of 2TH65 Type) in bridge circuit attached to the wall of the cuvette. The accuracy of the ultrathermostat (of Höppler Type) was better than $\pm$ 0.2°C. The values of the lifetime τ' of the excited molecules were measured with a phase-fluorometer.[1] The true values of the lifetime τ were calculated from τ' according to the method given in Refs. 2 and 3.

In accordance with our objective the dependence of the relative yield of luminescence F/F_o

TABLE I

No.	Dyes (mole/l)	Additive agent	Quencher (mole/l)	Temperature (^oK)
1.	Fluorescein (1.10^{-4})	3 vol % NaOH	KI (0 - 1)	(293 - 333)
2.	Fluorescein (1.10^{-4})	3 vol % NaOH	KI (3.10^{-1})	(298)
3.	Fluorescein (1.10^{-4})	3 vol % NaOH	KBr (0 - 2)	(303 - 333)
4.	Trypaflavin ($1.25 \cdot 10^{-4}$)	1.10^{-3} mole/l HCl	Rhodamine B ($0 - 2.10^{-3}$)	(303 - 323)
5.	Rhodamine B (1.10^{-4})	3 vol % NaOH	KI (0 - 1)	(303 - 323)

on the quencher concentration c, on the temperature T and the viscosity η_ν of the solutions and on the mean lifetime τ of the excited molecules was studied. The average value of the empirical constant a was determined from the experimental data by means of the relation (7) and was used to obtain the values of the calculated relative yield of luminescence (F/F_o)(c). The validity of the modified Jabłoński's relation (9) was verified by comparing the measured values of the relative yield of luminescence (F/F_o)(m) with the calculated (F/F_o)(c).

Fig. 3a shows a plot of the relative yield of luminescence (measured at five different temperatures with 436 nm wavelength of excitation) versus lg c_{KI} (concentration of KI) for the first series of solutions (cf. in Table I). It can be seen from Fig. 3a that there is a good agreement between the measured values and the calculated ones. (The points in all the figures give the measured values and the continuous lines represent the calculated ones). (The values of (F/F_o)(m) and (F/F_o)(c) for this solutions measured with 495 nm wavelength of excitation at different temperatures were given in Ref. 8). Fig. 3b shows the relative lifetime τ/τ_o of first series of solutions measured at 20°C.

In Figs. 3c and 3d the values of (F/F_o) (m.), (F/F_o) (c.), and τ/τ_o are plotted versus the the glycerin concentration ($c_{glyc.}$ %) for the second series of the solutions. (Here τ_o and F_o are the mean lifetime and the quantum yield of the solution in water, respectively). The increase in the values of F/F_o and τ/τ_o with increasing glycerin concentration could be explained by taking into consideration the influence of the mutual diffusion of the interacting molecules on the quenching of luminescence. It was supposed in Ref. 12 that there is an inverse relationship between the efficiency of the quencher and the viscosity of the luminescent system; the results in Figs. 3c and 3d prove the validity of this assumption.

Figs. 3e and 3f show the plots of F/F_o (calculated and measured) and τ/τ_o versus lg c_{KBr}

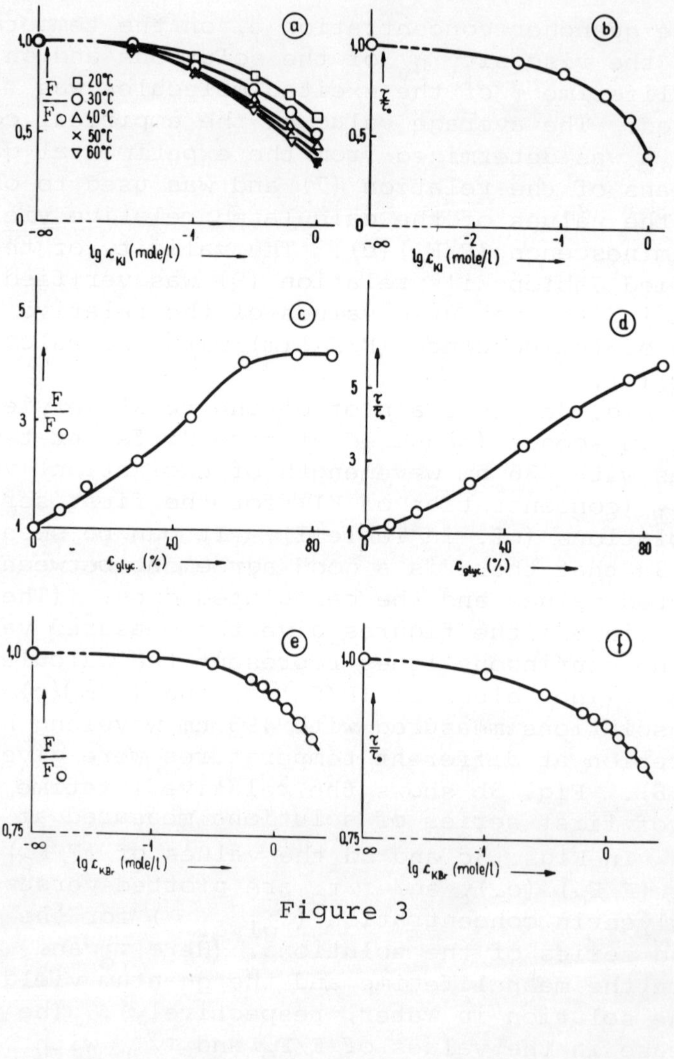
a
b
c
d
e
f
F/F₀
τ/τ₀
20°C
30°C
40°C
50°C
60°C
lg c_KJ (mole/l)
c_glyc. (%)
lg c_KBr (mole/l)

Figure 3

for the third series of solutions of Table I. By comparing Figs. 3a and 3e it can be seen that KBr is a less effective quencher than KI. As the change in the relative yield of luminescence with variation of the temperature of the solutions in this series is small, only the values of $(F/F_o)(m)$ and $(F/F_o)(c)$ for 30°C are plotted on Fig. 3e.

Figs. 4a and 4b respectively give the plots of $(F/F_o)(m)$, $(F/F_o)(c)$ and of τ/τ_o versus lg $c_{Rh.B}$ for the fourth series of the solutions. It can be seen from the figures that the quenching efficiency of Rhodamine B is very high. Already 10^{-3} mole/l concentration of this dye was enough to quench the luminescence of trypaflavine solution by 50%. It is apparent from this figure too that the values of the relative yield of luminescence are maximum at a small (6.10^{-5} mole/l) concentration of Rhodamine B instead of at the unquenched solutions. It suggests that the addition of a small quantity of an absorbing quencher to the luminescent solution causes an increase of the luminescence-intensity. This phenomenon was also observed by the authors of Refs. 4 and 7. They explained these results by supposing the existence of a proton-transfer process in the system, competing with the process of quenching. At a higher quencher concentration the increase in the luminescence-intensity is covered by the quenching of luminescence. The phenomenon observed in our system may also be interpreted in the same manner.

It can be seen from Figs. 3 and 4 that the dependence of F/F_o and τ/τ_o on the quencher or the glycerin concentration is different in all the examined cases, although it is equal in non-viscous solutions. Particularly big deviation exists between F/F_o and τ/τ_o for the fourth series of solutions (See Fig. 4) which can be explained by taking into consideration that in this system the quenching mechanism is also different (quenching by absorbing substances). This was probably the reason that the degree of polarization as a function

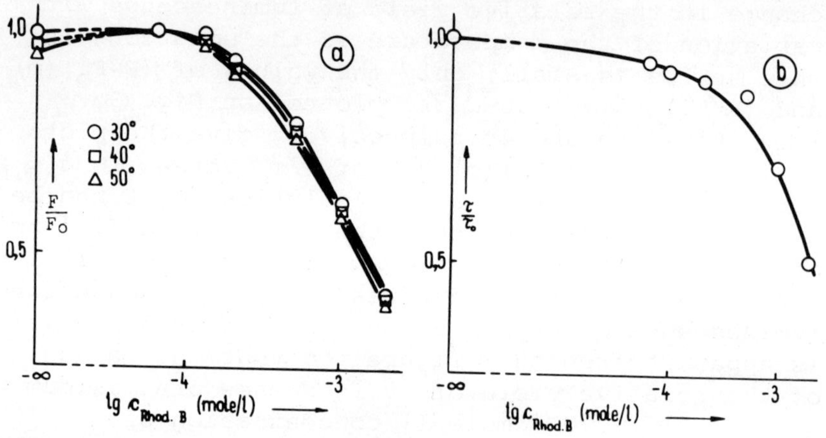

Figure 4

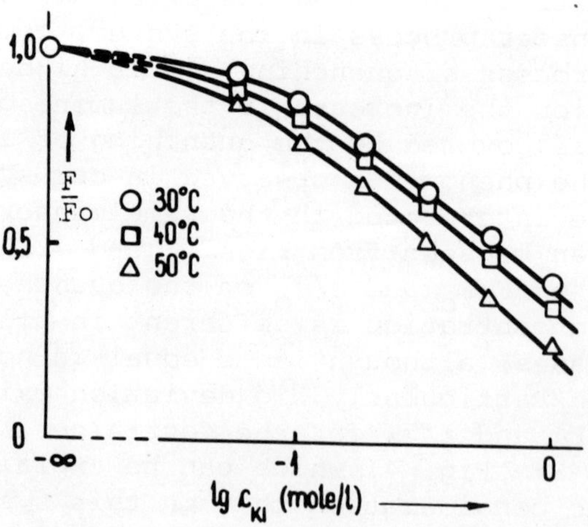

Figure 5

of the temperature and viscosity of the solution also showed a little anomaly in this system.[11]

For a better comparison the corresponding values of the relative yield of luminescence and the relative lifetime of the excited molecules measured at room-temperature are given in Table II. It is clear from the data that there is no equality between F/F_o and τ/τ_o even at a given quencher concentration. It suggests that in the case of viscous quenched solutions the decay of the luminescence seems to be non-exponential.

Table III contains the calculated and the measured values of F/F_o for the fifth series of solutions. In this system the values of $(F/F_o)(c)$ were determined by using the empirical values of $a(30^oC) = 3.11$; $a(40^oC) = 3.70$ and $a(50^oC) = 4.91$ ($\times 10^{-20}$ cm^3) calculated from the experimental data. It can be seen from the data given in Table III and plotted in Fig. 5 that (disregarding the values at the higher quencher concentration) there is a very good agreement between the measured and the calculated values of the relative yield of luminescence. The relation between v and $\sqrt{(T/\eta_\nu) \times \tau}$ was quite linear. These observations signify the important role of the mutual diffusion of the interacting molecules in the quenching of luminescence of solutions.

It is also clear from the data given in Table III and in Fig. 5 that the quenching efficiency of KI is higher than that of KBr (cf. series No. 3 of Table I). This result is in a good agreement with the result established in Ref. 16. From series No. 1 of Table II and series No. 5 of Table III it is clear that the quenching efficiency of quencher (KI) also depends on the nature of the luminescent substances.

The above-mentioned experimental results justify the modification of Jabłoński's relation[1] to describe the dependence of the relative yield of luminescence on the quencher concentration, on the temperature and the viscosity of the solutions

TABLE II

1st series of solutions			2nd series of solutions			3rd series of solutions			4th series of solutions		
KI (mole/l)	τ/τ_o	F/F_o	Glyc. (%)	τ/τ_o	F/F_o	KBr (mole/l)	τ/τ_o	F/F_o	Rhod. B (mole/l)	τ/τ_o	F/F_o
0.0	1.00	1.00	0.0	1.00	1.00	0.0	1.00	1.00	0.0	1.00	0.99
3×10^{-2}	0.92	0.99	7.5	1.21	1.31	1×10^{-1}	0.96	1.00	6.25×10^{-5}	0.95	1.00
1×10^{-1}	0.86	0.97	15.0	1.58	1.76	3×10^{-1}	0.94	0.99	1.25×10^{-4}	0.93	0.99
3×10^{-1}	0.74	0.75	30.0	2.39	2.24	6.3×10^{-1}	0.93	0.97	2.5×10^{-4}	0.91	0.94
6×10^{-1}	0.61	0.62	45.0	3.4	3.09	7.9×10^{-1}	0.92	0.96	5×10^{-4}	0.88	0.80
1.00	0.41	0.50	60.0	4.45	4.12	1.00	0.90	0.95	1×10^{-3}	0.72	0.62
-	-	-	75.0	5.32	4.27	1.58	0.87	0.91	2×10^{-3}	0.51	0.42
-	-	-	85.0	5.75	4.27	1.99	0.85	0.89	-	-	-

TABLE III

KI (mole/1)	303 (^oK) (F/F_o) (c.)	303 (^oK) (F/F_o) (m.)	313 (^oK) (F/F_o) (c.)	313 (^oK) (F/F_o) (m.)	323 (^oK) (F/F_o) (c.)	323 (^oK) (F/F_o) (m.)
0.00	1.00	1.00	1.00	1.00	1.00	1.00
5.62×10^{-2}	0.94	0.92	0.90	0.90	0.87	0.87
1.00×10^{-1}	0.87	0.86	0.83	0.84	0.77	0.79
1.78×10^{-1}	0.77	0.76	0.73	0.73	0.66	0.67
3.16×10^{-1}	0.65	0.64	0.61	0.59	0.52	0.51
5.62×10^{-1}	0.54	0.47	0.48	0.42	0.38	0.34
1.00	0.43	0.31	0.36	0.26	0.26	0.20

(and consequently on the mutual diffusion of the interacting molecules) and on the mean lifetime of the excited molecules. It seems to be very convenient for application as this modified relation[9] also contains only one arbitrary parameter to be fitted to the experimental data.

ACKNOWLEDGEMENTS

The author is greatly indebted to Professor A. Budó, member of the Hungarian Academy of Sciences, director of the Institute for his interest in this work and for his various valuable suggestions. Thanks are due to Professor I. Ketskeméty and Professor L. Szalay for the helpful discussions during the work.

REFERENCES

1. R. Bauer and M. Rozwadowski, Bull. Acad. Polon. Sci., 7, 365 (1959).
2. A. Budo and I. Ketskemety, Acta Phys. Hung. 14, 167 (1962).
3. A. Budo and L. Szalay, Z. Naturforsch. 18a, 90 (1963).
4. Th. Förster, Fluoreszenz Organischer Verbindungen (Vandenhoeck & Ruprecht, Göttingen, 1951).
5. I. M. Frank and S. I. Wawilow, Z. Phys. 69, 100 (1931).
6. M. D. Galanin, Trudy Phys. Inst. Akad. Nauk. USSR., 5, 339 (1950).
7. J. Glowacki and U. Kaminska, Acta Phys. Polon. Sci. 23, 43 (1963).
8. J. Hevesi, Acta Phys. et Chem. Szeged, 8, 16 (1962).
9. J. Hevesi, Acta Phys. et Chem. Szeged, 10, 59 (1964).
10. J. Hevesi, Thesis, Szeged (1965).
11. J. Hevesi, Acta Phys. et Chem. Szeged, 12, 3 (1966).
12. J. Hevesi and L. Kozma, Acta Phys. et Chem. Szeged, 8, 103 (1962).
13. A. Jablonski, Bull. Acad. Polon. Sci. 5, 13 (1957); ibid 6, 663 (1958).
14. I. Ketskemety, J. Dombi, J. Hevesi, R. Horvai and L. Kozma, Acta Phys. et Chem. Szeged, 7, 88 (1961).
15. V. L. Levshin, Photoluminescence of Liquid and Solid Substances (Moscow-Leningrad, 1951).
16. B. I. Stepanov, Luminescence of Complex Molecules (Izd. Akad. Nauk BSSR, Minsk, 1955).
17. B. Ja. Sveshnikov, Acta Physico-Chim. USSR 3, 453 (1936).
18. S. I. Wawilow, Z. Phys. 53, 665 (1929).

FLUORESCENCE QUENCHING OF TRYPTOPHAN AND PROTEINS

J. Eisinger

Bell Telephone Laboratories, Incorporated
Murray Hill, New Jersey

The fluorescence properties of proteins differ greatly one from another even though it has been shown that the emission of polypeptides generally originates from their tryptophan residues. The differences in fluorescence spectra and quantum yields can therefore be traced to different molecular environments of the one or more emitting tryptophans in the polypeptides and empirical correlations between molecular environments of fluorescence parameters have been suggested.[1-4] Behind these endeavors is of course the hope that the measurement of emission spectra can eventually become an analytical tool in the study of the electronic structure of proteins.

In spite of the interest in these problems, the excited states of tryptophan and their non-radiative de-excitations (quenching) in different environments are not well understood.

The fluorescence of tryptophan in polar solvents at room temperature shows a large red shift compared to the emission spectrum in non-polar solvents or frozen polar glasses. The origin of this red shift has been variously ascribed to dielectric effects in the solvent shell of the excited molecule[5,6] and to the formation of an excited complex (exciplex)[7,8] between the excited molecule and one or two solvent molecules. Either mechanism could cause a lowering of the energy of the excited molecule. Evidence for the existence of an exciplex is drawn from experiments in which a small amount of polar solvent is added to a nonpolar solvent. While an exciplex may well be formed under these conditions, it is clear that when the polar solvent concentration is increased to 100%, much greater red shifts than were observed for the exciplex are observed suggesting that in polar solvents several solvent molecules contribute to the lowering of the energy of the excited state when the solvent viscosity is low enough to permit their reorientation[9] during the lifetime of the excited state. Thus, Longworth[10] reported an exciplex at 320 nm for 1,2-dimethyl indole but in water this molecule emits at about 360 nm.[16]

We have measured the temperature dependence of the spectral changes of the tryptophan fluorescence using ethylene glycol: water (1:1) glass as a solvent. From the results shown in Fig. 1, it is seen that the red shift which occurs as the glass softens is progressively greater as the solvent viscosity decreases. This behavior is consistent with a red shift originating from the solvent reorientation in the solvent shell of the excited tryptophan, with the number of solvent molecules which can be reoriented during the excited state lifetime increasing with decreasing viscosity (see Fig. 2). There is no evidence for isosbestic points as would be expected in a 1:1 exciplex. Such exciplexes have been reported in

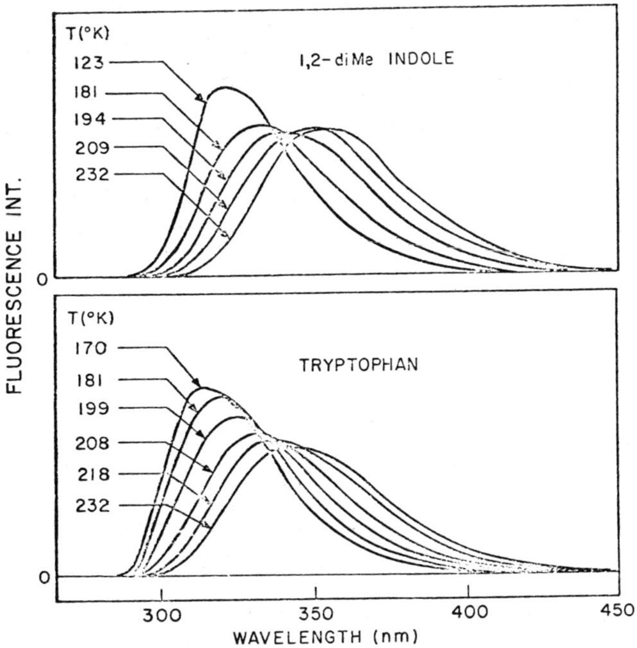

Figure 1 The emission spectra 1,2 dimethyl indole and of tryptophan in EGW glass at various temperatures which cover the range in which the solvent reorientation occurs in times comparable to the fluorescence lifetime. Note that the spectrum shifts and broadens gradually as solvent reorientation is more and more complete prior to emission with the fluorescence quantum yield remaining almost constant. The series of spectra have no isosbestic points so that 1:1 exciplexes are precluded.

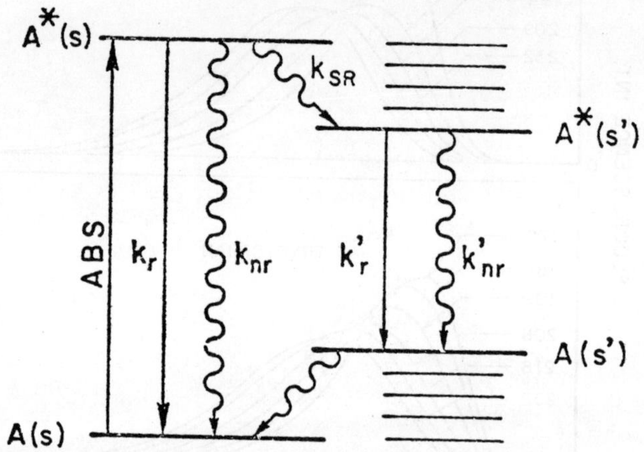

Figure 2 Schematic diagram of the processes by which reorientation of several polar molecules in the solvent shell of an excited molecule (indicated by a series of levels) leads to a lowering of the excited electronic state ($A^*(s) \rightarrow A^*(s')$). After fluorescence emission whose spectrum is red shifted compared to the low temperature spectrum, another solvent reorientation ($A(s') \rightarrow A(s)$) occurs before the lowest energy of the molecule and its solvent shell is attained.

nonpolar solvents with a small polar solvent addition but this system cannot be considered a valid model for tryptophan in a polar solvent. The other interesting result which emerges from Fig. 1 is that the quantum yield which is proportional to the area under the fluorescence curves remains virtually constant at temperatures below that at which solvent orientation is complete. This is seen more clearly in Fig. 3 which shows the temperature dependence of the fluorescence quantum yield (Φ_F) and the wavelength of maximum emission (λ_{max}). The main features of these curves (the near constancy of Φ_F at temperatures below those at which the red shift occurs and the strong temperature dependent quenching above them) are very similar for several indole and tryptophan derivatives which we have investigated and are all consistent with a model in which solvent reorientation is a prerequisite for the activated fluorescence quenching observed in water. Φ_F at 80^oK is between 0.5 and 0.6 for all the molecules we have studied. At temperatures above that at which solvent reorientation occurs, the fluorescence intensity of the red-shifted emission can be fitted by a nonradiative activated[11] quenching rate

$$k'_{nr} = c\ \exp(-E_A/kT)$$

in addition to the temperature independent radiation rate, k'_r. E_A is the quenching activation energy and c is a constant. Figure 2 gives a schematic view of this kinetic scheme: A and A* represent the tryptophan molecule in its ground and excited states and the solvent shell before and after solvent reorientation is indicated by s and s'.

It can readily be shown that according to this model, k'_{nr} is proportional to $(\Phi_F^{-1} - 1)$ so that E_A may be determined from the slope of the straight line which is obtained by plotting

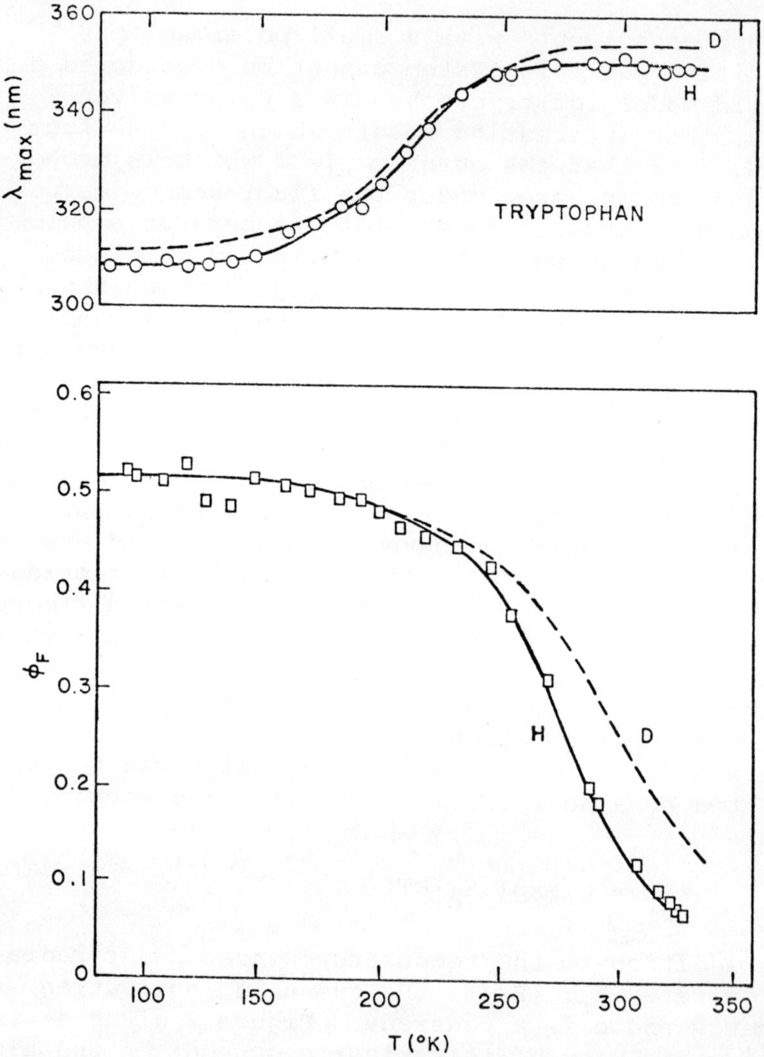

Figure 3 The temperature dependence of the wavelength of maximum emission (λ_{max}) and the fluorescence quantum yield (Φ_F) of tryptophan in EGW. The points and solid curves refer to EGW(H) and the dashed curve to EGW(D).

log $(\Phi_F^{-1} - 1)$ vs T^{-1}. Figure 4 shows such a plot for tryptophan in ordinary and heavy water and yields a value of E_A = 7 kcal/M for both solvents.

Stryer[12] has recently pointed out that appreciable solvent isotope effects for the fluorescence of aromatic molecules occur. He suggested proton transfer in the excited state as a possible mechanism for this effect, and it is likely to be important in some molecules.[13] We have compared the solvent isotope effect of tryptophan and of 1-methyl-tryptophan, which has no exchangeable protons on the indole ring and found them to be virtually the same (see Table I). This shows that for tryptophan proton transfer in the excited state is not an important quenching mechanism.

I would now like to describe a model which can account for all of the fluorescence properties of tryptophan which we have discussed including the isotope effect and will then discuss how this model might be applicable to proteins and other polypeptides.

Figure 5 is a schematic representation of a section through the potential surfaces of the ground and excited states of the molecule. The dashed curves, A(s') and A*(s'), indicate how these potential surfaces approach each other in energy as a result of solvent reorientation in the excited state. If they approach each other sufficiently to make nonradiative transitions between them a fast process and if this tunnelling occurs at an energy E_A above the lowest vibrational level of the excited state, an activated quenching of the state A*(s'), from which the red-shifted fluorescence originates, would occur. The mechanism by which the tunnelling occurs is thought to involve the solvent shell and isotopic differences occur as a result of different vibrational overlap factors in ordinary and heavy water.[14,15] These ideas are described in greater detail elsewhere.[16]

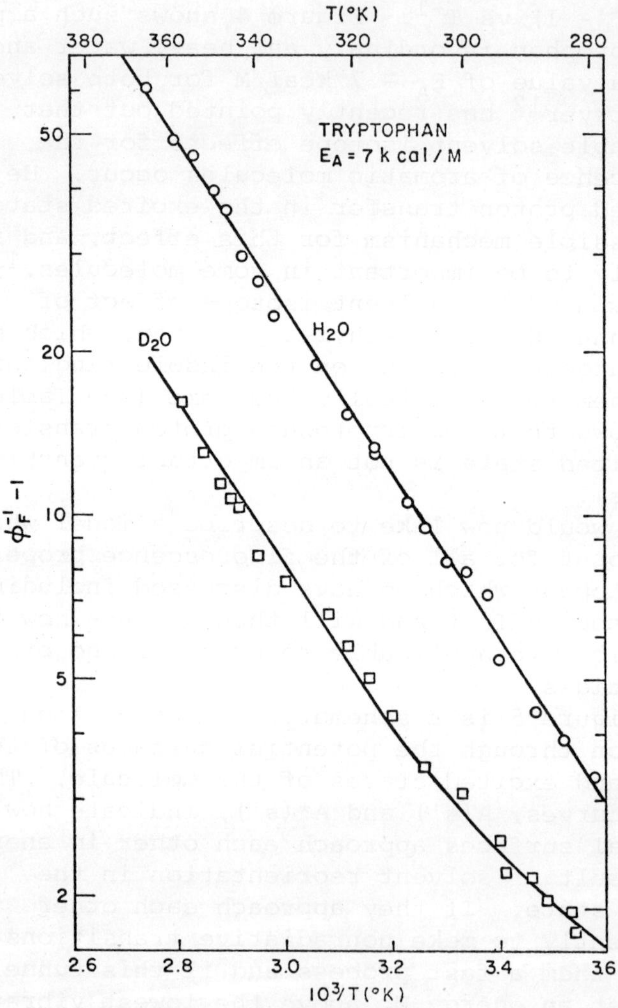

Figure 4 The temperature dependence of $\Phi_F^{-1} - 1$, which is proportional to the nonradiative de-excitation rate, for tryptophan in H_2O and D_2O. Note that the isotope effect is a factor of 3 but that the activation energy is the same in H_2O and D_2O.

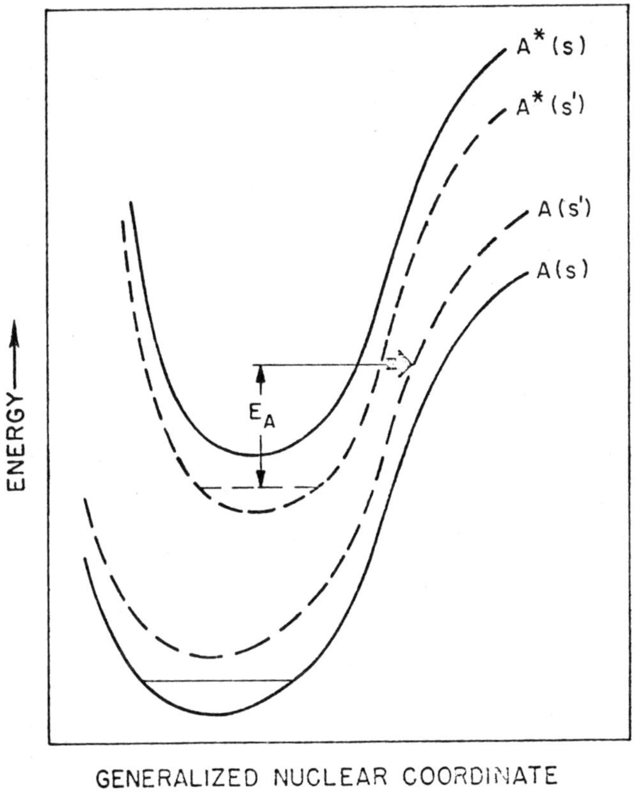

Figure 5 Schematic diagram illustrating the motion of the potential surfaces of a molecule in its ground and excited states (A and A*) as a result of the reorientation of surrounding polar solvent molecules. s represents the solvent shell in its ground state configuration and s' represents the solvent shell following solvent reorientation in the excited state. The short heavy arrow indicates where tunnelling between the potential surfaces A*(s') and A(s') might occur, leading to nonradiative de-excitations characterized by an activation energy E_A which is indicated in the figure.

TABLE I

	ΔE^a (10^4 cm^{-1})	$\Phi_F{}^b$ (H_2O, 300°K)	$\Phi_F{}^b$ (EGW, 80°K)	$\Phi_F(D_2O)/\Phi_F(H_2O)$		$\tau(H_2O)$ (10^{-9} sec)	$\tau(D_2O)/\tau(H_2O)$	$R = k'_{nr}(H_2O)/k'_{nr}(D_2O)$
Indole	0.35	0.23	0.6	1.30[c]	1.29[d]	-	-	1.44
1-Me-Indole	0.26	0.38	0.6	1.19[c]	1.09[d]	-	-	1.36
Tryptophan	0.40	0.14[e]	0.6	2.15[c]	1.65[d]	2.8	1.8	3.0
1-Me-Tryptophan	0.37	0.22	0.6	1.97[c]	-	4.5	1.9	2.4
1,2 di Me-Indole	0.34	0.43[f]	0.6	1.5[c,f]	-	-	-	-

[a] ΔE is the red shift due to solvent reorientation in the excited state.
[b] See Experimental section for uncertainties.
[c] Present work: 5 percent uncertainty.
[d] See reference 12.
[e] This value for the quantum yield is much smaller than the commonly accepted value obtained by Teale and Weber[2] (0.20) but agrees with two other determinations that are recent.[27,28]
[f] With EGW as solvent. Isotope effect is the limiting value at high temperature. At room temperature it is 1.1.

An important result of this investigation is the equality of E_A in H_2O and D_2O. This is consistent with the model presented above in that the approach of the energy levels as a result of solvent reorientation can be estimated from the magnitude of the red shift and is about the same in H_2O and D_2O. The difference in the nonradiative rates in the two solvent (k'_{nr}) is therefore in the pre-exponential factors (c) and not in the activation energy. A rational way of defining the isotope effect according to this model is

$$R = k'_{nr}(H_2O)/k'_{nr}(D_2O) = c(H_2O)/c(D_2O)$$

At high temperatures in water, R approaches a value of 3 for tryptophan and 2.4 for 1-methyl-tryptophan.

The polypeptides which offer the best hope for being able to derive structural information from their fluorescence spectra are clearly the ones with only a single tryptophan residue since this eliminates the uncertainties of heterogeneities among the emitting tryptophans. We have investigated several such proteins and hormones and here present some results for two of these.

The first step in these investigations is to ensure that the emission does, in fact, originate from the single tryptophan residue and this was done by comparing the fluorescence spectra obtained by exciting the molecule at several wavelengths between 265 and 292 nm. Since the absorption spectrum of tyrosine has a threshold at about 280 nm and that of tryptophan is at about 290 nm, one may conclude that if the fluorescence spectrum is independent of excitation wavelength, the contribution of tyrosine is negligible. (For the sake of brevity we will ignore the role of phenylalanine and take for granted that singlet energy can be transferred only from tyrosine to tryptophan).

Figure 6 shows the relative contributions of tyrosine and tryptophan to the absorption of ribonuclease T_1 which contains one tryptophan and nine tyrosines if it may be assumed that their absorption spectra in solution and in the proteins are the same. The fact that the protein absorption spectrum is red shifted by about 3 nm compared to that of the dummy solution with the same aromatic amino acid constitution shows that this assumption is only approximately correct. Figure 6 also shows the result of quantum yield determinations for the enzyme using different excitation wavelengths and it is seen that at the long wavelengths where most of the light is absorbed by tryptophan, but where the sample is still optically thick, Φ_F increases. This means that the energy transfer from tyrosine to tryptophan is not completely efficient. If the difficulty of the absorption spectrum shift explained above is ignored, one may obtain a quantitative result for the efficiency of this transfer and it turns out to be approximately 0.5. A somewhat smaller efficiency (0.33) has been reported by Longworth.[17]

In Table II, the fluorescence characteristics of ribonuclease T_1 and porcine corticotropin (ACTH), both of which are polypeptides with only a single tryptophan, are compared with those of tryptophan. It is seen that the fluorescence of ribonuclease T_1 has a large quantum yield and a small red shift which indicates that the emitting species has undergone very incomplete solvation or solvent reorientation. This is probably due to the tryptophan finding itself in a hydrophobic environment, as has been suggested by Longworth.[10] In agreement with this view, the solvent isotope effect is much smaller than for tryptophan in water.

Turning now to ACTH in which tryptophan is known to be in a strongly polar region of the polypeptide, we note that the emission spectrum is virtually the same as that of tryptophan in an

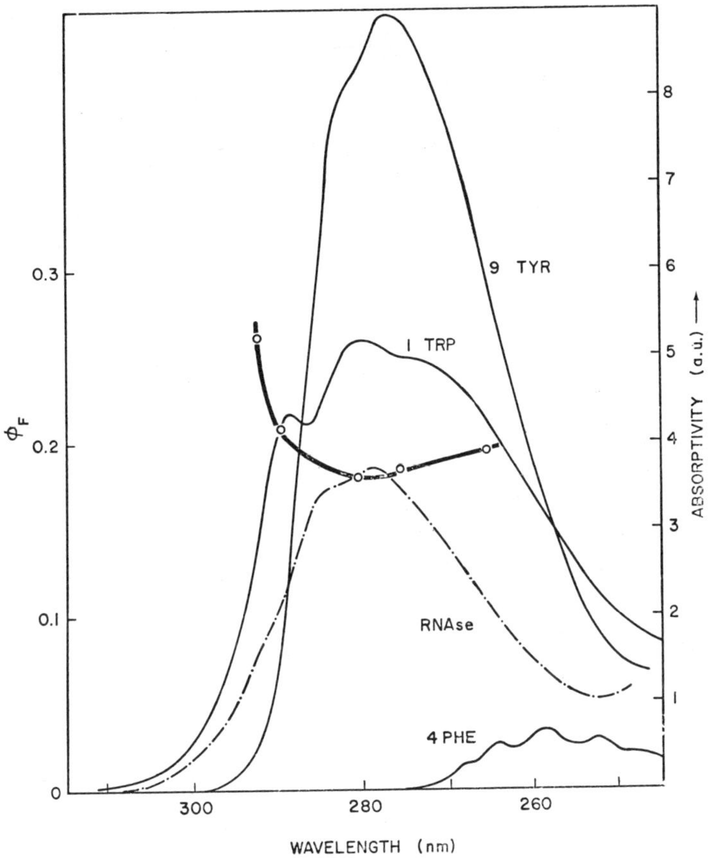

Figure 6 The room temperature absorption spectra of ribonuclease T_1 and those of the three aromatic amino acids it contains in their correct proportions. The latter three spectra are shown with their correct relative intensities. The heavy line shows the excitation wavelength dependence of the fluorescence quantum yield of the enzyme. Since the emission originates from the tryptophan residue at all excitation wavelengths, this shows that the singlet energy transfer from tyrosines (TYR) to tryptophan (TRP) is not 100% efficient.

TABLE II

	λ_{max} (nm)	$\Phi_F(H_2O)$	$\frac{\Phi_F(D_2O)}{\Phi(H_2O)}$
Tryptophan	356	0.14	2.15
Corticotropin (ACTH)	350	0.05	1.22
Ribonuclease T_1	320	0.18	1.11
Tryptophan (80^oK)	319	0.6	1.0

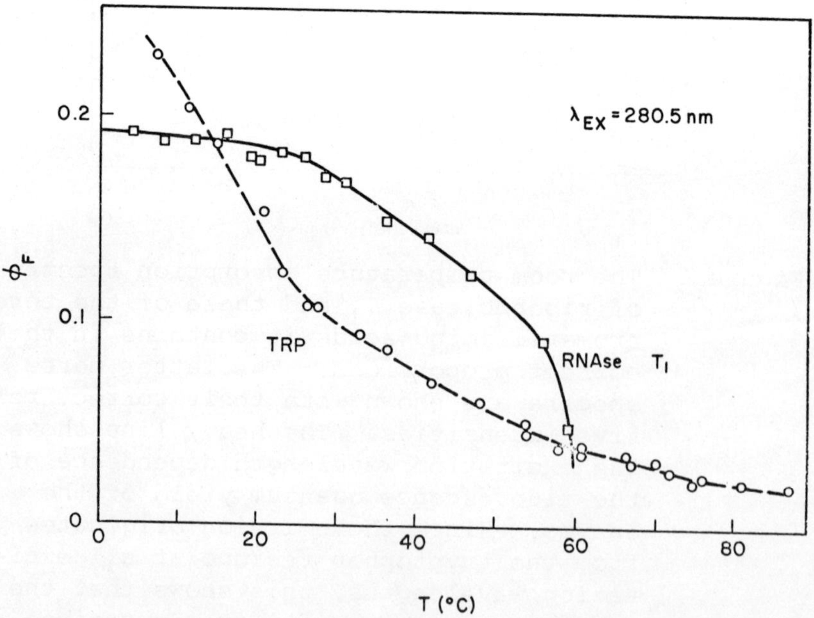

Figure 7 The temperature dependence of the fluorescence quantum yield of ribonuclease T_1 contrasted with that of tryptophan.

aqueous solution but that the isotope effect is nevertheless much smaller. This paradox can be resolved by noting that the quantum yield is quite low and postulating that in the peptide chain, tryptophan in a polar environment is subject to an isotope-independent quenching mechanism (k''_{nr}) in addition to the normal activated quenching (k'_{nr}) described above. To test this hypothesis, we note that for this model

$$\Phi^{-1}_{ACTH} = 1 + (k'_{nr} + k''_{nr})/k'_r = \Phi^{-1}_{TRP} + k''_{nr}/k'_r$$

We can now substitute the experimentally determined values for Φ_{ACTH} for H_2O and D_2O and find that k''_{nr}/k'_r is equal to 12.9 and 13.1 for H_2O and D_2O, respectively in agreement with our hypothesis that k''_{nr} should be independent of the isotopic constitution of the solvent. What the physical basis of the polypeptide specific nonradiative rate k''_{nr} might be remains obscure.

In Fig. 7, we show without much comment the temperature dependence of Φ of ribonuclease T_1. As might be expected, Φ varies rather slowly in the native protein which in this case (hydrophobic environment) resembles the conditions to which obtain in the frozen glass, where Φ was seen to be temperature independent. For the same reason, the quantum yield of the enzyme is also seen to be greater than that of tryptophan in this region. At higher temperatures, the tryptophan of the enzyme becomes more accessible to water and starts to resemble tryptophan in water, until at about 60°C the protein denatures and the fluorescence drops catastrophically. At the same time, the protein loses its tertiary structure and as the energy transfer from the tyrosines to the tryptophan becomes inefficient, the tyrosine fluorescence appears at about 304 nm in addition to the tryptophan emission.

ACKNOWLEDGEMENT

We wish to thank G. Navon who collaborated on the early work on the isotope effect, A. A. Lamola for many illuminating discussions and Mrs. B. Feuer for her technical assistance.

REFERENCES

1. S. V. Konev, Fluorescence and Phosphorescence of Proteins and Nucleic Acids (Plenum Press, New York 1967).
2. F. W. J. Teale and G. Weber, Biochem. J. 65, 476 (1957).
3. R. W. Cowgill, Biochim. Biophys. Acta 75, 272 (1963).
4. R. W. Cowgill (this symposium).
5. M. Mataga, Y. Torihashi and K. Ezumi, Theoret. Chim. Acta (Berl.) 2, 158 (1964).
6. E. Lippert, W. Luder and H. Boos, Advan. Mol. Spectry. 1, 443 (1962).
7. M. S.Walker, T. W. Bednar and R. Lumry, J. Chem. Phys. 45, 3455 (1966).
8. M. S. Walker, T. W. Bednar and R. Lumry, J. Chem. Phys. 47, 1020 (1967).
9. D. M. Hercules and L. G. Rogers, J. Chem. Phys. 64, 397 (1960).
10. J. Longworth, Photochem. and Photobiol. 7, 587 (1968).
11. E. J. Bowen, Disc. Faraday Soc. 27, 40 (1959).
12. L. Stryer, J. Am. Chem. Soc. 88, 5708 (1966).
13. Th. Förster and K. Rokos, Chem. Phys. Letters 1, 279 (1967).
14. G. W. Robinson and R. P. Frosch, J. Chem. Phys. 38, 1187 (1963).
15. M. Gouterman, J. Chem. Phys. 36, 2846 (1962).
16. J. Eisinger and G. Navon (to be published).
17. J. Longworth, Photochem. Photobiol. 8, (1968) (to be published).

CLASSIFICATION AND FORMATION OF CHARGE-TRANSFER COMPLEXES IN THE TRIPLET STATE

Henk Beens

Chemisch Laboratorium
der Vrije Universiteit
Amsterdam, Netherlands

Albert Weller*

Max-Planck-Institut für Spektroskopie
Göttingen, Germany

INTRODUCTION

The phenomenon of charge-transfer (CT) complex formation in the excited singlet state involving an electron donor molecule, D, and an electron acceptor molecule, A, has been studied extensively since, in 1963, the concentration dependent association of perylene (A) in its excited singlet state with dialkylaniline (D) giving rise to the emission of a broad structureless fluorescence band some 5000 cm^{-1} to the red of the normal structured fluorescence of the aromatic hydrocarbon was reported.[1] These studies[2] have shown that the diffusion-controlled formation of such complexes in solvents of low polarity according to

*To whom correspondence should be addressed.

$$^{1}\overset{*}{D} + A \rightarrow {}^{1}(D^{+}A^{-}) \qquad (1)$$

or $$^{1}\overset{*}{A} + D \rightarrow {}^{1}(A^{-}D^{+}) \qquad (2)$$

is the rule rather than the exception provided that the energy of the CT state is below the locally excited singlet states of both A and D. Lifetime measurements yielding 10^{-8}-10^{-7} sec for the structureless long wavelength emission indicate the singlet character of the emissive state.[3,4] Moreover it has been found[5] that the complex maximum emission frequencies observed in hexane and other inert solvents are directly related to the differences of the polarographic oxidation and reduction potentials measured in polar solvents like acetonitrile.

$$\tilde{\nu}^{max}(CT) = E(D/D^{+}) - E(A^{-}/A) - \Delta \qquad (3)$$

with $\Delta = 0.7 \pm 0.3$ kK if the emission is from the pure CT state.[6] Mixing of the CT state with locally excited states, $^{1}(\overset{*}{A}D)$ and $^{1}(A\overset{*}{D})$, however, results in $\Delta > 0.7$ kK, whereas interaction with the "no bond" ground state $^{1}(AD)$ will raise the fluorescent state (and lower the ground state) so that Δ can become considerably smaller than 0.7 kK and even negative.

Entirely analogous to fluorescence from the singlet CT state phosphorescence from the triplet CT state may be expected if this state, $^{3}(A^{-}D^{+})$, is energetically below the locally excited triplet states, $^{3}(\overset{*}{A}D)$ and $^{3}(A\overset{*}{D})$. This implies a relatively large energy gap between CT singlet and locally excited singlet states, so that their mixing may become small or even negligible. As the two unpaired electrons in a typical excited CT complex occupy different orbitals which are more or less localized in the complex components the singlet-triplet splitting of the CT state will be small and, in fact, will be zero for the zero-order CT state.

Therefore, equation (3) and its corollaries with respect to variations in Δ will be applicable also to triplet states and can be used to arrive at an interpretation of the triplet CT complexes similar to that obtained for singlet CT complexes.[5]

Generally, phosphorescence is observable only in rigid media where diffusion is extremely slow. Hence CT phosphorescence can be studied only with complexes which are present in the ground state already, and it is under these conditions that phosphorescence from CT complexes, indeed, has been observed.[7,8] ESR measurements[9,10] which have been carried out with two of these complexes (9 and 10 of Table II) to determine the zero-field-splitting parameters $|D|$ and $|E|$ establish their triplet state character. The values of $|D|$ obtained for these complexes are smaller by a factor of four than those of the triplet states of the components and, thus, corroborate the concept of triplet CT states with considerable spin separation.

EMISSION CHARACTERISTICS AND CLASSIFICATION

Two series of triplet CT complexes will be discussed, one with a common acceptor: tetrachlorophthalic anhydride (cf. Table I) and another one with a common donor: N,N-diethylaniline (cf. Table II). The complexes of Table II have been investigated with solutions of the acceptors in diethylaniline which, when rapidly cooled to 77°K, forms a clear rigid glass. Other acceptors which show similar emission characteristics in diethylaniline are: phthalic, isophthalic, and terephthalic dimethylester, 4-cyanopyridine, benzaldehyde, acetophenone, benzophenone. These and the complexes of Table I and II exhibit a delayed emission which is not observed with the donor and acceptor components alone and whose maximum frequency, $\tilde{\nu}_{ph}^{max}(CT)$, is lower than that of the

TABLE I: Data on complexes between tetrachlorophthalic anhydride (acceptor) and methylated benzenes (donors) in Me-cyclohexane at 77°K. $c_A = 5 \times 10^{-4}$ M. Phosphorescence maxima of the methylated benzenes are above 25 kK.

no.	donor	c_D	$\tilde{\nu}_{ph}^{max}$ (CT) (kK)	$E(D/D^+) - E(A^-/A)$ (kK)	Δ (kK)	
-	none	0	22.2	-	-	
1	toluene	5 vol%	21.45	24.65	3.20	(I)
2	m-xylene	5 vol%	20.55	22.25	1.70	(II)
3	p-xylene	5 vol%	20.3	21.95	1.65	(II)
4	o-xylene	5 vol%	21.0	22.10	1.10	(II)
5	mesitylene	5 vol%	20.7	21.55	0.85	(II)
6	durene	10^{-3} M	19.85	19.75	-0.10	(III)
7	pentamethyl-benzene	10^{-3} M	20.8[a]	19.10	-1.70	(IV)
8	hexamethyl-benzene	10^{-3} M	20.3[a]	18.70	-1.60	(IV)

[a] Delayed emission spectrum identical with fluorescence spectrum.

TABLE II: Data on complexes formed in N,N-diethylaniline (donor) with some acceptors at 77°K

no.	acceptor	$_{ph}^{max}(^3A^*)$ (kK)	c_A (M)	$_{ph}^{max}$(CT) (kK)	$E(D/D^+)$ $-E(A^-/A)$ (kK)	(kK)	$_{ph}$ (sec)	
-	none	-	0	24.8	-	-		
9	benzonitrile	24.9	6.6×10^{-3}	21.6	25.0	3.4	2.8	(I)
10	s-triazine	22.5	4.2×10^{-4}	21.1	22.4	1.3	1.1	(II)
11	1,4-dicyanobenzene	23.0	5.0×10^{-4}	20.1[a]	20.6	0.5	0.05	(IV)

[a] Delayed emission spectrum identical with fluorescence spectrum.

phosphorescence spectra of the components. This new structureless band, therefore, is assigned to the CT complex. The corresponding CT fluorescence spectrum, generally, occurs at somewhat higher frequencies except with the complexes 7, 8, and 11 where the "prompt" and delayed amission coincide within experimental accuracy (see Fig. 1). It is also in these three cases only that the lifetime of the delayed emission is shorter than 0.05 sec, whereas in the other cases the shortest lifetime is 0.25 sec (complex 6).

Application of equation (3) yields the values of Δ given in Tables I and II. On the basis of these values four typical situations can be distinguished. Their interpretation in terms of different types of mixing of zero-order states is outlined in Fig. 2 for the complexes of Table I where the ionization potential, IP_D, of the donor decreases from top (toluene) to bottom (hexamethylbenzene).

Case I is characterized by a Δ value considerably larger than 0.7 kK as with complexes 1 and 9. The zero-order CT state presumably lies above the locally excited state $^3(\overset{*}{A}D)$ so that the latter predominates in the emitting state.

In case II Δ is smaller than in case I but still larger than 0.7 kK as with complexes 2, 3, 4, 5, and 10. The emitting state, therefore, can be assumed to be predominantly $^3(A^-D^+)$, mixed with $^3(\overset{*}{A}D)$.

With decreasing ionization potential, IP_D, the zero-order CT state comes closer to the ground state so that interaction between $^1(A^-D^+)$ and $^1(AD)$ becomes increasingly important. This leads to increased stabilization of the ground state which for the complexes 6-8, indeed, has been observed experimentally.[11]

In case III (complex 6) where Δ is smaller than 0.7 kK, evidently as a result of this increased ground state stabilization, the emitting state is predominantly $^3(A^-D^+)$ as in case II. Thus, the

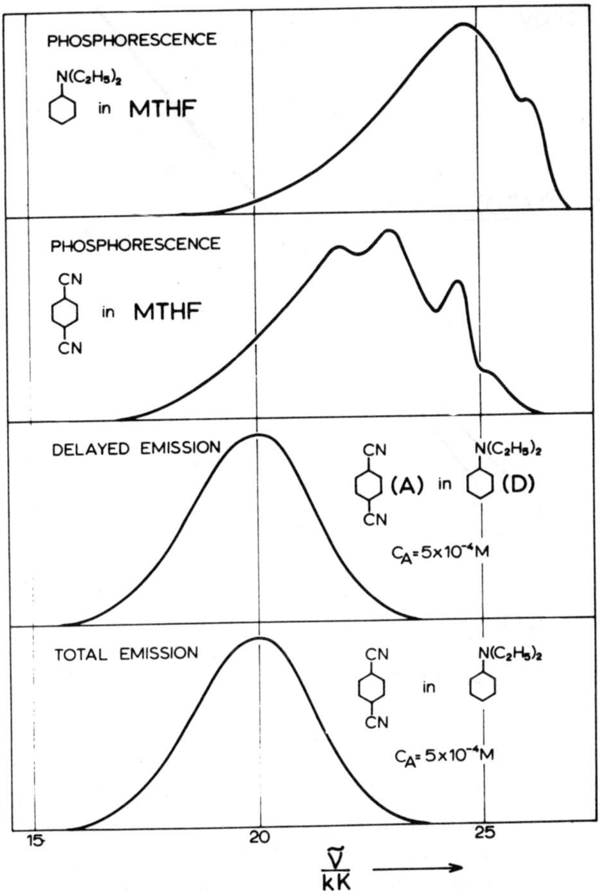

Figure 1 Emission spectra at 77°K. From top to bottom: Phosphorescence spectrum of diethylaniline (donor) in Me-tetrahydrofurane. Phosphorescence spectrum of 1,4-dicyanobenzene (acceptor) in Me-tetrahydrofurane. Delayed emission spectrum (lifetime 0.05 sec) of 1,4-dicyanobenzene (5×10^{-4} M) in diethylaniline (excitation 365 nm). Total emission spectrum of 1,4-dicyanobenzene (5×10^{-4} M) in diethylaniline (excitation 365 nm) observed without phosphoroscope.

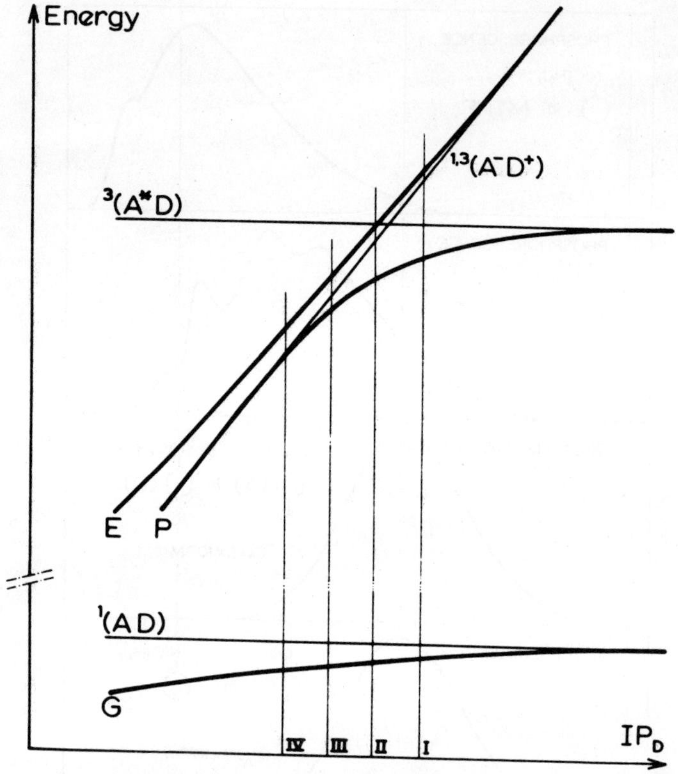

Figure 2 Energy diagram showing the interaction between the zero-order states $^1(AD)$, $^{1,3}(A^-D^+)$, and $^3(\overset{*}{A}D)$ (thin lines) for complexes with a common acceptor (as in Table I) and a series of donors characterized by their ionization potentials IP_D. The resulting states (heavy lines) are denoted by G (ground state), P (triplet state), and E (lowest excited singlet state).

differentiation between cases II and III, which is simply based on a "normal" value of Δ - 0.7 kK, may, in fact, not be distinct enough to be further retained.

Case IV: With the complexes 7, 8, and 11 a completely new situation is encountered in that here the phosphorescence and fluorescence spectra coincide. For complexes with a relatively strong ground state stabilization and, hence, a corresponding destabilization of the fluorescent state this can be understood only if one assumes that the delayed emission does not occur from the triplet CT state directly but as an E-type delayed fluorescence[12] from the singlet CT state which is thermally populated from the triplet state. This assumption is in agreement with the observation that the decay times of these delayed emissions are substantially shorter than those of the other complexes. The difference in Δ values between complex 7 and 8 on the one hand and complex 11 on the other hand is expected on account of a much smaller ground state stabilization in the latter complex.

KINETIC MEASUREMENTS OF TRIPLET CT COMPLEX FORMATION

The occurrence of E-type delayed emission from some CT complexes makes it possible to measure CT complex formation in the triplet state, e.g.

$$^3\overset{*}{D} + A \xrightarrow{k_A} {}^3(D^+A^-) \tag{4}$$

by emission spectroscopy in fluid solution. As the E-type delayed emission due to the endothermic reaction

$$^3(D^+A^-) \rightarrow {}^1(D^+A^-) \tag{5}$$

occurs at $77^{o}K$ with a decay time smaller than 0.05 sec the rate of reaction (5) at room temperature can be expected to be at least of the order of 10^4 sec^{-1} and hence comparable to or faster than other deactivation processes of $^3(D^+A^-)$.

The results of spectroscopic measurements which have been carried out with the system: N,N-diethylaniline (D) and 1,4-dicyanobenzene (A) in Me-cyclohexane at room temperature are shown in Fig. 3. In addition to the ultraviolet fluorescence of the donor (maximum at 29.6 kK), which is primarily excited and does not change in intensity, a new blue-green emission occurs around 20.4 kK, whose intensity, I, increases with increasing acceptor concentration, c_A, according to the Stern-Volmer type relation

$$I(c_A) = \frac{I(\infty)}{1 + c_h/c_A} \tag{6}$$

with a half value concentration $c_h = 1.3 \times 10^{-6}$ M. These findings, in particular the constant intensity of the diethylaniline fluorescence and the low half value concentration, can only be accounted for by the assumption that diethylaniline in the triplet state, $^3\overset{*}{D}$, which is generated in constant yield from the primarily excited singlet state reacts with 1,4-dicyanobenzene, A, to form the triplet CT complex according to (4). This is followed by the fast thermal reaction (5) and subsequent emission from the excited singlet CT complex.

There are two possible back reactions of $^3(D^+A^-)$:

$$^3(D^+A^-) \rightarrow {}^3\overset{*}{D} + A \tag{7}$$

$$^3(D^+A^-) \rightarrow D + {}^3\overset{*}{A} \tag{8}$$

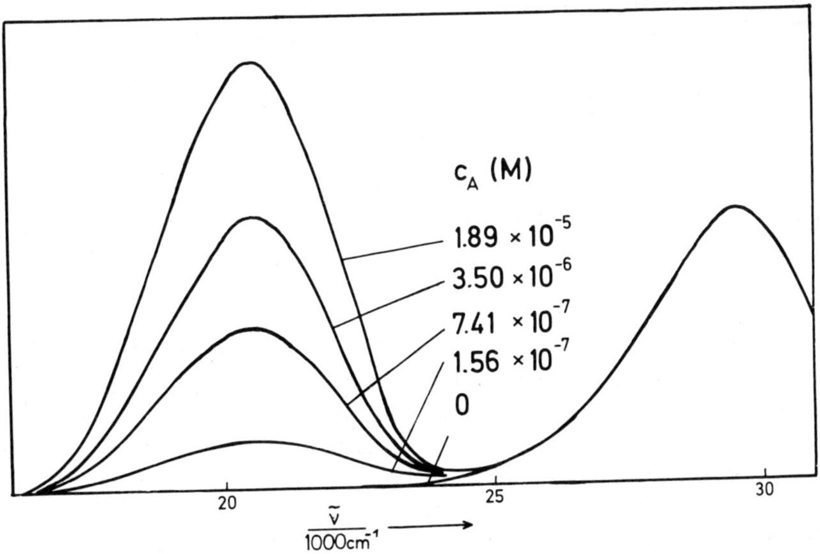

Figure 3 Emission spectra of 1.26×10^{-4} M N,N-diethylaniline (donor) in Me-cyclohexane (de-aerated) at room temperature with increasing amounts (0, 0.156×10^{-6}, 0.741×10^{-6}, 3.50×10^{-6}, 18.9×10^{-6} M) of 1,4-dicyanobenzene (acceptor) added (excitation 313 nm).

of which probably (8) may not be neglected. Hence, if k_A is the (presumably diffusion-controlled) rate constant of reaction (4) and τ_o the lifetime of $^3\overset{*}{D}$ in the absence of acceptor, one has

$$k_A\tau_o \geq \frac{1}{c_h} = 8 \times 10^5\ M^{-1}$$

This interpretation is confirmed by the results of quenching experiments which have been carried out with biphenyl as the quencher Q. Its triplet energy (69.5 kcal)[13] is below that of diethylaniline (76.8 kcal) whereas its singlet energy is higher (98.7 kcal vs 90.0 kcal). Addition of small amounts (up to 5×10^{-5} M) of biphenyl to a Me-cyclohexane solution which, containing 1.26×10^{-4} M diethylaniline and 3.78×10^{-5} M 1,4-dicyanobenzene (c_A), exhibits an emission spectrum very similar to the highest curve in Fig. 3 causes a strong decrease of the intensity, I, of the blue-green emission but does not affect the fluorescence band in the ultraviolet. Accounting for this effect by the triplet energy transfer reaction

$$^3\overset{*}{D} + Q \overset{k_Q}{\rightarrow} D + {}^3\overset{*}{Q} \tag{9}$$

with the rate constant k_Q, one obtains the Stern-Volmer equation

$$I(c_Q) = \frac{I(o)}{1 + c_Q/c_h'} \tag{10}$$

with

$$\frac{1}{c_h'} = \frac{k_Q\tau_o}{1 + c_A/c_h} \tag{11}$$

where τ_o, again, is the lifetime of $^3\overset{*}{D}$. Plotting 1/I versus quencher concentration one obtains a straight line with the slope $1/c_h' = 6.0 \times 10^4\ M^{-1}$, so that with $c_A/c_h = 29$ equation (11) yields

$$k_Q \tau_o = 18 \times 10^5\ M^{-1}$$

It should be noted that triplet quenching via CT complex formation: $^3\overset{*}{D} + Q \rightarrow {}^3(D^+Q^-)$ can be ruled out for energy reasons since for Q = biphenyl $E(^3\overset{*}{D}) < E(D^+Q^-)$. Similarly, since $E(D^-A^+) < E(^3\overset{*}{Q})$ biphenyl cannot quench the triplet CT state directly. As may be expected no quenching effect has been found with Q = benzene or p-xylene whose triplet energies are much higher than that of diethylaniline.

As the triplet lifetime, τ_o, of diethylaniline in Me-cyclohexane at room temperature has not yet been determined absolute values of the rate constants k_A and k_Q cannot be calculated. The only conclusions which can be drawn at this moment are that k_A and k_Q which very probably are diffusion-controlled ($\leq 10^{10}\ M^{-1}\ sec^{-1}$) are of the same order of magnitude and that $\tau_o \geq 10^{-4}$ sec.

Very similar results have been obtained with phthalic and terephthalic dimethylester instead of 1,4-dicyanobenzene.

ACKNOWLEDGEMENT

This work was supported by the Netherlands Organization for Pure Research (Z.W.O.) through the Netherlands Foundation for Chemical Research (S.O.N.).

REFERENCES

1. H. Leonhardt and A. Weller, Ber. Bunsenges. Physik. Chemie 63, 791 (1963).
2. H. Knibbe, D. Rehm and A. Weller, Paper presented to 8th Intern. Conf. Mol. Spectry., Copenhagen, 1965; Z. Phys. Chem. NF. 55, 95 (1967); Ber. Bunsenges. Physik. Chem. 72, 257 (1968); N. Mataga, K. Ezumi and T. Okada, Mol. Phys. 10, 201 and 203 (1966); H. Knibbe and A. Weller, Z. Physik. Chem. NF 55, 99 (1967); A. Weller, Nobel Symposium 5, Fast Reactions and Primary Processes in Chemical Kinetics, S. Claesson, Ed. (Almqvist and Wiksell, Stockholm, 1967) p. 413.
3. H. Knibbe, K. Röllig, F. P. Schäfer and A. Weller, J. Chem. Phys. 47, 1184 (1967).
4. N. Mataga, T. Okada and N. Yamamoto, Chem. Phys. Letters 1, 119 (1967).
5. H. Beens and A. Weller, Acta Phys. Polon. 34 (1968).
6. Evidently, solvation energies in polar solvents of the separate radical ions, D^+ and A^-, are of the same magnitude as the Coulomb interaction (mutual solvation) of the ions in the complex.
7. S. Iwata, J. Tanaka and S. Nagakura, J. Chem. Phys. 47, 2203 (1967).
8. H. Beens, (unpublished results).
9. H. Beens, J. de Jong and A. Weller, Paper presented to the XVe Colloque Ampere, 1968 and unpublished results.
10. During this investigation H. Hayashi, S. Nagakura and S. Iwata (Mol. Phys. 13, 489 (1967)) reported a D^* value of 0.050 cm^{-1} for the complex 1,2,4,5-tetracyanobenzene + durene.
11. J. Czekalla and K.-O. Meyer, Z. Physik. Chem. NF 27, 185 (1961): J. Czekalla and K. J. Mager, Ber. Bunsenges. Physik. Chem. 66, 65 (1962).

12. C. A. Parker and C. G. Hatchard, Trans. Far. Soc. 59, 284 (1963).
13. P. J. Wagner, J. Am. Chem. Soc. 89, 2820 (1967).

SOME PHOTOPHYSICAL PROCESSES IN TOLUENE

J. B. Birks

Shuster Laboratory
University of Manchester
Manchester, England

I. INTRODUCTION

This paper summarises and discusses the results of some recent studies of photophysical processes in toluene, a compound with several interesting features. It is the simplest of the alkyl benzenes; it is liquid from -95°C to 110°C it emits molecular and excimer fluorescence; it is commonly used as the solvent in liquid solution scintillators, where it exhibits intermolecular excitation migration, leading to efficient transfer of its singlet π-electronic excitation energy to a fluorescent solute; and its fluorescence quantum yield depends on the excitation wavelength.

II. MOLECULAR AND EXCIMER FLUORESCENCE

The first investigation, undertaken with J. R. Greenleaf and M. D. Lumb,[1] involved measurements from -85°C to +50°C of the fluorescence lifetimes, spectra and quantum yields of deoxygenated n-hexane solutions of toluene of molar concentration from [M] 5×10^{-3} M to ∿9.4 M (pure toluene). All observations were made in "reflection" to minimise self-absorption effects. The fluorescence lifetime τ was measured with the pulsed light fluorometer,[2,3] using a coaxial 30 kV, 16 atm hydrogen flash lamp, with appropriate filters, to obtain adequate excitation intensity in the toluene absorption region. The fluorescence spectra were observed under constant excitation conditions as a function of [M] and temperature. They were separated into their molecular and excimer components,[4,5] and the relative fluorescence quantum yields were evaluated, applying corrections for the geometrical refractive index effect.[6] Particular attention was paid to the purification of the toluene. Two physical properties were used as criteria of purity: the fluorescence lifetime (τ_L) of the liquid, and the "half-value" concentration $[M]_h$, the inverse of the Stern-Volmer self-quenching coefficient, K. The 20°C values of τ_L = 39.2 ns, $[M]_h$ = 8.3 M, are higher than those reported by previous observers,[4,7,8] indicating an improved standard of purity.

Excimer (D^*) formation from singlet-excited molecules (M^*)

$$M^* + M \rightleftharpoons D^* \tag{1}$$

in fluid solutions is described by the following parameters:[3,4]

$$1/\tau_M = k_M = k_{FM} + k_{IM} = k_{FM}/q_M \tag{2}$$

$$1/\tau_D = k_D = k_{FD} + k_{ID} = k_{FD}/q_D \tag{3}$$

$$\Phi_M = q_M/(1 + [M]/[M]_h) \tag{4}$$

$$\Phi_D = q_D/(1 + [M]_h/[M]) \tag{5}$$

$$K_e = k_{DM}/(k_{MD} + k_D) \tag{6}$$

$$K = 1/[M]_h = k_D K_e/k_M \tag{7}$$

$$K_1 = \Phi_D/\Phi_M[M] = k_{FD}K_e/k_{FM} \tag{8}$$

τ_M and q_M are the fluorescence lifetime and quantum efficiency of M* as $[M] \to 0$. τ_D and q_D are the fluorescence lifetime and quantum efficiency of D* as $1/[M] \to 0$. k_{FM}, k_{FD} and k_{IM}, k_{ID} are the rate parameters of fluorescence and internal quenching of M*, D*, respectively. Φ_M and Φ_D are the fluorescence quantum yields of M* and D*. $[M]_h$ is the "half-value" concentration at which $\Phi_M = \frac{1}{2}q_M$, $\Phi_D = \frac{1}{2}q_D$. $k_{DM}[M]$ and k_{MD} are the forward and backward rates of (1).

In the "high temperature region,"[4] where

$$k_{DM}[M],\ k_{MD} >> k_M,\ k_D \tag{9}$$

(6) becomes

$$K_e \to (K_e)_o = k_{DM}/k_{MD} = \exp(\Delta S/R - \Delta H/RT) \tag{10}$$

where $(K_e)_o$, ΔS and ΔH are the molar equilibrium constant, entropy and enthalpy, respectively, of (1), R is the gas constant and T the absolute temperature. Under condition (9) M* and D* have a common fluorescence lifetime,[4]

$$\tau = \frac{\tau_M + \tau_D[M]/[M]_h}{1 + [M]/[M]_h} \tag{11}$$

At $[M] = [M]_h$,

$$\tau = \tau_h = \tfrac{1}{2}(\tau_M + \tau_D) \tag{12}$$

At $[M] = [M]_e = 1/(K_e)_o$,

$$1/\tau = 1/\tau_e = \tfrac{1}{2}(k_M + k_D) \tag{13}$$

Equations (9)-(13) are valid for toluene in n-hexane over the temperature region studied.

Table 1 lists k_M and k_{FM} as functions of temperature. At 20°C $k_M = 1.98 \times 10^7$ sec^{-1}, $q_M = 0.12$ (Ref. 5), so that

$$k_{FM} = 2.40 \times 10^6 \text{ sec}^{-1} \text{ (at 20°C)}$$

At other temperatures k_{FM} is taken as proportional to n^2 (Ref. 9), where n is the refractive index of n-hexane at 270 nm wavelength. Expressing k_{IM} in the form,[4]

$$k_{IM} = k^o_{IM} + k'_{IM}\exp(-W_{IM}/kT) \tag{14}$$

where k is Boltzmann's constant, a plot of $\ell n\ k_{IM}$ against 1/T gives

$$k^o_{IM} = 1.28 \times 10^7 \text{ sec}^{-1}$$

$$k'_{IM} = 4.7 \pm 1.3 \times 10^9 \text{ sec}^{-1}$$

$$W_{IM} = 0.175 \pm 0.005 \text{ eV}$$

A similar value of $W_{IM} = 0.185 \pm 0.008$ eV is obtained from a plot of $-\ell n\ q_M (= \ell n\ k_M - \ell n\ k_{FM})$ against 1/T.

The parameter k_D (Table 1) was obtained from observations of[4] τ_M and τ_h, using (12). Expressing k_D in the form,

$$k_D = k_{FD} + k^o_{ID} + k'_{ID}\exp(-W_{ID}/kT) \tag{15}$$

a plot of $\ell n\ k_D$ against 1/T gives

$$k_{FD} + k^o_{ID} = 2.97 \times 10^7 \text{ sec}^{-1}$$

$$\log_{10}k'_{ID} = 10.9 \pm 0.3$$

$$W_{ID} = 0.24 \pm 0.02 \text{ eV}$$

The parameter K (7) was observed to be slightly dependent on [M], and the mean values of $[M]_h$ are listed in Table 1. $[M]_e$ (= k_{MD}/k_{DM}) was

TABLE 1: Toluene in n-hexane[1]

Temperature (^{o}C)	k_M (10^7 s^{-1})	k_{FM} (10^6 s^{-1})	k_D (10^7 s^{-1})	$[M]_h$ (M)	k_{MD}/k_{DM} (M)
-85	1.55	2.63	2.97	0.046	0.078
-70	1.56	2.59	2.98	0.086	0.114
-55	1.58	2.56	3.00	0.17	0.32
-40	1.62	2.53	3.03	0.38	0.90
-25	1.67	2.49	3.09	0.84	1.98
-10	1.74	2.46	3.18	1.87	4.5
+ 5	1.86	2.43	3.34	4.37	10.7
+20	1.98	2.40	3.60	8.3	19
+35	2.15	2.36	4.05	23.1	-
+50	2.41	2.33	5.29	42	-

obtained from a plot of $1/\tau$ against ℓn [M], using (13) or taking the point of maximum gradient, where (13) is valid. The values of k_{MD}/k_{DM} are listed in Table 1. A plot of ℓn (k_{MD}/k_{DM}) against 1/T yields the excimer binding energy

$$B = -\Delta H/N_o = 0.292 \pm 0.01 \text{ eV}$$

where N_o is Avogadro's number. A similar value of

$$B = 0.29 \pm 0.005 \text{ eV}$$

was obtained from a plot of ℓn K_1 against 1/T, indicating that k_{FD}/k_{FM} is independent of T.

From (2), (3), (7) and (8)

$$q_D = q_M K_1 [M]_h \qquad (16)$$

Substitution of the experimental values in (16) gives

$$q_D = 0.045 \pm 0.005 \text{ at } 20^{\circ}\text{C}$$

corresponding to

$$k_{FD} = 1.6 \times 10^6 \text{ sec}^{-1}$$

$$k^o_{ID} = 2.81 \times 10^7 \text{ sec}^{-1}$$

III. EXCIMER FORMATION AND DISSOCIATION

Because of condition (9), the rate parameters of excimer formation and dissociation, k_{DM} and k_{MD}, cannot be determined directly from fluorescence lifetime or quantum yield measurements. The second investigation, undertaken with J. C. Conte,[10] provided an indirect means of evaluating these rate parameters.

Observations were made of the rate parameter k_t of solvent-solute energy transfer from deoxygenated liquid toluene to a fluorescent solute (2,5-diphenyloxazole) at 20°C. A mean value of

$$k_t = 5.5 \times 10^{10}\ M^{-1}\ sec^{-1}$$

was obtained from these results, and from those of four independent observers, using five different solutes. This value is identical, within the experimental error, with the mean rate parameter

$$k_q = 5.6 \pm 0.1 \times 10^{10}\ M^{-1}\ sec^{-1}$$

of collisional quenching of the toluene fluorescence by three impurity solutes (oxygen, biacetyl, carbon tetrabromide), each of which have unit collisional quenching probability, p = 1. The identity of k_t and k_q shows that the solvent-solute energy transfer process is also collisional, with p = 1. The rate parameters of the two processes, which are controlled by diffusion and solvent excitation migration, are given by[8]

$$k_t = k_q = 4\pi N_o (D + \Lambda) R \times 10^{-3}\ M^{-1}\ sec^{-1} \quad (17)$$

$$= k_{diff} + k_{mig} \quad (18)$$

where

$$k_{mig} = 4\pi N_o \Lambda R \times 10^{-3}\ M^{-1}\ sec^{-1} \quad (19)$$

R is the collisional interaction distance, D is the sum of the diffusion coefficients, Λ is the solvent excitation migration coefficient,[8] and k_{diff} and k_{mig} are the components of k_t due to D and Λ, respectively. Substitution of $D = 4 \times 10^{-5}$ cm^2 sec^{-1}, R = 6 Å and $k_t = 5.5 \times 10^{10}\ M^{-1}\ sec^{-1}$ in (17) gives

$$\Lambda = 6.5 \times 10^{-5}\ cm^2\ sec^{-1}$$

$$k_{mig} = 3.4 \times 10^{10}\ M^{-1}\ sec^{-1}$$

It has been proposed[10,11] that the solvent excitation migration process is due to successive excimer formation and dissociation,

$$M_1^* + M_2 \rightleftharpoons D_{12}^* \rightarrow M_1 + M_2^* \text{ etc.} \tag{20}$$

where suffixes denote individual molecules. The mean time $\bar{t}$ from the formation of M_1^* to the dissociation of D_{12}^* is

$$\bar{t} = \frac{1}{k_{DM}[M]} + \frac{1}{k_{MD}} = \frac{1}{k_{mig}[M]} \tag{21}$$

From the elementary diffusion theory

$$\Lambda = \bar{\alpha}^2/6\bar{t} \tag{22}$$

$$= \frac{\bar{\alpha}^2 k_{DM}[M]}{6(1 + (K_e)_o[M])} \tag{23}$$

$$= \bar{\alpha}^2 k_{mig}[M]/6 \tag{24}$$

where $\bar{\alpha}$ is the r.m.s. displacement of M* due to excimer formation and dissociation. Substitution of the experimental values of Λ, k_{mig}, [M] and $(K_e)_o$, in (23) and (24) gives

$$\bar{\alpha} = 3.5 \text{ Å}$$

$$k_{DM} = 5.1 \times 10^{10} \text{ M}^{-1} \text{ sec}^{-1}$$

$$k_{MD} = 9.7 \times 10^{11} \text{ sec}^{-1}$$

for liquid toluene at 20°C.

The value of k_{DM} is higher than that for a diffusion-controlled process because of the short-range excimer interaction, and the high concentration [M] of adjacent unexcited molecules which may interact with M* in liquid toluene. Dilution of toluene with n-hexane reduces k_{DM} towards its diffusion-controlled value[3]

$$k_{DM} = \frac{8RTp}{3000\eta} \tag{25}$$

where η is the viscosity of n-hexane (η = 0.32 cP at 20°C.) The molar equilibrium constant $(K_e)_o$ is unaffected by dilution, so that values of

$$k_{DM} = 2.0 \times 10^{10} \ M^{-1} \ sec^{-1}$$

$$k_{MD} = 3.9 \times 10^{11} \ sec^{-1}$$

are estimated for toluene in dilute solution in n-hexane at 20°C, taking p = 1.

IV. EXCITATION INTO HIGHER STATES

The total fluorescence quantum yield Φ_F ($= \Phi_M + \Phi_D$) of toluene depends on the excitation wavelength λ_E (Ref. 12). In the third investigation, undertaken with J. C. Conte and G. Walker,[13] the fluorescence excitation spectra of deoxygenated toluene and of deoxygenated solutions of toluene in cyclohexane were observed at $\lambda_E \geq 195$ nm. The spectra were evaluated in terms of the parameter β, defined by

$$\beta = \Phi_F/(\Phi_F)_1 \tag{26}$$

where

$$(\Phi_F)_1 = (\Phi_M)_1 + (\Phi_D)_1 \tag{27}$$

and suffix 1 refers to excitation at a wavelength $(\lambda_E)_1$ into the first excited singlet state, where $\beta = 1$. Corrections were applied to Φ_F for the dependence of the specimen reflectivity on λ_E. The fluorescence excitation spectra are plotted in

Figure 1.

The data were analysed in terms of the kinetic scheme shown in Figure 2. M** and D** are higher excited singlet states of M* and D*, respectively, and $k_{JH}[M]$ and k_{HJ} are the forward and backward rates of the $M^{**} \rightleftharpoons D^{**}$ process. k_{MH} is the rate of internal conversion from M^{**} to M^*, which competes with k_{IH}, the rate of M^{**} internal quenching. k_{IH} includes all dissipative processes which do not yield M^* (or D^{**}). k_{DJ} is the rate of internal conversion from D^{**} to D^*, which competes with k_{IJ}, the rate of D^{**} internal quenching. k_{IJ} includes all dissipative processes which do not yield D^* (or M^{**}).

Under photostationary conditions and condition (9), a kinetic analysis[13] gives the following expressions:

$$\frac{\Phi_D}{\Phi_M} = \frac{(\Phi_D)_1}{(\Phi_M)_1} = K_1[M] \qquad (28)$$

i.e. the fluorescence spectrum is independent of λ_E, (provided the latter is below the ionization threshold), a result which has been confirmed experimentally,[13] and

$$\frac{1}{\beta} = \frac{(\Phi_F)_1}{\Phi_F} = \frac{k_H + k_J K_{JH}[M]}{k_{MH} + k_{DJ} K_{JH}[M]} \qquad (29)$$

where

$$k_H = k_{MH} + k_{IH} \qquad (30)$$

$$k_J = k_{DJ} + k_{IJ} \qquad (31)$$

$$K_{JH} = k_{JH}/(k_{HJ} + k_H) \qquad (32)$$

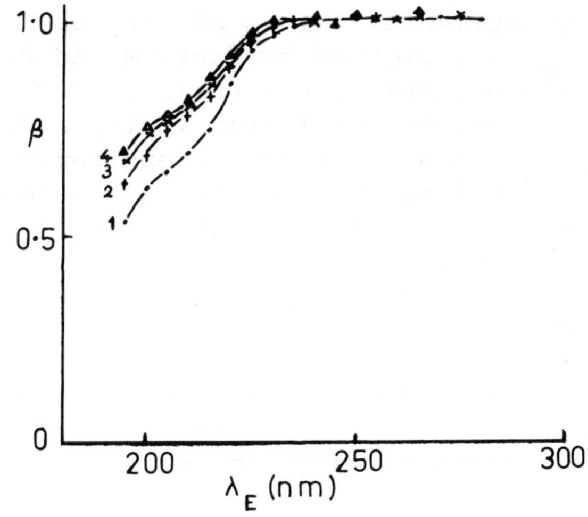

Figure 1 Fluorescence excitation spectra of deoxygenated cyclohexane solutions of toluene (1) · 9.4 M (pure toluene); (2) + 4.7 M; (3) x 2.35 M; (4) △ 1.18 M.

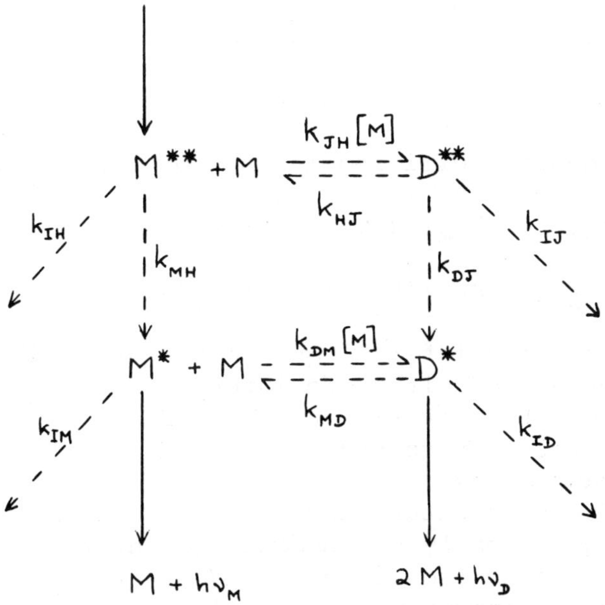

Figure 2 Kinetic scheme used in analysis of fluorescence excitation spectra.

The experimental values of $1/\beta$ at different values of λ_E, are plotted against $[M]$ in Figure 3. The results are consistent with (29), with the values of the parameters listed in Table 2. Similar analyses of the fluorescence excitation spectra of benzene, p-xylene and 2-methylnaphthalene[13] yielded the other parameter values listed in Table 2. The behavior of benzene differs from the other compounds in that the quantum efficiency k_{MH}/k_H of the $M^{**} \rightarrow M^*$ internal conversion is less than the quantum efficiency k_{DJ}/k_J of the $D^{**} \rightarrow D^*$ internal conversion. In benzene $1/\beta$ increases with decrease in $[M]$, while in toluene and the other compounds $1/\beta$ decreases with decrease in $[M]$.

V. DISCUSSION

Figure 4 summarises diagrammatically the energy levels (obtained from the fluorescence and absorption spectra) and the activation energies and rates of the various processes in toluene at 20°C. The D^{**} energy levels are estimated from the theoretical levels of the benzene excimer.[14]

The limiting values of the M^* and D^* fluorescence quantum efficiencies at low temperatures are

$$(q_M)_o = k_{FM}/(k_{FM} + k^o_{IM}) = 0.17$$

$$(q_D)_o = k_{FD}/(k_{FD} + k^o_{ID}) \simeq 0.054$$

The zero-point internal quenching rates, k^o_{IM} and k^o_{ID}, correspond either to intersystem crossing to the lowest triplet $^3M^*$ and $^3D^*$ (or $^3M^* + {}^1M$) states, respectively, or to radiationless transitions to the ground state.

The temperature-dependent M^* internal quenching (k'_{IM}) probably corresponds to intersystem crossing to an isoenergetic higher triplet state $^3M^{**}$, at an energy of 4.71 eV (= 4.53 $\pm$0.18 eV), following thermal activation through the energy

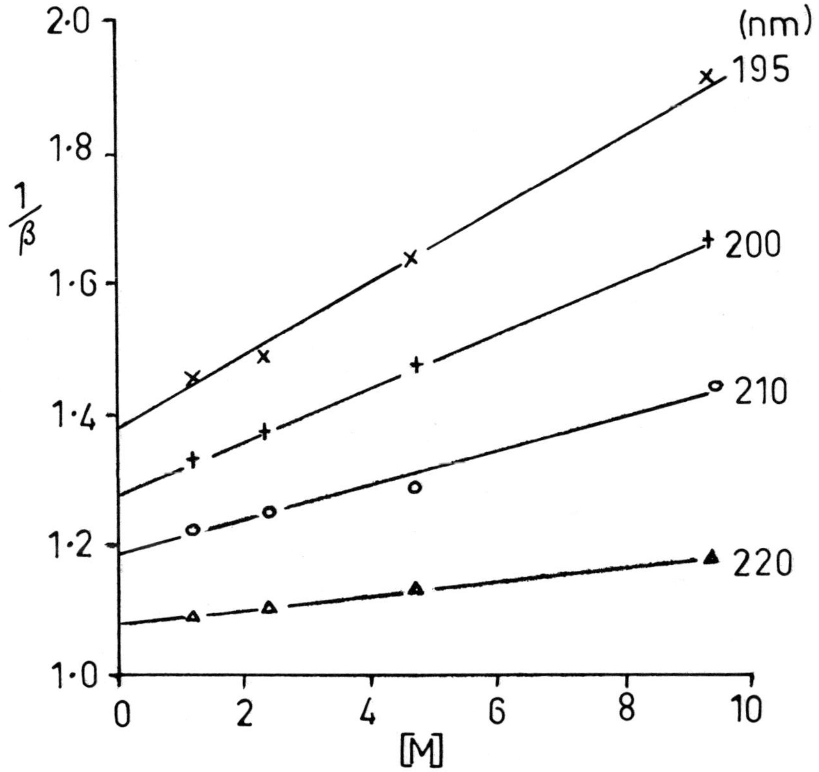

Figure 3 Deoxygenated cyclohexane solutions of toluene. $1/\beta$ against molar concentration [M] at various excitation wavelengths

x	195 nm	+	200 nm
·	210 nm	Δ	220 nm

TABLE 2: Cyclohexane Solutions at Different Excitation Wavelengths (λ_E)[13]

Compound	λ_E (nm)	k_{MH}/k_H	$(k_J/k_H)\,K_{JM}$ (M^{-1})	k_{DJ}/k_J
toluene	195	0.73	0.055	0
	200	0.78	0.041	0
	210	0.84	0.027	0
	220	0.93	0.011	0
benzene	195	0.28	0.26	0.48
	200	0.31	0.26	0.56
	205	0.35	0.22	0.56
	210	0.44	0.20	0.62
_p_-xylene	195	0.91	0.11	0.14
	200	0.97	0.053	0
	205	0.99	0.036	0
	210	1.00	0.026	0
2-methyl naphthalene	195	1.00	0.034	0
	200	1.00	0.063	0.06
	205	1.00	0.093	0.10
	210	1.00	0.12	0.13
	215	1.00	0.14	0.16
	220	1.00	0.16	0.16
	230	1.00	0.11	0.10

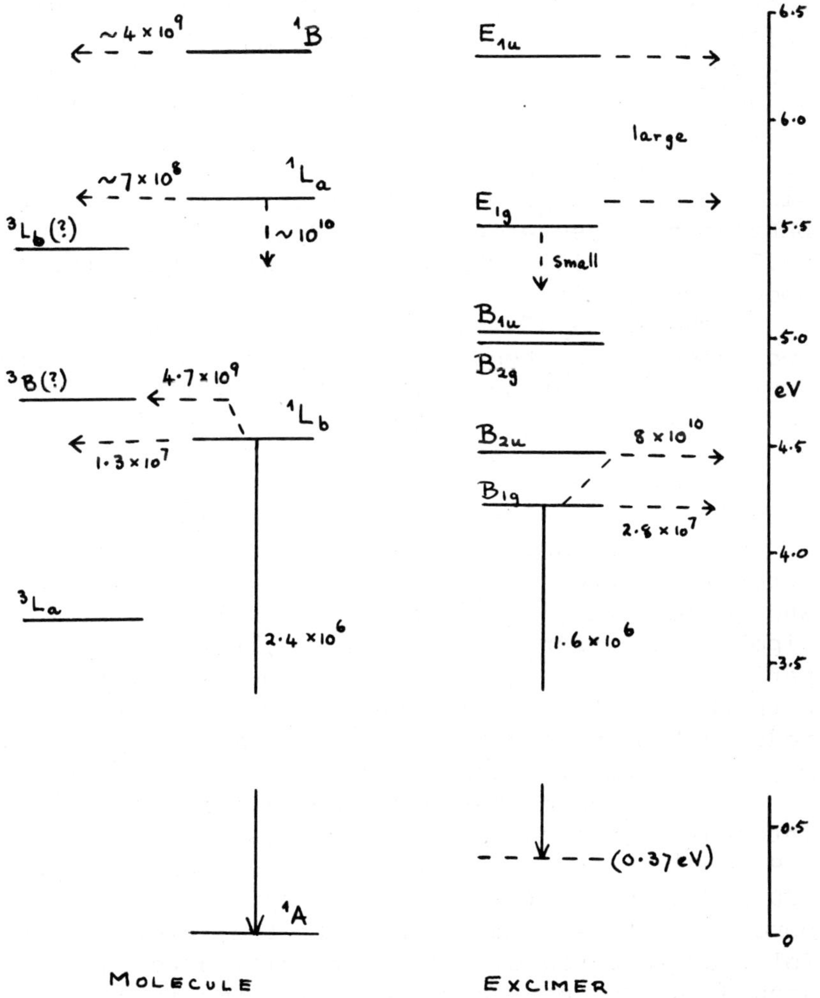

Figure 4 Molecular and excimer energy levels and rate parameters.

gap W_{IM} (= 0.18 eV). Comparison with benzene[15] suggests the identification of $^3M^{**}$ as the ^3B state (= 4.58 eV in benzene).

The temperature-dependent D^* internal quenching (k'_{ID}) may similarly correspond to intersystem crossing to an isoenergetic excimer triplet state $^3D^{**}$, at an energy of 4.48 eV (= 4.24 ± 0.24 eV), following thermal activation through the energy gap W_{ID} (= 0.24 eV). An alternative explanation is suggested by the theory of the benzene excimer,[14] namely that W_{ID} corresponds to activation from the lowest excimer singlet state B_{1g} to the next excimer singlet state B_{2u}, which may then dissociate. In benzene the theoretical $B_{1g} - B_{2u}$ energy gap is ∿0.2 eV (Ref. 14), which is consistent with the above hypothesis.

The $M^{**} \rightarrow M^*$ internal conversion involves two consecutive steps, (a) radiationless conversion from a low vibrational level (M_o^{**}) of the M^{**} state to a high vibrational level (M_v^*) of the M^* state, and (b) thermal dissipation of the excess vibrational energy of M_v^*. In solution step (b) is rapid (∿10^{13} sec^{-1}), and this rate is sometimes incorrectly equated to k_{MH}. Step (a), which is the rate-determining process, may be much slower. In benzene and toluene the $^1L_a(^1B_{1u}) \rightarrow {}^1L_b(^1B_{2u})$ electric dipole transition is spin-allowed, but it is parity-forbidden.[15] The latter factor, together with the relative large energy gap (∿1.1 eV) which reduces the overlap of the M_o^{**} and M_v^* wavefunctions, may reduce k_{MH} to about 10^{10} sec^{-1}.

If we assume k_{MH} ∿10^{10} sec^{-1}, then the M^{**} internal quenching rate k_{IH} increases from ∿7 x 10^8 sec^{-1} to ∿4 x 10^9 sec^{-1} as λ_E decreases from 220 nm to 195 nm (Table 2). k_{IH} probably corresponds to intersystem crossing to the triplet manifold, or to a radiationless transition to the ground state, possibly via an intermediate state of different molecular configuration.

The order and spacing of the excimer (D^{**}) energy levels in benzene (and probably toluene) are similar to those of the molecular (M^{**}) states from which they originate.[14] The excimer molecular separation r_m is determined by equilibrium between the gradient (dV'/dr) of the attractive excimer interaction potential V' as a function of the interplanar separation r of the two parallel molecules, and the gradient (dR/dr) of the intermolecular repulsive potential R (Ref. 16). (dV'/dr) is greater for the D^{**} states, originating from the higher molecular ^1L_a and $^1B(M^{**})$ states, than for the D^* states originating from the lowest molecular $^1L_b(M^*)$ state, so that r_m is less in the D^{**} states than in the D^* state, where $r_m \leq \overline{\alpha} = 3.5$ Å. The closer approach of the two molecules in the D^{**} state will facilitate the internal quenching (k_{IJ}) of D^{**}, by radiationless dissociation to the ground state or by intersystem crossing to the excimer triplet or quintet manifolds, and it will tend to inhibit $D^{**} \rightarrow D^*$ internal conversion (k_{DJ}).

Experimental evidence supporting the theoretical excimer model,[14] which has been used in the interpretation of the present results, is obtained from the nanosecond pulse radiolysis of benzene and toluene.[17] A structureless transient absorption band at ∿500 nm, which decays in the same manner as the fluorescence, is observed in each of these liquids, and this has been shown to be consistent with the theoretical $B_{1g} \rightarrow E_{1u}$ transition to a higher (D^{**}) excimer state.[18]

ACKNOWLEDGEMENTS

I wish to thank my colleagues Dr. J. C. Conte, Mr. J. R. Greenleaf, Dr. M. D. Lumb and Mr. G. Walker who undertook the experimental work described in this paper.

REFERENCES

1. J. R. Greenleaf, M. D. Lumb and J. B. Birks, J. Phys. B (Proc. Phys. Soc.), submitted for publication.
2. J. B. Birks, T. A. King and I. H. Munro, Proc. Phys. Soc. (London) 80, 355 (1962).
3. J. B. Birks, D. J. Dyson and I. H. Munro, Proc. Roy. Soc. A 275, 375 (1963).
4. J. B. Birks, C. L. Braga and M. D. Lumb, Proc. Roy. Soc. A 283, 83 (1965).
5. M. D. Lumb and D. A. Weyl, J. Mol. Spectrosc. 23, 365 (1967).
6. J. J. Hermans and S. Levinson, J. Opt. Soc. Am. 41, 460 (1951).
7. T. V. Ivanova, G. A. Mokeeva and B. Ya. Sveshnikov, Opt. Spectrosc. 12, 325 (1962).
8. R. Voltz, J. Klein, F. Heisel, H. Lami, G. Laustriat and A. Coche, J. Chim. Phys. 63, 1259 (1966).
9. J. B. Birks and D. J. Dyson, Proc. Roy. Soc. A 275, 135 (1963).
10. J. B. Birks and J. C. Conte, Proc. Roy. Soc. A 303, 85 (1968).
11. J. B. Birks, J. C. Conte and G. Walker, I.E.E.E. Trans. Nucl. Sci. NS 13, No. 3, 148 (1966).
12. C. L. Braun, S. Kato and S. Lipsky, J. Chem. Phys. 39, 1645 (1963).
13. J. B. Birks, J. C. Conte and G. Walker, J. Phys. B (Proc. Phys. Soc.), in press.
14. M. T. Vala, I. H. Hillier, S. A. Rice and J. Jortner, J. Chem. Phys. 44, 23 (1966).
15. J. B. Birks, L. G. Christophorou and R. H. Huebner, Nature (London), 217, 809 (1968).
16. J. B. Birks, Chem. Phys. Lett. 1, 304 (1967).
17. R. Cooper and J. K. Thomas (Argonne Nat. Lab. preprint) in press.
18. J. B. Birks Chem. Phys. Lett. 1, 625 (1968).

EXCIMER FLUORESCENCE OF ALKYL SUBSTITUTED BENZENES

Fumio Hirayama and Sanford Lipsky*

Department of Chemistry
University of Minnesota
Minneapolis, Minnesota

I. INTRODUCTION

Following the first report of excimer emission from pyrene by Förster and Kasper,[1] similar emissions have been observed for a variety of aromatic compounds.[2] For benzene and its alkyl derivatives, excimer formation has been reported by Ivanova, Mokeeva and Sveshmikov,[3] Helman,[4] Birks, Braga and Lumb,[5] and more recently by Lumb and Weyl.[6] Results of these investigations show that excimer formation in the alkylbenzenes is relatively inefficient compared to that of higher polyacenes such as pyrene. At room temperature, reliable excimer bands have only been observed weakly superimposed on the long wavelength tail of the

*This work was supported by the U. S. Atomic Energy Commission COO-913-27.

benzene and toluene monomer emissions. At lower temperatures it has been possible to obtain excimer spectra from some of the other alkyl substituted benzenes.[5,6] These studies, however, have been limited to the bulk state of the low temperature liquid.

In order to determine the probabilities for monomer emission and association and for excimer emission and dissociation to excited monomer, we have studied the concentration dependence of the fluorescence from benzene and nine alkyl substituted benzenes in methylcyclohexane at $-78^{o}C$.

II. EXPERIMENTAL

A 900 watt Osram high pressure xenon lamp was used as excitation source. The 260 mμ radiation from the lamp was isolated by a Bausch and Lomb 250 mm f/4.4 grating monochromator followed by a chlorine gas filter (1 atm., 2 cm length), and focused onto the face of the sample cell enclosed within a specially designed Dewar vessel. The fluorescence from the front face of the sample was viewed by an aluminized spherical concave mirror and focused onto the entrance slit of a Beckman DU monochromator. The remainder of the analyzing system consisted of an EMI 6256B photomultiplier, Keithley picoammeter, and Bristol chart recorder.

The correction-factor curve for spectral response of the entire analyzing system was determined with an NBS tungsten ribbon-strip lamp standard (U-103). The optical arrangement employed for this calibration was as suggested by Stair et al.[7] For low concentrations of aromatics the measured intensity was corrected for change in collection efficiency due to increased penetration depth of the exciting light. The concentration invariant emission of p-terphenyl in methylcyclohexane was used for this purpose. Quantum yields were determined against 9,10-dephenylanthracene

(2×10^{-3} M in cyclohexane; degassed) assuming its quantum yield is 1.00 after correction for reabsorption.[8] For low temperature measurements the solutions were cooled with a dry ice-methanol mixture (-78°C). Dissolved oxygen was removed by bubbling pre-purified nitrogen through the solution.

Matheson, Coleman and Bell benzene (fluorometric grade), toluene (fluorometric grade), m-xylene (spectrograde) and methylcyclohexane (spectrograde) were used without further purification. Eastman White Label ethylbenzene, cumene, o-xylene, and Aldrich mesitylene, 1,2,3- and 1,2,4-trimethylbenzene were purified by distillation under N_2 atmosphere. Matheson p-xylene was purified by recrystallization followed by distillation.

III. RESULTS AND DISCUSSION

We define ϕ_a as the probability for formation of excimer via the monomer association reaction and ϕ_d the probability for formation of excited monomer via the excimer dissociation reaction. The emission yields ϕ_S and ϕ_L of excited monomer and excimer respectively may be written quite generally as

$$\phi_S = (1 - \phi_a)\phi_m + \phi_a\phi_d(1 - \phi_a)\phi_m + \cdots$$

$$= \frac{(1 - \phi_a)\phi_m}{1 - \phi_a\phi_d} \qquad (1)$$

$$\phi_L = \phi_a(1 - \phi_d)\phi_e + \phi_a\phi_d\phi_a(1 - \phi_d)\phi_e + \cdots$$

$$= \frac{\phi_a(1 - \phi_d)\phi_e}{1 - \phi_a\phi_d} \qquad (2)$$

where ϕ_m and ϕ_e are the intrinsic* quantum yields of excited monomer and excimer.

From Eqs. (1) and (2) it is simple to derive that

$$\frac{\phi_S}{\phi_m} + \frac{\phi_L}{\phi_e} = 1 \qquad (3)$$

Equation (3) remains valid however under much weaker assumptions than are required for the validity of Eqs. (1) and (2). It is not difficult to demonstrate that a necessary and sufficient condition for the validity of Eq. (3) is that there be only two excited species which are interconvertible. Equations (1) and (2) assume additionally that the monomer is the exclusive precursor of the excimer. Alternatively, were the solution to contain dimer configurations which could be excited directly to the excimer state, Eqs. (1) and (2) would have to be appropriately modified, but Eq. (3) would remain valid. On the other hand, were it possible to form an excimer via triplet-triplet annihilation, the condition for validity of Eq. (3) would be violated.

Equation (3) predicts the existence of a concentration isoemissive point (i.e., a frequency in the fluorescence spectrum at which the intensity is invariant to concentration).[9] We define $P_m(\nu)$ and $P_e(\nu)$ to be the probabilities (per unit frequency) that monomer and excimer emit a photon of frequency ν, i.e.,

$$P_j(\nu) = I_j(\nu)/\int_0^\infty I_j(\nu')d\nu' \qquad (4)$$

---

*By intrinsic we imply that these probabilities are conditional on their being neither association nor dissociation reaction, i.e., $\phi_m = \lim_{\phi_L \to 0} \phi_S$ and

$\phi_e = \lim_{\phi_S \to 0} \phi_L$.

where j refers to either monomer or excimer and $I_j(\nu)$ is the intensity of monomer or excimer emission in arbitrary units. The total emission intensity at frequency ν is then given by

$$I(\nu) = A\left[\phi_S P_m(\nu) + \phi_L P_e(\nu)\right], \tag{5}$$

where A is some instrumental constant. For a frequency ν_o such that

$$\phi_m P_m(\nu_o) = \phi_e P_e(\nu_o) \tag{6}$$

it follows from Eqs. (3) and (5) that

$$I(\nu_o) = A\phi_m P_m(\nu_o). \tag{7}$$

Since neither ϕ_m nor $P_m(\nu_o)$ are expected to depend strongly on aromatic concentration, the intensity of emission at ν_o will be independent of concentration. It should be emphasized that the appearance of an isoemissive point is independent of any assumption concerning the existence of a monomer-excimer "equilibrium." Magnitudes of rate constants are not specified in the derivation.

Figure 1 shows the emission spectra of benzene-methylcyclohexane solutions at 25°C and -78°C. Isoemissive points are clearly obtained at ν_o = 308 mμ (25°C) and ν_o = 314 mμ (-78°C). It will be noted that at -78°C the spectrum is predominantly an excimer emission even at a benzene concentration of 0.5 M. At -78°C a distinct excimer emission has been found for all compounds studied at concentrations below 1 M, whereas for many of these compounds no reliable excimer emission could be found at 25°C even in the pure liquid. Isoemissive points have been obtained for all compounds at -78°C (toluene 317 mμ; ethylbenzene 317 mμ; cumene 321 mμ; p-xylene 320 mμ; m-xylene 320 mμ; o-xylene 316 mμ; mesitylene 317 mμ; 1,2,3-trimethylbenzene 316 mμ; 1,2,4-trimethylbenzene 321 mμ).

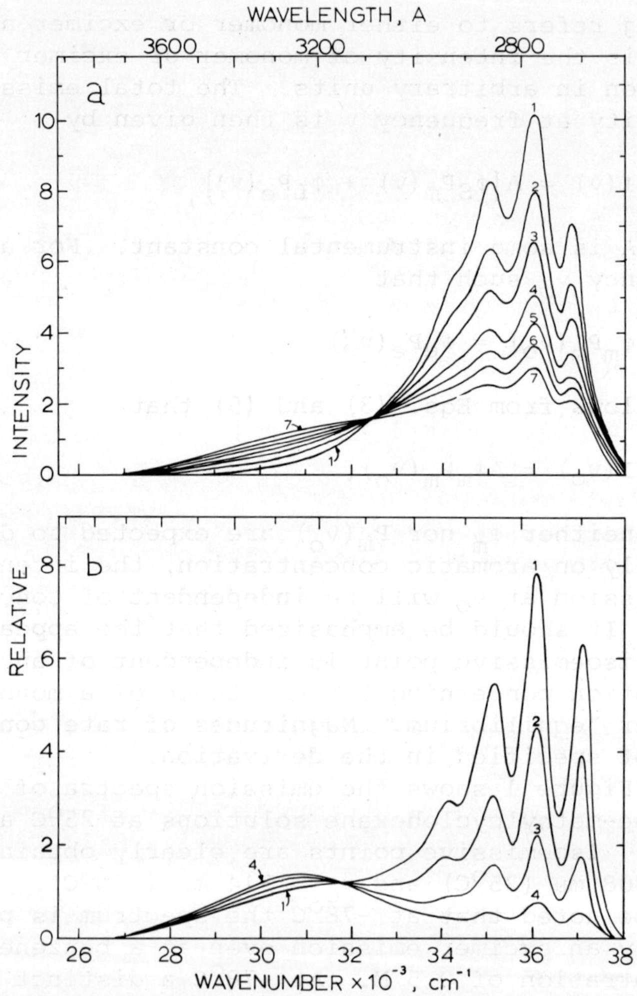

Figure 1 Emission Spectra of Benzene in Methylcyclohexane (relative photons/cm^{-1} vs. wavenumber).
a) at 25°C. Benzene concentration: (1) 0.112 M; (2) 1.12 M; (3) 2.24 M: (4) 4.48 M; (5) 6.72 M; (6) 8.96 M· (7) 11.2 M.
b) at -78°C. Benzene concentration: (1) 0.05 M· (2) 0.1 M; (3) 0.2 M· (4) 0.5 M.

From Eqs. (4) and (6) it follows that the ratio ϕ_e/ϕ_m can be directly determined from the position of the isoemissive point. In this way we have obtained for benzene at 25°C and -78°C ϕ_e/ϕ_m = 0.26 and 0.080, and for toluene and p-xylene at -78°C ϕ_e/ϕ_m = 0.11 and 0.17, respectively.

The quantum yields ϕ_c and ϕ_m can also be separately determined directly from Eq. (3). It will be noted that a plot of ϕ_L vs ϕ_S is predicted to be linear with intercepts of ϕ_e and ϕ_m at $\phi_S = 0$ and $\phi_L = 0$ respectively. An example of such a plot is shown in Fig. 2 for benzene for concentrations ranging from 0.112 M to 11.2 M at 25°C and 0.01 M to 0.5 M at -78°C. The ratio ϕ_e/ϕ_m obtained from Fig. 2 is 0.23 at 25°C and 0.075 at -78°C in good agreement with the results obtained from the isoemissive points. Similar agreement has been obtained for the other alkylbenzenes.

From Fig. 2 it can be seen that ϕ_e decreases as temperature decreases, contrary to the behavior of ϕ_m. The behavior of ϕ_m is typical of other compounds and is usually explained as due to an activation energy for some nonradiative process. Assuming such activation energy to be similarly required for nonradiative de-excitation of the excimer, it follows that the excimer radiative transition probability/sec must decrease sharply as the temperature is reduced. Such temperature dependence is to be expected were the transition symmetry forbidden and require thermal excitation of torsional oscillations to provide some allowedness.

If in Eqs. (1) and (2) it be additionally assumed that the association reaction is first order in unexcited monomer, it is simple to derive that

$$\phi_e/\phi_L = 1 + (1/\overline{K}c) \quad (8)$$

where $\overline{K} = \phi_m(1 - \phi_d)k_a/k_e$, and k_a and k_e are the rate constants for the monomer association and radiative processes. Using Eq. (8) we have obtained for benzene and toluene $\overline{K}$ = 45.0 l.mole^{-1}

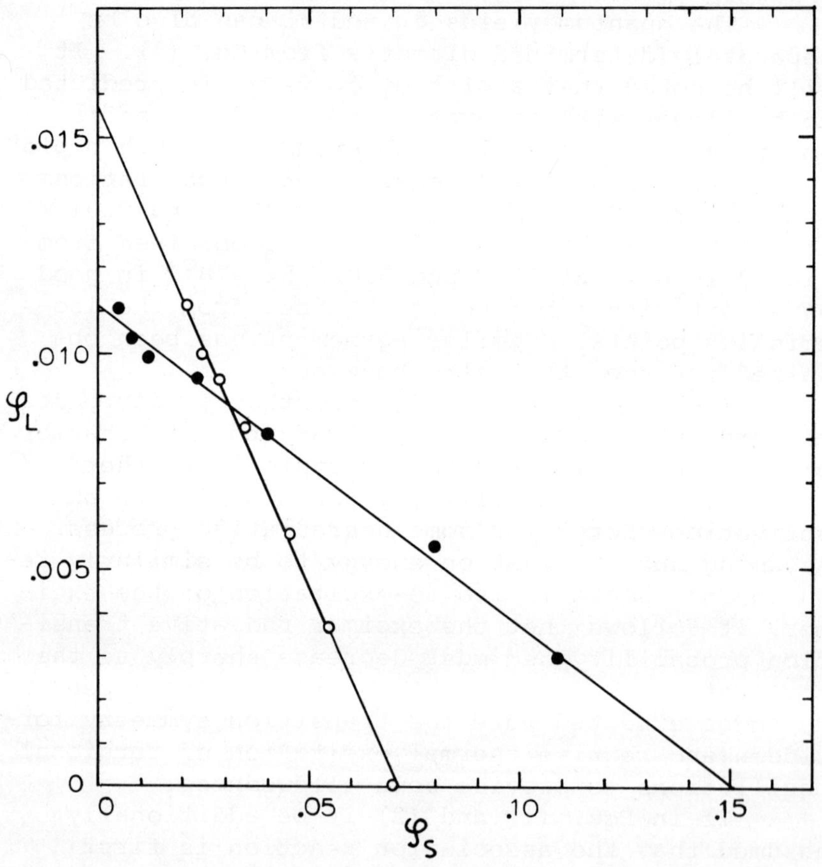

Figure 2 Plots of excimer emission quantum yield (ϕ_L) vs monomer emission quantum yield (ϕ_S) for solutions of benzene in methylcyclohexane at 25°C (0) and -78°C (●).

and 15.7 l.mole^{-1}* at -78°C compared to 0.18 and 0.14 l.mole^{-1} at room temperature.[10] This drastic change in $\overline{K}$ with temperature can be shown to be due to a pronounced decrease in ϕ_d. Whereas 0.1 M CCl_4 has no effect on the emission spectrum of benzene at room temperature, at -78°C it is found to reduce the ratio ϕ_L/ϕ_S by a factor of 1.5. This is most plausibly attributed to an increase in the lifetime of excimer resulting from a reduced rate of dissociation to excited monomer. Analysis of the dependence of ϕ_L/ϕ_S and $1/\phi_S$ on CCl_4 concentration indicates that at -78°C ϕ_d is negligible compared to unity. This permits an estimate to be made of the association rate constant.

From the definition of $\overline{K}$ (Eq. (8)), it follows that if $\phi_d = 0$ then

$$k_a = \overline{K}\tau_m^{-1} \tag{9}$$

where τ_m is the lifetime of excited monomer at -78°C. From Berlman's[8] value of τ_m = 29 nsec for benzene in cyclohexane at room temperature we can calculate τ_m at -78°C if the monomer radiative transition probability/sec is assumed independent of temperature. It then follows that $\tau_m(25°C)/\tau_m(-78°C) = \phi_m(25°C)/\phi_m(-78°C) = 0.47$ (see Fig. 2) giving $\tau_m(-78°C) = 62$ nsec. Substituting this and the value for $\overline{K}$ previously obtained into Eq. (9) we calculate that $k_a = 7.3 \times 10^8$ l.mole^{-1} sec^{-1} for the benzene association reaction at -78°C.

The viscosity of methylcyclohexane at -78°C has been measured to be 5.82 cp (which agrees with a value obtained by extrapolation of reported data[11] from 50°C to -25°C). Using this value, the diffusion limited rate constant at -78°C is calculated to be 7.4 x 10^8 l.mole^{-1} sec^{-1}. Comparison

---

*These values have been corrected for a 10% increase in concentration on cooling to -78°C.

with k_a indicates that the probability per encounter, p, for formation of excimer must be close to unity. Assuming p is temperature independent, we calculate from the viscosity of methylcyclohexane at 25^oC (η = 0.685 cp) that $k_a = 9.6 \times 10^9$ l.mole^{-1} sec^{-1} at 25^oC. A similar analysis has been made for other alkylbenzenes. The probability per encounter for excimer formation is found to decrease with alkyl substitution (e.g., toluene p = 0.51; p-xylene p = 0.27; mesitylene p = 0.033). This effect of alkyl substitution is consistent with the steric requirements of sandwich-type excimer configurations. A more complete account of this work including the analysis of data for all of the alkyl substituted benzenes and an extension of measurements to other temperatures will be presented elsewhere.

REFERENCES

1. Th. Förster and K. Kasper, Z. Elektrochem. 59, 977 (1955).
2. See review by J. B. Birks, Nature 214, 1187 (1967).
3. T. V. Ivanova, G. Mokeeva and B. Y. Sveshnikov, Opt. Spectry., USSR (English transl.) 12, 325 (1962).
4. W. P. Helman, Ph.D. thesis, University of Minnesota, 1964.
5. J. B. Birks, C. L. Braga and M. D. Lumb, Proc Roy. Soc. 283, 83 (1965).
6. M. D. Lumb and D. A. Weyl, J. Mol. Spectry. 23, 365 (1967).
7. R. Stair, R. G. Johnston and E. W. Halbach, J. Research NBS 64A, No. 4, 291 (1960).
8. I. B. Berlman, Handbook of Fluorescence Spectra of Aromatic Molecules (Academic Press, New York, 1965).
9. With temperature as the variable, similar invariant frequencies have been analyzed for the fluorescence spectra of some aromatic hydrocarbons by B. Stevens and M. I. Ban, Trans. Faraday Soc. 60, 1515 (1964).
10. These values of $\overline{K}$ at room temperature are considerably smaller than those obtained by Birks et al.: $\overline{K} = 0.48$ l.mole^{-1} for benzene; $\overline{K} = 0.24$ l.mole^{-1} for toluene (Ref. 5).
11. Selected Values of Physical and Thermodynamic Properties of Hydrocarbons and Related Compounds, API Research Project 44 (Carnegie Press, 1953).

EXCIMER LUMINESCENCE

A. K. Chandra* and E. C. Lim*

Department of Chemistry
Loyola University
Chicago, Illinois

I. INTRODUCTION

In a recent publication (paper I)[1] a semi-empirical theory of excimer luminescence in which all π-electrons of the two interacting aromatic molecules are treated using Hückel orbitals for dimers. The theory makes use of a complete Hamiltonian and considers the configuration interaction among various states using the formalism developed by Dewar and Longuet-Higgins[2] and by Pople[3] for the electronic states of alternant hydrocarbons. It has been shown[1] that the theory accounts for the more prominent features of the excimer luminescence of polycyclic hydrocarbons. Thus, in addition to yielding energies of excimer fluorescence which are in good agreement with experiments, the model shows that the lowest energy excimer state is of p (L_a) state parentage for both the singlet and triplet manifold. The linear relation between the energies of excimer fluorescence and monomer p band, which is believed to

---

*Address after November 1, 1968: Department of Chemistry, Wayne State University, Detroit, Michigan 48202.

be related to the near constancy of the energy gap between the monomer and excimer fluorescence, is also adequately accounted for. More recently, the theory has been shown[4] to be formally equivalent to, but much simpler than, the previous theories based on the molecular exciton-charge resonance concept. On the basis of an assumption that excimers possess D_{2h} equilibrium conformation, the question of the stability of the excimer triplet state and the thermal distortion of the excimer as the possible source of dipole allowed character of excimer fluorescence was examined. The results indicate that excimer triplet states of many polycyclic hydrocarbons are very likely unstable with respect to dissociation into monomer triplet and monomer ground state, and that thermal excitation of torsional distortion can account for the observed radiative lifetime of excimer fluorescence in naphthalene.

In this paper, we present a brief account of the results leading to the above conclusions.

II. OUTLINE OF THE THEORY

We assume that excimers have the D_{2h} configuration in which one molecule is exactly superposed over the other, in a perfect sandwich structure. Let the number of π-electrons in one molecule be 2m and the molecular orbitals these electrons occupy in the ground state be 1, 2, 3,.. ..,m where m is the highest filled orbital. Using a super-molecule approximation we designate the Hückel-type dimer orbitals as $\phi_1, \phi_2, \ldots, \phi_{2m}$ so that ϕ_{2m} represents the highest filled orbital. In addition to the orthogonality between the highest filled (m or m') and the lowest vacant molecular orbital m + 1 or (m + 1)' of the same molecule, it is assumed that orthogonality exists between m and (m + 1)' and between (m + 1) and m'. The coordinates of the two molecules in the excimer are so chosen that $S' > 0$ and $\beta' < 0$ where S' and β' are respectively the intermolecular overlap and resonance integrals. The energies and the normalized wave functions of the dimer orbitals related to those of monomer, after neglecting S' are as follows

$$E_{2(m+n)} = E_{m+n} - \beta'$$
$$E_{2(m+n)-1} = E_{m+n} + \beta' \qquad (1)$$

$$\phi_{2(m+n)} = \frac{1}{\sqrt{2}}\left[(m+n) - (m+n)'\right]$$
$$\phi_{2(m+n)-1} = \frac{1}{\sqrt{2}}\left[(m+n) + (m+n)'\right] \qquad (2)$$

where $n = 0, 1, 2, 3, \ldots.$ The dimer orbitals are therefore split by an energy $2\beta'$.

The configurational wavefunctions for the excited states of the dimer can be constructed from these dimer orbitals. Thus for the four low-lying excited singlet states, we write

$$X_1 = \phi_{2m}\phi_{2m+1} \qquad A$$
$$X_2 = \phi_{2m}\phi_{2m+2} \qquad S$$
$$X_3 = \phi_{2m-1}\phi_{2m+1} \qquad S$$
$$X_4 = \phi_{2m-1}\phi_{2m+2} \qquad A \qquad (3)$$

where $\phi_k\phi_l$ represents a configuration in which an electron is promoted from an occupied orbital ϕ_k to an unoccupied orbital ϕ_l. These wavefunctions are essentially the sum of two Slater determinants and are either symmetric or antisymmetric with respect to reflection in a plane that lies midway between, and parallel to, two monomers. The configurations X_2 and X_3 are degenerate. The matrix elements of the total Hamiltonian between two configurations of different symmetry are zero but do not vanish for those having the same symmetry. An interaction element of this type removes the degeneracy between X_2 and X_3 and lead to following four configurational interaction wavefunctions for the excited states of dimer

$$\sigma: \quad \frac{1}{\sqrt{1 + \lambda^2}}(X_1 + \lambda X_4)$$

$$\rho: \quad \frac{1}{\sqrt{1 + \lambda'^2}}(X_1 + \lambda' X_4)$$

$$\delta: \quad \frac{1}{\sqrt{2}}(X_2 - X_3)$$

$$\gamma: \quad \frac{1}{\sqrt{2}}(X_2 + X_3) \qquad (4)$$

where λ and λ' are the configurational mixing coefficients in the lower and higher excited states respectively. The method of determining λ or λ' and the excitation energies to the various dimeric states were discussed in paper I. The difference between the transition energy of the singlet p-band of monomer and excitation energies of the various dimeric singlet states are

$$E(p) - E(\sigma) = 2\left(\frac{1 - \lambda^2}{1 + \lambda^2}\right)|\beta'| + \left(1 - \frac{2\lambda}{1 + \lambda^2}\right)$$

$$\left[\langle m, m + 1|m, m + 1\rangle - \tfrac{1}{2}\langle m, m|m + 1, m + 1\rangle\right.$$

$$\left.+ \tfrac{1}{2}\langle m, m|(m + 1)'(m + 1)'\rangle\right] + \left(1 + \frac{2\lambda}{1 + \lambda^2}\right)$$

$$\langle m, m + 1|m', (m + 1)'\rangle \qquad (5)$$

$$E(p) - E(\gamma) = -2\langle m, m + 1|m', (m + 1)'\rangle \qquad (6)$$

$$E(p) - E(\delta) = 2\langle m, m + 1|m, m + 1\rangle -$$

$$\langle m, m|m + 1, m + 1\rangle + \langle m, m|(m + 1)',$$

$$(m + 1)'\rangle \qquad (7)$$

The energy of the dimeric state ρ is given by an expression similar to (5) except that λ is replaced by λ'.

The singlet-triplet splittings in the various excimer states under consideration are given by

$$E(^1\sigma) - E(^3\sigma) = (1 + \frac{2\lambda}{1 + \lambda^2})\left[<m,m + 1|m,m + 1> - <m,m + 1|m',(m + 1'>\right] \quad (8)$$

$$E(^1\gamma) - E(^3\gamma) = 2<m,m + 1|m,m + 1> + 2<m,m + 1|m',(m + 1)'> \quad (9)$$

$$E(^1\delta) - E(^3\delta) = 0 \quad (10)$$

$$E(^1\sigma) - E(^3\gamma) = -2(\frac{1 - \lambda^2}{1 + \lambda^2})|\beta'| + (1 + \frac{2\lambda}{1 + \lambda^2})\left[<m,m + 1|m,m + 1> - <m,m + 1|m',(m + 1)'>\right] + \tfrac{1}{2}(1 - \frac{2\lambda}{1 + \lambda^2})\left[<m,m|m + 1,m + 1> - <m,m|(m + 1)',(m + 1)'>\right] \quad (11)$$

Using expressions (5) to (11) it is possible to draw the general effect of configuration interaction on the positions of singlet and triplet excimer states. This is illustrated in Figure 1.

III. ENERGY OF EXCIMER FLUORESCENCE

The energy gap between the p state of the monomer and the σ state of the dimer is given by Eq. (5). Since no unique relationship is known between β' and D, the interplanar separation, we choose the arbitrary values of β' to give the best agreement with the observed energies. The values of β' (in eV) and the interplanar separation D

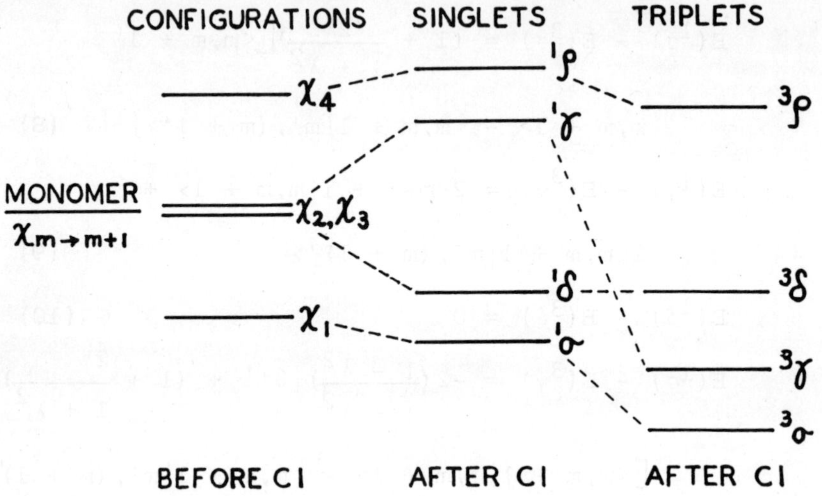

Figure 1 Effect of configuration interaction on the singlet and triplet states of excimer.

(in Å) at which the calculated values of E(p) - E(σ) give a reasonably good agreement with the observed energy gap are listed in Table I. The results indicate that for values of interplanar distance between 3 and 4 Å and the values of β' between 0.3 and 0.5 eV, the energy of σ state can satisfactorily account for the energy of excimer fluorescence. It happens that these values of β' are very close to what has been estimated[5] for paracyclophanes in which the interplanar separation is roughly 3.1 Å.

From Eq. (5) the transition energies of excimer fluorescence are related to those of the monomer p band by

$$E(\sigma) = (1 - K)E(p) + K\left[\Delta E - \langle m,m|(m + 1)', (m + 1)'\rangle\right] - 2\left(\frac{1 - \lambda^2}{1 + \lambda^2}\right)\beta' - \left(1 + \frac{2\lambda}{1 + \lambda^2}\right) \langle m,m + 1|m', (m + 1)'\rangle \qquad (12)$$

in which ΔE represents the energy difference between the lowest vacant and highest filled orbitals of the monomer and K is given by $\frac{1}{2}\left(1 - \frac{2\lambda}{1 + \lambda^2}\right)$. The sum of the second, third, and the fourth terms appearing on the right-hand side of Eq. (12) has been shown[1] to be generally small compared with the first terms, so that Eq. (12) may be approximated by

$$E(\sigma) \cong (1 - K)E(p). \qquad (13)$$

If the value of K (therefore, λ) does not change much from molecule to molecule, Eq. (13) predicts linear relationship between the transition energy of excimer fluorescence and that of the p absorption band of monomer. This behavior has indeed been observed,[1] and it has been suggested[1] to be responsible for the near constancy ($\sim$ 6000 cm^{-1})[6] of the energy gap between the 0,0 band of the

TABLE I: Values of β' (eV) and D (Å) at which Calculated E(p) - E(σ) Agree with the Observed Energy Gap Between the Monomer p-band and Excimer Fluorescence

	D	-β'	E(p) - E(σ) (eV)	ΔE obsv. (eV)
Naphthalene	3.0	0.50	1.20	1.22
Anthracene	3.5	0.40	0.94	0.94
Pyrene	4.0	0.30	1.28	1.13
Perylene	4.0	0.30	0.81	0.71

monomer fluorescence and the peak of the excimer fluorescence.

IV. COMPARISON WITH PREVIOUS THEORIES

Almost all previous theoretical work on the excimer electronic states of polycyclic hydrocarbons are based on the configuration interaction between molecular exciton states and charge-resonance states,[7] and thus it is desirable to compare the present semiempirical method with those based on the configuration-interaction model.

We have chosen naphthalene for comparison because the excimer electronic states of this molecule have been the subject of the most extensive theoretical treatments.

Both our semiempirical theory in the Pariser-Parr-Pople scheme and the alternate method based on the molecular exciton-charge resonance approach predict four low-lying excimer states of p-parentage in monomer. They are, according to our notation, the σ, δ, γ and ρ states of excimer which correspond to B_{3g}^-, B_{2u}^-, B_{2u}^+ and B_{3g}^+ respectively.

The wavefunctions of the $^1\sigma$ state given by

$$^1\sigma: \quad \frac{1 + \lambda}{\sqrt{1 + \lambda^2}} X_1 + \frac{\lambda}{\sqrt{1 + \lambda^2}} X_4 \tag{14}$$

can be translated into a group theoretical language for an excimer belonging to the D_{2h} point group. The wave function for the $^1\sigma$ state expressed as a linear combination of molecular exciton (Exc) and charge resonance (CR) takes the form

$$^1\sigma: \quad \frac{1 + \lambda}{\sqrt{1 + \lambda^2}} |B_{3g}(\text{Exc})\rangle + \frac{1 - \lambda}{\sqrt{1 + \lambda^2}} |B_{3g}(\text{CR})\rangle \tag{15}$$

where

$$|B_{3g}(\text{Exc})\rangle = \tfrac{1}{2}\{|m(\overline{m+1})| - |\overline{m}(m+1)|$$
$$- |m'(\overline{m+1})'| + |\overline{m}'(m+1)'|\}$$

$$|B_{3g}(\text{CR})\rangle = \tfrac{1}{2}\{|m(\overline{m+1})'| - |\overline{m}(m+1)'|$$
$$- |(m+1)\overline{m}'| + |(\overline{m+1})m'|\}$$

The coefficients of $|B_{3g}(\text{Exc})\rangle$ and $|B_{3g}(\text{CR})\rangle$ for the σ and ρ states (corresponding to B_{3g}^- and B_{3g}^+ of naphthalene excimer according to McGlynn et al.[7]) are compared in Table II.

In addition to furnishing wavefunctions which are very similar, both treatments predict that at large interplanar separation the σ and ρ states converge to pure $|B_{3g}(\text{Exc})\rangle$ and pure $|B_{3g}(\text{CR})\rangle$ states respectively. Though this convergence is slow in our treatment, the general form of wavefunctions, however, remain the same.

The above comparison therefore shows that the semiempirical theory of paper I is formally equivalent to the treatment based on the Exc-CR configuration interaction. However, the treatment of paper I has a definite advantage not only for its simplicity from the computational point of view but also for its ability to explain and predict the general features of excimers of polycyclic hydrocarbons, which are seemingly not possible by the other treatment.

V. TORSIONAL VIBRATION AS THE POSSIBLE SOURCE OF DIPOLE-ALLOWED CHARACTER FOR EXCIMER FLUORESCENCE

In excimers of D_{2h} a configuration, fluorescence from the lowest excited state is dipole-forbidden.[7] The measured radiative lifetimes of the excimer fluorescence of pyrene and 1,6-dimethyl naphthalene are, on the other hand, quite short (10^{-7} sec and 10^{-6} sec, respectively),[8] and they suggest that either fluorescence originates

TABLE II: Comparison of Wavefunctions of Naphthalene Excimers at Various Interplanar Separations

	Coefficient of $\|B_{3g}(Exc)>$ in		Coefficient of $\|B_{3g}(CR)>$ in	
	$^1\sigma(B_{3g}^-)$	$^1\rho(B_{3g}^+)$	$^1\sigma(B_{3g}^-)$	$^1\rho(B_{3g}^+)$
D = 3.0 Å				
Chandra and Lim[1]	0.8040	0.5981	0.5981	-0.8040
Azumi, Armstrong and McGlynn[4]	0.7489	0.6744	0.5763	-0.8267
D = 3.5 Å				
Chandra and Lim	0.8576	0.5157	0.5157	-0.8576
Azumi, Armstrong and McGlynn	0.8836	0.4709	0.4255	-0.9064
D = 4.0 Å				
Chandra and Lim	0.9116	0.4182	0.4182	-0.9116
Azumi, Armstrong and McGlynn	0.9790	0.2408	0.1858	-0.9827

from excimers having non-sandwich configuration, or the emission is induced by torsional vibration which destroys the high symmetry. It is equally probable that excimer fluorescence obtains its dipole allowed character via vibronic coupling to a dipole allowed state. The available data are far too few and incomplete to discriminate various possibilities although Birk et al.[6] and Azumi and Azumi[9] have suggested that the excimer has a stable configuration which is non-sandwich in conformation. In this section, we consider the energy and the transition probability of the emitting excimer state of naphthalene as a function of the angle of rotation about the common D_{2h} principal axis to see if torsional vibration can account for the observed radiative lifetime of excimer fluorescence.

The total transition moment between the singlet σ state and the dimeric ground state X_o of excimer is given by

$$P_\sigma^o = \left\langle \frac{1}{\sqrt{1+\lambda^2}}(X_1 + \lambda X_4) \middle| \sum_\mu r_\mu \middle| X_o \right\rangle \tag{16}$$

where r_μ is the position vector of μth electron. The matrix element of the electric moment, $\langle X_1 | \sum_\mu r_\mu | X_o \rangle$ and $\langle X_4 | \sum_\mu r_\mu | X_o \rangle$ can be shown, after neglecting the intermolecular overlap, to be equal to

$$\frac{1}{\sqrt{2}}(\vec{A}_1 - \vec{A}_2)$$

where $\vec{A}_1$ and $\vec{A}_2$ are the transition moment vectors for the p-band of the two monomers. The probability of excimer emission is equal to the square of dipole strength P_σ^o and it is given by

$$L = (P_\sigma^o)^2 = \left\langle \frac{1}{\sqrt{1+\lambda^2}}(X_1 + \lambda X_4) \middle| \sum_\mu r_\mu \middle| X_o \right\rangle^2$$

$$= \tfrac{1}{2}\left(1 + \frac{2\lambda}{1+\lambda^2}\right)\{\vec{A}_1 - \vec{A}_2\}^2 \tag{17}$$

If the angle between two vectors A_1 and A_2 is Θ, then

$$L = \left(1 + \frac{2\lambda}{1 + \lambda^2}\right) R (1 - \cos \Theta) \tag{18}$$

in which $R = A_1^2 = A_2^2$.

The result indicates that the transition probability of the excimer emission is zero if one of the monomers is exactly superposed above but at some distance from the other monomer. On the other hand, if we retain the principal axis of the two monomers common and rotate one molecule by Θ with respect to this principal axis the transition moment does not vanish.

The calculation of the energy of the emitting excimer state as a function of angle Θ is straightforward. The difference between the energy of the p-band of monomer $E(p)$ and the energy of excimer fluorescence $E(\sigma)$ for distortion by Θ is given by Eq. (5) where β' is replaced by $\beta' \cos \Theta$. Both the intermolecular integrals and λ appearing in Eq. (5) depend on Θ. The intermolecular integrals in naphthalene excimer were evaluated by Azumi and Azumi[10] for interplanar separation of 3 Å, while the value of λ can be evaluated from Eq. (15) of paper I using $\beta' \cos \Theta$ in place of β' and considering the dependence of $\langle X_1|H|X_4\rangle$ on Θ. The values of λ and $E(p) - E(\sigma)$ are summarized in Table III using $\beta' \approx 0.5$ eV. It is evident that the energies are not much affected by a slight distortion.

The above results make it possible to examine theoretically if the thermal excitation of torsional vibrations in D_{2h} excimers can account for the observed radiative lifetime of excimer fluorescence in naphthalene.

Writing Eq. (18) using oscillator strength, one obtains

$$\frac{f(\sigma)}{\nu(\sigma)} = \left(1 + \frac{2\lambda}{1 + \lambda^2}\right) \frac{f(p)}{\nu(p)} (1 - \cos \Theta) \tag{19}$$

TABLE III: Calculated Values of λ and $E(p) - E(\sigma)$ for Different θ (naphthalene excimer)[a]

θ	λ	$E(p) - E(\sigma)$ (eV)
0	0.147	1.20
5°	0.137	1.16
10°	0.136	1.15
15°	0.129	1.12
20°	0.120	1.10

[a] Observed value of $E(p) - E(\sigma)$ is 1.22 eV.

TABLE IV: The Sum of the First Two Terms (I_1, I_2) Appearing on the Right-hand Side of Eq. (29)

Compound	D(Å)	λ[a]	$\lvert\beta'\rvert$[b] (eV)	$I_1 + I_2$ (eV)
Naphthalene	3.0	0.15	0.5	-0.23
Anthracene	3.5	0.16	0.4	-0.07
Perylene	4.0	0.20	0.3	-0.01
Pyrene	4.0	0.03	0.3	+0.41

[a] Calculated from Eq. (15) of paper I.
[b] Values taken from paper I.

where f and ν represent oscillator strength and frequency of an electronic transition, respectively.

According to the results given in Table III the ambient thermal energy of 0.04 eV (value of $3/2 \cdot kT$ at room temperature) can effect torsional distortion of $\theta = 5^{o}$. Taking $\lambda = 0.137$ for $\theta = 5^{o}$ and using the value of 1.23[11] for $\nu(p)/\nu(\sigma)$, Eq. (19) assumes the form

$$f(\sigma) = 0.0039f(p) \tag{20}$$

Since the radiative lifetime τ is related to the oscillator strength f and the frequency ν by

$$\tau = \frac{1.499}{f\nu^2} \tag{21}$$

Eq. (20) leads to

$$\tau(\sigma) \simeq 385\tau(p) \tag{22}$$

The radiative lifetime of the p electronic state of naphthalene can be estimated from Eq. (21) using the mean frequency (ca. 36,770 cm^{-1})[12] and the oscillator strength (f = 0.13)[13] of the absorption band, and it is found to be ca. 0.61×10^{-8} sec. The use of this value of $\tau(p)$ in Eq. (25) yields a radiative lifetime of 2.35×10^{-6} sec for excimer fluorescence of naphthalene. This is in good agreement with the experimental radiative lifetime of ca. 1.2×10^{-6} sec reported for excimer fluorescence of 1,6-dimethylnaphthalene, and the result indicates that torsional thermal motion of the two molecules in excimer can account for the dipole-allowed character of excimer fluorescence in naphthalene. This conclusion contradicts an earlier conclusion of Azumi and Azumi[9] who have considered the same problem using the molecular exciton-charge resonance approach.

VI. STABILITY OF EXCIMER TRIPLET STATES

To examine the stability of the lowest energy excimer triplet state against dissociation into monomer triplet and monomer ground states we need to examine the difference between the energy of the triplet σ state of the excimer and the sum of the energies of the triplet p state and the ground state of the monomer.

The difference between the energy of the triplet σ state, $E_{3\sigma}$, and the energy of the ground state, E_D, of excimer can be written, from Eqs. (16) and (23) of paper I as

$$E_{3\sigma} - E_D = E(^3\sigma) = \Delta E - 2\left(\frac{1 - \lambda^2}{1 + \lambda^2}\right)|\beta'| - \tfrac{1}{2}\left(1 + \frac{2\lambda}{1 + \lambda^2}\right)\langle m,m|m + 1, m + 1\rangle - \tfrac{1}{2}\left(1 - \frac{2\lambda}{1 + \lambda^2}\right)\langle m,m|(m + 1)',(m + 1)'\rangle \tag{23}$$

where $E(^3\sigma)$ represents the excitation energy for the triplet state. The transition energy between the ground state of monomer with energy E_M and the triplet p state of monomer with energy E_{3p} is given by[3]

$$E_{3p} - E_M = \Delta E - \langle m,m|m + 1,m + 1\rangle \tag{24}$$

When the overlap repulsion is included, the ground state energy of the dimer E_D takes the form

$$E_D = 2E_M + x \tag{25}$$

in which x represents the repulsion energy of the dimeric ground state. Combining Eqs. (23), (24), and (25) we obtain

$$E_{3\sigma} - E_{3p} - E_M = -2\left(\frac{1 - \lambda^2}{1 + \lambda^2}\right)|\beta'|$$
$$- \tfrac{1}{2}\left(1 - \frac{2\lambda}{1 + \lambda^2}\right)\Big[\langle m,m|(m+1)',(m+1)'\rangle$$
$$- \langle m,m|m+1,m+1\rangle\Big] + x = I_1 + I_2 + x \tag{26}$$

The first two terms on the right-hand side of Eq. (26) can be evaluated using the values of λ, β', and molecular integrals from paper I, and they are summarized in Table IV.

The values of the repulsion energy of the ground dimeric state is not accurately known, but they may be taken to be of the order of 0.3-0.5 eV[14] at interplanar separations of 3.0-3.5 Å. When there values of the repulsion energies are used the sum of the three terms on the right-hand side of Eq. (26) becomes positive, and the results suggest that the excimer triplet state of many polycyclic hydrocarbons may be unstable with respect to dissociation into a monomer triplet and a monomer ground state. This may account for the failures[15] to observe excimer phosphorescence of pyrene and anthracene in rigid glasses at low temperatures under conditions in which excimer fluorescence was readily detectable.

REFERENCES

1. A. K. Chandra and E. C. Lim, J. Chem. Phys. 48, 2589 (1968).
2. M. J. S. Dewar and H. C. Longuet-Higgins, Proc. Phys. Soc. (London) A67, 795 (1954).
3. J. A. Pople, Proc. Phys. Soc. (London) A68, 81 (1955).
4. A. K. Chandra and E. C. Lim, J. Chem. Phys. (in press).
5. J. Koutecky and J. Paldus, Tetrahedron 19, Suppl. 2, 201 (1963).
6. J. B. Birks, M. D. Lumb and I. H. Munro, Proc. Roy. Soc. (London) A291, 244 (1966).
7. T. Azumi, A. T. Armstrong and S. P. McGlynn, J. Chem. Phys. 41, 3839 (1964), and references therein.
8. J. B. Birks and T. A. King, Proc. Roy. Soc. (London) A291, 244 (1966).
9. T. Azumi and H. Azumi, Bull. Chem. Soc. (Japan) 39, 2317 (1966).
10. T. Azumi and H. Azumi, Bull. Chem. Soc. (Japan) 39, 1829 (1966).
11. The value based on the 0,0 transition frequency of p band (ca. 35,100 cm^{-1})[12] and the assumed 0,0 position (ca. 28,600 cm^{-1}) of excimer fluorescence.
12. R. A. Friedel and M. Orchin, Ultraviolet Spectra of Aromatic Compounds (John Wiley and Sons, New York, 1951).
13. D. E. Mann, J. R. Platt, and H. B. Klevens, J. Chem. Phys. 17, 481 (1949).
14. J. B. Birks, D. J. Dyson and I. H. Munro, Proc. Roy. Soc. (London) A275, 575 (1963).
15. E. C. Lim and S. K. Chakrabarti (unpublished results).

LUMINESCENCE BEHAVIOR OF THE MIXED CHELATES OF EUROPIUM

K. K. Rohatgi and S. K. Sen Gupta

Physical Chemistry Laboratories
Jadavpur University
Calcutta-32, India

The luminescence characteristics of the chelates of Eu, Tb, Sm and Dy has become an active field of research due to their possible use as laser materials.[1] In these chelates the mechanism of emission is suggested to be excitation of the ligand to the singlet energy state by absorption of the pump radiation, followed by transfer to the higher energy states of the central metal ion via the triplet level of the ligand.[2] Emission then occurs from these energy states on combination with the ground state. As a potential laser material Eu has received the greatest attention.

The energy level scheme for Eu^{3+} ion has been worked out by Ofelt[3] and its absorption and emission spectra in $LaCl_3$ matrix have been reported by De Shazer and Dieke.[4] The ground state of Eu^{3+} is $^7F_0$ which is the lowest member of the energy levels obtained from Russell-Saunders coupling for the $4f^6$ electron system. The upper energy state is

^5D_J where J ranges from 0 to 4. The transitions between these 4f levels are forbidden by Laporte selection rule. $^5D_o \leftrightarrow F_{2,4,6}$ are electric dipole transitions and $^5D_o \leftrightarrow {}^7F_1$ and $^5D_1 \leftrightarrow {}^7F_o$ are magnetic dipole transitions. Some mixed transitions also occur. The electric dipole transitions are spin and parity forbidden, whereas the magnetic dipole transitions are only spin forbidden. $^5D_o \leftrightarrow {}^7F_o$ is forbidden in absorption and cannot directly be excited. But in emission ^5D_o is the most likely emitting state and $^5D_o \leftrightarrow {}^7F_2$ electric dipole transition becomes allowed by the electric dipole effects of the surrounding ligand fields. In distorted symmetry, specially in absence of a center of inversion these transitions are highly permitted. Thus, the nature of emission bands is to a large extent dependent upon the symmetry of the electric field imposed by the ligands on the 4f electrons.

It has been shown by Brecher, Samelson and Lempicki,[5] that eight coordinated tetrakis-chelates are better emitting systems than six coordinated tris-chelates of β-diketones. The addition of dimethyl formamide to tetrakis compound enhances the strong emission and generally sharpens the spectrum. The formamide adduct is nine coordinated and utilises all the nine available bonding orbitals constructed from 4d, 5s and 5p atomic orbitals. We have prepared some mixed chelates of high coordination number of the type ML_1L_2 where M is the rare-earth metal ion, L_1, a neutral ligand and L_2, a valence neutralizing ligand. In this paper the luminescence behavior of these complexes is reported where M = Eu, L_2 = salicylaldehyde or salicylate group and L_1 = phenanthroline, bipyridine, quinoline, pyridine and piperidine, all of which are N-coordinating neutral ligands of different sizes and are therefore expected to control the symmetry around the central metal ion. The spectrum of the ion reflects the symmetry of its immediate environment. The mixed chelates of phenanthroline with salicylaldehyde and salicylate group are analysed to have the formula Eu(phen)(saldd)$_3$ and Eu(phen)$_2$(sal)$_3$, respectively.

RESULTS AND DISCUSSION

The fluorescence and excitation spectra of the complexes in the benzene solution and in the solid state were obtained by the recording spectrofluorometer of Ferrand Optical Co. Ltd. Absorption measurements were made with Beckman DU spectrophotometer.

SPECTRAL STUDY IN SOLUTION. Simple salicylaldehyde in benzene solution absorbs at 325 nm but on complexation or salt formation, the absorption maximum shifts to 392 nm. The excitation spectra of all the mixed complexes of salicylaldehyde in benzene solution are obtained at 392 nm as a broad well-defined band. (Fig. (1)). Therefore in these complexes energy absorption by the salicylaldehyde moiety is responsible for excitation of rare-earth emission. The role of neutral ligand appears to be only to adjust the symmetry around the central ion. Eu^{3+} absorption at 394 nm is normally weak and corresponds to $^5D_3 \leftrightarrow {}^7F_0$ transition. It is hidden under the broad band of the salicylaldehydato group, but in salicylato complex it is observable and is found to increase eight fold on complexation. Since in Eu-phen-salicylate, excitation wavelength corresponds to 335 nm which is the region of absorption by the salicylate group. Therefore, this group should be mainly responsible for excitation of the central ion.

Simple tris-salicylaldehydato complex of Eu is very weakly fluorescent in the red region and insoluble in benzene. But when phenanthroline moiety is introduced in the coordination sphere the complex becomes benzene soluble and red emission is highly intensified. Main bands appear at 589

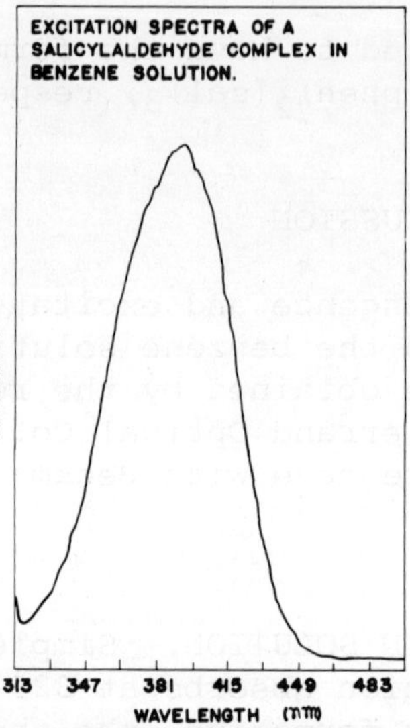

Figure 1

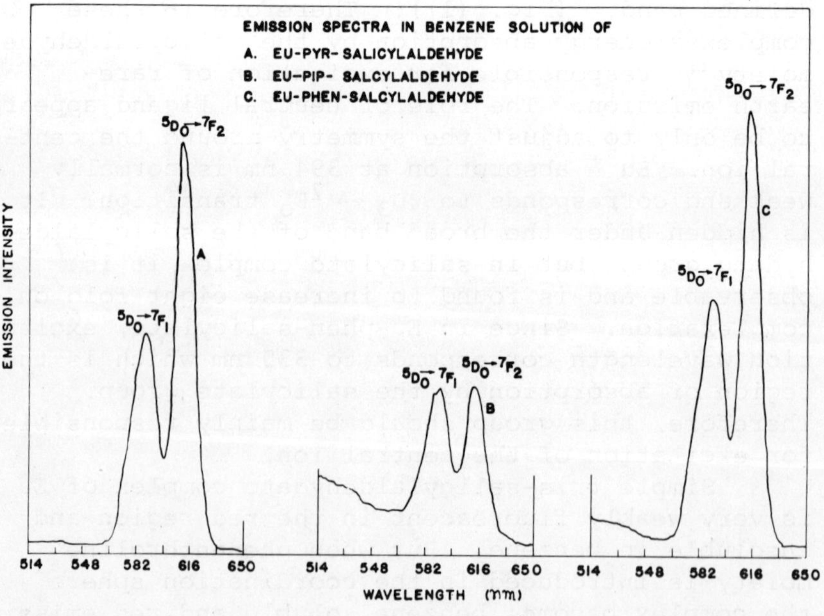

Figure 2

and 612 nm corresponding to $^5D_o \rightarrow {}^5F_1$ and $^5D_o \rightarrow {}^5F_2$ transitions respectively in Eu^{3+} (Fig. (2)). Of these, the first is the magnetic dipole (M.D.) and the second the electric dipole (E.D.) transition. The ratio of intensities, I_{612}/I_{589}, is calculated to be 1.9. Very similar emission characteristics were obtained when other neutral groups were introduced in the sphere of coordination. Of these groups, phenanthroline and bipyridine are bidentate and others monodentate. The results are tabulated in Table I.

Whereas the spectra in benzene solution for all the complexes were more or less similar, the spectra of the crystalline powder differed widely from one another (Figs. (3), (4)), exhibiting a marked effect of the sizes of the neutral ligands. For the microcrystalline system the excitation spectra were recorded at 410 nm for all the complexes including $Eu(saldd)_3$. But the nature of the excitation band differed in details when the fluorescence monochromator was adjusted for different emission peaks (Fig. (5)). The excitation band for 611 and 589 nm peaks had one broad band at 410 nm but for 526 nm region in fluorescence, the band was more complex with sharp peaks at 405, and other small peaks in short wavelength region superimposed on broad background envelope.

From the analysis of the spectra (Figs. 3A to 3D) it is found that for the different neutral ligands the fluorescence spectra are different and since in all the complexes the excitation is through salicylaldehydato group, the neutral ligands are responsible for the differences in the fluorescence spectra, evidently by creating fields of different symmetry. The fluorescence spectra of the complexes with monodentate neutral ligands, pyridine, quinoline and piperidine and simple Eu-salicylaldehyde are almost similar, with a strong band at 526 nm corresponding to the magnetic dipole transition $^5D_1 \rightarrow {}^7F_o$. Transitions from the ^5D_o level are weak and the magnetic dipole transition, $^5D_o \rightarrow {}^7F_1$,

TABLE I: Emission Intensity Ratios of Electric Dipole and Magnetic Dipole Transitions From $^5D_0$ Level in Mixed Chelates of Eu in Benzene Solution and Corresponding Excitation Maxima.

Name of the Compound	Intensity Ratio of $^5D_0 - {}^7F_2/{}^5D_0 - {}^7F_1$ Transitions	Excitation Maximum (nm)
Eu-Pyr-Salicylaldehyde	1.9	392
Eu-Quin-Salicylaldehyde	1.5	392
Eu-Piper-Salicylaldehyde	1.0	392
Eu-Bipyr-Salicylaldehyde	1.5	392
Eu-Phen-Salicylaldehyde	1.7	392
Eu-Phen-Salicylalate	1.5	335

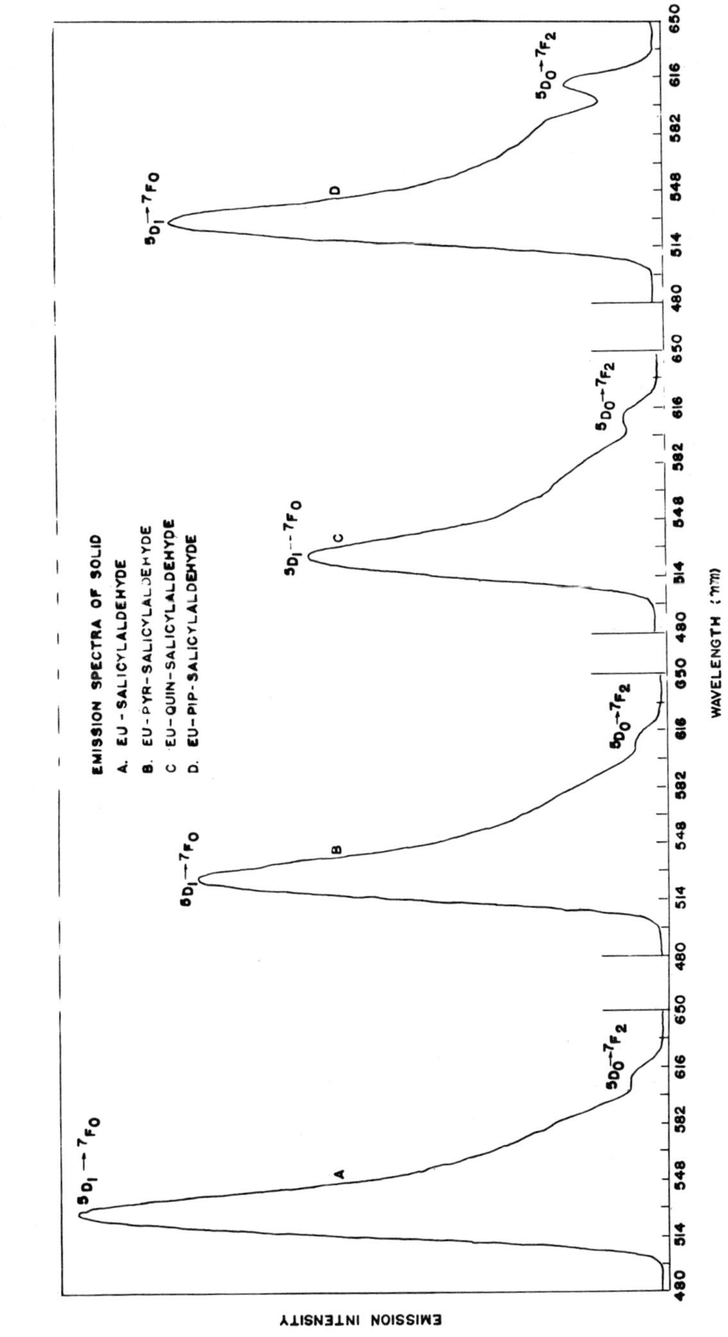
EMISSION SPECTRA OF SOLID
A. EU-SALICYLALDEHYDE
B. EU-PYR-SALICYLALDEHYDE
C. EU-QUIN-SALICYLALDEHYDE
D. EU-PIP-SALICYLALDEHYDE
A
B
C
D
$^5D_1 \rightarrow {}^7F_0$
$^5D_0 \rightarrow {}^7F_2$
480 514 548 582 616 650
WAVELENGTH (nm)
EMISSION INTENSITY

Figure 3

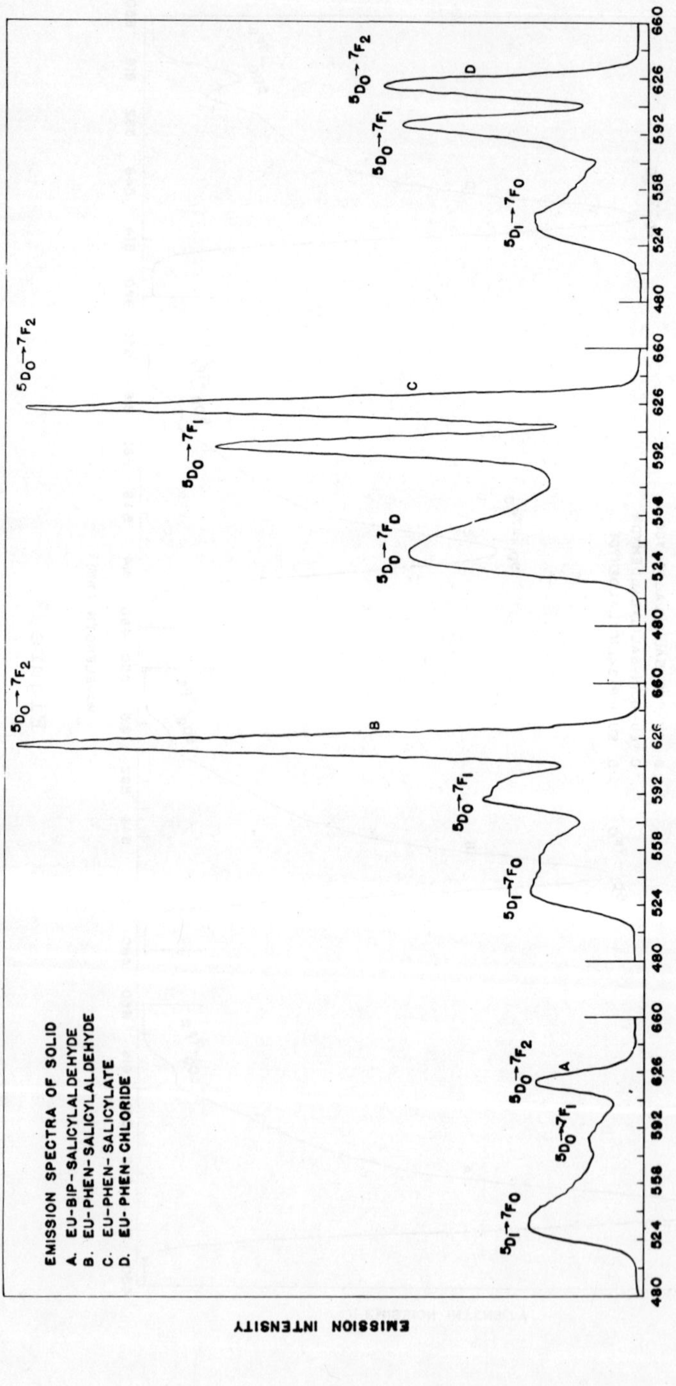

EMISSION SPECTRA OF SOLID
A. EU-BIP-SALICYLALDEHYDE
B. EU-PHEN-SALICYLALDEHYDE
C. EU-PHEN-SALICYLATE
D. EU-PHEN-CHLORIDE
EMISSION INTENSITY
WAVELENGTH (nm)

Figure 4

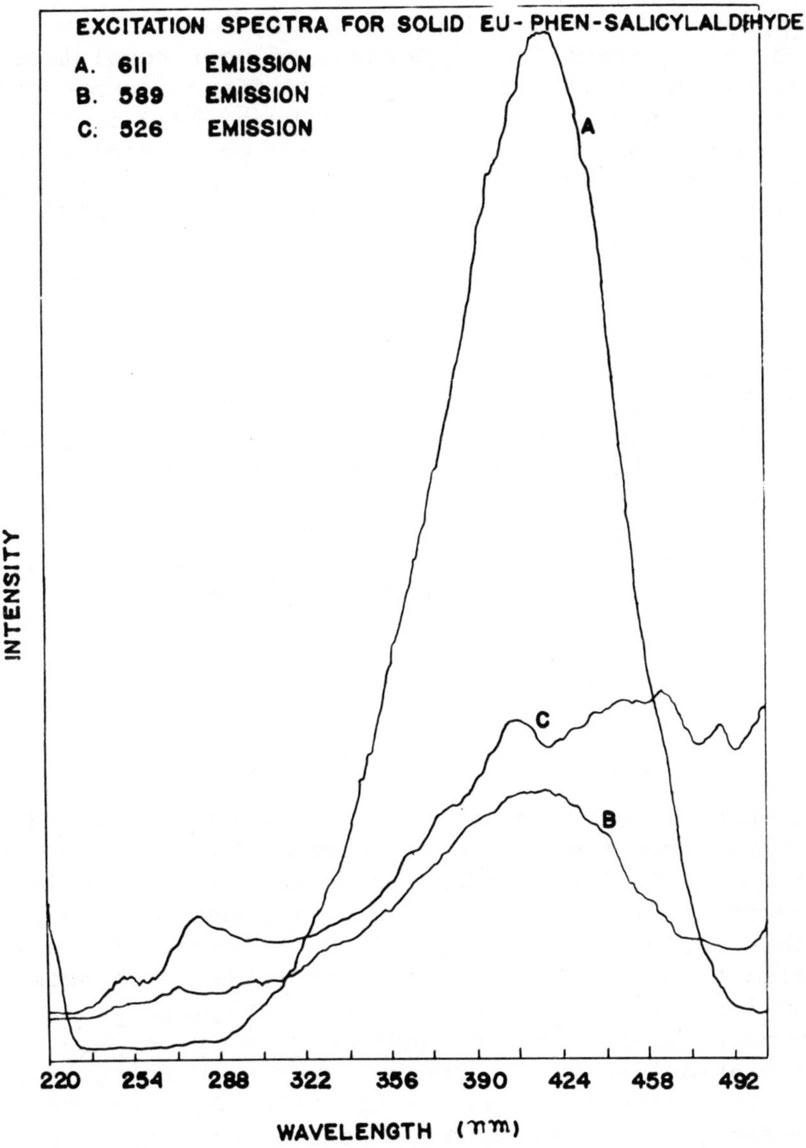
EXCITATION SPECTRA FOR SOLID EU-PHEN-SALICYLALDEHYDE
A. 611 EMISSION
B. 589 EMISSION
C. 526 EMISSION
A
B
C
INTENSITY
220
254
288
322
356
390
424
458
492
WAVELENGTH (nm)

Figure 5

appears as a hump under the strong band due to $^5D_1 \rightarrow {}^7F_o$ transition. Because of poor resolution of the spectrofluorometer, the different components of the bands overlap to form a broad band in this region. The $^5D_o \rightarrow {}^7F_2$ electric dipole transition is very weak in these complexes and the relative intensity increases from pyridine to piperidine through quinoline. As the introduction of pyridine has no effect on simple Eu-salicylaldehyde spectra, it appears that the available hole in the molecular geometry must be big enough to accomodate the flat pyridine molecule without any distortion. These neutral ligands being monodentate two molecules may enter the coordination sphere in a more symmetrical fashion and the complexes formed by them being less asymmetric, the magnetic dipole transitions are relatively stronger than the electric dipole one. Quinoline being more bulky than pyridine creates more asymmetry in its complex and piperidine being nonplanar distorts the field further. This must be the reason for the relative increase in electric dipole transition at 610 nm in piperidine complex (Table II).

The fluorescence spectra of the solid complexes formed with bipyridine and phenanthroline are completely different. Here the intensity of transitions from the ^5D_o level increases many times as compared to the monodentate neutral ligand series. Particularly in the complex with phenanthroline, this increase of efficiency is striking. It is also true for the other phenanthroline complexes, Eu-(phen)$_2$(salicylate)$_3$ and Eu(phen)$_2$Cl$_3$. It appears that in these complexes the $^5D_1 - {}^5D_o$ radiationless transition efficiency increases sufficiently or it may be that the ^5D_o level is directly populated through some other path. It may be noted in this connection that the excitation spectra for 526 nm emission band is more complex than that for 611 and 584 nm line. In the complex with monodentate neutral ligands vibronic coupling with the excited Eu^{3+} state may be different

TABLE II: Intensity Ratios of Emission Peaks of Polycrystalline Mixed Chelates of Europium.

Name of the Compound	Intensity Ratio of ${}^5D_1 - {}^7F_0 / {}^5D_0 - {}^7F_2$ Transitions	Intensity Ratio of ${}^5D_0 - {}^7F_2 / {}^5D_0 - {}^7F_1$ Transitions
Eu-Salicylaldehyde	15	0.45
Eu-Pyr-Salicylaldehyde	15	0.46
Eu-Quin-Salicylaldehyde	9	0.60
Eu-Piper-Salicylaldehyde	5	0.87
Eu-Bipyr-Salicylaldehyde	0.94	2.3
Eu-Phen-Salicylaldehyde	0.18	4.3
Eu-Phen-Salicylate	0.38	1.4
Eu-Phen-Chloride	0.44	1.1

leading to excitation of higher multiplets of the ^5D manifold. In the solution spectra of these complexes the radiative transition from $^5D_1$ is completely quenched by solvent molecules and the transitions are mainly from ^5D_o to $^7F_{1,2}$. A smaller ratio for ED/MD transitions from ^5D_o in benzene solution, imply a more symmetrical field in a solvent environment. This is not unexpected since the arrangement of atoms bonded to Eu will be more distorted in solid from otherwise favored configurations to accomodate crystal packing requirements.

The ratios of the intensities of electric dipole transition to magnetic dipole transition, I_{611}/I_{589}, in emission for the complexes with bidentate neutral ligands are given in Table II. It is found that for Eu(phen) $(Saldd)_3$ this ratio is the highest, showing a maximum of asymmetric field in this complex. In $Eu(phen)_2(salicylate)_3$ and $Eu(phen)_2Cl_3$ these ratios are low indicating the existence of a more symmetric field. This is apparent from the consideration that since only one phenanthroline is attached to Eu in the salicylaldehydato complex it creates more asymmetry in this complex than that in the salicylato or chloride complex where the two phenanthroline can be symmetrically arranged. A smaller ratio for the bipyridine-salicylaldehydato complex compared to that of the corresponding phenanthroline complex appears to be due to reduced rigidity of bipyridine. That this ratio of emission intensities increases with increasing deviation from the inversion symmetry was shown in the interesting paper by Blasse et al.[6] in the case of some Eu^{3+}-activated inorganic phosphors.

Salicylaldehyde being bidentate and phenanthroline or bipyridine having two lone pairs of electrons per molecule the ligands occupy the eight orbitals obtained from vacant 4d, 5s and 5p orbitals. Consequently, three electronic configurations can arise, e.g., d^5sp^2, d^5p^3 and d^4sp^3 which produce face centered isosceles prism (D_{2v}),

Archimedean antiprism (D_{4d}) and tetragonal dodecahedron (D_{2d}) or antiprism respectively. Brecher et al.[5] have discussed the selection rules for these spatial configurations when all the coordinating groups are oxygen. In this case two orbitals will be occupied by two lone pairs of nitrogen and will cause considerable lowering of symmetry. Comparing the resolved spectra in the $^5D_o \rightarrow {}^7F_2$ region (Fig. 4) of Eu(phen)(saldd)$_3$ with that of the dihydrate of the tris Eu-diketonate it appears that it may have C_{2v} symmetry still lowered due to rigid phenanthroline molecule where all the transitions are allowed. In fact, we observe definite bands at 622, 616 and 611 nm and closer examination of the asymmetric nature of the bands show that they can be further resolved into more bands. We have failed to resolve them due to the insufficient resolution of our instrument. Eu(phen)$_2$(salicylate)$_3$ on the other hand have only one band around 614 nm, supporting a more symmetric nature of the complex due to symmetric placement of two phenanthroline groups. From the composition which has been established by suitable analytical methods, the latter compound should have a coordination number of ten. A coordination number of ten in La(EDTAH)$(H_2O)_4$ has also been established from X-ray studies.[7] This is possible only with the help of a 5f orbital of more or less symmetric geometry.

ACKNOWLEDGEMENT

The grant of Junior Research Fellowship to one of us (S.K.S.) by the Council of Scientific and Industrial Research is gratefully acknowledged.

REFERENCES

1. A. Lempicki and H. Samelson, Phys. Letters. 4, 133 (1963).
2. G. A. Crosby, R. E. Whan and R. M. Alire, J. Chem. Phys., 34, 743 (1961).
3. G. S. Ofelt, J. Chem. Phys. 38, 2171 (1963).
4. L. G. De Shazer and G. H. Dieke, J. Chem. Phys. 38, 2190 (1963).
5. C. Brecher, H. Samelson and A. Lempicki, J. Chem. Phys. 42, 1090 (1965).
6. G. Blasse, A. Bril and W. C. Nieuwpoort, Int. Conf. on Luminescence, 1966 Budapest, p. 7, Vol. D9.
7. J. L. Hoard, J. Am. Chem. Soc. 87(6), 1611 (1965).

ENERGY TRANSFER AND ELECTRON TRANSFER IN SOME LANTHANIDE COMPLEXES

Marcos Kleinerman

Research Center
American Optical Corporation
Southbridge, Massachusetts

INTRODUCTION

It has been shown recently[1] that some organic dyes, including fluorescein, show the phenomenon of delayed fluorescence in a low temperature glass, caused by the photo-oxidation of the dye by radiation of higher energy than needed to excite the lower vibrational sublevels of the first excited singlet level S_1 of the dye, and subsequent recombination of the photo-ejected electron with the oxidized molecule-ion. Some such dyes can form complexes with rare earth ions. In this paper we show that these dyes can sensitize the fluorescence of some rare earth ions when excited with radiation of the same energy required to produce the above mentioned delayed fluorescence. This sensitized fluorescence may take place even when the emissive level of the rare earth is higher than the lowest triplet level T_1 and, at least in one case, the S_1

level of the dye. The energy donors studied in this work are fluorescein and the ligand 1,5 diphenyl 1,3,5 pentanetrione (DPT).

EXPERIMENTAL

Fluorescein was obtained from Distillation Products Industries, and was purified by repeated dissolution in dilute aqueous NaOH followed by precipitation with dilute HCl. Finally, it was recrystallized from absolute ethanol.

DPT, from Distillation Products Industries, was several times recrystallized from absolute ethanol. The rare earth acetates $MAc_3 \cdot XH_2O$ from American Potash and Chemical Corporation had a purity of 99.9 percent in metal ion content. The gadolinium, terbium and europium chelates of DPT were prepared by refluxing the rare earth acetate with an excess of DPT in ethanol for three hours. The insoluble chelate was filtered, washed with boiling ethanol and dried for two hours at $100^{o}C$. Chemical analysis indicated the composition $M(DPT)_2 \cdot Ac$.

Fluorescence excitation and emission spectra, and relative fluorescence efficiencies and lifetimes were obtained as described in another paper from our laboratory.[2]

It was observed that the solutions of EuDPT tended to photodecompose on prolonged standing. Therefore, all the fluorescence measurements in this work were performed on freshly prepared solutions.

RESULTS AND DISCUSSION

Paramagnetic rare earth ions other than Gd^{3+} quench the $S_1 \rightarrow S_o$ fluorescence of both fluorescein and EPT, as shown in Tables I and II. Such quenching is of general occurrence for fluorescent

TABLE I

$S_1 \rightarrow S_o$ fluorescence efficiencies ϕ of the lanthanide complexes of fluorescein, relative to the Lu^{3+} complex, in solutions containing 10^{-4} Molar fluorescein (as the disodium salt) and 10^{-2} Molar rare earth acetate in a 1:19 mixture of DMSO:Ethanol. The excess of rare earth ion was added to minimize the concentration of dissociated fluorescein. Temperature: 300°K ± 2°K.

Rare Earth	ϕ
Pr	0.085
Nd	0.018
Sm	0.18
Eu	0.065
Gd	1.0
Tb	0.30
Dy	0.37
Ho	0.06
Er	0.02
Tm	0.29
Yb	0.32
Lu	1.0

TABLE II

$S_1 \rightarrow S_o$ fluorescence efficiencies ϕ of the lanthanide complexes of DPT, relative to the Lu^{3+} complex, in solutions containing 10^{-3} Molar ligand and 10^{-2} Molar rare earth acetate in a 1:19 mixture of DMSO:Ethanol. The excess of rare earth ion was added to minimize the concentration of dissociated ligand.

Rare Earth	ϕ 300°K	ϕ 77°K
Pr	0.07	$<10^{-3}$
Nd	0.04	$\sim10^{-3}$
Sm	0.09	$\sim10^{-3}$
Eu	$<10^{-2}$	$<10^{-3}$
Gd	0.48	0.58
Tb	0.12	0.005
Dy	0.13	0.007
Ho	0.04	$<10^{-3}$
Er	0.03	$\sim10^{-3}$
Tm	0.18	0.007
Yb	0.21	0.08
Lu	1.0	1.0

ligands, as described in greater detail in reference 2, and shows direct energy transfer to a rare earth ion from the S_1 level of the ligand.

It was shown[2] that in rare earth chelates the rate of this energy transfer process is usually of the order of 10^{11} sec.$^{-1}$ or higher. Such value is approached in the DPT systems used in this work, if it is assumed that the radiative component of the fluorescent decay of DPT is of the order of 10^{-8} seconds or shorter.

Of special interest is the luminescent behavior of the complexes of fluorescein and DPT in low temperatures solutions. Figures 1 and 2 show the phenomena of delayed fluorescence from the Gd^{3+} complexes of these dyes. This behavior is similar to the one described by Lim and co-workers.

When Tb^{3+} is substituted for Gd^{3+} the delayed fluorescence is quenched, and instead the characteristic luminescence of Tb^{3+} appears. Like the delayed fluorescence of the Gd^{3+} complexes, this process occurs from energy levels of the ligand higher than the lower vibrational sublevels of the S_1 states, as shown in Figures 3 and 4.

An additional energy transfer mechanism occurs from DPT to Eu^{3+} whose emissive level, unlike the $^5D_4$ level of Tb^{3+}, lies lower than the T_1 level of DPT. To our knowledge this is the first demonstration of two different mechanisms of intramolecular fluorescence sensitization in lanthanide complexes by the same ligand species.

In order to discuss the phenomena described above the following additional information should be taken into consideration.

(1) The sensitized luminescence of Tb^{3+} by fluorescein is a monophotonic process, as is the sensitized luminescence of both Tb^{3+} and Eu^{3+} by DPT. The delayed fluorescence of both fluorescein and DPT, and that of their gadolinium complexes are also monophotonic.

(2) The quantum yield of sensitized Tb^{3+} fluorescence in the Tb^{3+}-fluorescein system is

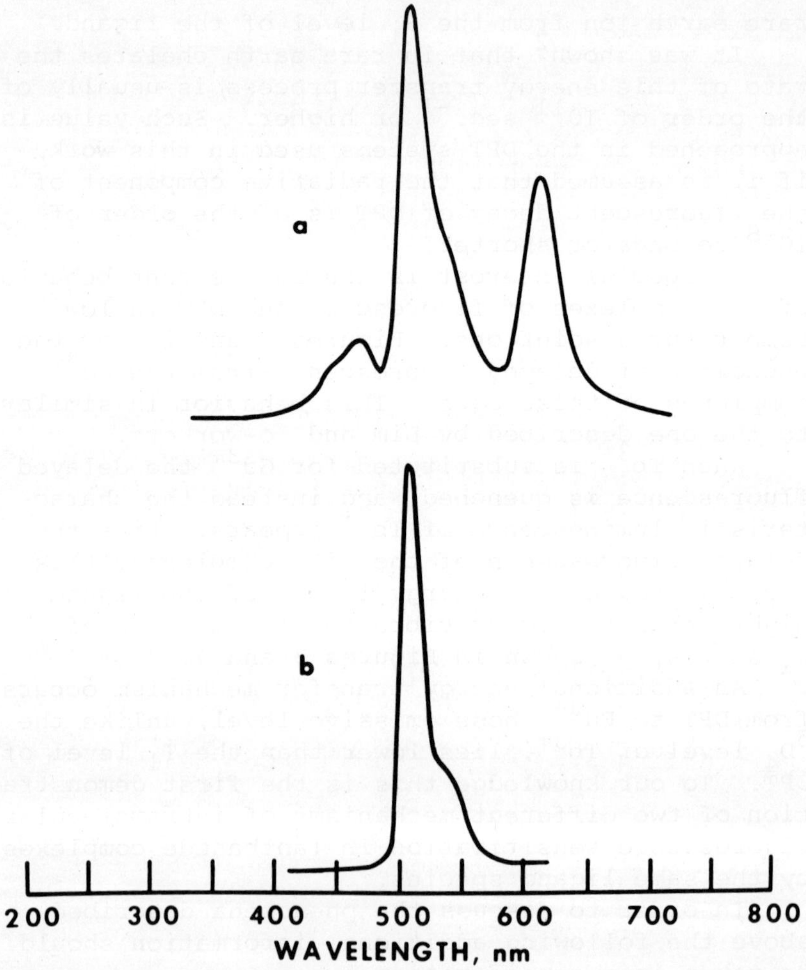

Figure 1 (a) Delayed fluorescence (peak at ∿512 nanometers) and phosphorescence (peak at ∿615 nanometers) in a solution containing 10^{-4} Molar Uranine (Fluorescein disodium salt) and 10^{-2} Molar Gadolinium acetate in 1:19 DMSO:ethanol mixture at $77^{\circ}K$. (b) Instantaneous $S_1 \rightarrow S_o$ fluorescence of the same solution.

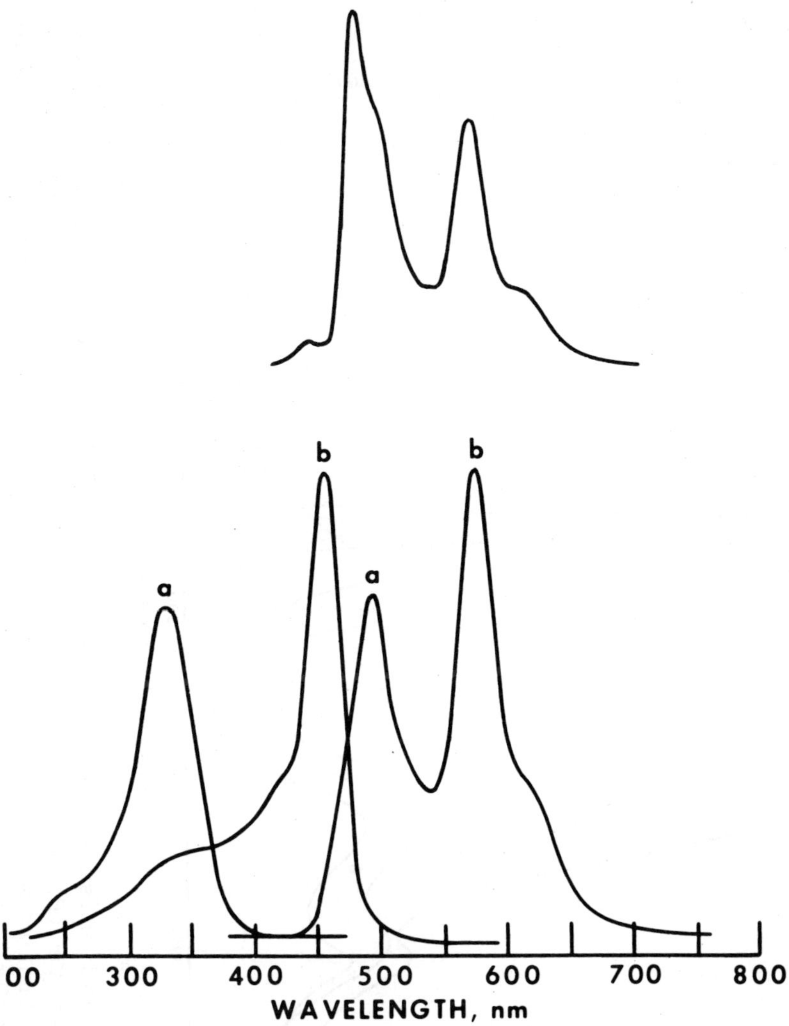

Figure 2 Upper Graph: Total emission (instantaneous fluorescence plus phosphorescence) in a 10^{-3} M solution of Gd DPT in a 1:19 DMSO:ethanol mixture at $77^{O}K$. Excitation wavelength: 370 nanometers.
Lower Graph: Excitation and emission spectra of the same solution; (a) delayed fluorescence, (b) phosphorescence.

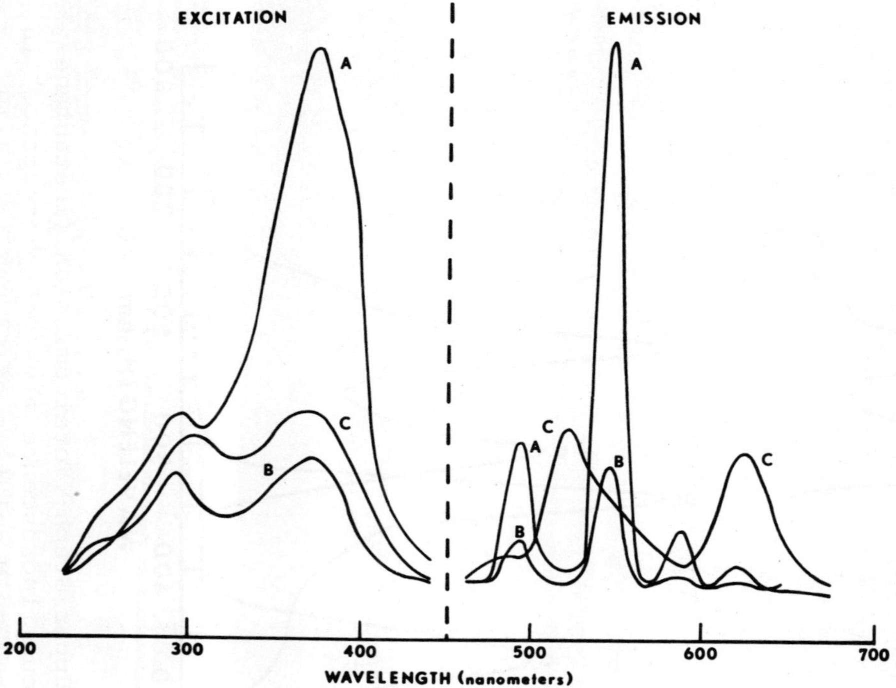

Figure 3 Excitation and emission spectra in; (A) 10^{-4} M Fluorescein, 10^{-3} M Terbium acetate; (B) 10^{-3} M Terbium acetate; (C) 10^{-4} M Fluorescein, 10^{-3} M Gadolinium acetate. Solvent: 1:19 DMSO:ethanol mixture. Temperature: 77°K. A rotating drum was used to cut out the instantaneous fluorescence from these solutions.

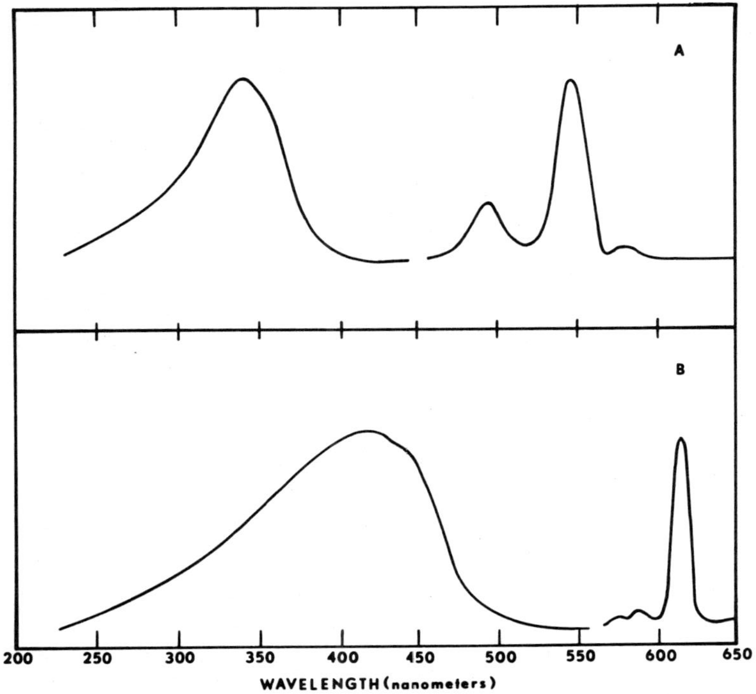

Figure 4 Excitation and emission spectra in; (A) 10^{-3} M TbDPT; (B) 10^{-3} M EuDPT. Solvent: 1:19 DMSO:ethanol mixture at 77°K. A rotating drum was used to cut out the instantaneous fluorescence from these solutions.

rather low, of the order of 10^{-2} or lower. This fact makes it difficult to study the chemical changes in the dye by spectroscopic techniques.

The quantum yield of sensitized Tb^{3+} fluorescence is higher ($\sim 10^{-1}$) in the TbDPT systems. Perhaps as a result of this fact the DPT systems show a greater tendency to undergo irreversible changes upon prolonged ultraviolet irradiation. We are at present studying the nature of such chemical changes.

(3) There is no measureable build-up time, down to 5×10^{-6} seconds, of the sensitized fluorescence of either Tb^{3+} or Eu^{3+} in both the fluorescein and the DPT systems.

(4) The fluorescence yield of Tb^{3+} in the TbDPT system increases as the ligand-to-Tb^{3+} ratio is decreased from its original value of 2.

(5) Substitution of toluene for the alcohol solvent in either the fluorescein or the DPT systems does not essentially change their behavior. The sensitization of the Tb^{3+} fluorescence in the TbDPT system takes place even in an acrylic matrix.

Both the monophotonic character and the spectral dependence of the fluorescence sensitization of Tb^{3+} in both dye systems are consistent with a mechanism involving an electron transfer from the dye to the lanthanide ion. There may appear to be a conflict between this interpretation and the fact that the rare earth emissive species is still the trivalent ion. In particular, the absence of a build-up time for the lanthanide fluorescence does not provide any evidence for the formation of a divalent metastable rare earth ion. However, we know of no reason why a reoxidation of the lanthanide ion to its more stable oxidation state of three could not take place in times shorter than 5×10^{-6} seconds.

An apparently more puzzling question is why should Tb^{3+} show sensitized fluorescence at all, even after energy transfer from the dye. One would expect efficient quenching by the energy levels of the dye which are lower than the $^5D_4$ Tb^{3+} level.[2] One way out of this puzzle lies in the hypothesis that at least during the fluorescence lifetime of Tb^{3+}, of the order of 10^{-3} seconds, the dye molecule is a different chemical species from the one prior to the electron transfer process. Consistent with this interpretation is the increase in the fluorescence yield of Tb^{3+} in the TbDPT system when the ligand-to-Tb^{3+} ratio in solution is decreased to unity or less. With a ratio of 2, after the electron transfer process there is still an unchanged ligand molecule capable of quenching the Tb^{3+} emission.[3] With a ratio of ≤ 1 we are effectively removing the quenching centers. This lends support to an electron transfer mechanism.

Although the phenomena described above have been observed in only a limited number of systems we should not rule out electron transfer as an important energy transfer mechanism in more familiar systems. In most of these, the phenomena described above would not occur after an electron transfer process if the ligand undergoes a very rapid rearrangement to its initial state, or to a different species having energy levels capable of drawing energy from the lanthanide ion emissive levels. Considering the wealth of information on electron transfer processes to rare earth ions in inorganic systems it is indeed strange that such processes have not been proposed for lanthanide complexes, especially in those systems having ligands which are strong electron donors.

CONCLUSION

Fluorescein and 1,5 diphenyl 1,3,5 pentanetrione can transfer excitation energy to lanthanide ions from their first excited singlet level S_1. In addition they can sensitize the fluorescence of Tb^{3+} in low temperature glasses when excited to levels higher than the lower vibrational sublevels of their S_1 states. The experimental results appear consistent with a mechanism involving electron transfer from the dye to the lanthanide ion.

ACKNOWLEDGEMENTS

The author has greatly benefited from discussions with Professor S. I. Choi. Competent experimental assistance was provided by Mrs. Donald Gauthier.

REFERENCES

1. E. C. Lim and G. W. Swenson, J. Chem. Phys., 36, 118 (1962); E. C. Lim and W. Y. Wen, J. Chem. Phys., 39, 847 (1963); E. C. Lim, C. P. Lazarra, M. Y. Yang and G. W. Swenson, J. Chem. Phys., 43, 970 (1965).
2. M. Kleinerman (to be published in J. Chem. Phys).
3. In the Tb-fluorescein systems no stable solutions can be obtained unless there is an excess of Tb^{3+}.

LUMINESCENCE OF PHTHALOCYANINES. I.

K. E. Rieckhoff and E. M. Voigt

Departments of Physics and Chemistry
Simon Fraser University
Burnaby 2, British Columbia, Canada

INTRODUCTION

Phthalocyanine and the metal-phthalocyanines are of interest on account of their structural similarity to the porphyrins and their usefulness as passive Q-switches in laser technology. Their fluorescence in solution in the region of 7,000 Å has been reported in a number of publications. Terenin et al.[1] determined the fluorescence lifetime of phthalocyanine (H_2Pc) and of the Mg and Zn substituted molecules (MgPc and ZnPc) to be of the order of 10^{-9} sec. In a more recent publication[2] the 7,000 Å fluorescence of H_2Pc at 77°K was shown to have additional weaker bands at 7350 Å and 7775 Å respectively. Copper phthalocyanine (CuPc) did not show fluorescence. These results were confirmed by more extensive vapor phase and solution studies of Eastwood et al. which included H_2Pc, MgPc, ZnPc and CuPc.[3] The phosphorescence of H_2Pc, MgPc, and ZnPc was searched for by Becker and Kasha[4] in EPA glass at 77°K using a photographic technique out to 9000 Å. They did not find any phosphorescence. Similarly, Eastwood, Edwards, Gouterman and Steinfeld did not find phosphorescence, even though their experimental arrangements were quite sensitive. However, they worked at high temperatures, in the vapor phase or at room temperature in solutions. Indirect evidence for the existence of a triplet state below the fluorescent state was obtained by Kosonocky, Harrison and Stander[5] who, in fact made a lifetime measurement of the triplet state of H_2Pc by observing the recovery of the ground state absorption after saturating this absorption with a Q-switched ruby laser pulse. They found the lifetime to be 10^{-6} sec and 1.5×10^{-4} sec at room temperature and 77^oK respectively. The reflection spectra and photoconductivity work of Day and William[6] on CoPc, NiPc, CuPc and ZnPc in the solid state also indicated the existence of an excited state near 10,000 Å. One may conclude from the past failure to observe phosphorescence and the measured short lifetime that radiationless transitions dominate the depopulation of the triplet state in these compounds, and if phosphorescence was to be found, a very sensitive technique would have to be used. We made a deliberate attempt at finding the phosphorescence of phthalocyanines using an intense He-Ne laser operating at 6328 Å to excite the lowest known singlet state although the excitation occurs at the short wavelength edge of the absorption band. Using the sensitive technique described in the next paragraph we succeeded in observing phosphorescence in a number of phthalocyanines in various solvents at 77^oK.

EXPERIMENTAL ARRANGEMENT (SEE FIG. 1)

Light from a Spectra-Physics Model 125 He-Ne Laser (∿80 mW output) was passed through a 6328 Å interference filter to remove residual light at other wavelengths originating in the

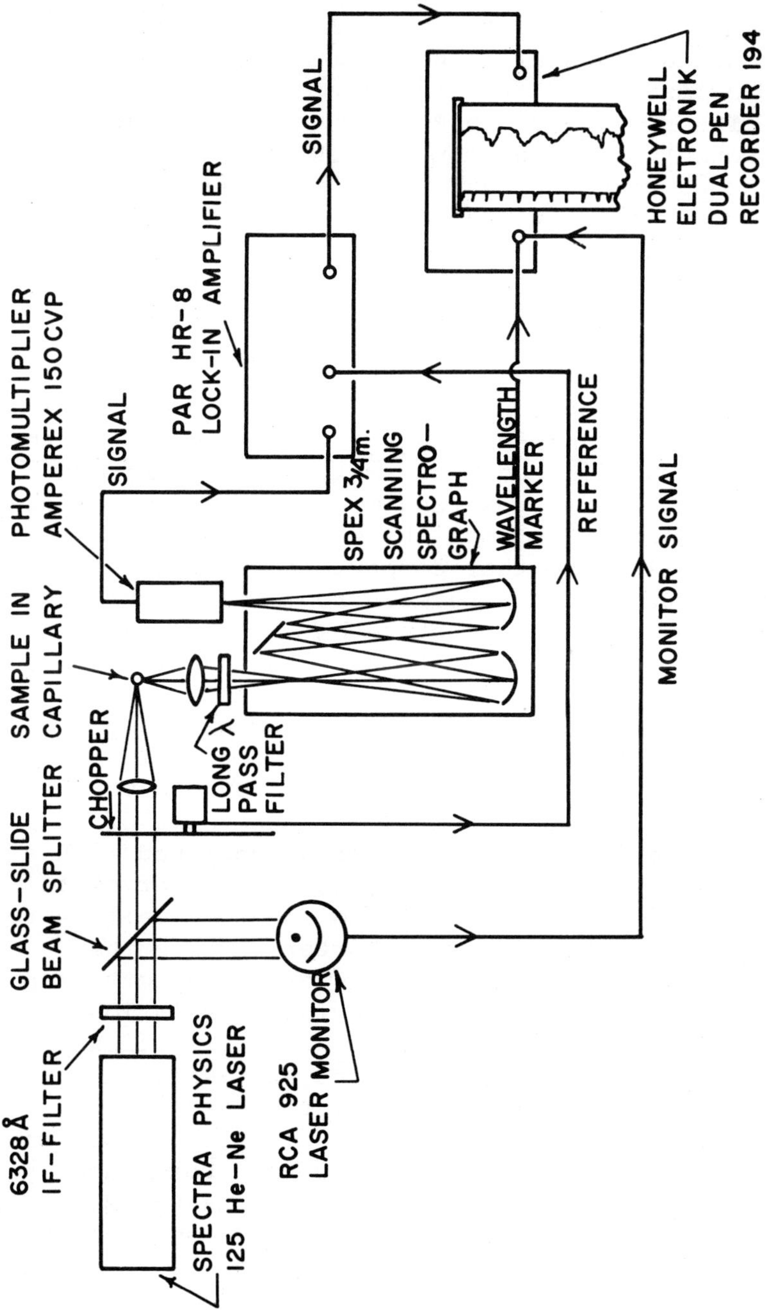

Figure 1 Experimental Arrangement

plasma tube of the laser. The light then passed through a glass slide beam splitter which removed approximately 8% from the beam for monitoring of the laser output. An RCA 925 photodiode (S-1 response) served as monitor and its output was recorded simultaneously with the observed spectra on one channel of a Honeywell Elektronik 194 dual-pen recorder. The major portion of the laser beam passed through the beam splitter and was chopped at 75 cycles per second and then focused with a cylindrical lens onto the sample.

The samples were contained in capillaries with O.D. of approximately 1 mm, oriented vertically and for measurements at 77°K located in the unsilvered tail-end of a small liquid nitrogen dewar. The latter arrangement resulted in considerable losses in both the exciting and the emitted light so that comparisons of the intensity of the luminescence between room temperature and liquid nitrogen temperature have to be made with great caution and are at best qualitative in nature.

The luminescence from the sample was focused at right angles to the exciting laser beam, with a lens of f = 15 cm through a Corning 2-64 glass filter onto the entrance slit of a 3/4 m Spex Scanning Spectrograph equipped with a grating blazed at 7500 Å. The filter served to reduce the scattered exciting light as well as to eliminate stray light at shorter wavelengths.

Entrance and exit slits of the spectrograph were set at 500 μ, resulting in a resolution of 5 Å according to manufacturers specifications.

The detector used at the exit slit was an Amperex 150 CVP photomultiplier cooled by dry nitrogen to approximately 100°K. The signal from the photomultiplier together with a reference signal from the chopper were fed to a PAR Model HR-8 Lock-In Amplifier whose output was recorded on the remaining channel of the dual-pen recorder.

Intensity measurements on the luminescence are relative and were corrected for the response of the 2-64 filter and the photomultiplier response, but not for the unknown response of the grating. Wavelength measurements are accurate within ± 5 Å, but for broad and noisy peaks their exact location may be in error by as much as ± 50 Å in the worst cases.

The phthalocyanine compounds used were obtained from K & K Laboratories and Eastman-Kodak (reagent grade). They were purified by sublimation. The solvents used were spectrograde, except for isopentane which was reagent grade. The samples were not deoxygenated.

RESULTS AND DISCUSSION

The only luminescence observed at room temperature in solution was fluorescence in the region 6,700-7,800 Å (Table 1). For most phthalocyanines this fluorescence is strong and well-defined. However, vanadyl (VOPc) and copper phthalocyanine (CuPc) show no or practically no fluorescence. We observe similar behavior at 77°K where the CoPc fluorescence was found to be extremely weak as well. The fluorescence spectra are solvent and temperature dependent and for phthalocyanine itself also strongly concentration dependent. This is probably due to dimer formation and a more detailed study of these fluorescence features will be published separately.

The low temperature luminescence spectra showed additional emissions in the region 8,000-9,500 Å. These bands were generally very broad and structureless and often much weaker than the fluorescences. We associate these emissions with the $S_0 \leftarrow T_1$ phosphorescence which had not been observed until now. The luminescences and their relative intensities have been summarized in Tables 2, 3 and 4.

TABLE 1: Luminescence Spectra of Phthalocyanines in Benzene at 293°K

Phthalocyanine	Fluorescence (Å)	Relative peak Intensities
Metal-Free	6685, 6975, 7325, 7770	1:30:5:4
Lithium	6665, 6975, 7310, 7772	2:44:4:3
Sodium	6655, 6965, 7310, 7760	1:40:4:3
Magnesium	6662, 6976, 7310, 7760	2:34:3:2
Aluminum (Chloro-)	6685, 6972, 7287, 7755	3:59:7:4
Vanadyl	----------------------	--------
Cobalt	6700, 6968, 7303, 7763	1:18:2:1
Copper	6960 (very weak)?	--------
Zinc	6777, 6968, 7290, 7745	18:38:2:1
Platinum	---- 6965, 7297, 7755	-:16:2:1

TABLE 2: Luminescence Spectra of Phthalocyanines in Benzene at 77°K

Phthalocyanine	Fluorescence (f) Position of first intense band(s), Å	Fluorescence (f) Intensity	Phosphorescence (p) Position of band(s), Å	Phosphorescence (p) Intensity	Relative Intensity f/p
Metal-Free	6960		8180, 9050	13:8	9:1
Lithium	6975		-		-
Sodium	6950		-		-
Magnesium	6945		-		-
Aluminum	6910		8000, 9350	1:3	3:4
Vanadium (II)	6933		9075 (?)	very weak	9:1
Vanadyl	-		9100	-	-
Cobalt	6868	very weak	-		-
Copper	-		-		-
Zinc	68 6923	1:1	-		-
Platinum	6942, 7040	1:2	-		-

TABLE 3: Luminescence Spectra of Phthalocyanines in Hydrocarbon Glass[a] at 77°K

Phthalo-cyanine	Fluorescence (f) Position of first intense band(s), Å	Fluorescence (f) Intensity	Phosphorescence (p) Position of band(s), Å	Phosphorescence (p) Intensity	Relative Intensity f/p
Metal-Free	7030		8180		2:3
Lithium	6842, 6933	1:6	-		-
Sodium	6930		-		-
Magnesium	6730, 6870	1:13	-		-
Aluminum	6845		9420		
Vanadium (II)	6925		-		-
Vanadyl	-		9138		-
Cobalt	6865	very weak	-		-
Copper	-		-		-
Zinc	6783		-		-
Platinum	6930, 7012	3:2			-

[a] Methylcyclohexane (4):isopentane (1).

TABLE 4: Luminescence Spectra of Phthalocyanines in Carbon Tetrachloride at 77°K

Phthalo-cyanine	Fluorescence (f)		Phosphorescence (p)		Relative Intensity f/p
	Position of first intense band(s), Å	Intensity	Position of band(s), Å	Intensity	
Metal-Free	6955		8115		60:1
Lithium	7005		(9225) ?	weak	10:1
Sodium	6933		-	-	-
Magnesium	6775, 6970	1:8	8568, 9150	weak (2:1)	30:1
Aluminum	6860, 6950	2:3	9390		3:1
Vanadium (II)	6950		9310		4:3
Vanadyl	-		9155		-
Cobalt	6840		-		-
Zinc	6745, 6930	9:5	-		-
Copper	-		9050 (?)	weak	-
Platinum	6957		-		-

It is apparent from the data that we deal generally with three classes of phthalocyanines

(1) Those which fluoresce but do not phosphoresce in any solvent reported: CoPc, ZnPc and PtPc.

(2) Those which phosphoresce but do not fluoresce in any solvent reported: VOPc and CuPc.

(3) All other phthalocyanines which show simultaneous fluorescence and phosphorescence of varying relative intensity depending upon the solvent used.

Phthalocyanine itself has a phosphorescence which in benzene solutions shows a maximum and a shoulder of similar intensities (Table 2). Since such double structure is apparent in a few instances for the metal phthalocyanines in benzene as well (but with opposite relative intensities of the two peaks), further studies are required to determine whether it is due to an external or internal perturbation of the molecules involved. It is to be noted that the phosphorescence maxima of the metal phthalocyanines are observed between 8,800 and 9,500 Å, while the principal phosphorescence of H_2Pc occurs at somewhat higher energy, i.e. 8,100-8,200 Å.

In order to discuss the division of the data into three classes, it must be remembered that we are dealing with extremely complex systems (a) in which the singlet/triplet conversions are highly dependent upon the spin-orbit coupling in most cases and (b) in which at least four <u>competing</u> decay processes occur simultaneously according to the relative lifetimes measured. The first excited singlet state, S_1, is depopulated by three competing mechanisms: fluorescence and radiationless transitions to the ground state and by internal conversion to the triplet manifold. The latter is depleted by radiationless transitions and phosphorescence to the ground state (Fig. 2). Generally, we expect fluorescence to be observed preferentially whenever k_{r_1} and k_i are

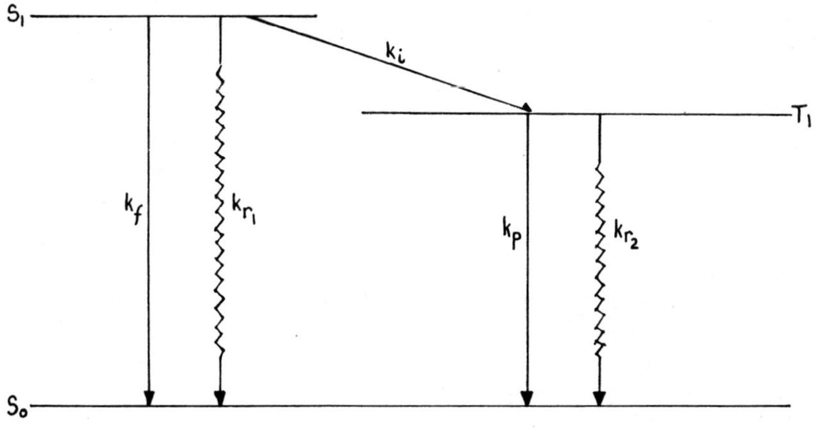

Figure 2 Decay rates involved in the depopulation of the first excited states of the phthalocyanines:
S_o, S_1 = ground and first excited singlet states
T_1 = lowest triplet state
k_f = rate of fluorescence
k_p = rate of phosphorescence
k_{r1}, k_{r2} = rates of radiationless transitions.

considerably smaller than k_f. Given a favorable k_{r1}, then, or a very high population of the S_1 level, as is true for direct laser excitation, k_i is small for diamagnetic transition metal phthalocyanines and for ionic metal phthalocyanines. This applies to the compounds in class (1) with exception of CoPc which has a very low extinction value at the laser excitation frequency in the solvents studied. We predict, therefore, that CoPc in a "suitable" solvent, i.e. one which shifts the absorption spectrum into the laser excitation region, will show either fluorescence or fluorescence and phosphorescence.* The argument above applies also to class (3) compounds such as Na_2Pc, Li_2Pc, MgPc, and to some degree to phthalocyanine itself.

Phosphorescence is expected to occur preferentially whenever $k_f, k_{r1} << k_i >> k_{r2}$. k_i is large for phthalocyanines containing paramagnetic transition metal ions with d-orbitals of suitable symmetries and energies to mix with the phthalocyanine levels. Generally, this holds for the substances in class (2) and for those of class (3) which were not discussed in the previous paragraph. It is, however, reasonable to assume k_i and k_f to be of comparable magnitude for a number of these phthalocyanines, so that simultaneous phosphorescence and fluorescence is expected, as long as k_{r2} is not fast, as was observed. Lifetime and polarization measurements are planned to clarify the energy transfer processes involved in these interesting cases.

Given the situation, then, that k_i is sufficiently large to populate T_1 adequately, it is still necessary that $k_{r2} < k_i$ so that phosphorescence can be observed. It has been found[7] that

*We have observed both fluorescence and phosphorescence of CoPc in propanol glass at 77°K.

the quantum yield and lifetime of phosphorescence decrease with increasing shift of the transition toward longer wavelengths. This suggests for the substances investigated here which have relatively low emission energies, that the smaller the $\lambda_{phosph.}$, the more competitive k_{r_2} and k_p become. Our data in the various solvents (Tables 2,3,4) bear this out when it is remembered that k_i is much less dependent on external factors such as solvent and temperature, than is k_{r_2}. This becomes apparent in the slight variations observed for the fluorescence to phosphorescence ratio of a given phthalocyanine from solvent to solvent.

In summary we can state that under the excitation and detection conditions usually employed for phthalocyanines most of the photon energy was lost in radiationless processes and the remaining radiation could not be detected. By increasing both, intensity of excitation and sensitivity of detection, we could observe radiative emission, with lifetimes not longer than milliseconds, from the lowest excited states of the phthalocyanines.

ACKNOWLEDGEMENTS

This work was supported by grants of the National Research Council of Canada to the authors.

REFERENCES

1. Terenin et al., Dokl. Akad. Nauk SSSR. 114, 751 (1957).
2. J. M. Assour, S. E. Harrison, J. Am. Chem. Soc. 87, 652 (1965).
3. D. Eastwood, L. Edwards, M. Gouterman and J. Steinfeld, J. Mol. Spectroscopy 20, 381 (1966).
4. R. S. Becker, M. Kasha, J. Am. Chem. Soc. 77, 3669 (1955).
5. W. F. Kosonocky, S. E. Harrison and R. Stander, J. Chem. Phys. 43, 831 (1965).
6. (a) P. Day and J. P. William, J. Chem. Phys. 37, 567 (1962).
   (b) P. Day, G. Scregg and R. J. P. William, ibid. 38, 2779 (1963).
7. W. H. Melhuish, J. Opt. Soc. Am. 54, 183 (1964).

LUMINESCENCE FROM RHODIUM (III) AND IRIDIUM (III) COMPLEXES[1]

G. A. Crosby and D. H. W. Carstens

Department of Chemistry
Washington State University
Pullman, Washington 99163

INTRODUCTION

The spectroscopic properties of transition-metal compounds, molecules having organic and inorganic ligands bonded to a central ion, have in recent years received much attention. The studies of such species are providing insight into the electronic structures and bonding characteristics of complexes. Originally most of the investigations were carried out with absorption techniques, but many of these complexes have been found to luminesce when excited by uv light providing additional experimental information on the electronic structures. Some examples include Cr(III),[2] Mo(III),[3] Ru(II),[4] and Os(II).[5]

Often minor differences in the structures or geometries of complexes lead to a reordering of the energies of the corresponding excited states present in the molecules resulting in major changes in the types of emissions observed. In general three types of luminescences are obtained from complexes: ligand emission arising from electronic excited states derived primarily from the ligand electronic system; d-d emission occurring from excited states essentially localized on the central-metal ion; and charge-transfer (CT) emission arising from excited states having mixed ion-ligand character.

In the present manuscript we present emission studies on $[Ir(phen)_3]^{3+}$, $[Rh(phen)_3]^{3+}$, and trans-$[Rh(phen)_2Cl_2]^+$. Each ion exhibits one of these general types of luminescence. Assignments are also given for the multiplicity of the emitting state for each molecule.

EXPERIMENTAL

The complexes were prepared using standard techniques. $[Rh(phen)_3](ClO_4)_3 \cdot H_2O$ was made following the procedure used by Harris and McKenzie[6] to prepare the analogous $[Rh(bipy)_3]^{3+}$ ion. Light tan microcrystals were obtained by recrystallization from water and drying in vacuo at 50°.

Analysis: Calculated for $[Rh(phen)_3](ClO_4)_3 \cdot H_2O$: C, 45.0; H, 2.73; N, 8.75. Found: C, 44.7; H, 3.71; N, 9.06.

$[Ir(phen)_3]I_3 \cdot 2H_2O$ was prepared according to Chiswell and Livingstone.[7] The canary yellow product was obtained by recrystallization from water following treatment with activated charcoal.

Analysis: Calculated for $[Ir(phen)_3]I_3 \cdot 2H_2O$: C, 37.6; H, 2.4; N, 7.3. Found: C, 36.7; H, 2.1; N, 7.1.

The pale yellow needles of trans-$[Rh(phen)_2Cl_2]Cl \cdot 2H_2O$ were obtained by the method of Gillard et al.[8]

Analysis: Calculated for $[Rh(phen)_2Cl_2]Cl \cdot 2H_2O$: C, 47.59; H, 3.32; N, 9.25. Found: C, 46.72; H, 3.54; N, 9.02.

The purity of $[Ir(phen)_3]I_3 \cdot 2H_2O$ and _trans_-$[Rh(phen)_2Cl_2]Cl \cdot 2H_2O$ was checked by thin-layer chromatographic techniques using aluminum oxide adsorbent and methanol as a solvent. In both cases only one component was seen on the chromatogram. Unfortunately this technique could not be used with $[Rh(phen)_3](ClO_4)_3 \cdot H_2O$ as no appropriate solvent and adsorbent system could be found.

Room-temperature absorption spectra of water solutions were measured in matched, quartz cells using a Cary Model 14 spectrophotometer. Because of the limited solubilities of the ionic complexes in organic solvents, all low-temperature studies were carried out on a water-methanol (1:4 by volume) glass. Emissions were recorded photographically using a Steinheil Universal spectrograph on Kodak 103a-F and I-N plates. Exciting light from a GE AH-6 1000-watt lamp was passed through a filter train consisting of 5 cm of $CuSO_4$ solution (100 g/liter) and a 5840 Corning filter. This limited the exciting radiation to a band centered around 3600 A. Whenever a molecular emission occurred below 7000 A, the spectrum was also recorded on a Hitachi Model MPF-2A recording spectrophotofluorimeter.

Lifetimes shorter than 5 msec were measured using a xenon-flash apparatus having a 0.5 μsec resolution time. Mean lives longer than 5 msec were measured on the Hitachi apparatus.

ELECTRONIC STATES OF COMPLEXES

In the type of transition-metal complex studied here ligand ($\pi-\pi^*$), ligand-field (d-d), and charge-transfer (CT) electronic states are predicted. The relative energies of these states vary and are dependent upon several factors dictated by the nature of the ion, the types of ligands bonded, and the geometry of the molecule. It is possible to predict the relative ordering of these states through approximate calculations, comparisons between similar compounds, or chemical intuition.

Ligand states arising from promotions of electrons within the π-orbitals of the ligands vary in energy only slightly from those of the free ligand because of the relatively small perturbation caused by the presence of the central ion. Transitions among these states lead to intense absorption bands in the ultraviolet region of the spectrum which often resemble closely the absorption bands of the uncoordinated ligands. Luminescence arising from these states in complexes would be expected to resemble closely luminescence from the corresponding free ligand.

The number and energies of the d-d states depend upon the symmetry of the complex and the coordinating strength of the ligands. Although it is certainly not correct, it is usually assumed that the symmetry of a complex can be approximated by considering only the ligand atoms bonded directly to the central ion,[9] in these cases the N atoms. Tris complexes of 1,10-phenanthroline and 2,2-bipyridine will therefore be considered to possess octahedral (O_h) symmetry and <u>trans</u> complexes, to possess tetragonal (D_{4h}) symmetry. To calculate the positions of the states the octahedral crystal-field perturbation is first applied to the free ion d orbitals causing them to split into two sets, a lower triply degenerate t_{2g} set and a higher doubly degenerate e_g pair. Since both Rh(III) and Ir(III) are normally low-spin ions, the ground states of the complexes studied have $(t_{2g})^6$ configurations. Promotion of an electron leads to an excited configuration $(t_{2g})^5(e_g)^1$ which lies at an energy of 10 Dq or Δ above the ground configuration. Application of the electrostatic perturbation (e^2/r) gives the ground state, $^1A_{1g}$, and four excited states, $^3T_{1g}$, $^3T_{2g}$, $^1T_{1g}$, and $^1T_{2g}$.[9] In the tetragonal complexes the ligand perturbation causes further splittings as indicated in Fig. (1).[10]

In octahedral complexes the energies of the d-d states are determined by the value of 10 Dq and two electronic repulsion parameters, B and C. Since 10 Dq for these strong-field complexes is larger than the other terms, the positions of the states are roughly proportional to this value. Furthermore, on going from the second to the third transition series, 10 Dq increases by a factor of about 1.2. Thus bands attributed to d-d transitions in an Ir(III) complex are expected to be blue shifted with respect to the corresponding bands in the analogous Rh(III) molecules.

In the trans complexes where the tetragonal perturbation is large and 10 Dq is not too high, d-d states may lie at significantly lower energies than the parent octahedral levels (see Fig. 1). In this case two other parameters, D_s and D_t, must be introduced to account for the additional splitting of the states.

Unfortunately the prediction of the energies of CT states is more difficult. It is possible to estimate their energies by a consideration of the chemical stability of the ligands and the central ions toward oxidation and reduction. Generally the CT states for complexes of Rh(III) would be expected to lie at far greater energies than CT states for the corresponding Ir(III) complexes because of the ease with which Ir(III) can be oxidized to Ir(IV).[11]

OPTICAL TRANSITIONS IN COMPLEXES

In organic spectroscopy the rule that a molecule emits from the lowest state of a given multiplicity is rarely violated.[12] Although the applicability of this generalization to transition-metal complexes has not been tested widely, in all compounds studied thus far in our laboratory the rule appears to hold.

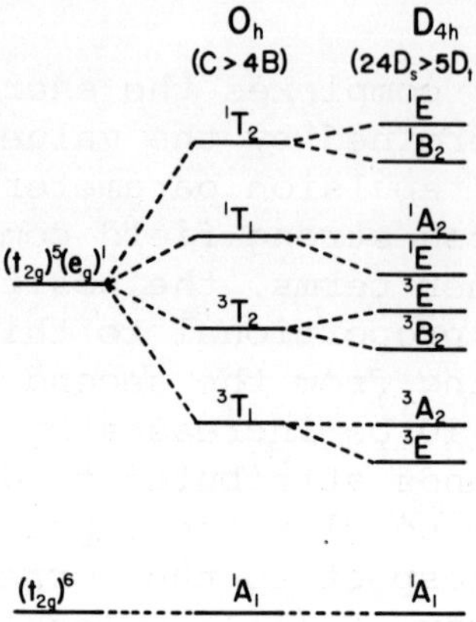

Figure 1 Excited (d-d) states for d^6 ion in octahedral (O_h) and tetragonal (D_{4h}) fields. In the first case the splittings are dependent upon two repulsion parameters, B and C. On lowering the symmetry two additional terms, D_s and D_t, are present. The ordering of the states is contingent upon the relative values of these parameters (schematic only).

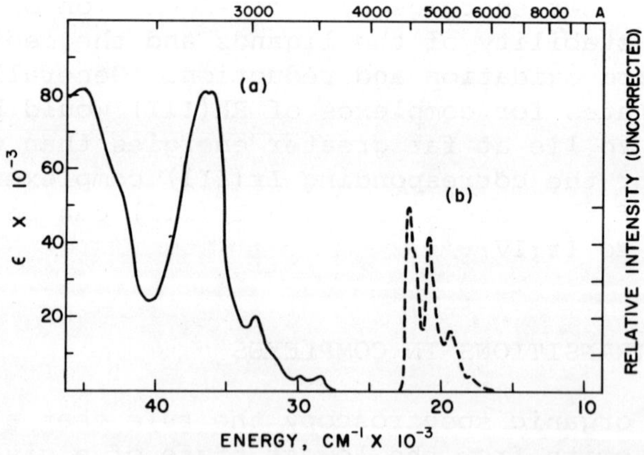

Figure 2 (a) Room-temperature aqueous absorption spectrum of $[Rh(phen)_3](ClO_4)_3 \cdot H_2O$ (9.83 x 10^{-6} M in 1 cm cell); (b) Low-temperature emission spectrum (∿5 x 10^{-5} M in H_2O-MeOH, 1:4 by volume) measured on Hitachi MPF-2A.

In principle both spin-allowed (fluorescence) and spin-forbidden (phosphorescence) emissions can occur, but in all the molecules we have studied only the latter has been seen. The lifetime of a phosphorescence is considerably shortened from that usually observed in hydrocarbons probably owing to the increased spin-orbit coupling effected by the heavy-metal ion.

Each type of luminescence observed from a transition-metal complex has distinguishing characteristics. Ligand-localized phosphorescence from a complex has about the same vibrational structure and energy as the free-ligand phosphorescence; the lifetime is shortened somewhat from the free-ligand value. Emission arising from d-d transitions generally has little or no structure.[13] CT phosphorescence has a short lifetime, but since the transition occurs between states having some ligand character, prominent vibrational structure is usually seen.[4]

RESULTS AND ASSIGNMENTS

$[Rh(phen)_3]^{3+}$. The absorption and emission spectra for this ion are shown in Fig. 2. Since all the absorption bands have intensities greater than those usually found for Laporte-forbidden d-d bands and since no CT transitions are expected in the near uv, all bands can be assigned to ligand-localized transitions. This assignment for the four bands beginning at 28,400 cm^{-1} and spaced $\sim$1500 cm^{-1} apart might be questioned, but comparison with other Rh(III) complexes justifies the identification. If these transitions involved either CT or d-d states, one would expect similar bands in the corresponding $[Rh(bipy)_3]^{3+}$ ion, because of the similar chemical properties and crystal-field strengths of these two closely related ligands. In fact, the bands in question are absent in the bipyridine complex. Furthermore, a similar progression of four bands is seen in the absorption spectra for the trans-$[Rh(phen)_2X_2]^+$ series.

The similarity between emission from the $[Rh(phen)_3]^{3+}$ ion and the free 1,10-phenanthroline phosphorescence is striking. Both bands have essentially the same structure and vibrational progressions. The luminescence for the complex is only slightly shifted, the first peak occurring at 22,300 cm^{-1} vs. 22,200 cm^{-1} for the free ligand. The lifetime of the complex emission is shortened to 48.0 ±1.1 msec compared to 1.55 sec for 1,10-phenanthroline but is obviously characteristic of a spin-forbidden process. The emission definitely arises from a ligand-localized triplet state, which for this complex is the lowest electronic excited state.

$[Ir(phen)_3]^{3+}$. The results for this complex are shown in Fig. (3). Again most of the bands appearing in the uv absorption spectrum are primarily ligand-localized transitions, although there is distinct evidence that CT bands are overlapping the lower π-π^* transitions. The region between 28,500 and 35,000 cm^{-1} shows the same general features as observed for the rhodium complex, but the structure is significantly blurred. An additional feature in the spectrum is the appearance of two bands at 27,800 and 26,300 cm^{-1} that are believed to be CT singlet-singlet transitions and two nuances at lower energies [(3), (4) in Fig. (3)] that cannot be ligand-localized bands and are too low for ligand-field transitions $[^1A_1 \rightarrow {}^3(CT)?]$.

The emission observed from $[Ir(phen)_3]^{3+}$ is strong, has a well-defined vibrational structure beginning at 21,600 cm^{-1}, and possesses a short mean life (~12 μsec). The single vibrational progression of 1400 cm^{-1} resembles closely the main progression observed in the emission spectrum of the $[Rh(phen)_3]^{3+}$ ion and is remarkably similar to the emission spectra measured for tris(1,10-

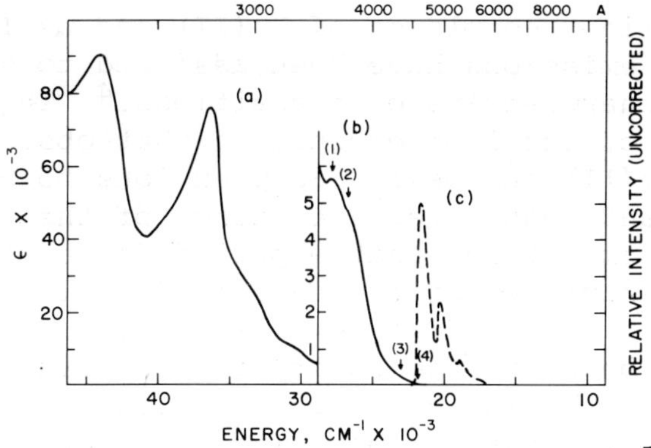

Figure 3 Aqueous absorption spectra for $[Ir(phen)_3]I_3 \cdot 2H_2O$. (a) 7.93×10^{-5} M in 0.1 cm cells. (b) 4.94×10^{-4} M in 0.1 cm cells. Four shoulders are seen in the near uv absorption spectrum with approximate maxima and extrapolated molar extinction coefficients (in parentheses) as follows: (1) 27,800 (1400); (2) 26,300 (1800); (3) 23,000 (30); (4) 21,900 (10). (c) Low-temperature emission spectrum measured photoelectrically on Hitachi MPF-2A ($\sim 9 \times 10^{-6}$ M in H_2O-MeOH).

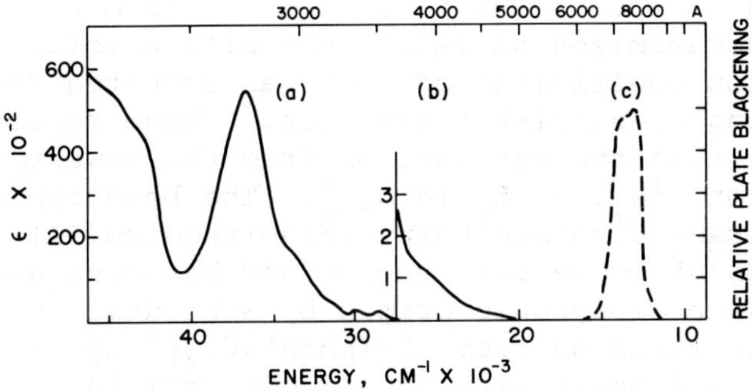

Figure 4 Aqueous absorption spectra of trans-$[Rh(phen)_2Cl_2]Cl \cdot 2H_2O$. (a) 1.04×10^{-5} M in 1 cm cell. (b) 2.59×10^{-4} M in 10 cm cell. (c) Low-temperature emission spectrum measured photographically on I-N plates ($\sim 9 \times 10^{-5}$ M in H_2O-MeOH, 1:4 by volume).

phenanthroline) complexes of Ru(II) and Os(II). The latter emissions have been assigned to spin-forbidden charge-transfer transitions.[4] The similarity of the luminescence to that observed from the Ru(II) and Os(II) complex ions both in structure and mean life, the energy of the transition (∿700 cm^{-1} below that expected for a ligand-localized triplet-singlet transition analogous to that seen in the Rh(III) complex), and the proximity of CT bands in the absorption spectrum lead us to assign the luminescence to a triplet-singlet charge-transfer transition. The emission appears even at room temperature in fluid solution as has been noted by Wunschel and Ohnesorge.[14]

trans-$[Rh(phen)_2Cl_2]^+$. The absorption spectrum for this complex, shown in Fig. 4, again displays the usual ligand bands. Another band is seen, however, which appears only as a broadening of the tail of the first ligand band and lends a slight yellow color to the solid complex. This band appears in all three complexes of the series trans-$[Rh(phen)_2X_2]^+$, progressively red shifting on going from Cl to Br to I. In the iodo complex the band maximizes at 24,000 cm^{-1} with a molar extinction coefficient of ∿1000 as expected for a d-d singlet-singlet transition. These results indicate that the band arises from the lowest d-d transition $[^1A_{1g} \rightarrow {}^1E_g$ in $D_{4h}]$. The band appears in the trans-dihalotetra(pyridine)rhodium(III) complexes at comparable energy and has been assigned to the same electronic origin by Schmidtke.[15]

The emission from $[Rh(phen)_2Cl_2]^+$ appears as a broad band maximizing at ∿13,000 cm^{-1} in the near IR region. This maximum is difficult to determine precisely owing to variations of plate sensitivity which also account for the apparent structure. The emission has a lifetime of 20.2 ± 1.2 μsec. We assign it to a forbidden $[^3E_g \rightarrow {}^1A_{1g}]$ spin-orbit perturbed phosphorescence. The low energy of the $^{3}E_{g}$ state in comparison with the energy of the parent state in $[Rh(phen)_3]^{3+}$ ($^{3}T_{1g}$ in O_h) shows a large tetragonal distortion.

OTHER COMPLEXES. Because of the similarities in electronic structures and crystal-field strengths of the two organic ligands, the spectra of complexes with 2,2'-bipyridine are analogous to the 1,10-phenanthroline spectra reported here. The major variations occur in the uv ligand absorption bands. $[Rh(bipy)_3]^{3+}$ exhibits ligand-localized phosphorescence. The series $[Rh(bipy)_2X_2]^{+}$ (X = Cl, Br, I) manifests the same spectrscopic behavior as the $[Rh(phen)_2X_2]^{+}$ series, and $[Ir(bipy)_3]^{3+}$ displays a charge-transfer luminescence.

DISCUSSION

In all the complexes of Rh(III) and Ir(III) that we have investigated a unique luminescence is observed. This is in contrast to the general behavior of organic molecules for which both fluorescence and phosphorescence often occur. The results are similar, however, to those for Ru(II) and Os(II) $(d)^6$ complexes.

In each complex the energy of the luminescence and the lifetime support the assignment of a spin-orbit perturbed, spin-forbidden transition. In every case the emission appears to arise from the lowest excited triplet state of the complex irrespective of whether the orbital type is d-d, π-π^*, or CT. These results demonstrate that, for complexes of Rh(III) and Ir(III), intersystem crossing between the singlet and triplet manifolds is enhanced to the point that the molecules rapidly and completely cross from the singlet system to the lowest triplet state, from which they combine radiatively with the ground state exhibiting phosphorescence.

REFERENCES

1. Research sponsored by AFOSR(SRC)-OAR, USAF, Grant No. AFOSR-68-1342.
2. H. L. Schläfer, H. Gausmann, and H. Witzke, J. Chem. Phys. 46, 1423 (1967).
3. H. L. Schläfer, H. Gausmann, and H. Witzke, J. Mol. Spectry. 21, 125 (1966).
4. D. M. Klassen and G. A. Crosby, J. Chem. Phys. 48, 1853 (1968).
5. G. A. Crosby, D. M. Klassen, and S. L. Sabath, Mol. Crystals 1, 453 (1966).
6. C. M. Harris and E. D. McKenzie, J. Inorg. Nucl. Chem. 25, 171 (1963).
7. B. Chiswell and S. E. Livingstone, J. Inorg. Nucl. Chem. 26, 47 (1964).
8. R. D. Gillard, J. A. Osborn, and G. Wilkinson, J. Chem. Soc. 1965, 1951.
9. G. A. Crosby, W. G. Perkins, and D. M. Klassen, J. Chem. Phys. 43, 1498 (1965).
10. R. A. D. Wentworth and T. S. Piper, Inorg. Chem. 4, 709 (1965).
11. B. Martin and M. Waind, J. Chem. Soc. 1958, 4284.
12. M. Kasha, Radiation Res. Suppl. 2, 243 (1960).
13. M. Mingardi and G. B. Porter, J. Chem. Phys. 44, 4354 (1966).
14. R. Wunschel, Jr. and W. E. Ohnesorge, J. Amer. Chem. Soc. 89, 2777 (1967).
15. H. H. Schmidtke, Z. Physik. Chem. (Frankfurt) 34, 295 (1962).

OPTICAL DETECTION OF MAGNETIC RESONANCE IN RANDOMLY ORIENTED TRIPLET STATE MOLECULES*

Arthur Forman and Alvin L. Kwiram**

Department of Chemistry
Harvard University
Cambridge, Massachusetts 02138

The magnetic resonance of the lowest excited triplet state of organic molecules has been detected optically.[1,2,3] The three Zeeman components of the triplet state can have different radiation properties, both with respect to polarization and intensity, so that changing their relative populations changes the optical emission[4] characteristics of the system.

The general experimental considerations are quite straightforward.[2] The sample under study is irradiated in a microwave cavity with ultraviolet light. The experiments are conducted in the liquid helium temperature range in order to get long spin

* Supported in part by a grant from the National Science Foundation, GP-7428, and in part by the Advanced Research Projects Agency.

** Alfred P. Sloan Fellow.

lattice relaxation times and large population differences. The population change is effected by partially saturating an ESR transition between two of the Zeeman levels. The resulting change in the phosphorescence is monitored with a photomultiplier tube whose output is fed to a signal averager which scans synchronously with the magnetic field-sweep through the resonance condition. Appropriate filters can be used to restrict the observation to a single vibrational band. In this way the optical detection of magnetic resonance (ODMR) is effected. It is a simple matter to determine whether the peaks correspond to an increase or decrease of emission.

Our first experiments[2] were done on single crystals of durene and biphenyl doped with naphthalene, quinoxaline, or phenanthrene. The orbital symmetry of the lowest triplet state of naphthalene[5,6] and quinoxaline[7] are B_{2u} and B_2 respectively and that of phenanthrene[8] is B_2 (See footnote 9). The phosphorescence is polarized predominantly perpendicular to molecular plane.[10,11] The spin Hamiltonian parameters for these triplets are known.[5,7,12,13] Making use of the above data one would predict that at zero field emission is mainly from the top Zeeman level of naphthalene and quinoxaline and from the middle level of phenanthrene. In the presence of a magnetic field these zero field states are mixed, and the optical properties of the resulting states can be predicted since their composition is an easily determined linear combination of the zero field states, t_x, t_y, and t_z. In Figure 1 the axis system used for the molecules under discussion are shown. Figure 2 depicts schematically the energy levels, versus magnetic field, for naphthalene and quinoxaline. From Figure 2 it can be seen that for $H||z$, pumping the low $\Delta m = 1$ transition should produce an increase in emission whereas pumping the high field transition should produce a decrease if t_z is the principal emitter. For this orientation the strongly

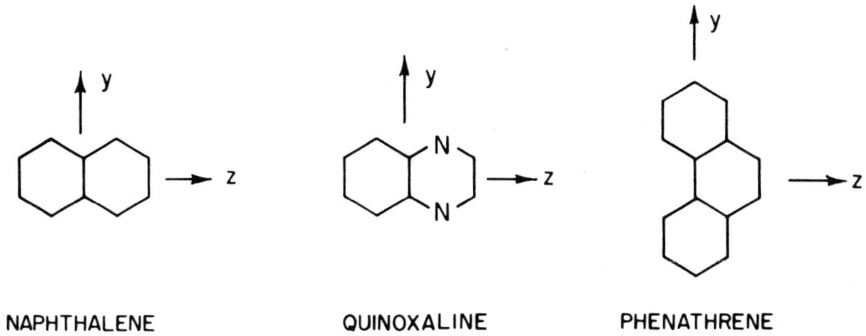

Figure 1 The choice of axes used in this discussion. In each case the x axis is perpendicular to the molecular plane.

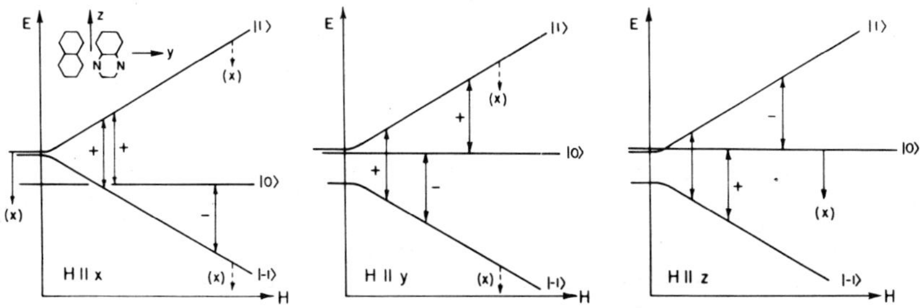

Figure 2 The energies of the Zeeman levels of naphthalene and quinoxaline triplet states as a function of magnetic field. The zero-field states are listed at the left and the usual high field states at the right. The ESR transitions are indicated with the appropriate sign of the ODMR signal. The polarization of the emission, x, from the Zeeman levels is indicated in parentheses.

emitting level is not involved at all in the $\Delta m = 2$ transition (which is a forbidden ESR transition if the magnetic field, H, is parallel to one of the principal axes of the fine-structure tensor, and the microwave field is perpendicular to this direction). For the cases $H||x$ or $H||y$ inducing the $\Delta m = 1$ transitions gives rise to various changes in emission as shown in the Figure. However, inducing the $\Delta m = 2$ transition produces an increase in emission for both cases. These results have been consistently confirmed in extensive ODMR studies on single crystal and the data imply that t_z is the principal emitter.

In a sample of randomly oriented triplet state molecules the $\Delta m = 1$ transitions are spread over a wide range of magnetic fields and are correspondingly weak. On the other hand, the $\Delta m = 2$ transitions occur over less than a 200 gauss range (at X band for these parameters). Furthermore, for the majority of the randomly oriented molecules the resonance condition occurs within a few gauss of the minimum resonance field possible. The result is a narrow and intense $\Delta m = 2$ ESR signal. Although the differences in the emission properties of the two states connected in a $\Delta m = 2$ transition are not as large as for the most favorable cases in $\Delta m = 1$ transitions, the ESR signal is very much stronger; this makes the $\Delta m = 2$ transition a better candidate for ODMR in a glass.

The phosphorescence of naphthalene and quinoxaline in EPA glasses is polarized perpendicular to the molecular plane, indicating that these molecules emit from t_z, the top zero-field state. This state cannot decrease in energy when a magnetic field is applied, so that for any arbitrary direction of the magnetic field relative to the molecular axes, the magnitude of the coefficient of t_z in the uppermost state can never be less than in the lowest one. Since the $\Delta m = 2$ transition connects the top and bottom levels, the ODMR should never give rise to a decrease in emission if

t_z is the only emitter. The optical signals corresponding to the $\Delta m = 2$ transition were easily detected at the position of the $\Delta m = 2$ ESR transition. Figure 3 shows such a signal for naphthalene d-8 in EPA. The signal corresponds to an increase in emission due to microwave pumping.[4]

On the contrary a system which emits from the bottom zero-field level would give a negative ODMR signal (for the $\Delta m = 2$ transition) in a sample of randomly oriented molecules. In general, if the lowest zero-field state of an alternant hydrocarbon is t_x, where x is perpendicular to the molecular plane, and the phosphorescence of the π^*-π transition is polarized parallel to x (as it is in all known cases with the possible exception of guests in a durene host), then t_x <u>cannot</u> be the emitter. This follows from the fact that the lowest triplet is formed by promoting an electron from the highest filled π to the lowest unoccupied π^* orbital, which is identical except for the reversal in sign of the coefficients of the atomic $p\pi$ orbitals on the "unstarred" atoms. (Cases where degeneracy occurs are excluded.)

The third and last case to be considered is that of emission from the middle Zeeman level. In this case the sign of the ODMR $\Delta m = 2$ signal does depend on the orientation of the molecule in the magnetic field as can be seen by studying Figure 4. In a randomly oriented sample this would lead to a certain amount of cancellation of the ODMR signals which would therefore be considerably weaker. However the regions of + and - ODMR signals tend to be separated, giving two peaks of opposite sign for the randomly oriented sample. This phenomenon can only occur if the molecules are emitting from the middle zero-field level.

This case is nicely illustrated by phenanthrene. The relevant energy level diagrams for this molecule are shown in Figure 4. The polarization, ESR, and ODMR data are consistent with t_z, the middle zero-field level, being the principal

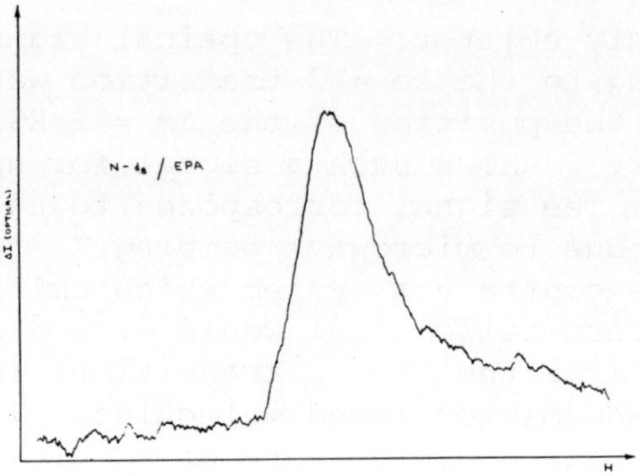

Figure 3 The ODMR signal for the $\Delta m = 2$ transition of naphthalene-d_8 in EPA. The figure shows the change in emission as a function of magnetic field.

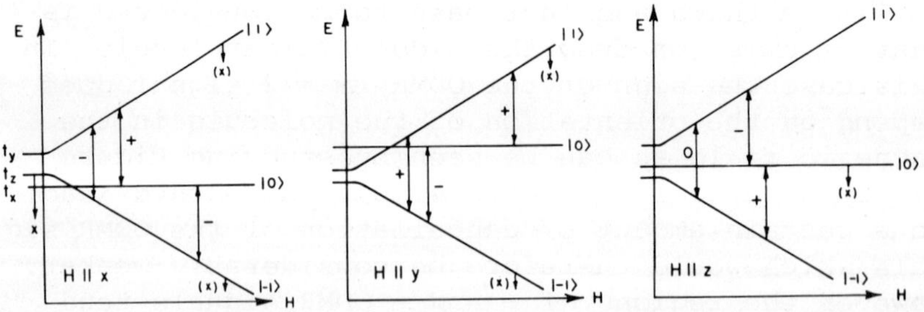

Figure 4 The energies of the Zeeman levels of the phenanthrene triplet state as a function of magnetic field. The zero-field states are listed at the left and the polarization of emission, x, from the Zeeman levels is indicated. The ESR transitions and the signs of the ODMR signals are shown.

emitter. The effect this has on the $\Delta m = 2$ ODMR signals is shown in the ODMR spectrum ($\Delta m = 2$ transitions) for a single crystal of phenanthrene in biphenyl, in which there are 2 magnetically inequivalent sites per unit cell for this particular orientation. (See Figure 5). The magnetic field is parallel to the x axis for one site and makes an angle of about 30° with the z-axis for the other site. Two $\Delta m = 2$ ODMR peaks of opposite sign are obtained. The ODMR results ($\Delta m = 2$) for phenanthrene dissolved in EPA are shown in Figure 6. Two weak ODMR peaks appear; a negative one coincident with the position of the maximum $\Delta m = 2$ ESR signal, and a positive one about 140 gauss to high field. From the positions of these two peaks an estimate of the zero field splittings can be made. In addition the fact that the low field peak corresponds to a decrease in emission means that the smallest zero-field splitting is between the lowest two states; (See Figure 4) i.e. the ordering of the levels is thus determined.

Calculations were made to simulate the spectrum. A uniform distribution of molecular orientations in the field was chosen and for each of these the lowest resonance field was calculated by the method of Kottis and Lefebvre,[14] using the known spin Hamiltonian values for phenanthrene. The eigenstates were calculated and from these the ODMR signal strength was determined for each orientation. This was taken to be proportional to the ESR transition probability and to the difference in the absolute value of the squares of the coefficients of t_z (the emitting level) in the upper and lower states. In other words, it was assumed that the population change is proportional to the ESR transition probability and that t_z was the only emitting level. (As the radiationless transition rates from the different spin components are not known, these were not taken into account. These factors could affect the relative intensities of the 2 peaks.) A histogram was constructed with

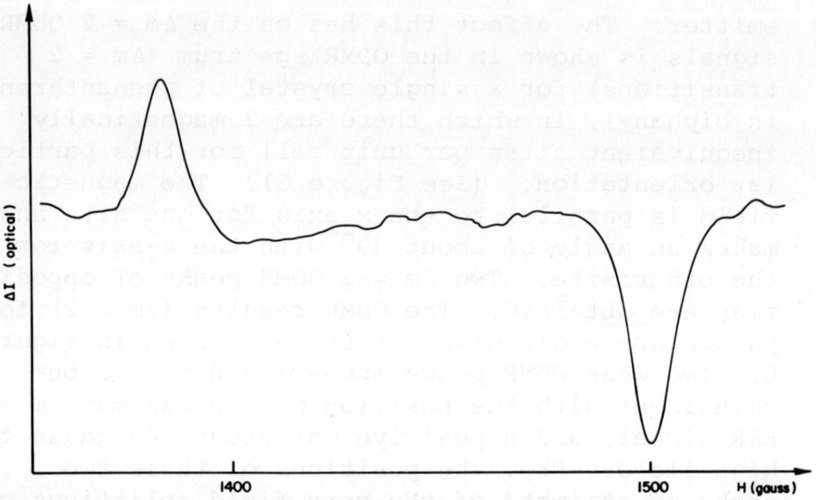

Figure 5 The ODMR signals from the $\Delta m = 2$ transitions of the two magnetically inequivalent triplet state sites of phenanthrene-d_{10} in a single crystal of biphenyl. The magnetic field is parallel to the x axis for one site and makes an angle of about 30° with the z axis of the other site.

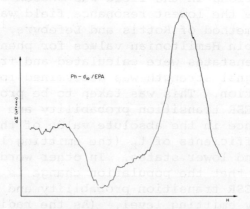

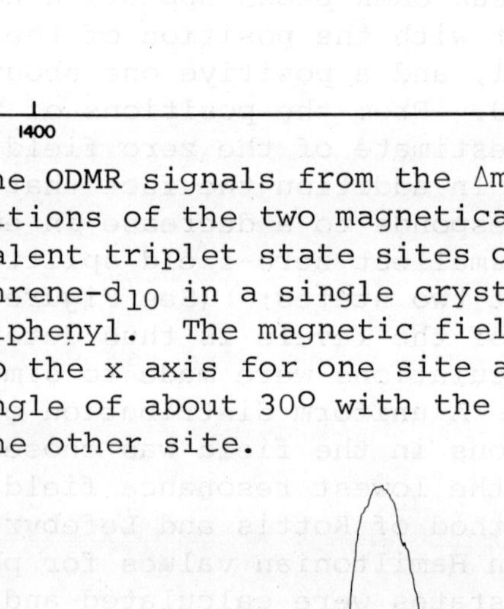

Figure 6 The ODMR signals for the $\Delta m = 2$ transition of phenanthrene-d_{10} in EPA. The figure shows the change in emission as a function of magnetic field.

the optical signal intensities placed in "boxes" 2 gauss wide. The polarizations of the incoming radiation and the singlet-singlet transition were taken into account. The histogram shows the existence of 2 peaks, with a negative ODMR signal at the minimum resonance field and a positive signal 160 gauss up field. The agreement with the experimental results is quite good.

In the above discussion we were able to show that the ODMR spectra from $\Delta m = 2$ transitions in glasses are consistent with the known ESR and optical polarization data. However, it should be possible in principle to deduce the spin Hamiltonian parameters independently of ESR data by using simply the polarization and ODMR data for $\Delta m = 2$ transitions in randomly oriented samples. One can estimate the zero-field splittings from the separation of the ODMR peaks. The fact that the low field peak is a negative ODMR signal means that the smallest splitting separates the lowest two levels. The problem is to assign the labels t_x, t_y, and t_z to the proper zero-field states (where the state t_x is unaltered in energy by a magnetic field along the x axis, etc.). Above we showed that the emitting level is the middle one which must be t_z for the radiation from the $^3B_2$ to be polarized perpendicular to the molecular plane.

The remaining assignment can be made by using the photoselection technique. The strong singlet-singlet transition is known to be long axis (y) polarized.[8] If a polarizer is placed in the path of the exciting light, the high field ODMR peak should be strongest when the polarization is parallel to the magnetic field if t_y is the top zero-field state and weakest if t_x is. (This results from the deficiency of paramagnetic molecules with their long axes perpendicular to the field). The highest field peak is obtained from the transition between the two states which start out closest together at zero field while the third state is unaltered in energy (refer to Figure 4).

Since it is the lowest two levels which are closest together, t_y is the top zero-field state.

Thus from ODMR experiments on $\Delta m = 2$ transitions together with the appropriate optical data it is possible to determine the spin Hamiltonian fine structure terms including their signs. In other "sign of D" experiments the relative intensities of the ESR transitions are measured. Here the "direction" of the transition is determined from the sign of the ODMR signal.

Unfortunately for systems such as naphthalene the $\Delta m = 2$ ODMR would seem to give insufficient information to deduce the spin Hamiltonian parameters since only one line is observed. For those cases the relevant information could, of course, be obtained from the $\Delta m = 1$ transitions. Preliminary results on the latter seem to indicate that this is indeed possible.

The above results have been interpreted in terms of a simple model in which only one of the zero-field levels is emitting. In fact there may well be non-negligible contributions from the other levels, but we do not feel these will basically alter our conclusions. Furthermore, since ODMR signals are determined by the ratio of radiative to radiationless decay rates one may anticipate complications in a more quantitative study.

We would like to acknowledge the valuable technical assistance of Mr. I. W. Hill.

REFERENCES

1. M. Sharnoff, J. Chem. Phys. 46, 3263, (1967).
2. A. L. Kwiram, Chem. Phys. Letters, 1, 272, (1967).
3. J. Schmidt, I. A. M. Hesselman, M. S. de Groot, J. H. van der Waals, Chem. Phys. Letters, 1, 434, (1967).
4. In this discussion emission will always mean optical emission. Pumping will always refer to microwave pumping.
5. C. A. Hutchison, Jr., B. W. Mangum, J. Chem. Phys. 34, 908, (1961).
6. N. S. Ham, K. Ruedenberg, J. Chem. Phys. 25, 13, (1956).
7. J. S. Vincent, A. H. Maki, J. Chem. Phys. 39, 3008, (1963).
8. T. Azumi, S. P. McGlynn, J. Chem. Phys. 37, 2413, (1962).
9. Vectors parallel to the short axis of naphthalene (D_{2h}) and quinoxaline (C_{2v}) transform as B_{2u} and B_2 respectively. For phenanthrene (C_{2v}) the vector parallel to the long axis transforms as B_2.
10. M. A. El-Sayed, R. G. Brewer, J. Chem. Phys., 39, 1623, (1963).
11. N. K. Chaudhuri, M. A. El-Sayed, J. Chem. Phys., 43, 1423, (1965).
12. R. W. Brandon, R. E. Gerkin, C. A. Hutchison, Jr., J. Chem. Phys., 41, 3717, (1964).
13. A. W. Hornig, J. S. Hyde, Mol. Phys., 6, 33, (1963).
14. P. Kottis, R. Lefebvre, J. Chem. Phys., 39, 393, (1963).

REFERENCES

1. M. Sharnoff, J. Chem. Phys., 46, 3263, (1967).
2. A. L. Kwiram, Chem. Phys. Letters, 1, 272, (1967).
3. J. Schmidt, I. A. M. Hesselmann, M. S. de Groot, J. H. van der Waals, Chem. Phys. Letters, 1, 434 (1967).
4. In this discussion emission will always mean optical emission. Pumping will always refer to microwave pumping.
5. C. A. Hutchison, Jr., B. W. Mangum, J. Chem. Phys. 34, 908, (1961).
6. N. S. Ham, K. Ruedenberg, J. Chem. Phys. 25, 13, (1956).
7. D. S. Vincent, A. H. Maki, J. Chem. Phys. 39, 3088, (1963).
8. T. Azumi, S. P. McGlynn, J. Chem. Phys. 37, 2413, (1962).
9. Vectors parallel to the short axis of naphthalene (D_{2h}) and quinoxaline (C_{2v}) transform as B_2 and B_1 respectively. For phenanthrene (C_{2v}), the vector parallel to the long axis transforms as B_2.
10. M. A. El-Sayed, R. G. Brewer, J. Chem. Phys., 39, 1623, (1963).
11. P. K. Chaudhuri, M. A. El-Sayed, J. Chem. Phys., 43, 1423, (1965).
12. R. W. Brandon, R. E. Gerkin, C. A. Hutchison, Jr., J. Chem. Phys., 41, 3717, (1964).
13. A. W. Hornig, J. S. Hyde, Mol. Phys., 6, 33, (1963).
14. P. Kottis, R. Lefebvre, J. Chem. Phys., 39, 393, (1963).

QUANTITATIVE ESR STUDIES OF ORGANIC TRIPLET STATES. EXTINCTION COEFFICIENTS OF T → T' TRANSITIONS

J. S. Brinen

Central Research Division
American Cyanamid Company
Stamford, Connecticut 06904

INTRODUCTION

Electronic transitions between the lowest triplet state and higher lying triplet states have been the subject of considerable study during the last two decades. These transitions, initially identified by Lewis and co-workers,[1] have subsequently been investigated by McClure,[2] Craig and Ross[3] and Porter and Windsor[4] and have led to increased information regarding higher excited triplet states.

The greatest emphasis to date has been expended on locating the higher lying triplet states with somewhat less concern as to the strength of the transitions. Only a few determinations of extinction coefficients have been reported for triplet-triplet transitions in rigid glasses at low temperatures[2-7] and for molecules studied by more than one worker, the results are in poor agreement. The disagreement stems from the inability to obtain a direct experimental value for the concentration of triplet molecules involved in the absorption process.

Basically two different methods have been employed and both obtain the concentration of triplet molecules by indirect means. The first involves analysis of the kinetic expressions for populating the lowest excited singlet and triplet states and was initially employed by McClure,[2] and used by Lavalette,[7] and with modification, by Keller and Hadley.[5] Values obtained by these workers for naphthalene and phenanthrene, the most studied molecules, differ by up to two orders of magnitude. Major difficulties in the kinetic analysis approach may be due to any of the following: (1) photochemical decomposition, (2) the assumption of no radiationless losses (other than intersystem crossing) from the lowest excited singlet state, (3) variations in the rate of formation of triplet molecules due to competition with strong T-T' absorption bands at the wavelengths of excitation, and (4) variation in the exciting light intensity across the sample due to absorption by ground state molecules. (This may be minimized when dilute solutions are employed.)

The second indirect approach used to measure triplet concentration is to measure the depletion of the ground state. Craig and Ross[3] used this technique to obtain a lower limit for the extinction coefficients of naphthalene, phenanthrene and anthracene. The ground state depletion in their experiments was too small to determine and they used an upper limit of 5% conversion to the triplet state. A major source of difficulty in the depletion technique arises when a T-T' absorption band occurs in the same wavelength region as the ground state absorption bands. If this situation arises (and it is very common), then assumptions regarding the shape of the T-T' bands must be made[6] and measurements at many wavelengths throughout the S-S' spectrum are necessary.

In this communication, a technique is described for measuring extinction coefficients for triplet-triplet transitions which employs electron spin resonance techniques to measure the triplet state concentration directly. The results of the extinction coefficient measurements are then compared with published values.

EXPERIMENTAL

Naphthalene $-d_8$, phenanthrene $-d_{10}$ and pyrene $-d_{10}$ were obtained from Merck Sharpe and Dohme, Ltd., and were not further purified. A sample of zone refined anthracene-d_{10} was generously donated by Drs. R. A. Keller and S. G. Hadley. Phenanthrene was purified by the method described by Kooyman and Farenhorst.[8] Zone refined and vacuum sublimed chrysene was obtained from James Hinton. Coronene, 1,2,5,6 dibenzanthracene and 1,2 benzocoronene were chromatographed on alumina. Triphenylene, 1,2 benzanthracene, 1,2,3,4 dibenzanthracene, fluorene, carbazole and picene were obtained commercially. ESR triplet, luminescence and absorption measurements indicated these were of reasonable purity and they were used without further purification.

Measurements were made at liquid nitrogen temperature in dilute rigid glass solutions

(∿1-5 x 10^{-4} M/l). Phenanthrene and naphthalene were measured in 3-methylpentane, which had been passed through a three-foot silica column. The other compounds studied were examined in 2-methyltetrahydrofuran which had been passed through alumina, with the exception of anthracene -d_{10} which was measured in EET (2:1:1 ether, ethanol and toluene).

The apparatus used for the simultaneous ESR and optical measurements is shown in Figure 1 and has been described in detail in previous publications.[9,9a] In brief, a partially aluminized quartz plate is used to transmit the UV excitation light (from a 200W Hg arc with a Corning 7-54 filter and a 5-cm $NiSO_4$-$CoSO_4$ solution filter) and to reflect the monitoring tungsten light into (and out of) a Varian optical transmission cavity. Appropriate quartz lenses focus the transmitted light onto the slit of a Perkin Elmer Model 13 spectrometer, modified for use in the visible and ultraviolet regions. The UV and tungsten light impinge on the sample along the same axis, an arrangement similar to the experimental conditions described by Keller and Hadley.[5] A Varian spectrometer with a 9" magnet and Fieldial was used to obtain the ESR spectra. The tungsten light source was chopped to permit subsequent AC amplification.

SPECTROSCOPIC MEASUREMENTS

A. CONCENTRATION DETERMINATIONS. The method used here involves the measurement of the steady state triplet concentration using electron spin resonance and the simultaneous measurement of the ESR triplet spectrum and the triplet-triplet absorption spectrum. The concentration determination was initially described by Aleksandrov and Pukhov[10] and depends on comparing the integrated absorption of the Δm

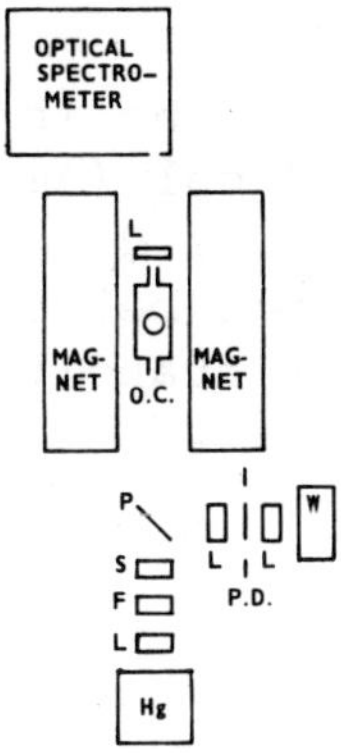

Figure 1 Schematic diagram of the apparatus used for obtaining simultaneous ESR and optical spectra of triplet molecules: Hg represents a 250 W mercury arc, L-lenses, S-shutter, F-filter system, P-a pellicle, O.C.-the optical transmission cavity in which the sample is kept (at 77°K), W-the tungsten arc used for the measurement of triplet-triplet absorption spectra, and P.D.-the chopper used for phase detection.

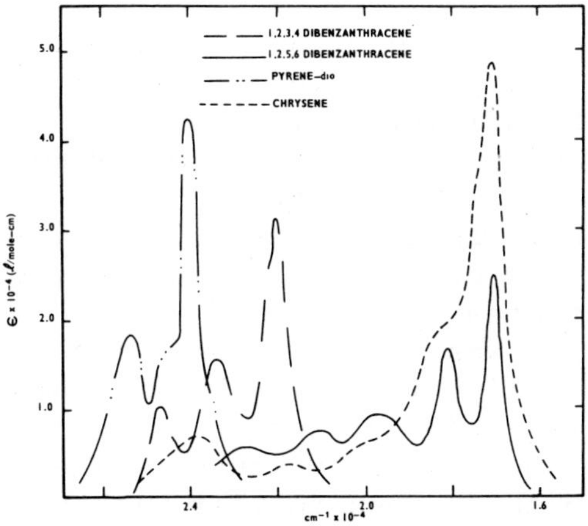

Figure 2 Triplet-triplet absorption spectra of 1,2,3,4-dibenzanthracene; 1,2,5,6-dibenzanthracene; pyrene-d_{10}; and chrysene in 2-methyltetrahydrofuran at 77°K.

= 2 triplet signal with the integrated absorption of a standard free radical ($\Delta m = 1$). The ratio of the areas is then corrected for the difference in transition probabilities between $\Delta m = 1$ (allowed) and $\Delta m = 2$ (forbidden) transitions. The working equation[10] is $N_T = N_r \frac{15}{8} \frac{(h\omega)^2}{D^2 + 3E^2} \frac{I_T}{I_r}$ where N_r and N_T are concentrations of standard and triplet, respectively, I_r and I_T the corresponding integrated absorptions, $h\omega$ the microwave energy and D and E the zero-field splitting parameters. The standard used in these experiments was a 10^{-2} M/l solution of di-t-butyl nitroxide[11] in toluene. At this concentration the standard solution was found to be stable to within a few percent over the period of months.[11] Checks on the stability were performed periodically by comparing the standard with a freshly prepared solution (10^{-2} Molar) after measuring the purity of the nitroxide by magnetic susceptibility determinations. The standard spectrum was measured at 77^oK.

The technique involves comparing a uniformly distributed standard with one which is generated via light absorption. The triplet molecules can not truly be uniformly distributed. To minimize this difficulty, dilute solutions were employed so that only a small fraction of the exciting light was absorbed. In all cases less than 10% of the total starting concentration was converted to triplets at steady state. As a check, the triplet concentration was monitored as a function of ultra-violet excitation intensity by interposing neutral density screens (of different transmission) between the sample and the light source. The ratio of the signal with the screen to that without the screen was found to be equal to the transmission of the screen, showing that the triplet concentration was linear with the light intensity used.

B. OPTICAL MEASUREMENTS. The T-T' spectra were obtained by scanning the visible spectrum of the sample with and without ultraviolet excitation. The percent transmission and the optical density were then calculated from these spectra and from the 0% transmission line, which was determined by replacing the sample with a blackened ESR tube. For the 0% transmission line, the amplification was increased by an order of magnitude to make certain that visible light was not entering the spectrometer from around the sample tube.

Once the T-T' spectra were scanned (the ESR triplet spectra were measured simultaneously), optical densities used for the ε measurements were obtained as follows. At a particular fixed wavelength in the T-T' spectrum, the rise and decay of the T-T' absorption (and ESR signal) was obtained by use of a shutter placed in the path of the UV exciting light. The transmission values with triplets present at steady state and with no triplets present were then determined and the optical density calculated. Identical measurements were then performed throughout the entire wavelength range of interest. In this manner, variations in the transmitted light brought about by slight movement in the dewar (liquid nitrogen bubbling) were minimized if not eliminated. The T-T' spectrum could then be plotted point by point as a function of optical density. The interposing of neutral density screens in the UV excitation beam produced identical optical density and triplet concentration changes, demonstrating that both optical density and triplet concentration varied linearly with light intensity levels used in the experiment.

Since conventional ESR tubes are cylindrical (∿3 mm od), the definition of path length to be used in the calculations becomes somewhat difficult. Although this problem has been treated in some detail,[12] the procedure used here was somewhat less rigorous. A 1 mm aperture was centered at the rear of the optical cavity ∿3-3.5" from the center of the sample. The tungsten light was passed through a 2mm aperture placed in front of the optical cavity and was slightly convergent on the sample. The transmitted light which reached the spectrometer passed through the center of the sample tube. Room temperature solution absorption measurements on naphthalene solutions in these cylindrical tubes indicated that the path length was between 0.23 and 0.25 mm. The value 0.25 mm was chosen for the calculations, but it must be recognized that this could be as much as 10% in error. It is planned in the future to use a laser as a spectral source to determine accurately the optical path length.

The concentration measurements were found to be reproducible to within ± 10%, the principle limitation being the double integration of the spin resonance signal. The accuracy of the overall technique is believed to be governed by the assumptions involved in the quantitative application of ESR.

RESULTS

The results of the extinction coefficient measurements for the triplet-triplet transitions are tabulated in Table I along with the triplet concentration obtained at steady state. The spectra of several molecules for which there is little or no literature data, are shown in Figure 2 and 3. Spectra of the other molecules discussed (except for anthracene $-d_{10}$) are given in Reference 9a.

The extinction coefficient for a random distribution of molecules (fluid solutions) differs from a photoselected distribution of molecules involved in the determination of the triplet-triplet spectrum. This problem has been examined by Albrecht[13] and by Keller and Hadley.[5] The latter authors conclude that only a small correction due to photoselection is needed for the case where both the exciting UV light and the monitoring

TABLE I: Steady State Triplet Concentration and Triplet-Triplet Extinction Coefficients

Compound	Triplet Concentration[a] 10^{-5} M/l	Band Max[b] cm^{-1}	$\varepsilon \times 10^{-4}$ (l/mole cm) This work	Literature
Naphthalene-d_8	2.7	24100	3.19	>1.0;[c] 1.4;[d] 2.3;[e] 4.5[f]
Phenanthrene	2.5	20410	4.15	>1.8;[c] 2.7[d]
Phenanthrene-d_{10}	4.2	20470	4.29	2.0[e]
Anthracene-d_{10}	1.3	23530	7.5	>4.5;[c] 9.0;[f] 11.5[g]
1,2-Benzanthracene	2.1	20300	4.4	2.9[h]
Triphenylene	2.9	23200	1.65	0.7;[d] 1.7[e]
Chrysene	7.2	17100	4.86	
Pyrene-d_{10}	3.6	24050	4.36	
1,2,3,4-Dibenzanthracene	5.8	22050	3.10	
1,2,5,6-Dibenzanthracene	3.1	17050	2.50	
Picene	4.4	15730	7.55	
Coronene	3.6	20650	1.58	
1,2-Benzocoronene	5.6	17000	2.55	2.5[h]
		23650	3.88	3.8[h]
Fluorene	6.6	26050	2.07	
Carbazole	7.8	23100	1.22	

a Steady state concentration determined by ESR experimental reproducibility ± 10%.
b Most intense visible T-T' absorption band maximum.
c Reference 3.
d Reference 5. More recent unpublished results[13] are in substantial agreement with the values obtained using the ESR data.
e Reference 7.
f Reference 21.
g Reference 20.
h Reference 6.

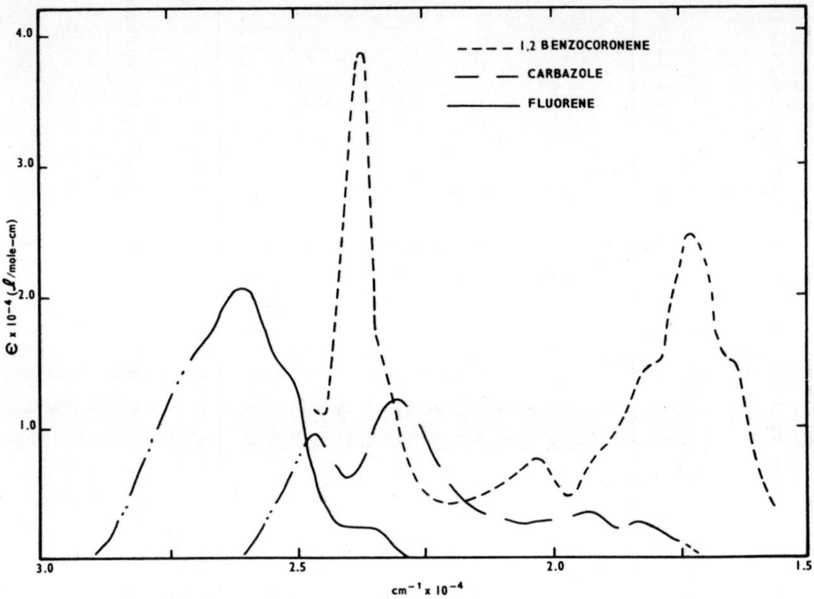

Figure 3 Triplet-triplet absorption spectra of 1,2-benzocoronene; fluorene; and carbazole in 2-methyltetrahydrofuran at 77°K.

tungsten light are not polarized.

The effect of photoselection on the ESR triplet signal ($\Delta m = 2$) was investigated by exciting the sample with polarized light and determining the triplet concentration. For deuterated phenanthrene, at very low triplet levels, a deviation of $\sim$10% was observed as a function of the angle of polarization. The corrections due to photoselection, although considered, have not been included in the results given in Tables I and II. The corrections are considerably larger when polarized light is used in both the exciting and monitoring beams,[5] and such measurements are now in progeess at these laboratories.

The extinction coefficients previously reported for naphthalene and phenanthrene using the kinetic analysis approach are generally lower than those reported here. Unpublished measurements by Keller and Hadley[14] using ground state depletion are within experimental error of the results determined by ESR. The measurements on phenanthrene-h_{10} and -d_{10} giving extinction coefficients which are identical within experimental error support the general feeling that deuteration has little effect on radiative transition probabilities. Recent values for triphenylene using both kinetic[7] and ground state depletion[13] approaches agree closely with the results reported here.

Of the less studied molecules, excellent agreement with literature data[6] is obtained for 1,2-benzocoronene.[6] The extinction coefficients are given for two "bands" in the spectrum since polarization measurements on the T-T' spectrum[15] show these have opposite polarization with respect to 3100 A excitation. The ε values reported here for the T-T' bands in chrysene, 1,2,3,4 dibenzanthracene, picene and coronene are in agreement with those reported by Windsor[17,18] et al. using ground state depletion methods. The values for 1,2,5,6 dibenzanthracene are lower by $\sim$30% than those previously reported.[17] Extinction coefficients have not been reported previously for pyrene-d_{10},[3] fluorene[3] and carbazole[19] although the low temperature T-T' spectra have been.

Since the measurements discussed here depend entirely on the observation of a steady state ESR signal, it was of additional interest to determine the short lifetime limitation (since short τ_{ph} implies low triplet concentration) of the technique. To test this, anthracene-d_{10} (τ_{ph} = 0.15 sec.) and 1,2 benzanthracene (τ_{ph} = 0.4 sec.) were measured. As expected, low triplet concentrations were obtained, 1.3×10^{-5} M/l for anthracene-d_{10} and 2.1×10^{-5} M/l for 1,2 benzanthracene. Using these concentrations, extinction coefficients were calculated. The results for 1,2 benzanthracene are considerably higher than reported.[6] The weak triplet ESR signal may be a contributor to this discrepancy. However, 1,2 benzanthracene does have strong T-T' absorption bands overlapping the S-S' spectrum which could make the triplet concentration estimates using ground state depletion uncertain. The value for anthracene-d_{10} is, as Craig and Ross predicted, (for anthracene-h_{10}) greater than 4.5×10^4 l/mole-cm. It is lower (by∿25%) than the value reported by Windsor and Novak[20] and is within experimental error of the work of Astier and Meyer[21] and the unpublished work of Keller and Hadley.[13] Thus, even for these short lived triplet states good agreement with reported results is obtained.

It is often commented that T-T' bands are in general considerably broader than S-S' absorption bands. From the spectra reported here, it is not uncommon for T-T' bands to have half intensity widths of ∿400-500 cm^{-1}. Examination of S-S' transitions which terminate 35,000-40,000 cm^{-1} above the ground state (as do the T-T' transitions under discussion) show that the half intensity widths are comparable (if not larger in some instances) to those of the T-T' absorption bands.

The oscillator strengths for the triplet-triplet transitions have been calculated from the measured extinction coefficients. These are indicative of strongly allowed transitions and are in agreement with the theoretical predictions of Orloff.[22] Orloff's assignments and the measured f values are tabulated in Table II. The measured oscillator strengths indicate that the theoretical values[22] should be reduced by a scale factor of ∿1/6. This would result in agreement between experimental and theoretical values.

Two f values are given for 1,2,5,6 dibenzanthracene because theoretical calculations predict the presence of two electronic transitions in this region. The larger value is obtained using the entire spectrum observed while the smaller value is derived by considering the two low energy bands only. Oscillator strengths are also given for both allowed T-T' transitions in 1,2 benzocoronene. The value for the 17,000 cm^{-1} band is in agreement with reported work.[6]

A comparison of fluorene and carbazole shows that both the maximum extinction coefficient and the f values are seriously effected with the heteroatom substitution. Both of these spectra are broad so that the relatively low ε values still give rise to rather large oscillator strengths. The larger value given for carbazole is obtained attributing the entire spectrum to a single electronic transition.

In addition, the experimental oscillator strengths (f) have been used to estimate the radiative lifetime of the upper triplet state ($^{\tau}T'$) involved in the triplet-triplet absorption process. These are tabulated in the last column of Table II. The frequency used in the expression to calculate $^{\tau}T'$ from f[23] was taken to be at the maximum ε of the $T' \leftarrow T$ transition. The radiative lifetimes calculated vary between five and twenty nanoseconds and are of the same magnitude as radiative lifetimes for allowed singlet-singlet transitions.[17] The observed mean lifetime of the upper triplet will be much shorter than the

TABLE II: Oscillator Strengths[a] for Triplet-Triplet Transitions

Compound	Assignment[b]	Oscillator Strength	$\tau_{T'}^{c}$ (sec)
Naphthalene-d_8	$^3B_{2u} \rightarrow {}^3B_{3g}$	.12	1.2×10^{-8}
Phenanthrene-d_{10}	$^3B_2 \rightarrow {}^3A_1$	.23	0.9×10^{-8}
Anthracene-d_{10}	$^3B_{2u} \rightarrow {}^3B_{3g}$	.27	0.6×10^{-8}
1,2-Benzanthracene	$^3A_1 \rightarrow {}^3A_1$	.43	0.5×10^{-8}
Triphenylene		.085	1.8×10^{-8}
Chrysene	$^3B_u \rightarrow {}^3A_g$	.40	0.7×10^{-8}
Pyrene-d_{10}	$^3B_{2u} \rightarrow {}^3B_{3g}$	.21	0.7×10^{-8}
1,2,3,4-Dibenzanthracene		.20	0.8×10^{-8}
1,2,5,6-Dibenzanthracene	$^3B_u \rightarrow {}^3A_g$	.25 (.12)[d]	$1.2\ (2.4) \times 10^{-8}$
Picene	$^3B_2 \rightarrow {}^3A_1$	.40	0.8×10^{-8}
1,2-Benzocoronene	$^3B_2 \rightarrow {}^3B_2$	.28[e]	1.0×10^{-8}
	$^3B_2 \rightarrow {}^3A_1$	.18[e]	0.8×10^{-8}
Fluorene		∿.25	$\sim 0.5 \times 10^{-8}$
Carbazole		.18 (.14)[f]	$0.9\ (1.1) \times 10^{-8}$

a Computed from the equation; $f = 4.33 \times 10^{-9} \int \varepsilon_{\tilde{\nu}} d\tilde{\nu}$
b Reference 19.
c Reference 20.
d See discussion in text.
e See discussion in text.
f See discussion in text.

radiative lifetimes because of internal conversion to lower lying triplet states[16] and possible intersystem crossing back to the singlet manifold. For allowed singlet-singlet transitions, the former process is absent (for $S_1 \rightarrow S_o$ emission) so it might be expected that lifetimes of the upper triplet state (involved in a $T' \rightarrow T$ fluorescence) would be considerably shorter than lifetimes of allowed singlet states ($S_1 \rightarrow S_o$), even though the calculated radiative lifetimes are similar.

CONCLUSION

A method for measuring extinction coefficients for triplet-triplet transitions has been described which employs electron spin resonance techniques to determine steady state triplet concentrations. Since the triplet concentration is determined directly, the uncertainties inherent in the indirect approaches, which are functions of the individual molecules and their electronic energy levels, are circumvented. The utility of this technique for measuring concentrations of triplet (π,π^*) molecules with lifetimes as short as 0.15 seconds has been demonstrated. Oscillator strengths calculated using these extinction coefficients demonstrate the strongly allowed nature of these transitions.

ACKNOWLEDGMENT

The author wishes to express his gratitude to Dr. W. G. Hodgson for constant encouragement throughout the course of this investigation, and specifically for guidance through the intricacies of quantitative ESR determinations. He also wishes to thank Dr. M. K. Orloff, Dr. S. G. Hadley and Dr. R. A. Keller for discussions regarding their unpublished observations.

REFERENCES

1. G. N. Lewis, D. Lipkin and T. J. Magel, J. Am. Chem. Soc. 63, 3005 (1941); G. N. Lewis and D. Lipkin, J. Am. Chem. Soc. 64, 2801 (1942).
2. D. S. McClure, J. Chem. Phys. 19, 670 (1951).
3. D. P. Craig and I. G. Ross, J. Chem. Soc. 1954, 1589.
4. G. Porter and M. W. Windsor, Proc. Roy. Soc. (London) A245, 235 (1958).
5. R. A. Keller and S. G. Hadley, J. Chem. Phys. 42, 2382 (1965).
6. W. R. Dawson, J. Opt. Soc. Amer. 58, 222 (1968).
7. D. Lavalette, C. R. Acad. Sc. Paris 266B, 279 (1968).
8. E. C. Kooyman and E. Farenhorst, Trans. Faraday Soc. 49, 58 (1943).
9. J. S. Brinen, W. G. Hodgson, J. Chem. Phys. 47, 2946 (1967).

9a. J. S. Brinen, J. Chem. Phys. (in press).

10. I. V. Aleksandrov and K. K. Pukhov, Opt. Spectry. 17, 513 (1964).
11. A. K. Hoffman, A. M. Feldman and E. Gelblum, J. Am. Chem. Soc. 86, 646 (1964); and W. G. Hodgson and W. Haugen (unpublished work).
12. I. G. Ross, J. Opt. Soc. Amer. 44, 40 (1954).
13. A. C. Albrecht, J. Mol. Spectry. 6, 84 (1961).
14. S. G. Hadley, and R. A. Keller (private communication). Values for naphthalene-d_8, phenanthrene, phenanthrene-d_{10} and triphenylene using ground state deletion agree quite closely with the measurements using the ESR method.
15. J. S. Brinen (unpublished work). The transition at 17,000 cm^{-1} is polarized parallel to 3100 Å and 3650 Å excitation, indicating "long" axis polarization, while the transition at 23,650 cm^{-1} is perpendicular to 3100 Å excitation indicating "short axis" polarization.

Theoretical calculations[16] of the T-T' spectrum of 1,2-benzocoronene are in complete agreement with these observations.
16. M. K. Orloff (unpublished results).
17. M. W. Windsor, W. R. Dawson and R. S. Moore, "Photochromic Eye-Protective Devices Based on Triplet Absorption," Ann. Rept., U. S. Air Force Contract AF-41 (609) 2908, Aug. 1966.
18. M. W. Windsor, W. R. Dawson, R. S. Moores and G. Weber, "Research on Triplet States and Photochromism for Flash Blindness Protection," Ann. Rept., U. S. Air Force Contract AF-41 (609) 2425, April, 1965.
19. B. R. Henry and M. Kasha, J. Chem. Phys. 47, 3319 (1967).
20. M. W. Windsor and J. R. Novak, The Triplet State, Proceedings of an International Symposium at American University of Beirut, Lebanon.
21. R. Astier and Y. H. Meyer, ibid.
22. M. K. Orloff, J. Chem. Phys. 47, 237 (1967).
23. S. J. Strickler and R. A. Berg, J. Chem. Phys. 37, 814 (1962). The form of the equation used in the present paper is that for atomic states since for the T-T' absorption maximum was used in the calculation.

PHOSPHORESCENCE AND ESR SPECTRA OF THE CHARGE-TRANSFER TRIPLET STATES OF SOME MOLECULAR COMPLEXES CONTAINING TETRACYANOBENZENE AS ELECTRON ACCEPTOR

Hisaharu Hayashi, Saburo Nagakura

Institute for Solid State Physics
University of Tokyo
Roppongi, Minato-ku
Tokyo, Japan

and Suehiro Iwata

Institute of Physical and Chemical Research
Yamato, Saitama, Japan

We have measured emission spectra for some molecular complexes containing tetracyanobenzene (TCNB) as electron acceptor and benzene or its methyl derivatives as electron donor. We have succeeded in finding long-lived emissions different from those of the component molecules. From the dependence of their maximum wavenumbers upon the ionization potentials of donors and from the consideration of the energy diagrams of these complexes, we have concluded that for some of the complexes the lowest triplet states have the charge-transfer (CT) characters and therefore that the observed emissions can be regarded as the CT phosphorescence. This is the first finding of a "CT triplet state."

In order to obtain further information of the CT triplet state, we have undertaken to observe ESR spectra for TCNB complexes with benzene or its methyl derivatives. In actuality, we have succeeded in observing the ESR spectra of their CT triplet states and in finding a vivid dependence of fine structure constants upon the ionization potentials of donors. Furthermore, we could determine the contribution of CT structure in the lowest triplet state from the analysis of the observed fine structure constants.

EMISSION SPECTRA

First we describe briefly the experimental results of phosphorescence observed for TCNB complexes with benzene, toluene, xylenes, mesitylene, durene, pentamethylbenzene and hexamethylbenzene. Some of our results are shown in Fig. 1. The observed phosphorescence maxima and lifetimes are shown in Table I together with the fluorescence maxima and the ionization potentials of donors. The observed phosphorescence spectra were interpreted as emissions from the lowest triplet states with various amounts of CT characters which are greatly dependent upon the ionization potentials of donors. The reasons for this are as follows: (1) For a fixed acceptor, the observed phosphorescence maximum shifts to the lower frequencies in parallel with the decrease in the ionization potential of donor. This tendency is similar to that observed with the case of the CT absorption and fluorescence spectra. (2) From the comparison of the observed CT fluorescence spectra of some TCNB complexes with the phosphorescence spectra of the component molecules, the zero order CT triplet state of the TCNB-hexamethylbenzene complex

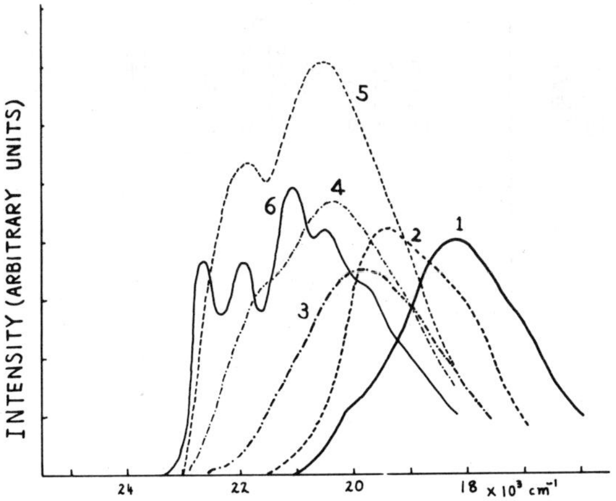

Figure 1 The phosphorescence spectra of TCNB complexes in EP solution at 77°K; (1) TCNB-HMB, (2) TCNB-durene, (3) TCNB-mesitylene, (4) TCNB-toluene, (5) TCNB-benzene, and (6) TCNB only.

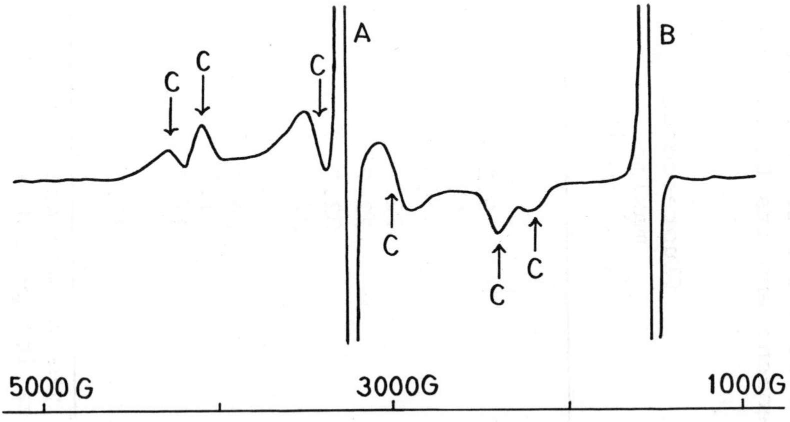

Figure 2 ESR spectrum of the TCNB solution in toluene-ethyl ether under ultraviolet light irradiation (a 500 W super-high pressure mercury lamp with UVD 25 filter) at 77°K: (A) TCNB anion; (B) $\Delta m = \pm 2$ line; (C) $\Delta m = \pm 1$ lines. (ν = 9178 MHz).

TABLE I: Emission spectra and the Related Properties of TCNB Complexes with Benzene and its Derivatives

	fluorescence maxima (10^3 cm^{-1})	phosphorescence maxima (10^3 cm^{-1})	τ [a] (sec)	I_p [b] (eV)
TCNB		21.2	3.6	
TCNB-HMB	19.3	18.2	0.4	7.85
TCNB-PMB	19.4	18.3	1.1	7.92
TCNB-DU	20.2	19.6	0.9	8.03
TCNB-ME	22.1	19.6	3.0	8.39
TCNB-PX	22.2	20.1	3.0	8.445
TCNB-OX	22.2	20.1	3.0	8.555
TCNB-MX	22.2	20.1	3.1	8.56
TCNB-TO	24.7	20.5	3.3	8.82
TCNB-BE	26.3	20.9	3.3	9.245
TCNB in ME	21.8	19.7	2.2	
TCNB in TO	23.5	20.0	2.0	
TCNB in toluene-ether	23.5	20.2	3.0	

[a] τ: Lifetimes of phosphorescent states.
[b] I_p: Ionization potentials of donors.

for example is undoubtedly lower than the lowest triplet states of the component molecules. This means that the lowest triplet state of this complex has predominantly the CT character.[1]

ESR SPECTRA

ESR spectra were measured with various TCNB solutions. First of all, we explain the ESR spectrum of the solution containing TCNB in toluene-ether (1:1) mixed solvent, because this is the only example showing ESR signals due to the both transitions of $\Delta m = \pm 1$ and $\Delta m = \pm 2$ for the triplet state. The result of this system is shown in Fig. 2. From the former transition spectrum (C in Fig. 2), we could determine the components of the g tensor and the fine structure constants D and E. The description on this point is completely omitted in this paper.[2]

Now let us turn to the ternary solutions of TCNB-hexamethylbenzene, TCNB-durene, TCNB-mesitylene, TCNB-o-xylene, TCNB-m-xylene and TCNB-p-xylene in ethanol. The results observed for some of them are shown in Fig. 3. Each of these solutions showed two $\Delta m = \pm 2$ signals.[3] One of them which appeared at ∿1400 G can safely be ascribed to the excited triplet state of TCNB itself which exists freely in the ternary solutions. This is because the ethanol solution of TCNB alone shows an ESR signal of the similar shape at 1424 G, and also because the lifetimes from the decay curves of the ESR signals observed for the ternary solution and the ethanol solution of TCNB are equal to the phosphorescence lifetime of TCNB itself. Another kind of signals appeared at higher field than 1400 G. Their positions are listed in Table II. These ESR signals which appeared in the wide magnetic field region of 1500-1610 G can be regarded as due to the lowest triplet excited states of the molecular complexes

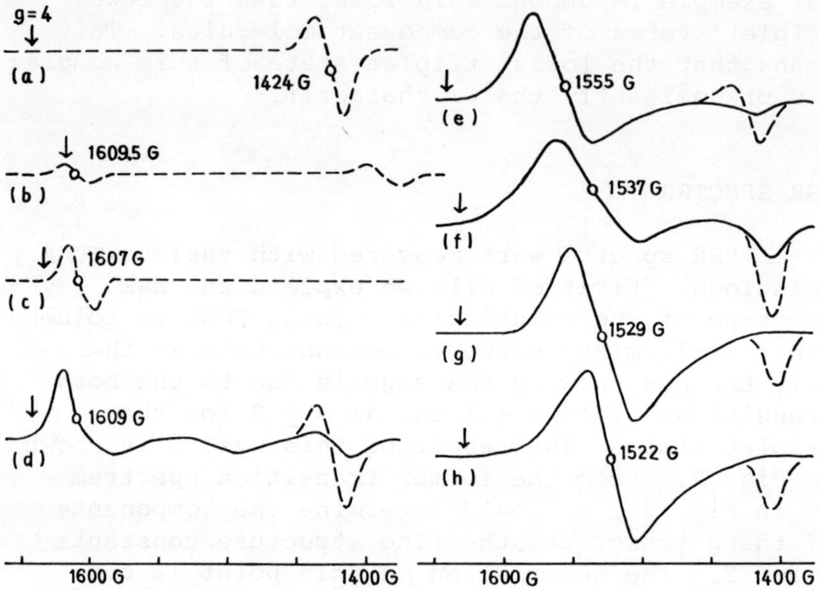

Figure 3 ESR spectra in the g ≃ 4 region of the ternary solutions containing TCNB and various donors in ethanol under ultra-violet light irradiation (a 500 W super-high pressure mercury lamp with UVDIA filter for solid lines and with UVD 25 filter for broken lines) at 77°K: (a) TCNB only (ν = 9193 MHz); (b) TCNB-HMB (ν = 9060 MHz); (c) TCNB-PMB (ν = 9145 MHz); (d) TCNB-DU (ν = 9193 MHz); (e) TCNB-ME (ν = 9193 MHz); (f) TCNB-PX (ν = 9144 MHz); (g) TCNB-OX (ν = 9143 MHz); (h) TCNB-MX (ν = 9146 MHz).

TABLE II: ESR Spectral Data and *x* values obtained with TCNB Complexes with Benzene and its Methyl Derivatives

	H_{min} (gauss)	(MHz)	τ_L[a] (sec)	τ_H[a] (sec)	D^* (cm^{-1})	*x*
TCNB	1424	9193	3.5	-	0.1317	0
TCNB-HMB	1609.5	9060			0.0231	0.95
TCNB-PMB	1607	9145		0.7	0.0452	0.77
TCNB-DU	1609	9193	3.3	1.4	0.0502	0.72
TCNB-ME	1555	9193	3.3	3.3	0.0844	0.42
TCNB-PX	1537	9144	3.5	2.7	0.0880	0.39
TCNB-OX	1529	9143		3.0	0.0918	0.36
TCNB-MX	1522	9146		3.3	0.0950	0.33
TCNB-TO	1455	9137	3.3		0.1189	0.11
TCNB-BE	1440	9141	3.7		0.1238	0.07
TCNB in ME	1554	9113	-	2.9	0.0772	-
TCNB in TO	1514	9113	-	2.9	0.0957	-
TCNB in toluene-ether	1502	9101	-	2.9	0.1015	-

[a] τ_L and τ_H are the lifetimes of the lowest triplet states of free TCNB and TCNB complexes obtained from the decay curves of ESR signals, respectively.

of TCNB and electron donors. The reasons for this are as follows:

First, these lines were observed only for the systems containing both electron donor and acceptor (TCNB). Second, they could be observed by the selective excitation in which only the complexes could mainly be excited. Third, the lifetimes obtained from the decay curves of the ESR signals under consideration are nearly equal to the phosphorescence lifetime of the respective complexes within the experimental errors, as is shown in Tables I and II.

The transition probability of the $\Delta m = \pm 2$ is generally proportional to the square of the fine structure constant D^*.[4] As described below, the D^* values of the molecular complexes under consideration are smaller than those of usual aromatic molecules. Therefore their $\Delta m = \pm 2$ transitions turn out to have small probability and are difficult to be detected. In actuality, the observation of the ESR signals due to the $\Delta m = \pm 2$ transitions of the triplet states was accompanied with several difficulties before the success for the molecular complexes, in particular for TCNB-hexamethylbenzene and TCNB-pentamethylbenzene, the D^* values of which are very small.

FINE STRUCTURE CONSTANTS

The value of the fine structure constant D^* can be obtained from the $\Delta m = \pm 2$ line of the rigid solution with the aid of the following relation[5]

$$D^* = \{3/4(h\nu)^2 - 3(g\beta H_{min})^2\}^{\frac{1}{2}} \qquad (1)$$

where

$$D^* = (D^2 + 3E^2)^{\frac{1}{2}} \qquad (2)$$

In order to obtain the D^* value experimentally, it is necessary to determine the g and H_{min} values. In the present study, the g value was assumed to be 2.000 for all the triplet states of the complexes under consideration. This seems to be reasonable from the fact that the three components of the g tensor were determined to be 2.001_3, 1.995_8 and 1.997_3 for the TCNB-toluene complex in the mixed solvent of ethyl ether and toluene.[2] The g value of the triplet state of TCNB itself was assumed to be 2.003. Usually, the g values of the triplet states of the aromatic molecules are isotropic and nearly equal to the free spin value.[6] The H_{min} of the $\Delta m = \pm 2$ line was assumed to be the mid-point between the maximum and the minimum of the derivative curve. The H_{min} values obtained on this assumption are shown in Table II.

From the above-mentioned H_{min} and g values, the D^* values corresponding to all the $\Delta m = \pm 2$ lines were obtained with the aid of Eq. (1) as is shown in Table II. The D^* value of the TCNB-toluene complex in toluene-ether obtained from the $\Delta m = \pm 2$ line was 0.1015 cm^{-1}. The same quantity was calculated to be 0.1045 cm^{-1} by the aid of the D and E values obtained from the $\Delta m = \pm 1$ lines.[2] The fact that the two D^* values are nearly equal to each other, seems to support the present method used for obtaining the D^* values from the $\Delta m = \pm 2$ lines.

CT THEORY AND FINE STRUCTURE CONSTANTS

According to Mulliken's theory, the lowest triplet excited state of the 1:1 molecular complexes containing TCNB and benzene or methyl-substituted benzenes can be represented by the following equation:[1]

$$\psi = a\Phi_a(D_a^+A^-) + b\Phi_b(D_b^+A^-) + c\Phi_c(DA^*) \qquad (3)$$

where Φ_a and Φ_b represent, respectively, the lowest two zero order CT triplet states Φ_{CT1} and Φ_{CT3} described in the previous paper.[1] They correspond, respectively, to the CT configurations from the highest two occupied orbitals of donor θ_2 and θ_3, to the lowest vacant one of TCNB, Φ_8. The wavefunction Φ_c represents the zero order locally excited triplet state corresponding to the lowest excitation within TCNB.

In order to calculate the fine structure constants D and E, only the spin-spin dipolar interaction was taken into account.[7] The geometries of the molecular complexes were taken from the X-ray crystal analysis data of the TCNB-hexamethylbenzene molecular complex obtained by Niimura, Ohashi, and Saito.[8] The distance between the TCNB and hexamethylbenzene molecular planes is 3.45 Å. The point charge approximation was used, i.e. the electronic charge was assumed to be placed on the positions of the nuclei. For the spin density of the TCNB anion, we used the lowest vacant MO of TCNB, Φ_8, calculated by the SCFMO method.[1] For the spin density of the cation of the donor, we used that of the benzene cation. The D^* value was evaluated by Eq. (2) after the calculation of the D and E values.

The D^* value can be written as follows:

$$D^* = \int \psi^* D(1,2) \psi d\tau \equiv \langle \psi | D | \psi \rangle \qquad (4)$$

where the two electron operator D(1,2) represents the dipole interaction between the two odd electrons, which corresponds to the fine structure constant D^*. We substitute Eq. (3) into Eq. (4) and define the values D_a^*, D_b^*, and D_A^* as follows:

$$D_a^* = \langle \Phi_a | D | \Phi_a \rangle$$

$$D_b^* = \langle \Phi_b | D | \Phi_b \rangle$$

$$D_A^* = \langle \Phi_c | D | \Phi_c \rangle$$

The D_a^* and D_b^* values were calculated to be 0.0213 cm^{-1} and 0.0230 cm^{-1}, respectively. The observed D^* value of TCNB (0.1317 cm^{-1}) was used for the D_A^* value. The off-diagonal terms such as $\langle \Phi_a | D | \Phi_c \rangle$, $\langle \Phi_b | D | \Phi_c \rangle$, $\langle \Phi_a | D | \Phi_b \rangle$, etc. were shown to be much smaller than D_a^*, D_b^*, and D_A^* and were disregarded.

Since D_a^* is nearly equal to D_b^*, we take the mean value as D_{CT}^*:

$$D_{CT}^* = \tfrac{1}{2}(D_a^* + D_b^*)$$

The overlap integrals $\langle \Phi_a | \Phi_c \rangle$ and $\langle \Phi_b | \Phi_c \rangle$ are very small compared with unity. Consequently, the D^* value can be expressed with the aid of the CT character $x = a^2 + b^2$ as follows:

$$D^* = xD_{CT}^* + (1 - x)D_A^* \tag{5}$$

This is the theoretical expression for the D^* values of the lowest triplet states of this kind of molecular complexes. The observed D^* values in Table II lie between the D_{CT}^* and D_A^* values.

RELATION BETWEEN THE D^* VALUES AND THE CT CHARACTERS OF THE MOLECULAR COMPLEXES

When the geometries of the various 1:1 molecular complexes are assumed to be the same as that of the TCNB-hexamethylbenzene complex, the theoretical D^* values of various 1:1 molecular complexes can be written by use of Eq. (5) as follows:

$$D^*(cm^{-1}) = 0.1317 - 0.1095x \tag{6}$$

The CT character x in the lowest triplet states of the TCNB complexes was obtained by use of Eq. (6) from the observed D^* values. The results are given in Table II.

According to the results given in Table II, the x values of various TCNB complexes decrease in the following order; TCNB-hexamethylbenzene > TCNB-pentamethylbenzene > TCNB-durene > TCNB-mesitylene > TCNB-p-xylene > TCNB-o-xylene > TCNB-m-xylene > TCNB-toluene > TCNB-benzene. This order is parallel to the decreasing order of the CT fluorescence and phosphorescence maximum wavelengths and also to the increasing order of the ionization potentials of the donors.[9] This is reasonable from the CT theory of molecular complexes.

As is clearly seen in Table II, the lowest triplet excited states of the TCNB-hexamethylbenzene, TCNB-pentamethylbenzene, and TCNB-durene complexes consist mainly of the CT configurations. The contributions of the CT configuration to the lowest triplet state is nearly close to 50% for the TCNB-mesitylene, TCNB-o-xylene, TCNB-m-xylene, and TCNB-p-xylene complexes. Particularly, it may be noticed that the x values for the TCNB complexes with the three xylene isomers were proved from the D^* values to decrease in the order of p- > o- > m-xylene in accordance with the order expected from their ionization potentials.[10] The lowest triplet excited states of the TCNB-toluene and TCNB-benzene complexes were shown to consist mainly of the locally excited configurations.

ACKNOWLEDGEMENT

The authors wish to thank Professor Sizuo Fujiwara of the University of Tokyo and Professor Koich Itoh of Osaka University for kindly putting ESR spectrometer at their disposal.

REFERENCES

1. S. Iwata, J. Tanaka and S. Nagakura, J. Am. Chem. Soc. 88, 894 (1966).
2. The result will be published in the near future in J. Chem. Phys.
3. For the pentamethylbenzene-TCNB, however, only one signal was observed.
4. J. H. van der Waals and M. S. de Groot, Mol. Phys. 2, 333 (1959).
5. M. S. de Groot and J. H. van der Waals, Mol. Phys. 3, 190 (1960).
6. For example, C. A. Hutchison, Jr. and B. W. Mangum, J. Chem. Phys. 34, 908 (1961); J. S. Vincent and A. H. Maki, J. Chem. Phys. 39, 3088 (1963).
7. J. Higuchi, J. Chem. Phys. 38, 1237 (1963).
8. N. Niimura, Y. Ohashi and Y. Saito, Bull. Chem. Soc. Japan (to be published). We are greatly indebted to them for their kindness in informing us the data prior to publication.
9. V. I. Vedeneyev, L. V. Gurvich, V. N. Kondrast'yev, V. A. Medvedev and Y. L. Frankevich, Bond Energies, Ionization Potentials, and Electron Affinities (Edward Arnold Ltd., London, 1966).
10. V. J. Hammond, W. C. Price, J. P. Teegan and A. D. Walsh, Disc. Farad. Soc. 9, 52 (1950); H. Baba, I. Omura, and K. Higasi, Bull. Chem. Soc. Japan 29, 521 (1956); K. Watanabe, J. Chem. Phys. 26, 542 (1957); R. Bralsford, P. V. Harris, and W. C. Price, Proc. Roy. Soc. A258, 459 (1960).

STUDIES OF RADIATIONLESS TRANSITIONS IN CORONENE USING NANOSECOND LASER PHOTOLYSIS AND SPECTROSCOPY

M. W. Windsor and J. R. Novak

Chemical Sciences Department
TRW Systems
One Space Park, Redondo Beach, California

INTRODUCTION

Transfer of excitation energy within complex molecules via non-radiative pathways is an important phenomenon in photochemistry and radiation chemistry. For many years the class of polycyclic aromatic hydrocarbons has provided a fertile testing ground for the comparison of theory and experiment on the subject of radiationless transitions. However, the elucidation of such pathways is hampered by the incomplete nature of our knowledge of the excited electronic states possessed by such

*Supported in part by the Aerospace Research Laboratories, USAF, under Contract AF 33 (615)-5331
*And in part by the Office of Naval Research, under Contract N00014-67-C0327

molecules. Because of considerations of symmetry and of spin, many excited electronic states are inaccessible, or accessible only with difficulty, by direct absorption of light from the ground state. For example, the selection rule prohibiting spin intercombinations in molecules containing only light atoms rules out direct transitions from the ground state to the manifold of triplet electronic states. Such states must be located by studies of triplet-triplet absorption using such techniques as flash photolysis or uv irradiation in rigid media to produce a large population of molecules in the lowest triplet state, T_1, by nonradiative cross-over from the singlet manifold.[1]

In many aromatic hydrocarbons which possess a center of symmetry, such as the linear polyacenes, benzene through pentacene, and also pyrene and coronene, transitions from the $\bar{A}_{1g}$ ground state to higher singlet states of $\underline{g}$ parity are forbidden by the $\underline{g} \nleftrightarrow \underline{g}$ selection rule.[2] Although the prohibition can be relaxed by the presence of asymmetric vibrations, the resulting transitions are still likely to be quite weak and in practice cannot be distinguished in the presence of strong broad absorption bands arising from transitions to higher states of $\underline{u}$ parity.

Two techniques have recently become available for locating higher singlet states of $\underline{g}$ parity. Both techniques depend on the use of lasers. The first is multiphoton spectroscopy[3] in which two or more photons of the same frequency are simultaneously absorbed by a single molecule.

The second, with which we are concerned here, is laser photolysis and spectroscopy,[4] in which a very short-duration laser pulse is used to obtain a population of molecules in the lowest excited singlet state, S_1, adequate to carry out absorption spectroscopy on this excited state. Since the lowest excited singlet state, for centro-symmetric molecules, has $\underline{u}$ parity, transitions to higher $\underline{g}$

states from this state are, unlike those from the ground state, fully allowed.

After summarizing the experimental technique, we describe how it can be used to obtain data on higher singlets of _g_ parity for coronene via the observation of the absorption spectrum of the lowest _excited_ singlet state. In addition, we show how nanosecond kinetic observations of the decay of S_1 and the appearance of T_1, both _in absorption_, can shed new light on the subject of intramolecular radiationless transitions.

EXPERIMENTAL

To study the excited singlet states of aromatic hydrocarbons in absorption, a very intense excitation source and time resolution of 10^{-7} sec or better are needed. Observations by flash photolysis and spectroscopy employing xenon-filled flash lamps are limited to a time resolution of about 1 μsec.[5] Nanosecond lamps used for fluorescence lifetime measurements are inadequate, in the intensity of light produced, by many orders of magnitude, either for photochemical excitation, or as sources of background continua for absorption spectroscopy. The present technique of laser photolysis and spectroscopy uses a single 30 nsec giant pulse from a ruby laser to provide both a monochromatic uv excitation flash and a synchronized continuum flash intense enough for spectroscopic recording.

The technique is shown schematically in Fig. 1. A Q-switched ruby laser provides a 30 nsec pulse of 6 Joules energy at 694 nm. By passing the primary laser beam through a crystal of potassium dihydrogen phosphate (KDP), between 1 and 10% of this energy is converted to the second harmonic at 347 nm. The primary and doubled laser pulses emerging from the KDP crystal are separated spatially using a hollow quartz prism filled with

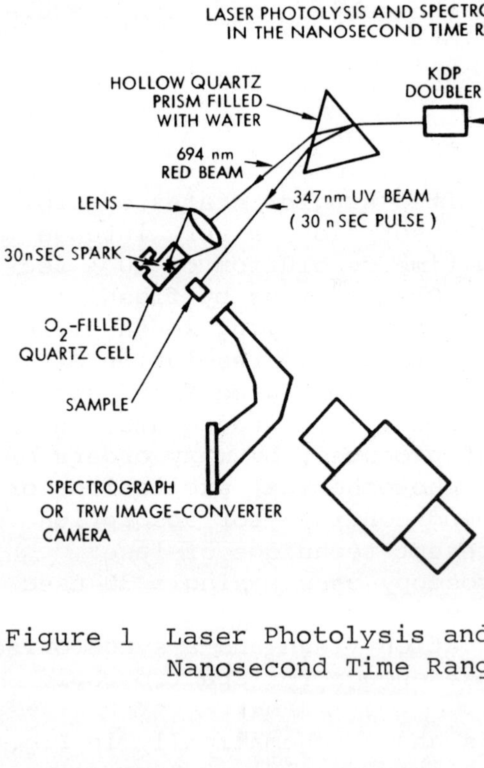

Figure 1 Laser Photolysis and Spectroscopy in the Nanosecond Time Range.

water. (A glass prism soon develops brownish streaks along the path of the beam, probably owing to production of F-centers by the intense uv light). The 30 nsec uv pulse is used to excite the sample. The primary red laser pulse is focused to a point in a quartz cell filled with oxygen at 1 atm pressure, using a 5 cm focal length lens. The consequent electric field intensity at the focus is so high that electrical breakdown of the gas occurs. The result is a very intense spark of short duration. In O_2 at 1 atm the light from the spark lasts only 30 nsec and is synchronized with the excitation flash. It provides a background continuum intense enough to record an absorption spectrum photographically in a single exposure, over the region 200 nm to 800 nm, using a small quartz Hilger spectrograph.

To obtain time-resolved spectra, the spectrograph is replaced by an image-converter camera (ICC).[6] A direct-vision combination of 5 prisms is used as a spectrograph to produce a low-dispersion spectrum on the photocathode of the ICC. The quartz cell in which the laser breakdown spark is produced is now filled with xenon instead of oxygen. In xenon the light output from the spark lasts several microseconds and provides a background source of almost constant intensity for times up to 1 μsec.

Different deflecting voltages applied to the image-tube, produce absorption spectra on the output phosphor screen of the image tube with continuous time-resolution over intervals ranging from 20 nsec to 1 μsec. To obtain a permanent record the screen is photographed with a Polaroid camera.

RESULTS

A time-resolved absorption spectrum for coronene dissolved in poly-(methylmethacrylate) plastic is shown in Fig. 2. The right-hand exposure shows

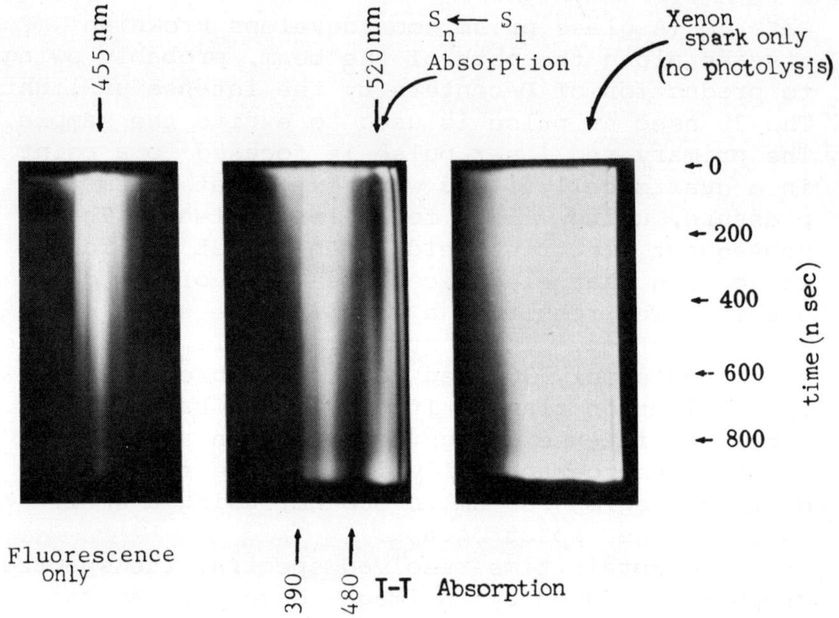

Figure 2 Decay of Fluorescence (Left Frame) and Decay of Excited Singlet Absorption and Build-up of Triplet-Triplet Absorption (Center Frame) for Coronene in Poly(methylmethacrylate) plastic at 23°C. Right Frame shows Background Spectrum of Xenon Spark only.

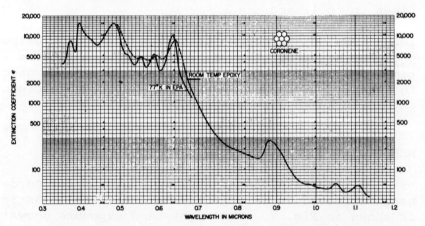

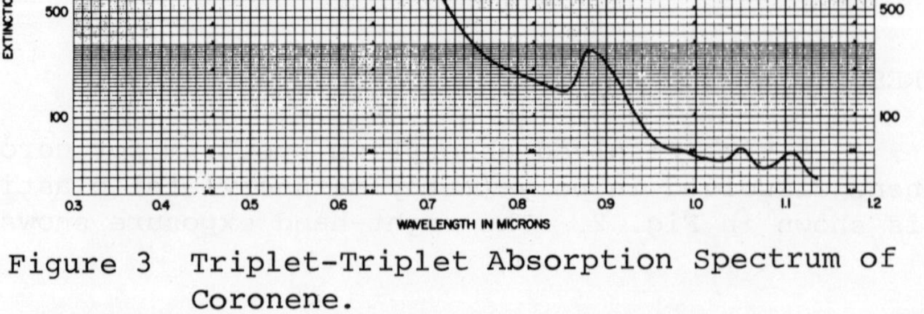

Figure 3 Triplet-Triplet Absorption Spectrum of Coronene.

the spectrum of the background spark alone. The center exposure shows the ICC streak spectrum over a time of approximately 900 nsec. A new absorption band at 520 nm is seen whose decay can be followed over a period of about 300 nsec. As this band decays it is replaced by bands at 480 nm and 390 nm which grow in intensity concomitantly with the disappearance of the 520 nm band. The left-hand exposure, taken with the uv excitation pulse alone, shows the decay of the fluorescence emission.

Comparison of the above results with the triplet-triplet absorption spectrum of coronene in epoxy plastic shown in Fig. 3, which was obtained by a double-beam recording technique using intense uv cross-irradiation from an AH-6 mercury arc to populate the triplet state,[7] discloses the following:

(1) The 480 nm and 390 nm bands which grow in after about 200 nsec on the ICC photograph, agree very well in wavelength with the T-T absorption bands at 484 nm and 390 nm in Fig. 3.

(2) The above bands are absent prior to about 200 nsec.

(3) The 520 nm band is present immediately after excitation and rapidly dies away as the triplet bands appear.

(4) The rates of disappearance of the 520 nm absorption band and the fluorescence emission are closely similar.

From (2) we infer that the lowest triplet state of coronene is not significantly populated immediately after the 30 nsec laser excitation pulse, but becomes so only after a delay of 200 nsec or more. From (3) we infer that the 520 nm band cannot result from absorption from the lowest triplet state. From (4) we conclude that the 520 nm band arises from absorption by the lowest excited singlet state[4] and, from (1), this state undergoes conversion to the lowest triplet state over a period of several hundred nanoseconds.

Laser photolysis experiments on 10^{-3} M coronene in acetonitrile solution disclose another excited singlet state absorption band at 380 nm.[4] The same experiments also show heavy bleaching of the coronene ground-state absorption band in the 340 nm region immediately following the excitation pulse. The 520 nm band must, therefore, have an extinction coefficient comparable to that of the ground-state bands. We estimate a value of 20,000 M^{-1} cm^{-1}. Thus the new bands arise from fully allowed transitions and must be attributed to absorption from the $^1B_{2u}^-$ state of coronene to higher singlet states of g parity.

Data on the energies of the singlet and triplet states of coronene are summarized in the energy level diagram of Fig. 4. Data for the singlet states accessible from the ground state are taken from the absorption spectra of Clar.[8] Presumably all of these states are of u parity. The triplet state data for coronene in epoxy plastic are from the T-T absorption spectrum at room temperature obtained in the present study, shown in Fig. 3. The T-T bands at 634, 484, 395 and 373 nm have been previously observed.[9] The bands between 500 and 600 nm and the much weaker infrared bands at 880, 980, 1050 have not been previously reported. The extinction coefficient scale has been normalized to a value of ε_T = 15,500 M^{-1} cm^{-1} for the 484 nm band obtained earlier in our laboratories[9] for coronene in EPA glass at 77°K. The use of this figure is supported by more recent studies of coronene in both epoxy plastic and poly (methylmethacrylate) (PMM) plastic.[10] These studies show that at 77°K the value of ε_T in PMM is the same as that in EPA; this value changes by less than 10% in going from 77°K to room temperature. Also, PMM and epoxy samples give the same value of $\varepsilon_T\Phi_T$, where Φ_T is the quantum yield of triplet formation. We conclude, therefore, that the ε_T for coronene has much the same value in epoxy plastic at room temperature as in EPA at 77°K.

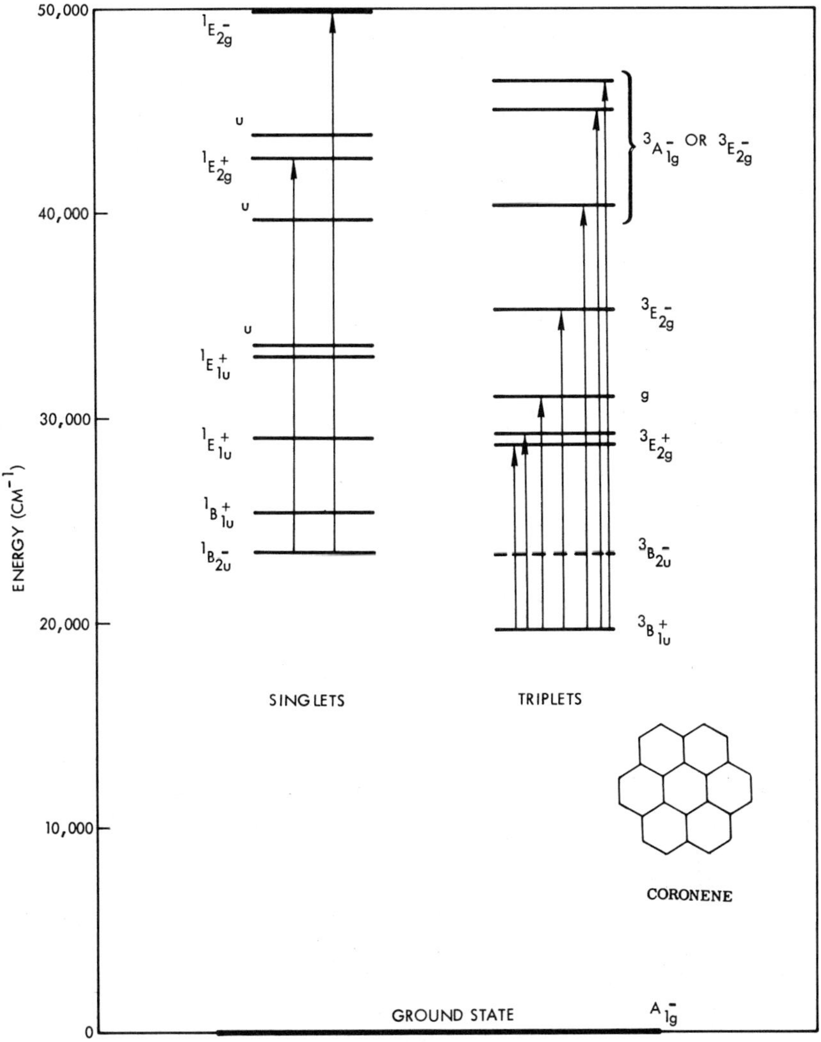

Figure 4 Singlet and Triplet Energy Levels of Coronene.

DISCUSSION

We have assigned the symmetry species of the various singlet and triplet levels in Fig. 4 by analogy with Pariser's assignments for benzene.[2] For benzene, Pariser predicts triplet minus states degenerate in energy with the corresponding singlet minus states. Thus, there may exist a $^3B_{2u}^-$ state close in energy to the lowest excited singlet ($^1B_{2u}^-$) state. The corresponding T-T absorption from the $^3B_{1u}^+$ lowest triplet state would be parity forbidden and be at about 2.5μ in the infra-red and, hence, be extremely difficult to observe. The lack of temperature-dependence of the fluorescence yield and the high value (0.64) of the triplet yield of coronene[10] supports the above possibility.

The newly-observed triplets at 28,740 and 29,230 cm^{-1}, which we have assigned as $^3E_{2g}^+$ are nearly degenerate with the $^1E_{1u}^+$ state at 29,000 cm^{-1}. In view of the negligible energy gap and the parity-allowedness of the transition, the intersystem crossing $^1E_{1u}^+ \rightsquigarrow {}^3E_{2g}^+$ should be very fast and might effectively compete with the internal conversion $^1E_{1u}^+ \rightsquigarrow {}^1B_{1u}^+$ which, while spin-allowed, is parity-forbidden and involves an energy gap of almost 4000 cm^{-1}. If this is the case, Φ_F and Φ_T will depend on the excitation wavelength. Below 345 nm Φ_T should be found to have increased at the expense of Φ_F. Also triplet formation via this route would be much more rapid than via cross-over from the lowest excited singlet state. The doubled-ruby laser wavelength of 347 nm used in the present work is slightly too long to test the above hypothesis.

Above 29,000 cm^{-1} and below 50,000 cm^{-1}, no further energy matches between the zero-point levels of the higher singlet and triplet states occur. However, the two new singlets of g parity, identified in the present work, are separated by a quite large energy gap (7100 cm^{-1}) and the ground-state absorption spectrum shows no absorption maxima between 43,800 and 50,000 cm^{-1}.[11] Thus an energy gap of 6000 cm^{-1} may exist between the highest singlet g state and the highest singlet u state identified so far. This is a sufficiently large gap that intersystem crossing from the 49,800 cm^{-1} singlet level to the triplet manifold could conceivably compete with internal conversion to lower singlets. Fast intersystem crossing to the triplet manifold from higher excited singlet states may offer an explanation for a current puzzle in radiation chemistry. Following nanosecond pulse radiolysis of naphthalene and anthracene, the majority of the triplet appears immediately and only a small fraction grows in at later times.[12] Similar behavior has been observed very recently for coronene.[13] Rapid cross-over from higher singlets could account for this phenomenon.

Finally, the present results shed new light upon the problem of the mechanism of intramolecular radiationless transitions. Rhodes, Henry and Kasha[14] (RHK) presented very recently a stationary-state model in which the phenomenon of a radiationless transition as a kinetically observable process was eliminated. In this model the absorption of light by the ground state carried the molecule to an excited state of mixed character. In the case of excitation to what we normally think of as the lowest excited singlet state, the terminal state subsequent to light absorption is actually a state of mixed singlet-triplet character. From this viewpoint, there should be no distinction between the time of formation of the excited singlet and the triplet state; both should be formed at the same time. We pointed out that our laser photolysis observations are at variance with this viewpoint.[15] As can be seen from Fig. 2, the triplet state of coronene is not formed promptly with the act of light excitation. The lowest excited singlet state, as shown by the immediate appearance of both fluorescence and of excited singlet absorption, is formed promptly. Subsequently, the decay of the singlet and the concomitant appearance of the triplet can be followed over a period of many hundreds of nanoseconds. There is no doubt then that, in our experimental system, the S_1 state and the T_1 state are physically distinct entities, that the process of intersystem crossing from S_1 to T_1 is physically meaningful, and that the progress of the conversion can be observed and followed in kinetic fashion.

More recently RHK[16] have stated that their viewpoint stated above applies only to the limiting case of a single-frequency radiation field interacting with the molecule. In other words, the time-independent picture of an excited state of mixed singlet-triplet character applies only to the situation where a single vibronic level of the upper state is populated. Such a level constitutes a true stationary state of the complete Hamiltonian, including the portions which are left out in making the Born-Oppenheimer approximation. Thus, in the absence of collisions or further radiative perturbation, the wave-function of this level will not evolve with time.

The above situation is of interest conceptually, but is usually far removed from situations of practical interest or attainability. The density of vibronic levels in the vibrationally excited T_1 state at an energy equal to the zero-point level of the S_1 state is extremely large. From the expressions used by Bixon and Jortner,[17] Jortner and Berry[18] and by Robinson,[19,20] in their theoretical treatments of radiationless transitions, we estimate a density of approximately 10^4 cm (states per wave-number) for the vibrationally excited lowest triplet ($^3B_{1u}^+$) of coronene at the zero-point level of the lowest excited singlet ($^1B_{2u}^-$) state. The density increases rapidly with increasing energy gap, so that at levels corresponding to excitation to a vibrationally excited $^1B_{2u}^-$ state, the density in the $^3B_{1u}^+$ state will be even higher. Thus, even using a pulsed ruby laser as an excitation source, with a typical bandwidth of 1 cm^{-1}, an excited state comprising a superposition of many thousands of the exact eigenstates will be produced. Such a state will be time-dependent. Its internal distribution among the assembly of eigenstates will change with time. From time-to-time the distribution will approximate the Born-Oppenheimer description of what we call the $^1B_{2u}^-$ state and the emission of fluorescence will be possible.[18] At other times it will approximate the B-O description of the vibrationally excited triplet and, provided the molecule can lose energy by collision or transfer to a lattice, it will become stabilized in the lower vibrational levels of the $^3B_{1u}^+$ triplet.

The collisional loss of vibrational energy by the excited triplet is probably very fast (10^{-12} sec). Thus the observable process of intersystem crossing depicted in Fig. 2 must correspond to the probability with which the ensemble of initially-excited eigenstates attains a distribution corresponding to the B-O vibrationally excited triplet. In other words, even using the stationary state model, the concept of intersystem crossing (or internal conversion) is still quite similar to earlier descriptions of a rate-controlling adiabatic crossing of potential energy surfaces, followed by collisional loss of excess vibrational energy. Thus, as stated recently by RHK,[16] in the limit of excitation by radiation of broad bandwidth relative to the manifold of B-O states, it becomes meaningful to speak of radiationless transitions as physically observable kinetic processes. The majority of intramolecular radiationless processes in aromatic hydrocarbons appear to lie in this limit, using presently available pulsed laser light sources.

REFERENCES

1. S. K. Lower and M. A. El-Sayed, Chem. Rev. 66, 199 (1966).
2. R. Pariser, J. Chem. Phys. 24, 250 (1956).
3. W. L. Peticolas, Ann. Rev. Phys. Chem. 18, 233 (1967).
4. J. R. Novak and M. W. Windsor, J. Chem. Phys. 47, 3075 (1967).
5. G. Porter, in Technique of Organic Chemistry, A. Weissberger, Ed. (Interscience, New York, 1963), Vol. VIII, Pt. 2, Chap. 19, p. 1059.
6. TRW Instruments, Model 1D, 139 Illinois Street, El Segundo, California 90245.
7. M. W. Windsor and J. R. Novak, The Triplet State, A. Zahlan, Ed. (Cambridge University Press, New York, 1967), p. 229.
8. E. Clar, Polycyclic Hydrocarbons (Academic Press, New York, 1964), Vol. 2.
9. M. W. Windsor, W. R. Dawson, R. S. Moore and D. Weber, "Research on Triplet States and Photochromism for Flash Blindness Protection, 1965, Annual Report, USAF Contract AF41(609)-2425. Available as ASTIC 026791.
10. W. R. Dawson and J. L. Kropp (unpublished results).
11. E. Clar (private communication).
12. J. W. Hunt and J. K. Thomas, J. Chem. Phys. 46, 2954 (1967).
13. J. K. Thomas (private communication).
14. W. C. Rhodes, B. R. Henry and M. Kasha, Symposium on the Nature of Excited States of Organic Molecules, U. of California, Riverside, December, 1967.
15. M. W. Windsor and J. R. Novak, Symposium on the Nature of Excited States of Aromatic Molecules, University of California, Riverside, December 1967.
16. B. R. Henry and M. Kasha, Ann. Revs. Phys. Chem. 00, 000 (1968).

17. M. Bixon and J. Jortner, J. Chem. Phys. 48, 715 (1968).
18. J. Jortner and R. S. Berry, J. Chem. Phys. 48, 2757 (1968).
19. G. W. Robinson, The Triplet State, A. Zahlan, Ed. (Cambridge University Press, New York, 1967), p. 213.
20. G. W. Robinson, J. Chem. Phys. 47, 1967 (1967).

DIRECT MEASUREMENT OF THE LIFETIME OF BENZENE IN ITS VIBRATIONLESS $^1B_{2u}$ STATE

Teh-hsuan Chen and E. W. Schlag

Department of Chemistry
Northwestern University
Evanston, Illinois 60201

Direct timing of the fluorescence emission from selected quantum levels gives one information about microscopic rate processes for excited vibronic states. Preferably one would like such information for all possible monochromatic excitations of the relevant electronic manifold. These lifetimes directly represent the cross-sections for the isolated systems initially prepared. In general they are expected to differ strongly from lifetimes which are a result of radiation from the ground vibronic state, or near thereto. One way to obtain information about vibronic states is from a measurement of yields, which is a competitive measurement between two or more microscopic processes. Alternatively one can obtain such information by timing these molecular processes against a laboratory clock. This would have the additional benefit that the cross-sections are absolute, in the sense that they are compared to a known laboratory time standard. Such measurements then must be performed with monochromatic light, with nanosecond timing definition, absorbed in a gas which is in the low pressure region. A sensitive apparatus was recently developed and the lifetime spectrum was observed for β-naphthylamine.[1] A similar study for benzene, however, is made considerably more difficult by its low absorptivity.

The only available data to our knowledge on the lifetime of benzene is the work of Donovan and Duncan,[2] who measured the lifetime of benzene excited in a low pressure discharge (p = 0.008-0.75 Torr). Under these conditions they observed that the inverse lifetime was given as

$$\tau^{-1} = \{1.69 + 20.7\ P(\mathrm{Torr})\} \times 10^{6}\ \mathrm{sec}^{-1} \qquad (1)$$

The interesting feature here is that τ^{-1} increases with pressure, whereas our previous experience[1] led us to expect a decrease of τ^{-1} with pressure. The limiting low pressure value of

$$\tau^{-1} = 1.69 \times 10^{6}\ \mathrm{sec}^{-1} \qquad (2)$$

was then taken as the lifetime. This lifetime is probably some average over the excited states initially prepared in the discharge, which may be more than just the lowest state. The limiting value (2) is close to the value for the radiative lifetime obtained by McClure,[3] suggesting, that in the low pressure limit no other processes are possible, all states, isolated from collisions, only leading to radiative emission. Other results appear to indicate, however, that other processes can occur, the quantum yield for fluorescence being considerably less than unity,[4] thus leading to apparently conflicting conclusions. For these reasons it was decided that it might be of interest to determine this lifetime by the techniques applied to β-naphthylamine.[1]

It was decided to attempt to populate benzene with the least possible energy in its first absorbing vibronic state, at 2590 Å, with sufficient monochromaticity to ensure that only this 523 cm^{-1} state is occupied. The experimental setup was similar to the one employed previously.[1] The monochromator was set for a bandwidth of 10 Å, which was considered sufficiently monochromatic. The pressure was varied between 5-85 Torr of pure benzene (zone refined material).

The process is represented as a simple two-level model (Fig. I) the solution to which was given previously[5] as

$$\cot\Phi = \beta + \frac{(\gamma - \beta)(1 + \beta^2)}{(\alpha p)^2 + \alpha p(\beta + \gamma) + (1 + \beta^2)} \tag{3}$$

where

$$\alpha = \frac{Z}{\omega}; \quad \beta = \frac{k_2 + k_f}{\omega}; \quad \gamma = \frac{k_1 + k_f}{\omega}$$

where Z is the collision frequency and ω is the light modulation frequency. In being a two-level solution one must observe the same cautions in the application of (3) as one does for applications of the Stern-Volmer relation and other two-level solutions. A many level theory for such processes is available,[6] but would lead to too many undetermined constants to be suitable here. For (3) it can be seen that the low pressure limit of (3) is just

$$\cot\Phi = \gamma \tag{4}$$

and the high pressure limit is

$$\cot\Phi = \beta \tag{5}$$

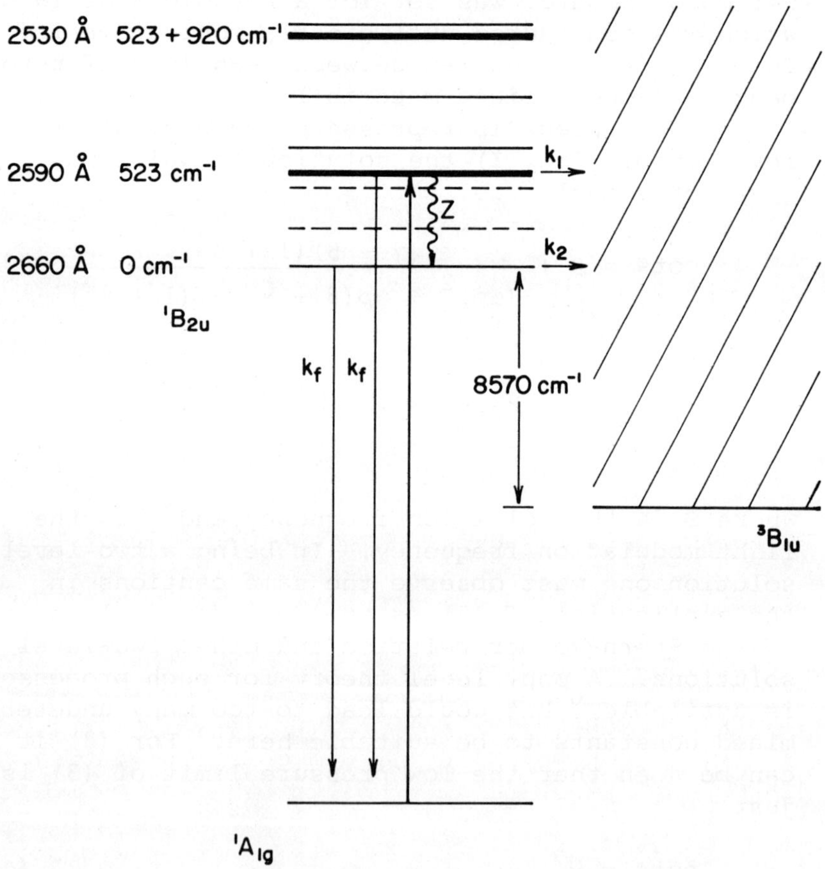
2530 Å 523 + 920 cm⁻¹
2590 Å 523 cm⁻¹
2660 Å 0 cm⁻¹
¹B₂ᵤ
k₁
k₂
Z
kf
kf
8570 cm⁻¹
³B₁ᵤ
¹A₁g

Figure 1

where (4) and (5) are just of the form

$$\omega\tau = \tan\Phi \tag{6}$$

sometimes referred to as the exponential decay relation. At intermediate pressures $\cot\Phi$ is seen to be pressure dependent, and hence an exponential relation such as (6) does not apply, but rather the full form (3) must be employed. It can also be seen that in the low pressure region $\cot\Phi$ falls linear with pressure, and in the high region $\cot\Phi$ rises linearly with $1/p^2$.[7] Both of these relations are useful limiting methods for graphical extrapolation to obtain γ and β respectively. Such linear extrapolation methods, however, require that there be sufficient data in the linear region to find a limiting slope. More seriously, limiting slope methods reject the data in the transition region, data which is usually known with higher accuracy. For these reasons it was decided to fit all the data to the exact equation (3) obtaining the best values for α, β, and γ by a non-linear least squares regression.[7] Such programs can display severe instabilities if the scatter in the data is large. Nevertheless it is usually possible, with various modifications,[7] to obtain good fits for α, β, and γ, this then having the advantage that all the data were used in the determination of the constants. For this case of benzene, γ is the reduced lifetime[8] of the 523 cm^{-1} state, and β is the reduced lifetime for the ground vibronic state for the $^1B_{2u}$ manifold. α is the collision cross section for depopulation of the 523 cm^{-1} state by benzene collisions. Upon inserting the known laboratory modulation frequency, these values become absolute values for the cross sections of the relevant processes.

The results can be seen in Fig. 2 (frequency = 10 MHz) for $\cot\Phi$ vs pressure for all the points of Table 1, Fig. 3 displays $\cot\Phi$ vs $1/p^2$ for a single run to illustrate the extrapolation for β.

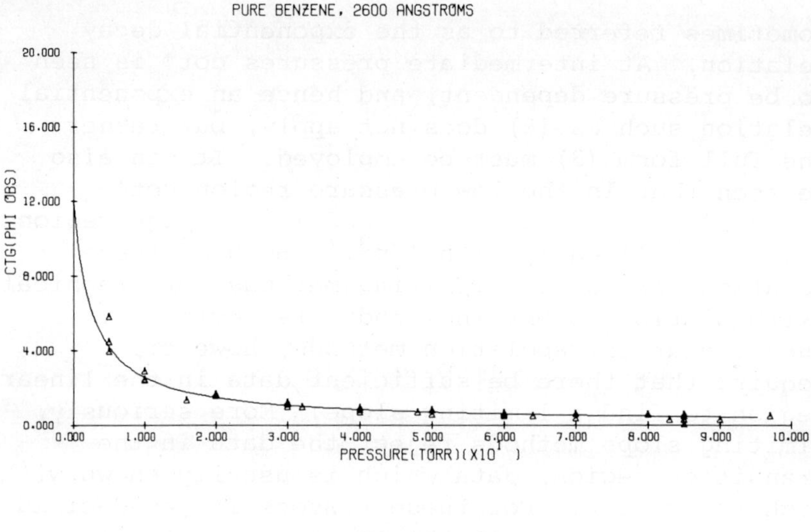

Figure 2

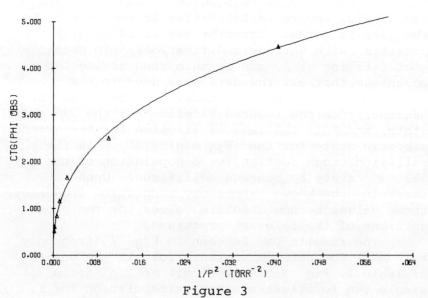

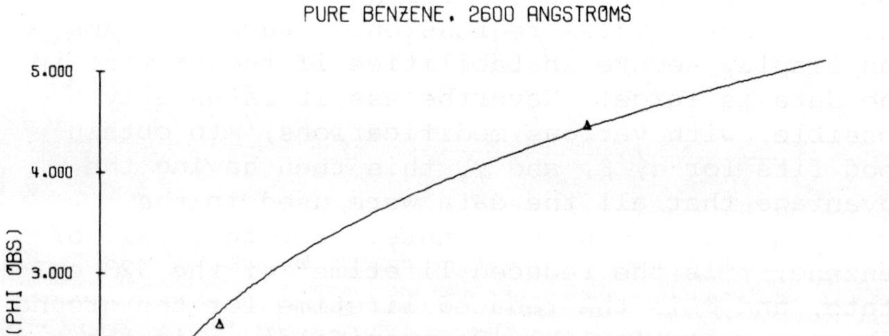

Figure 3

TABLE I: Observed Phase Angle (Φ) vs Pressure of Pure Benzene

Set No.	Φ(deg.)	cotΦ	Pressure (torr)
6	9.73	5.83	5.0
1	14.10	3.98	5.0
2	12.61	4.47	5.0
6	18.90	2.92	10.0
1	22.36	2.43	10.0
2	21.80	2.50	10.0
5	35.93	1.38	16.0
6	32.00	1.60	20.0
1	30.91	1.67	20.0
2	31.07	1.66	20.0
6	38.44	1.26	30.0
1	45.14	0.995	30.0
2	40.76	1.16	30.0
5	45.00	1.00	32.0
6	45.87	0.970	40.0
1	54.55	0.712	40.0
2	49.97	0.840	40.0
5	53.98	0.727	48.0
6	49.30	0.860	50.0
1	59.59	0.587	50.0
6	55.39	0.690	60.0
1	62.89	0.512	60.0
2	58.62	0.610	60.0
5	62.98	0.510	64.0
6	57.38	0.640	70.0
1	67.51	0.414	70.0
6	58.62	0.610	80.0
1	72.56	0.320	83.0
6	61.63	0.540	97.0
2	62.53	0.520	85.0
	72.52	0.315	85.0
	72.52	0.315	85.0
	62.35	0.524	85.0
	72.52	0.315	85.0
	87.02	0.052	85.0
	58.20	0.620	85.0
5	72.00	0.325	90.0

It should be noted that cotΦ falls with pressure as predicted by (3), and in distinction to (1). Furthermore the intercepts obtained from a use of all data so far taken are γ = 12 and β = 0.20 (line drawn in Fig. 2 and 3). This leads to

$$\tau_1 = (k_1 + k_f)^{-1} = 1.3 \text{ nsec} \qquad (7a)$$

$$\tau_2 = (k_2 + k_f)^{-1} = 80 \text{ nsec} \qquad (7b)$$

McClure's value[3,9b] for k_f leads to 1.42×10^6 sec^{-1}. Combining this with (7b) results in a high pressure fluorescence quantum yield of Φ_f = 0.12, in good agreement with the value of Noyes, Harter, and Mulac[4a] of $\Phi_f = 0.18 \pm 0.04$. Thus the vibrationless lifetime here determined is consistent with the known high pressure quantum yields and the known strength of the transition. If the value of k_f is now subtracted in (7), one obtains

$$k_1 = 7.5 \times 10^8 \text{ sec}^{-1} \qquad (8a)$$

$$k_2 = 1.1 \times 10^7 \text{ sec}^{-1} \qquad (8b)$$

Although, as can be seen from Fig. 2, (8b) is known far better than (8a), these differ approximately by a factor of 70 for a change in energy of only 523 cm^{-1} (∿1.5 kcal/mole). If all the rates are indeed homogeneous Poisson processes, and k_f is the same for both states, then the ratio of lifetimes in (7) must just be the ratio of the fluorescence quantum yields for the two levels.[10] It must, however, be observed that k_1 is obtained by extrapolation from relatively high pressures with a two-level model. A two level system leads to no problems as long as the system is studied near the limiting range. This is true for the high pressure value, but probably not the low pressure value (see Fig. 3). Experiments are in progress to extend the range to lower pressures. The Poisson nature of the process will be investigated by a change of modulation frequency.

It has been suggested by Robinson and Frosch[9] that rate constants for intersystems crossing in benzene be given by an application of the first order expression[11]

$$W = \frac{2\pi}{\hbar}\left| H \right|^2 \rho(E) \qquad (9)$$

where in addition the assumption is made that the interaction per final quantum state can be approximated by a constant $\overline{\beta}^2$. This has the effect that (9) is largely independent of the state density[9b] in contrast to a phase space theory which would be essentially linear with the state density. In this equation $\rho(E)$ is the relevant density of states for triplet benzene ($^3B_{1u}$), which start 8570 cm^{-1} below the ground vibronic state of $^1B_{2u}$.

The density of states is a rather complicated stair-case function with energy, due to the quantum levels of all the overtones and combinations of the 3n-6 normal vibrations. For many purposes, particularly at higher energies, these steps can be smoothed. A properly smoothed result is given by the finite series of Schlag and Sandsmark[12] as a geometric mean expanded about an arithmetic mean

$$\rho(E) = \sum_{i\,odd} A_i(\omega_1, \ldots, \omega_{3n-6})(E + E_z)^{s-i} \qquad (10)$$

$$E_z = \tfrac{1}{2}\sum_i hc\omega_i$$

of which three terms were evaluated explicitly. Some further terms were given by Haarhoff,[13] but the general form of the coefficients for the complete series was finally given by Thiele.[14] Equation (10) is easily written as a subroutine on the machine, and constitutes an unambiguous method of obtaining the densities for use in (9) from the spectroscopic normal vibrations of the molecule of interest. Some of these values for benzene are tabulated in Table II. It can be seen from this table that the density per cm^{-1} for

TABLE II: Densities of Energy Levels in Benzene

E (cm^{-1})	$^1A_{1g}$ $\rho(E) \times cm^{-1}$*	$^1B_{2u}$ $\rho(E) \times cm^{-1}$**
8600	5.71×10^4	7.89×10^5
8700	6.50×10^4	9.04×10^5
8800	7.39×10^4	1.04×10^6
8900	8.39×10^4	1.18×10^6
9000	9.53×10^4	1.35×10^6
9100	1.08×10^5	1.55×10^6
9200	1.23×10^5	1.76×10^6
9300	1.39×10^5	2.01×10^6
9400	1.57×10^5	2.29×10^6
9500	1.78×10^5	2.61×10^6
9600	2.01×10^5	2.97×10^6
9700	2.27×10^5	3.38×10^6
9800	2.57×10^5	3.83×10^6
9900	2.90×10^5	4.35×10^6
10000	3.27×10^5	4.94×10^6
10100	3.68×10^5	5.60×10^6
10200	4.15×10^5	6.34×10^6
10300	4.67×10^5	7.18×10^6
10400	5.25×10^5	8.12×10^6
10500	5.90×10^5	9.17×10^6
10600	6.63×10^5	1.04×10^7
10700	7.44×10^5	1.17×10^7
10800	8.35×10^5	1.32×10^7
10900	9.36×10^5	1.49×10^7

*Frequencies for the $^1A_{1g}$ state from J. H. Callomon, T. M. Dunn, and I. M. Mills, Phil. Trans. Roy. Soc. (London) 259A, 499 (1966), see also G. Herzberg, Electronic Spectra of Polyatomic Molecules, (Van Nostrand, Princeton, 1966), p. 666.
**Frequencies for $^1B_{2u}$ are known only below 1000 cm^{-1}, except for ν_1, and ν_{15}. These latter two indicate only a small change from the $^1A_{1g}$ state. Hence the $^1A_{1g}$ frequencies were used here for the unknown frequencies above 1000 cm^{-1}.

the lower vibronic state is 7×10^5, whereas for the upper state, 523 cm^{-1} higher, is 2×10^6. These numbers may be scaled down because not all vibrations contribute equally to this process.[9b] If one uses this full density of states and the value for k_2 in (8b) above, one obtains $\overline{\beta} = 3.7 \times 10^{-6}$ compared to the state spacing of 1.4×10^{-6}. These two numbers would tend to suggest that the intersystems crossing process alone may contribute sufficient broadening of states to behave as a large molecule. This result is essentially unchanged if the density were reduced by a factor of 7 due to Franck-Condon restrictions.[9b]

In conclusion, it was shown possible to observe a lifetime from benzene when it is populated with 2600 Å radiation, the first strong absorption line in the spectrum. From the pressure dependence high and low pressure lifetimes are obtained by extrapolation. The extrapolated high pressure value of 80 nsec represents the lifetime of the vibrationless ground state of the $^1B_{2u}$ manifold. The low pressure value of 1.3 nsec is obtained with less precision due to high scattered light, and more work on this is in progress. The ground state lifetime is in good agreement with the observed quantum yield for this state.

ACKNOWLEDGEMENT

We wish to thank Mr. Ben Blaney for performing many of the machine computations. We also with to thank the Air Force Office of Scientific Research for their sponsorship of this work.

REFERENCES

1. (a) H. von Weyssenhoff and E. W. Schlag, Ber. Bunsenges. 1178 (1967).
   (b) Ibid. 72, 153 (1968).
   (c) Ibid. 72, 155 (1968).
2. J. W. Donovan, A. B. F. Duncan, J. Chem. Phys. 35, 1389 (1961).
3. D. S. McClure, J. of Chem. Phys. 17, 905 (1949).
4. (a) W. A. Noyes, W. A. Mulac and D. A. Harter, J. Chem. Phys. 44, 2100 (1966).
   (b) E. M. Anderson and G. B. Kistiakowsky, J. Chem. Phys. 48, 4787 (1968).
   (c) A. E. Douglas and C. W. Mathews, J. Chem. Phys. 48, 4788 (1968).
5. E. W. Schlag, H. von Weyssenhoff and M. E. Starzak, J. Chem. Phys. 47, 1860 (1967).
6. E. W. Schlag, S. J. Yao and H. von Weyssenhoff, J. Chem. Phys. (in press).
7. (a) H. von Weyssenhoff and E. W. Schlag (unpublished results).
   (b) M. E. Starzak, Ph.D. thesis, Northwestern University, 1968.
8. $\gamma = (\omega\tau_1)^{-1}$, hence the lifetime is reduced by the period of the modulation.
9. (a) G. W. Robinson and R. P. Frosch, J. Chem. Phys. 37, 1962 (1962).
   (b) G. W. Robinson, J. of Chem. Phys. 47, 1967 (1967).
10. The observed quantum yield ratio appears to be somewhat smaller than this (C. S. Parmenter, private communication).
11. See for example C. Kittel, Elementary Statistical Physics, (Wiley, New York, 1958), p. 173.
12. E. W. Schlag and R. A. Sandsmark, J. Chem. Phys. 37, 168 (1962).
13. P. C. Haarhoff, Mol. Phys. 6, 337 (1963); 7, 101 (1963).
14. (a) E. Thiele, J. Chem. Phys. 39, 3258 (1963).
    (b) E. W. Schlag, R. A. Sandsmark and W. G. Valence, J. Phys. Chem. 69, 1431 (1965).

SOLVENT EXCITATION MIGRATION IN LIQUID SCINTILLATORS: A THEORETICAL STUDY

S. Georghiou

Laboratory for Biophysical Chemistry
Dcpartment of Chemistry
University of Minnesota
Minneapolis, Minnesota 55455

K. Razi Naqvi
Atomic and Molecular Physics Group
Schuster Laboratory
University of Manchester
Manchester 13, England

I. INTRODUCTION

That the excitation energy of a fluorescent solvent in a liquid scintillator flits from one solvent molecule to another has been established by numerous, and largely concordant, experimental investigations. But, despite the general agreement on the occurrence of solvent excitation migration, the mechanism through which an excited solvent molecule hands over its excitation to a similar but unexcited neighbor awaits settlement.

Voltz and his associates proposed that, in benzene and its methyl derivatives, the excitation migrates on account of octopole-octopole interaction between solvent molecules.[1,2] They estimated, from theoretical considerations, the magnitude of Λ, the coefficient of migration, and found it to be in rough agreement with experiment. However, the crudity of quantum mechanical calculations on interactions between large molecules prohibits any attempt to quantify the deductions based on their model. The proposed scheme cannot, for instance, be used to forecast the values of Λ for a particular solvent; or how Λ would vary when the concentration of the primary solvent is lowered by adding to it an inert secondary solvent.

Birks and his collaborators have suggested, as an alternative, a mechanism based on successive excimer formation and dissociation.[3,4] It is our aim to evolve, in this paper, a mathematical account of migration by using this model as the basis of our calculations; to see whether it gives reasonable values for Λ; and to study the dependence of Λ on the concentration of the primary solvent. We will treat migration first as a problem in the kinetics of a multistage reaction and then as a case of random walk in three dimensions.

II. THEORY

Consider a process in which a substance A_1 undergoes a reaction in the following successive stages

$$A_1 \underset{k_1'}{\overset{k_1}{\rightleftharpoons}} A_2 \underset{k_2'}{\overset{k_2}{\rightleftharpoons}} A_3 \cdots A_i \underset{k_i'}{\overset{k_i}{\rightleftharpoons}} A_{i+1} \cdots A_s \underset{k_s'}{\overset{k_s}{\rightleftharpoons}}$$
$$A_{s+1} \xrightarrow{k_{s+1}} \text{products} \qquad (1)$$

where k_i and k_i' denote the rate parameters for the forward and backward reactions involved in the ith stage of process (1).

Nikitin[5] has established, without assuming the existence of equilibrium conditions, the following relations which connect the effective rate parameter k for the overall reaction (1) with those for the individual stages:

$$k^{-1} = \sum_{i=0}^{s} k^{-1}_{(s+1-i)} \qquad (2)$$

where

$$k_{s+1-i} = \left[\frac{1}{k_{i+1}} + \frac{k_{i+1}'}{k_{i+1} k_{i+2}} + \cdots \right.$$

$$\left. \cdots + \frac{k_{i+1}' k_{i+2}' \cdots k_s'}{k_{i+1} k_{i+2} \cdots k_s k_{s+1}} \right] \qquad (3)$$

Equation (2) was derived by using the pseudo-stationary state approximation for the concentration of the reactants.

Let us now consider a liquid scintillator comprising an aromatic solvent and a solute, and let it be continuously illuminated by a light source of constant intensity so that a photostationary state is established. The mechanism under consideration can be represented as

$$M_1^* + M_2 \underset{\frac{1}{2}k_d}{\overset{k_a n}{\rightleftharpoons}} D_{12}^* \underset{k_a'}{\overset{\frac{1}{2}k_d}{\rightleftharpoons}} M_1 + M_2^* + M_3 \underset{\frac{1}{2}k_d}{\overset{k_a n}{\rightleftharpoons}}$$

$$D_{23}^* \underset{k_a'}{\overset{\frac{1}{2}k_d}{\rightleftharpoons}} M_2 + M_3^* + M_4 \underset{\frac{1}{2}k_d}{\overset{k_a n}{\rightleftharpoons}} D_{34}^* \cdots \qquad (4)$$

where M stands for an unexcited solvent monomer, M^* and D^* designate the excited monomer and the excimer respectively; n denotes the concentration (number of molecules per c.c.) of the solvent; $k_a n(\text{sec}^{-1})$ is the rate parameter for the formation of the excimer, $k_d(\text{sec}^{-1})$ that for its dissociation; k_a' represents the probability per second that, after its constituent monomers have been torn asunder, an excimer will be re-formed (from the same monomer units which originally associated to generate it). k_a and k_a' are both numerically equal to pk_e, where k_e is the number of encounters that would occur per unit time if there were just two molecules present (one in the ground state and the other electronically excited), and p is the probability that an encounter between these results in excimer formation. It is evident that for any system of practical interest the inequality

$$k_a n >> k_a' \tag{5}$$

is valid. We will assume, in keeping with experimental results,[6] that the processes of excimer formation and dissociation are much more rapid than the unimolecular processes of radiative and nonradiative decay which compete for the relaxation of M^* and D^*.

On comparing the processes (1) and (4) the following relations emerge:

$$k_1 = k_3 = k_5 = k_7 \ . \ . \ . = k_a n \tag{6}$$

$$k_2 = k_4 = k_6 = k_8 \ . \ . \ . = \tfrac{1}{2}k_d \tag{7}$$

$$k_1' = k_3' = k_5' = k_7' \ . \ . \ . = \tfrac{1}{2}k_d \tag{8}$$

$$k_2' = k_4' = k_6' = k_8' \ . \ . \ . = k_a' \tag{9}$$

The final expression for the sum $\sum_{i=0}^{s} k_{s+1-i}^{-1}$ will depend on whether s + 1, the total number of stages, is even or odd. Now migration is defined as the process whereby an unexcited molecule acquires energy from a similar but excited entity; hence the only physically meaningful case is that which terminates after an even number of stages, for an odd number of stages can only carry energy from a monomer to an excimer (and vice versa). It is also apparent that for process (1) $\Lambda_M \equiv \Lambda_D$ ($=\Lambda$, say), where the subscripts M and D refer to the monomer and the excimer respectively.

We now evaluate k for the case of interest, viz., that involving an even number of stages. It can be easily verified that:

We now evaluate k for the case of interest, viz., that involving an even number of stages. It can be easily verified that:

$$k^{-1}_{(s+1-i)} = \frac{2}{k_a n} \cdot \frac{\left(\frac{k_a'}{k_a n}\right)^{\frac{s-i+1}{2}} - 1}{\frac{k_a'}{k_a n} - 1} \qquad (10)$$

when i is even;

$$k^{-1}_{(s+1-i)} = \frac{2}{k_d} + \frac{2k_a'}{k_d k_a n} + \frac{k_a'}{k_a^2 n^2} \qquad (11)$$

$$+ \frac{2}{k_a n}\left(\frac{k_a'}{k_a n}\right)^2 \frac{\left(\frac{k_a'}{k_a n}\right)^{\frac{s-i-2}{2}} - 1}{\frac{k_a'}{k_a n} - 1}$$

when i is odd. By making use of the inequality (5), and of equations (2), (10) and (11), we deduce the following expression for the effective rate constant k:

$$k = \frac{k_a n}{(s+1)\left(1 + \frac{k_a n}{k_d}\right)} \qquad (12)$$

Transforming the units of concentration to the usual moles per liter, we rewrite equation (12) as

$$k = \frac{k_{DM}[M]}{(s+1)\left(1 + \frac{k_{DM}[M]}{k_{MD}}\right)} \qquad (13)$$

where k_{DM} is the rate parameter of excimer formation expressed in l $mole^{-1}$ sec^{-1}, [M] denotes the molar concentration of the solvent, and k_d has been replaced by k_{MD}. Substituting

$$K_e = \frac{k_{DM}}{k_{MD}}$$

one gets

$$k = \frac{k_{DM}[M]}{(s + 1)(1 + K_e[M])} \qquad (14)$$

We see from (4) that after every two stages the excitation energy traverses by one molecular diameter (=d, say). To calculate the total displacement of the energy after (s + 1) stages we make use of the well known relation derived for the analogous phenomenon of random flights in three dimensions[7] and write

$$6\Lambda t = Nd^2 \qquad (15)$$

where $N = (\frac{s + 1}{2})$ represents the total number of steps, and during each step the excitation energy suffers a displacement d of constant length but in a random direction.

Solving equation (15) for Λ, replacing N by $\frac{1}{2}(s + 1)$ and 1/t by the right-hand side of equation (14), we find

$$\Lambda = \frac{d^2 k_{DM}[M]}{12(1 + K_e[M])} \qquad (16)$$

It is instructive to note here that Birks and Conte[4] derived a similar expression through a less rigorous argument which took into account only the first two stages of process (4).

III. COMPARISON WITH EXPERIMENT

The experimental determination of k_{DM}, the bimolecular rate parameter of excimer formation, has hitherto been confined to solute molecules. It has been shown[8] that k_{DM} can be adequately expressed as

$$k_{DM} = pk_c \tag{17}$$

where p is the probability of excimer formation during a bimolecular encounter and k_c is the encounter frequency which can be calculated from the often used relation

$$k_c = \frac{8RT}{3000\eta} \tag{18}$$

Birks, Braga & Lumb[6] assumed that, for benzene, toluene, p-xylene and mesitylene, p = 1, and used equation (18) to calculate k_{DM} for these solvents. Later, Birks and Conte[4] inferred, from their studies on solvent-solute energy transfer, that equation (18) gives values ($\sim 10^{10}$ l mole^{-1}sec^{-1}) which are too low by a factor of ~ 10. Substitution of the numerical values of the different parameters in equation (16) indicates that agreement with reported values of Λ would result if $10^{10} < k_{DM} < 10^{11}$.

The influence of dilution of primary solvent by an inert solvent, such as cyclohexane, has been investigated by some workers.[9-11] Their results show that the addition of a diluent lowers the magnitude of Λ in a manner qualitatively consistent with that demanded by equation (16). Here again we are unable to make quantitative deductions for want of experimental values of k_{DM} at different concentrations of the primary solvent.

In sum, then, the validity of the expression derived by us can be checked only if experimental values of k_{DM} are known. However, the qualitative agreement with the published data indicates that the approach adopted in this paper leads to an acceptable description of the phenomenon of solvent excitation migration in liquid scintillators.

ACKNOWLEDGEMENT

We thank Dr. J. B. Birks for making a helpful comment about the use of equation (15).

REFERENCES

1. R. Voltz, G. Laustriat and A. Coche, C. R. Acad. Sci. 257, 1473 (1963).
2. R. Voltz, J. Klein, C. Tanielian, H. Lami, F. Heisel, G. Laustriat and A. Coche, Proc. Intern. Symposium Nuclear Electronics (European Nuclear Encrgy Agency, Paris, 1964), p. 71.
3. J. B. Birks, J. C. Conte and G. Walker, IEEE Trans. Nucl. Sci. NS-13, No. 3, 148 (1965).
4. J. B. Birks and J. C. Conte, Proc. Roy. Soc. A303, 85 (1968).
5. (a) E. E. Nikitin (private communication.)
   (b) E. A. Peshenichnov, Proc. Acad. Sci. USSR (Dokiady Akademii Nauk SSSR), Physical Chemistry Section, Engl. transl., 166, 91 (1966) and references cited therein.
6. J. B. Birks, C. L. Braga and M. D. Lumb, Proc. Roy. Soc. A194, 283 (1965).
7. S. Chandrasekhar, Rev. Mod. Phys. 15, 1 (1943).
8. J. B. Birks, M. D. Lumb, and I. H. Munro, Proc. Roy. Soc. A280, 289 (1964).
9. J. T. Dubois and J. W. van Loben Sels, Intern. Symposium. Org. Scint., Argonne Nat. Lab., 1964.
10. C. Tanielian, thesis, Strasbourg, 1965.
11. J. Nafisi-Movaghar, J. B. Birks and K. Razi Naqvi, Proc. Phys. Soc. 91, 499 (1967).

TRIPLET STATE QUENCHING OF STIMULATED EMISSION FROM ORGANIC DYE SOLUTIONS

A. V. Buettner, B. B. Snavely, and O. G. Peterson

Research Laboratories,
Eastman Kodak Company
Rochester, New York 14650

I. INTRODUCTION

The observation of stimulated emission from an organic dye solution excited by a giant-pulse ruby laser was first reported by Sorokin and Lankard.[1] Shortly after this initial publication similar results were reported by Schäfer et al.[2] and others.[3,4]

A careful investigation of the properties of the laser-pumped laser led Sorokin and Lankard[5] to the conclusion that the threshold for stimulated emission could also be reached by flash-lamp excitation of a dye solution. They subsequently observed stimulated emission from several organic dyes excited by a very fast flashlamp of their own design. Schmidt and Schäfer,[6] working independently but following an approach similar to that of Sorokin and Lankard, reported similar results. Since these early reports, many interesting, and poorly understood, phenomena have been observed in solutions exhibiting stimulated emission. Of these phenomena one of the most interesting, and important from a practical standpoint, is a marked quenching of stimulated emission attributed to the losses associated with the triplet state of the dye molecules.

Stimulated emission from flashlamp-excited dye solutions begins at a well-defined threshold of excitation intensity and is quenched at pump light intensities higher than that for which stimulated emission is initiated. The effect is clearly shown in the data of Schmidt and Schäfer and has been discussed in some detail by Sorokin et al. in a recent review article.[7] Sorokin et al., and Schmidt and Schäfer, proposed that optical absorption by dye molecules accumulating in a molecular triplet state by intersystem single-triplet crossing during the excitation of the dye is responsible for this quenching. The explanation is generally accepted.

This effect, detrimental as it is to the operation of a dye laser, may be used to study the dynamics of triplet formation and intersystem crossing on a time scale of less than a microsecond, a time domain which is difficult to reach with conventional flash photolysis techniques.

In this paper we report the results of measurement of triplet and singlet state concentrations and intersystem crossing rates in solutions of fluorescein (disodium salt), rhodamine B, and rhodamine 6G, deduced from the observation of stimulated, or laser, emission, from these dyes. The emission is used as a probe to determine optical losses within the dye at the time stimulated emission begins.

First we discuss the theoretical considerations involved in determining the "critical inversion" for the dye solutions, i.e., the number of excited singlet state molecules per unit volume required for stimulated emission. The number of excited molecules per unit volume required to obtain critical inversion is influenced by the number of molecules in the triplet state. By comparing the actual value of the critical inversion with that expected in the absence of triplet state molecules, the triplet state density can be deduced. Since the excited singlet and triplet state densities are known at a particular instant, the onset of stimulated emission, the intersystem crossing rate constant may be estimated.

II. THEORETICAL CONSIDERATIONS

A. CALCULATION OF THE CRITICAL INVERSION. The mechanism for stimulated emission, illustrated schematically in terms of the energy levels of a dye molecule, is shown in Fig. 1. Excitation occurs with the absorption of light from the flashlamp, which raises the energy of the dye molecules from the singlet ground state to a higher vibrational level of the first excited singlet state. The molecular energy decays non-radiatively to the lowest level, level 2, of the excited singlet state. The laser emission results from a stimulated transition from level 2 to level 1, which is an excited vibrational level of the lowest singlet state. Nonradiative decay from this level to the ground state terminates the process.

If we assume level 1 to be empty, the process of Fig. 1 is analogous to the four-level laser, or phonon-terminated maser, processes analyzed by Yariv and Gordon[8] and McCumber.[9] Applying the relationship for the "start oscillation" condition of Yariv and Gordon[8] gives the critical inversion

$$n_{2c} = \frac{8\pi\tau}{\lambda_\ell^4 E(\lambda_\ell) t_o} \qquad (1)$$

to initiate stimulated emission from an organic dye solution contained within an optical cavity. In this equation τ is the fluorescence decay time

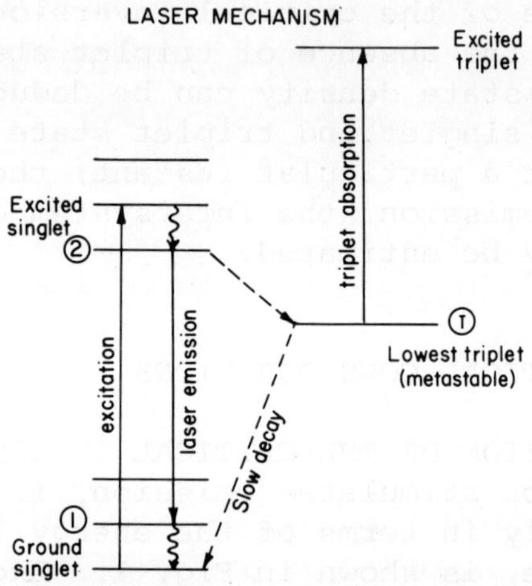

Figure 1 Mechanism by which stimulated emission is produced, illustrated schematically in terms of the dye molecule energy levels. The optical loss associated with the triplet state, produced by intersystem crossing, is also indicated.

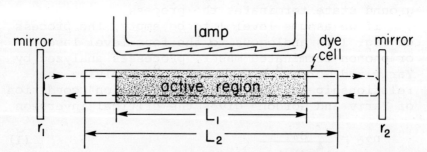

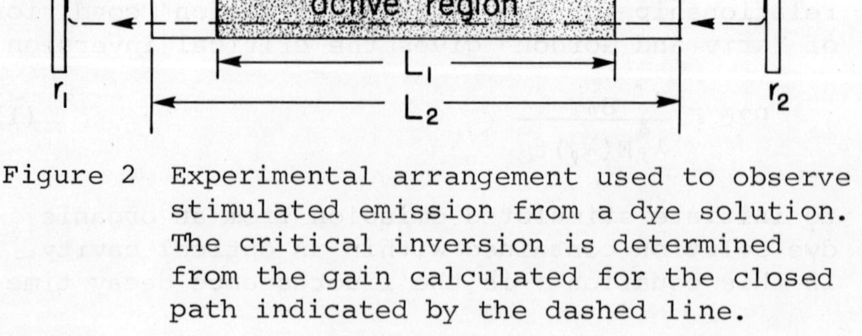

Figure 2 Experimental arrangement used to observe stimulated emission from a dye solution. The critical inversion is determined from the gain calculated for the closed path indicated by the dashed line.

for the transition from level 2 to level 1 of Fig. 1, λ_ℓ is the wavelength at which stimulated emission occurs, $E(\lambda_\ell)$ is the probability per unit wavelength that an excited molecule emits at the wavelength λ_ℓ, and t_o is the time required for the intensity of a radiation pulse of wavelength λ_ℓ to decay to 1/e of its initial value within the excited region of the cavity. The quantity t_o is calculated from the measured loss of the optical cavity including singlet state absorption, reflectance loss at the dye cell end windows, and transmission of the cavity mirrors, but excluding loss associated with the molecular triplet state. $E(\lambda_\ell)$ is determined from the measured fluorescence spectrum. The normalization of $E(\lambda)$ is defined by the relationship

$$\int_{\text{fluor.}} E(\lambda)d\lambda = \phi \qquad (2)$$

where ϕ is the fluorescence quantum yield and the integral is taken over the singlet emission spectrum.

The effects of intersystem crossing have been neglected in the derivation of Eq. (1). It is expected that molecules will accumulate in the lowest state of the triplet manifold level of Fig. 1, since the triplet state lifetime is much greater than that of the upper laser level. The effect of intersystem crossing upon the stimulated emission is twofold. First, the accumulation of molecules in the triplet state decreases the concentration of molecules available to participate in the laser process. Second, and more serious, is the triplet-triplet optical absorption which overlaps the singlet fluorescence. This introduces an optical loss which increases the critical inversion. In many dyes this loss is so large that critical inversion cannot be achieved. Thus, the pump light intensity required to reach or maintain critical inversion is increased with respect to that required in the absence of triplet state absorption.

B. CRITICAL INVERSION IN THE PRESENCE OF TRIPLET STATE LOSSES. We now develop an expression for the critical inversion which includes the triplet state losses and which can be evaluated experimentally. Here we briefly outline a development which has previously been presented in detail.[10]

The experimental arrangement of the flash-lamp-excited dye laser is illustrated schematically in Fig. 2. The system consists of a cell containing the dye in solution between two highly reflecting, plane-parallel mirrors which form the optical cavity. The dye cell is excited over part of its length, L_1, by a flashlamp. The inactive regions at the ends of the dye cell, contributing to the total length L_2, introduce an optical loss which must be considered.

We develop an expression for the critical inversion by considering the gain of the system, which we define as the number of photons produced by stimulated emission less the number lost by absorption and mirror transmission as we carry a radiation pulse of intensity $u(\lambda)$ around the closed circuit indicated by the dashed line in Fig. 2. This gain is expressed in Eq. (3) which reflects its wavelength dependence.

$$G(\lambda) = \frac{\lambda^4 u(\lambda) N_2 E(\lambda) 2L_1}{8\pi\tau} - u(\lambda)\, 2.3\frac{c}{\eta}\{2L_1 N_o \varepsilon_o + 2(L_2 - L_1) N\varepsilon_o + 2L_1 N_T \varepsilon_T - \log r_1 r_2\} \quad (3)$$

In this equation N_2 is the concentration of molecules in the upper laser level, N_o the concentration in the ground state, and N_T the concentration in the triplet state, all three measured in the active region. ε_o and ε_T are the extinction coefficients of the ground state and triplet state at the wavelength λ, and c/η is the speed of light in the medium. The factor of two associated with the lengths in Eq. (3) results from the length of the gain circuit considered which traverses the system twice. The last term of Eq. (3) is the transmission losses of the mirrors of reflectances r_1 and r_2.

We now assume that the threshold for stimulated emission is reached at the wavelength for which the gain per photon, $g(\lambda) = G(\lambda)/u(\lambda)$, is a maximum so that $dg(\lambda)/d\lambda = 0$ at this wavelength. The molecular concentration in the excited singlet state when the stimulated emission threshold is reached is the critical inversion which we designate by N_{2c}. Taking the wavelength derivative of (3) and setting it equal to 0, we obtain

$$g'(\lambda) = 0 = \frac{N_{2c}\lambda^4}{8\pi\tau}\left(E' + \frac{4E}{\lambda}\right)L_1 - 2.3\frac{c}{\eta}\{L_1N_o\varepsilon_o' + (L_2 - L_1)N\varepsilon_o' + L_1N_T\varepsilon_T' - \tfrac{1}{2}\frac{d}{d\lambda}\log r_1r_2\} \tag{4}$$

where the primes denote the derivative with respect to wavelength. Equation (4) may be solved for the critical inversion which yields, after some algebra,

$$N_{2c} = \frac{\varepsilon_o'(\lambda_\ell)}{\dfrac{\eta\lambda_\ell^3}{4.6c\pi\tau}\left[\dfrac{E'(\lambda_\ell)\lambda_\ell}{4} + E(\lambda_\ell)\right] + \varepsilon_o'(\lambda_\ell)}\frac{L_2}{L_1}N + \frac{(\varepsilon_T - \varepsilon_o)'(\lambda_\ell)}{\dfrac{\eta\lambda_\ell^3}{4.6c\pi\tau}\left[\dfrac{E'(\lambda_\ell)\lambda_\ell}{4} + E(\lambda_\ell)\right] + \varepsilon_o'(\lambda_\ell)}N_T$$

$$= K_1\frac{L_2}{L_1}N + K_2N_T \tag{5}$$

We have assumed that all the molecules in the active region are either in state N_o, N_2, or N_T, i.e., $N = N_o + N_2 + N_T$, where N is the molecular concentration of the dye solution. The mirrors are assumed to be nondispersive so that $d/d\lambda \log r_1 r_2 = 0$.

The dependence of N_{2c} upon the triplet concentration is seen clearly in Eq. (5). Since we wish to obtain both the critical inversion and the triplet state concentration, a second relationship between these quantities can be obtained from Eq. (3). At threshold, $G(\lambda) = 0$. Neglecting the mirror losses, the equation becomes

$$N_{2c} = \frac{(L_2/L_1)\varepsilon_o}{\alpha E\lambda^4 + \varepsilon_o} N + \frac{\varepsilon_T - \varepsilon_o}{\alpha E\lambda^4 + \varepsilon_o} N_T \tag{6}$$

where $\alpha = \eta/8\pi\tau c2.3$.

Solving equations (5) and (6) simultaneously for N_{2c} and N_T yields (7) and (8).

$$N_{2c} = \frac{N(L_2/L_1)\varepsilon_o'(\varepsilon_T - \varepsilon_o)}{(\alpha\lambda^4 E' + 4\alpha E\lambda^3 + \varepsilon_o')(\varepsilon_T - \varepsilon_o)} \qquad \frac{-\ N(L_2/L_1)\varepsilon_o(\varepsilon_T - \varepsilon_o)'}{-\ (\alpha E\lambda^4 + \varepsilon_o)(\varepsilon_T - \varepsilon_o)'} \tag{7}$$

$$N_T = \frac{N(L_2/L_1)\varepsilon_o'(\alpha\lambda^4 E + \varepsilon_o)}{(\alpha\lambda^4 E' + 4\alpha E\lambda^3 + \varepsilon_o')(\varepsilon_T - \varepsilon_o)} \qquad \frac{-\ (\alpha E'\lambda^4 + 4\alpha E\lambda^3 + \varepsilon_o')N(L_2/L_1)\varepsilon_o}{-\ (\alpha E\lambda^4 + \varepsilon_o)(\varepsilon_T - \varepsilon_o)'} \tag{8}$$

These equations will be used to find the singlet and triplet state concentrations at the stimulated emission threshold for the dyes.

C. DYNAMICS OF THE TRIPLET CONCENTRATION. Assume that the dye solution is excited by a flashlamp with an intensity which increases linearly with time. In this case the triplet concentration, N_T, will satisfy the differential equation

$$N_2 k_{S'T} = Ktk_{S'T} = \frac{dN_T}{dt} + \frac{N_T}{\tau_T} \quad (9)$$

where $k_{S'T}$ is the intersystem singlet-triplet rate constant, τ_T is the triplet state lifetime, and Kt is the concentration of excited singlet molecules at any given time. The solution of Eq. (9) is

$$\frac{N_T}{N_2} = k_{S'T}\tau_T \left[1 + \frac{\tau_T}{t}\{\exp(-t/\tau_T) - 1\}\right]$$

which becomes, in the limit of $t \ll \tau_T$,

$$\lim_{t\to 0} \frac{N_t}{N_2} = \frac{k_{S'T}}{2} t \quad (10)$$

This relationship will be used to estimate $k_{S'T}$ for the lasing dyes after calculation of N_2 and N_T at laser threshold from Eqs. (7) and (8).

III. EXPERIMENTAL

A. APPARATUS AND MEASUREMENTS. Accurate measurements of the absorption and emission spectra of the dye solutions are required for the evaluation of the parameters in Eqs. (1), (3), (4) and (6). Absorption spectra were measured with a Cary Model 14 Spectrophotometer at cell lengths of 0.2 cm and 10 cm. The long path measurements were required to obtain the optical absorption in the long wavelength region of the absorption spectrum with sufficient accuracy for the evaluation of the derivative, required for the evaluation of K_1 and K_2, at the stimulated emission wavelength.

Fluorescence spectra and quantum yields of fluorescein, rhodamine B, and rhodamine 6G were measured by F. Grum, of the Kodak Research Laboratories, with a specially constructed fluorimeter. This instrument yielded the fluorescence data in digital form for subsequent calculation of the quantum yield after correction of the fluorescence spectrum for the instrument variables.

The fluorescence lifetimes were measured for the same dyes by P. B. Gilman, also of the Kodak Research Laboratories, who used a TRW fluorescence decay apparatus capable of measuring decay times of several nanoseconds. The values of the fluorescence lifetimes and quantum yields are given in Table I.

The triplet spectra were measured by flash photolysis. The flash apparatus, which has been described,[11,12] was modified to dissipate 47J (1.7 μF, 7.5 KV) through an EG and G FX-1 flash tube with a flash intensity half-width of 7 μsec. and a 100th width of 35 μsec. To determine the triplet spectra, the absorption of the ground state plus triplet, directly after the flash, was constructed from a series of kinetic measurements at different wavelengths. The observed singlet plus-triplet spectrum of the dyes was resolved into the singlet component and a triplet component containing a negligible amount of singlet band in the region of overlap.[11,12] Since good laser dyes have a high fluorescence yield and a low triplet yield, they produce small optical density changes and much scattered light, and are therefore less than ideal dyes for flash photolysis measurements. Thus, there is considerable error in the absolute value of the extinction coefficient of the triplet.

TABLE I: Fluorescence Decay Time and Quantum Yield for Dyes Exhibiting Stimulated Emission

Dye and Solvent	Lifetime τ (10^{-9} sec)	Quantum Yield ϕ
Fluorescein 10^{-4} M water	4.5	.90
Rhodamine B 10^{-4} M methanol	2.0	.62
Rhodamine 6G 10^{-4} M ethanol	7.4	.84

However, the flash photolysis signal at each wavelength is proportional to $N_T(\varepsilon_T - \varepsilon_o)$, and the ratio $(\varepsilon_T - \varepsilon_o)'/(\varepsilon_T - \varepsilon_o)$, which is used to calculate N_{2c}, is independent of the absolute value of the extinction coefficient of the triplet. The triplet spectra of the Rhodamines in PMMA were used for the calculations in alcohol.

The dyes were excited by a fast coaxial flashlamp patterned after the design of Sorokin and co-workers.[7] The dye cell was 0.45 cm in diameter with an active length, L_1, of 10 cm and a total length, L_2 of 12.5 cm. The end windows of the dye cell were perpendicular to the dye cell axis and were not antireflection-coated. Plane dielectric mirrors were used to form the cavity. For each of the dyes studied, one mirror having a peak reflectance of 0.9 and a second with peak reflectance of 0.995 at the wavelength λ_ℓ were used.

The excitation flash reached peak intensity at approximately 0.7 microsecond after initiation. Total electrical energy in the flashlamp capacitor for these measurements was 112 joules.

Laser emission spectra were recorded with a Bausch and Lomb 1.5-meter grating spectrograph with a resolution of approximately 10 A/mm. The spectrographic plates were scanned with an Eastman Kodak densitometer to obtain the laser spectra.

Time development of the stimulated emission was observed with an ITT biplanar photodiode mounted to collect approximately equal intensities of the flashlamp and the laser emission. This enabled the time relationship between flash and laser pulses to be observed with a single-trace oscilloscope. This information was required for the evaluation of $k_{S'T}$.

B. RESULTS. For three dyes studied, very intense stimulated emission was observed on the long wavelength side of the fluorescence emission peak. The threshold flashlamp intensity to produce stimulated emission was quite clearly defined. The electrical energy required to reach threshold, stored in the flashlamp capacitor, was approximately 40 joules for the dyes reported. The light energy in the flash is considerably less than this value.

The use of the experimental data in the calculation of the critical inversion and triplet state concentrations has been described in detail in an earlier publication.[10]

Triplet absorption spectra obtained from these experiments and used in the analysis of the stimulated emission data for rhodamine B and rhodamine 6G are given in Figs. 3 and 4, respectively. The fluorescein data were analyzed by using the triplet absorption spectrum measured by Lindqvist.[13]

Bass and Steinfeld[14] have demonstrated that the wavelength of the 2-2'diethylthiatricarbocyanine iodide laser, excited by a giant-pulse ruby laser, sweeps with time from short to long wavelengths. Similar results have been obtained by Farmer et al.[15] In order to determine the wavelength at the threshold for stimulated emission in these experiments, it is assumed that the same process occurs in flashlamp-excited lasers. Accordingly, the wavelength λ_ℓ is taken as the short wavelength limit of the laser emission spectrum. The laser emission spectra are shown in Fig. 5 with the values of λ_ℓ for fluorescein disodium salt, rhodamine 6G, and rhodamine B obtained by a linear extrapolation of the short wavelength edge of the spectrum.

The values of critical inversion and triplet state concentration, as well as the wavelengths λ_ℓ at which stimulated emission is initiated, are given in Table II.

The intersystem crossing rate constant, $k_{S'T}$, may now be estimated by using the data of Table II in conjunction with Eq. (8). The values of the time at which threshold is reached, as well as the values for $k_{S'T}$, are given in Table III,

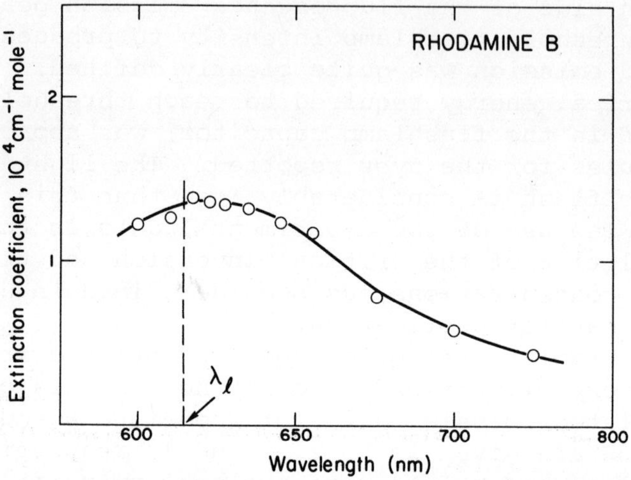

Figure 3 Molar extinction coefficient for triplet state optical absorption of rhodamine B in polymethyl methacrylate as determined from flash photolysis measurements.

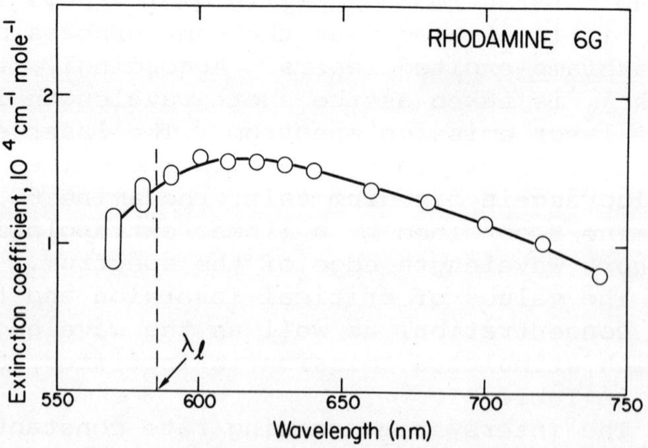

Figure 4 Molar extinction coefficient for triplet state optical absorption of rhodamine 6G in polymethyl methacrylate as determined from flash photolysis measurements.

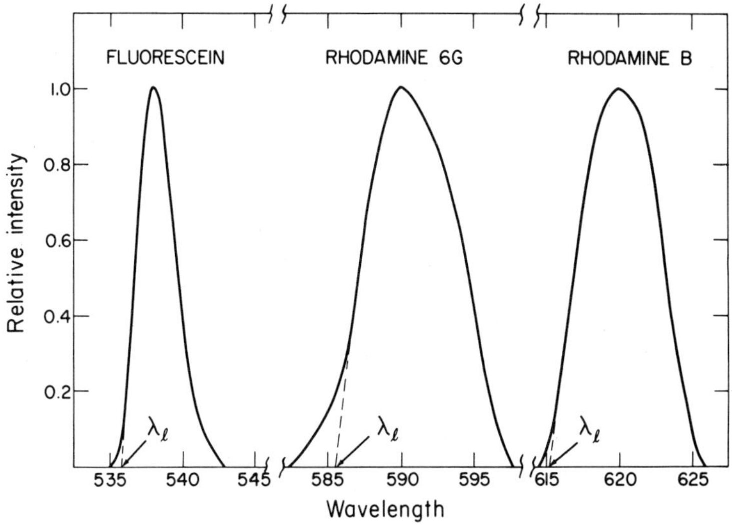

Figure 5 Stimulated emission spectra for
(a) Fluorescein disodium salt, 10^{-4} M in water
(b) Rhodamine 6G, 10^{-4} M in ethanol, and
(c) Rhodamine B, 10^{-4} M in methanol.
Excitation was by a flashlamp discharging 112 joules of electrical energy. The wavelengths λ_ℓ are indicated.

TABLE II: Excited Singlet (Critical Inversion) Concentration and Triplet State Concentration at the Stimulated Emission Threshold of Several Dyes Excited by a Flashlamp Discharging 112 Joules

Dye and solvent	λ_ℓ	N_{2c} (10^{15} cm^{-3})	N_t (10^{15} cm^{-3})	N_t (% of total)
Fluorescein (disodium salt) 10^{-4} M water	536	.6	5	8
Rhodamine B 10^{-4} M methanol	615	.22	2.0	3
Rhodamine 6G 10^{-4} M ethanol	586	.4	1.1	2

TABLE III: Time, t, at which stimulated emission threshold is reached using 112-joule flash peaking in .7 μsec. Intersystem crossing rate, $k_{S'T}$, calculated from $k_{S'T} = 2N_T/N_2t$ and compared with the value expected in the absence of internal conversion

Dye and Solvent	t (μsec)	$k_{S'T}$ (10^7 sec^{-1})	$1/\tau$ $(1 - \phi)$ (10^7 sec^{-1})
Fluorescein (disodium salt) 10^{-4} M water	.26	6	6
Rhodamine B 10^{-4} M methanol	.25	7	19
Rhodamine 6G 10^{-4} M ethanol	.25	2.0	2.2

where they are compared with the values of $k_{S'T}$ expected in the absence of internal conversion. The latter values are obtained from the relationship[16]

$$k_{S'T} = \frac{1}{\tau}(1 - \phi) \tag{11}$$

where ϕ is the fluorescence quantum efficiency. The values of the time, t, in Table III are taken from oscilloscope traces of the time dependence of the laser and flashlamp pulses.

IV. DISCUSSION AND CONCLUSIONS

The accuracy of the critical inversion and triplet state concentrations given in Table II is dependent upon the accuracy of the measurements of fluorescent decay time, of fluorescent quantum yield at various wavelengths, and of the extinction coefficients of the triplet and ground singlet states at various wavelengths. We would hesitate therefore to credit N_{2c} and N_T with better than $\pm$ 50% accuracy.

The values of $k_{S'T}$ calculated from N_{2c}, N_T and the time to reach threshold should also be accurate to $\pm$ 50% at best. They should be smaller than the values of $k_{S'T}$ calculated from Eq. (11), in which excited singlet to ground state nonradiative transitions are neglected. With this in mind, the agreement in Table III between the intersystem crossing rate constants calculated in different ways is good.

Saturation of the triplet state concentration could tend to yield a low measured value for $k_{S'T}$. Equation (10) represents the solution of Eq. (9) for small values of time, specifically for $t/\tau_T \ll 1$. This approximation may not be strictly applicable for the present results obtained with air-saturated dye solutions. Measurements of the flash intensity required to reach the stimulated emission threshold as a function of the time required to reach threshold for rhodamine B in methanol revealed that the required intensity begins to saturate for pumping times longer than about 0.5 μsec. If t approaches τ_T, the value of $k_{S'T}$ will be underestimated. For an oxygen-saturated solution it is expected that τ_T will be about a microsecond.

Measurements have been presented for dyes which can be excited to produce stimulated emission. The technique described, however, should not be restricted to the relatively small class of dyes that we have investigated. It should be possible to measure transient losses in nonlasing systems, or even nonfluorescent ones, by mixing them with dyes which will emit stimulated radiation. By choosing the proper lasing dye it should be possible to control the transient species produced.

The dynamics of the formation of transient losses, such as those to the triplet state, can be studied by varying the rise slope of the exciting flash, or by changing the losses of the optical cavity mirrors, so that the time at which threshold is reached may be varied. In this way it is possible to determine the value of the loss as a function of time. Lifetimes of transient species in the microsecond or submicrosecond range may be measured.

In this paper we have presented a new technique for measuring transient optical losses associated with the production of meta-stable molecular states. The technique utilizes stimulated emission from a flashlamp-excited organic dye to probe the optical losses of the cavity containing the dye. With this procedure it is possible to study transient losses persisting for times as short as several tenths of a microsecond, a range which is difficult to probe by conventional flash photolysis.

REFERENCES

1. P. P. Sorokin and J. R. Lankard, IBM Jour. Res. and Dev. 10, 162 (1966).
2. F. P. Schäfer, W. Schmidt, and J. Volze, Appl. Phys. Lett. 9, 306 (1966).
3. M. L. Spaeth and D. P. Bortfield, Appl. Phys. Lett. 9, 179 (1966).
4. B. B. McFarland, Appl. Phys. Lett. 10, 208 (1967).
5. P. P. Sorokin and J. R. Lankard, IBM Jour. Res. and Dev. 11, 148 (1967).
6. W. Schmidt and F. P. Schäfer, Z. Naturforschg. 22a, 1563 (1967).
7. P. P. Sorokin, J. R. Lankard, V. L. Moruzzi, and E. C. Hammond (to be published).
8. A. Yariv and J. P. Gordon, Proc. IEEE 51, 4 (1963).
9. D. E. McCumber, Phys. Rev. 134, A299 (1964).
10. B. B. Snavely and O. G. Peterson, Jour. Quantum Electronics QE-4 (to be published).
11. A. V. Buettner, J. Phys. Chem. 68, 3253 (1964).
12. A. V. Buettner, J. Chem. Phys. 46, 1398 (1967).
13. L. Lindqvist, Arkiv för Kemi, 16, 79 (1960).
14. M. Bass and J. I. Steinfeld, J. Quantum Electronics QE-4, 53 (1968).
15. G. I. Farmer, B. G. Huth, L. M. Taylor and M. R. Kagan, Appl. Phys. Lett. 12, 136 (1968).
16. N. J. Turro, Molecular Photochemistry (W. A. Benjamin, New York, 1967), p. 54.

THEORETICAL CALCULATION OF RADIATIONLESS TRANSITION RATES

Bryan R. Henry* and Willem Siebrand

Division of Pure Chemistry
National Research Council of Canada
Ottawa 2, Canada

I. INTRODUCTION

Quantum yields of emission processes are often smaller than unity. In polyatomic molecules most of them tend to be so small as to be zero for all practical purposes. The processes responsible for this regrettable loss of light are known as radiationless transitions.[1] Instead of light, these transitions produce heat. In a typical radiationless transition, a single large quantum of electronic energy is broken down into many small quanta of vibrational energy. The vibrations taking up the electronic energy may be molecular vibrations or vibrations in which the environment participates. As a rule, both are involved. If there is no environment, a radiationless process is strictly speaking, reversible, and hence not an actual transition. How much of an environment is needed to make it irreversible is an interesting question, which tends to arouse lively debate.[1]

*N.R.C.C. Post-doctoral Fellow, 1968- .

In the following discussions, it will not be a problem, however, because we will insist on a solid environment.

The interaction of a molecule with its environment divides the terms in the molecular Hamiltonian into two groups: zeroth-order terms, that are larger than the interaction term, and perturbation terms that are smaller than it. The eigen-functions of the zeroth-order terms represent almost-stationary states. These states interact with the environment whereby they lose vibrational energy. Since the environment may be taken infinitely large, its energy levels form a continuum, so that its interaction with molecular states will give rise to damping of these states by means of vibrational relaxation. The zeroth-order states do not only interact with the environment, but also, though more weakly, with each other. This latter interaction leads to a radiationless transition from one electronic state to another. Because of the vibrational relaxation in the manifold of the final electronic state, the transition is irreversible and fit for a formulation in terms of time-dependent perturbation theory. The result is that the initial electronic state decays according to a first-order rate constant of magnitude

$$k = (2\pi/\hbar)\rho_E |\langle\psi_f|H'|\psi_i\rangle|^2 \qquad (1)$$

Here ψ_i and ψ_f are the initial and final zeroth-order states, usually Born-Oppenheimer states, and H' is the nuclear kinetic-energy operator, which, in the case of states with different multiplicities, may be assisted or replaced by the spin-orbit coupling operator. The factor ρ_E, known as the density of states, is governed by the rate of vibrational relaxation, i.e., the fast process in the kinetic scheme.

By separating the Born-Oppenheimer states into electronic and vibrational parts, we can simplify (1) to

$$k = (2\pi/\hbar)\rho_E J^2 F(E) \tag{2}$$

where J is an electronic matrix element and F(E) is the sum of squares of vibrational overlap integrals, i.e., the Franck-Condon factor familiar from spectroscopy. F(E) tends to decrease very rapidly with increasing energy separation E between the electronic parts ϕ_i and ϕ_f of ψ_i and ψ_f.

There is a certain arbitrariness in the way one divides physical effects between the mathematical factors F(E) and ρ_E. The simplest physical picture is that of interaction between a single state ψ_i with no excess vibrational energy and a whole set of states $\psi_f(E)$, all with an excess vibrational energy E, so as to just match the energy of ψ_i. How accurate the matching must be is determined by ρ_E. Levels that are closer together than their uncertainty-principle halfwidths, which is calculated from their rate of vibrational relaxation, are clearly degenerate in the present context. Thus, ρ_E can be taken as the reciprocal of this halfwidth. In that case, F(E) must be summed over all matching levels of ψ_f, each with its own Franck-Condon factor, $f_n(E)$:

$$F(E) = \sum_n f_n(E) \tag{3}$$

In practice, this summation is so difficult that people often simplify (3) to

$$F(E) = G f_n(E) \tag{4}$$

where G is the total number of matching levels, which then is included in ρ_E. However, not all $f_n(E)$ are the same; in fact, they may be vastly different, and the problem of selecting a representative one is very difficult. In most cases, $f_n(E)$ is very small and G is very large, so that (4) will give very poor results. It is, therefore, important to select models which allow a direct summation of (3).[2]

II. TRIPLET-TO-GROUND STATE TRANSITIONS IN AROMATIC HYDROCARBONS

As a specific example, we consider the radiationless transition from the lowest triplet state to the ground state in aromatic hydrocarbons.[3] The main reason for choosing this example is the relative abundance of reliable data. Triplet lifetimes are known for more than 20 aromatic hydrocarbons, and there is no particular difficulty in separating the radiative from the radiationless rate constants. The dependence of k on the triplet energy E, and on the C/H ratio is accurately known, and so is the effect of deuteration on k. In fact, we know enough to accurately predict triplet lifetimes of any aromatic hydrocarbon once we know its triplet energy.

A qualitative interpretation of these data is readily given.[3] It is found that symmetry has no appreciable effect on k, from which it appears that J is reasonably constant between molecules. Thus, the variation of k over more than four orders of magnitude must be due to ρ_E and F(E). It appears that a small and fairly constant amount ($\approx$4000 cm^{-1}) of electronic energy is taken up by CC-stretching modes and that the bulk ($\approx$E-4000 cm^{-1}) goes into CH-stretching modes. The CC modes contribute through changes in molecular dimensions accompanying the electronic transition, the CH modes through their high frequency and anharmonicity.

In order to put these ideas in a quantitative form, it is very tempting to neglect all anharmonicity. Then one can treat the molecule as a system of uncoupled harmonic oscillators, which simplifies the calculations greatly. The only vibrational coupling that arises is harmonic coupling with the solvent, which is included in ρ_E. In the absence of molecular contributions to this coupling, ρ_E should be the same for all molecules if the solvent is the same. This leaves us with F(E) as the cause of all variations of k. Thus, if we can calculate F(E), we can calculate relative values of k for all aromatic hydrocarbons.

Expressions have been obtained for $f_n(E)$ and even for F(E) in the harmonic approximation.[2] Unfortunately, these expressions are in terms of spectroscopic parameters that are mostly unknown. What one can unequivocally determine, however, is the sign of $d^2\log F(E)/dE^2$. This may not seem very important, but it turns out to be enough to invalidate the harmonic approximation in the present case.[3] Thus, we have to allow for anharmonicity, which means that every oscillator will be coupled to every other oscillator in the molecule, so that the calculations are going to be complicated.

However, rather than entirely discarding the harmonic model, we may try to use it as a stepping stone towards an improved model. The simplest procedure would be to allow one or more parameters which are constant in the harmonic approximation to vary with the vibrational quantum number v. For example, the energy expression for a Morse oscillator is of the form

$$E = (v + \tfrac{1}{2})\hbar\omega + (v + \tfrac{1}{2})^2\hbar X = E_o + v\hbar\omega^o (1 + vX/\omega^o), \qquad (5)$$

where X is the anharmonicity constant. Thus, the energy of a Morse oscillator can be written in the same form as the energy of a harmonic oscillator if the frequency ω^o is allowed to vary linearly with v.

In the same vein we can deal with the harmonic approximation to the radiationless rate constant, which is[2,3]

$$k = k_o \left(\frac{\zeta}{N_C}\right)^v \frac{\Gamma(N_H + v)}{\Gamma(N_H)\Gamma(v + 1)} \tag{6}$$

In this equation N_C and N_H are the numbers of carbon and hydrogen atoms per molecule, $k_o = 3.5 \times 10^5$ sec.$^{-1}$ and

$$\zeta = z\Delta\omega/2\omega \tag{7}$$

where z is a factor of order unity. Here the frequency shift $\Delta\omega$, which the oscillators undergo as a result of the transition, is expected to be especially sensitive to changes in v. Let us, in analogy to (5), try the substitution

$$\zeta = \lambda v \tag{8}$$

in (6), where λ is an adjustable parameter. This is undoubtedly a very crude way of improving the harmonic results, but it works very well for the proper choice of λ. With $\lambda = 0.051$, which is the best choice, Eq. (6) accounts satisfactorily for all known triplet-to-ground state radiationless rate constants.[3]

The same equation with the same value of λ can also account for all known radiationless transition rates from the first excited singlet to the ground state.[4] In this case, one finds $k_o = 3 \times 10^{13}$ sec.$^{-1}$. Comparison with k_o for triplet-to-ground state transitions shows that the latter transitions are slowed down relative to the spin-allowed transition by a spin-prohibition factor of 10^8.

An attempt has been made[5] to justify (8), or at least compute λ, by a direct calculation of F(E) for a Morse oscillator. This can be done for a one-dimensional oscillator, where F(E) simplifies to f(E). The comparable form of Eq. (6) is obtained by taking $N_H = N_C = 1$, so that

$$k = k_o(\lambda v)^v \tag{9}$$

This amounts to extrapolating our semi-empirical results to a hypothetical aromatic hydrocarbon CH, which resembles but is not identical with the CH molecule. Such an extrapolation is drastic, but is not incompatible with the derivation of (5).

The theoretical f(E) for Morse oscillator is rather complicated and contains a number of unknown spectroscopic parameters. However, it can be reduced to a form similar to (9), if one is willing to introduce drastic approximations. These approximations cannot really be justified in the absence of precise knowledge of the spectroscopic parameters involved, in view of the severe cancellation among the terms of f(E). The final result is

$$f(E) \approx f(0)(ev\omega^o/X)^v, \tag{10}$$

where e = 2.72 is the basis of the natural logarithms. Comparison of (9) and (10) yields an estimate of the anharmonicity of aromatic CH-stretching modes

$$X \approx -\lambda\omega^o/e \approx -56 \text{ cm}^{-1} \tag{11}$$

for $\lambda = 0.051$ and $\omega^o \approx 3000$ cm^{-1}. This is a reasonable result if one believes the anharmonicity of aromatic CH-stretching modes to be comparable to the anharmonicity of the CH molecule which is given by $X = -64.3$ cm^{-1}.

Thus, it appears that we are on the right track with our extension of Eq. (6) so as to include anharmonicity. Before we can carry on along these lines, however, we need a better understanding of the magnitude of anharmonicity constants in aromatic hydrocarbons. In the next section we concentrate on this problem.

III. THE OVERTONE SPECTRUM OF BENZENE

The real test for the empirical anharmonicity constant (11) would be to check it against the anharmonicity constant obtained from spectroscopic observations. Perhaps, the most illuminating of these observations is the overtone spectrum of benzene, measured back in 1929 by Ellis.[6] Using optical path lengths up to 6 m, he obtained no less than 7 CH-stretching overtones. Their frequencies, together with the fundamental frequency, obeys rather accurately the following equation

$$\nu(v) = 25 + 3083v - 57.5v^2 (\mathrm{cm}^{-1}). \qquad (12)$$

Comparison with (5) leads to

$$X = -57.5 \ \mathrm{cm}^{-1} \qquad (13)$$

which compares well with (11).

However, before rushing to a favorable judgement, it is well to ponder for a moment the significance of Eq. (12). Except for the small constant term of 25 cm^{-1}, this is an expression characteristic of a single, anharmonic CH-stretching oscillator. In benzene, there are six equivalent CH bonds and their stretching vibrations can be grouped into two non-degenerate and two degenerate normal modes. Thus, it is not immediately clear to which vibration the value of X given in (12) should be assigned. Actually, one expects all four normal modes to contribute to the overtone spectrum. For large v, there are many combinations of normal modes which have the correct symmetry for an allowed transition, and there is no obvious reason to single out one of these combinations for every value of v as being the most importnat.

To solve this problem, we have to go more deeply into the nature of anharmonicity in polyatomic molecules. If we calculate the vibrational energy of such a molecule, we get by a straightforward generalization of (5)

$$E = \sum_{K} (v_K + \tfrac{1}{2})\hbar\omega_K + \sum_{K \geq L}\sum (v_K + \tfrac{1}{2})(v_L + \tfrac{1}{2})\hbar X_{KL} \tag{14}$$

where K and L label the normal modes. If some of the modes are degenerate additional terms occur which, however, need not concern us here. The important thing in (14) is that anharmonicity couples the normal modes. Thus, except for infinitesimal amplitudes, the molecule does not vibrate according to a pattern of independent normal modes, but according to a much more complicated pattern, in which the normal modes may or may not be recognizable. This will depend on the magnitude of the cross-terms $v_K v_L X_{KL}$: if they are large, the normal-mode description is a poor starting point and one may well look for a more appropriate representation.

For example, consider the CH-stretching vibrations in benzene. A typical normal mode is the totally symmetric one, whose vibration we represent by the notation C_6-H_6, where the bar denotes the vibrational coordinate. Let us compare this vibration with the vibration C_6H_5-H. The latter vibration is not a normal mode, i.e., it is not a stationary state for infinitesimal amplitudes. On the other hand, it is certainly a valid mode for large amplitudes, since it gives the correct description of the thermal dissociation of benzene, which C_6-H_6 certainly does not. It appears, therefore, that we have found a new description in terms of local CH-stretching vibrations, which is valid for values of v near the CH-dissociation limit. This description, which we call the local-mode representation,[4,7] is thus complementary to the normal-mode representation, which is valid only for small v.

In benzene, all six local CH-stretching modes are equivalent. Moreover, one expects on the basis of straightforward physical arguments[7] that their mutual coupling is weak, so that they vibrate almost independently. Thus, the vibrational energy can, to a good approximation, be written as the sum of the contributions of the local modes. This yields an immediate explanation of the main features of the overtone spectrum, as given by (12). The parameters in that equation simply refer to the local modes, and since all six of them are equivalent, there is only one frequency and one anharmonicity constant. The similarity of this constant [cf. (13)] and the anharmonicity constant of the CH molecule neatly fits into this picture.

To prove this interpretation, a much more elaborate assignment of the benzene overtone spectrum was carried out.[7] The local-mode anharmonicity constant, with and without anharmonic coupling between local modes, was transformed into a set of normal-mode anharmonicity constants. With these constants and the known fundamental frequencies, the overtone spectrum was calculated by standard methods. This involved writing down for a given v all combinations of normal CH-stretching modes which have an allowed component for optical transitions. To each of these combinations, we assigned a wavelength, an intensity and a Lorentzian shape. After summation, the maxima of the resulting band contours were compared with the observed maxima. An almost perfect matching, superior indeed to that of Eq. (12), was obtained by taking the local-mode anharmonicity constant to be

$$X = -55.2 \text{ cm}^{-1} \qquad (15)$$

which differs from (13) by 4%, but is virtually identical with (11).

It appears, therefore, that the overtone spectrum can be explained quantitatively on the basis of six independently vibrating CH-bonds. The anharmonicity constant associated with this vibration is given by (15).

IV. ANHARMONICITY AND RADIATIONLESS TRANSITIONS

Let us now try to apply the insight gained in the last section to the model of radiationless processes outlined in Section II. In some respects, the model has become more meaningful. In the harmonic approximation, the N_H CH-stretching modes of an aromatic hydrocarbon could be either normal or local modes. With the introduction of anharmonicity, the normal modes are no longer germane. We are left with N_H local modes, which are anharmonic, but essentially uncoupled. In benzene, these six local modes are equivalent and a single frequency and anharmonicity constant describes them all. In other aromatic hydrocarbons, not all CH bonds are equivalent, but the variations in frequency and bond-dissociation energy are relatively small, so that the same pair of parameters will be at least approximately valid. This explains why a single value of λ applies to all aromatic hydrocarbons, and demonstrates the correspondence between λ and the local-mode anharmonicity constant. Finally, the local-mode picture explains why symmetry has no effect on radiationless transitions of the type discussed in Section II: the Franck-Condon factors of these transitions are governed by local properties which are essentially independent of the overall structure of the molecule.

The role of anharmonicity in radiationless processes is also demonstrated by the well-known observation that molecules with weak bonds tend to be poor emitters. The weaker is a bond, the lower is its dissociation energy, and so, roughly speaking, the stronger is its anharmonicity. We have just seen that the more anharmonic is an oscillator the greater is the ease with which it accepts electronic energy. Thus, weak bonds, through their anharmonicity provide an efficient pathway for radiationless processes.

The correct theoretical procedure for calculating F(E) is fairly clear. Starting with anharmonic oscillators, e.g., Morse oscillators, we should calculate the Franck-Condon factor of a single oscillator and then generalize the result to a system of N_H oscillators. However, neither of these steps is easy. The dependence of f_n on v_n is complicated and is sensitive to the precise values of spectroscopic parameters which are not available at the present time. The complex dependence of f_n on v_n makes it very difficult to generalize the result from one to N_H oscillators. Besides, permutation of the v_n among the oscillators will, in general, give rise to a different energy. Hence, it will be necessary to specify an energy range in which the summation of the f_n is to be carried out, which amounts to specifying a value of ρ_E.

This effect of ρ_E on F(E) is characteristic for anharmonic oscillators because of their coupling. The reverse effect also occurs, since every oscillator not explicitly taken into account in calculating F(E) will contribute to ρ_E through anharmonic coupling with the oscillators in F(E). The implied conclusion, that ρ_E may be controlled as much by intramolecular vibrations as by coupling with the medium, is not in itself surprising. It is well-known that solvent effects on aromatic triplet lifetimes are generally small. However, the theoretical complexity of these couplings is discouraging and has so far prevented a truly satisfactory treatment of the vibrational relaxation process.

The present situation, then, can be summarized as follows. We have a model that, in principle, should be soluble, but has not been solved yet, partly because of computational problems, but mainly because the appropriate spectroscopic parameters are not known. We have, instead, a solution for a much simpler model, which by itself is not appropriate, but can be modified so as to give good agreement with experiment. The crucial difference between the two models is the manner in which anharmonicity is introduced.

REFERENCES

1. See e.g., B. R. Henry and M. Kasha, Ann. Rev. Phys. Chem. Vol. 19, (1968) (in press) for a recent review.
2. W. Siebrand, J. Chem. Phys. 46, 440 (1967).
3. W. Siebrand, J. Chem. Phys. 44, 4055 (1966); W. Siebrand and D. F. Williams, ibid 46, 403 (1967); W. Siebrand, ibid 47, 2411 (1967).
4. W. Siebrand and D. F. Williams, J. Chem. Phys. (in press).
5. W. Siebrand, Chem. Phys. Letters (in press).
6. J. W. Ellis, Trans. Faraday Soc. 25, 888 (1929).
7. B. R. Henry and W. Siebrand (submitted for publication).

NONRADIATIVE DECAY OF BENZENE'S LOWEST TRIPLET STATE AND CH ANHARMONICITY*

T. E. Martin and A. H. Kalantar

Department of Chemistry
University of Alberta
Edmonton, Alberta, Canada

I. INTRODUCTION

Observations that the lifetimes of the lowest triplet state of aromatic hydrocarbons increase upon perdeuteration[1] have stimulated a great deal of experimental and theoretical work on nonradiative decay processes.

The data available show CH motions to be important to nonradiative decay rates (β). Radiative lifetimes ($1/b$), which are rather long, appear to be unchanged upon perdeuteration.[2] Some recent work on partially deuterated molecules suggests that the decay rate ($1/\tau = b + \beta$) varies linearly with the degree of deuteration,[3] while others[4] report a large sensitivity of the decay

*Supported in part by The National Research Council of Canada.

processes to the position of any inequivalent hydrogens.

The so-called deuterium effect on the triplet decay time has been explained in terms of a relatively slow isoenergetic intersystem tunnelling from the vibrationless level of the phosphorescent state to a highly excited vibrational level of the ground singlet state, followed by a rapid decay to the vibrationless ground state.[5] When considering isomers of a given molecule, electronic and environmental factors are normally presumed to be the same. Therefore most theoretical treatments[6-8] have concentrated on the Franck-Condon factors (F), which have also been implicated experimentally.[9] For a particular decay route, F is the product of the squared vibrational overlap integrals appropriate to the particular nonradiative route from the triplet to some particular overtone-combination level in the ground singlet state. Many other routes also exist, involving other possible combinations of vibrational levels; these can be included with a statistical weighting factor obtained by permuting the vibrational quanta among the appropriate normal modes. Thus we regard F as a product of a vibrational overlap factor and a statistical factor. Careful discussions of the influence of these factors on F are given in the literature,[5-8] assuming simple harmonic oscillators. Briefly, the overlap can be greater if the normal modes have different equilibrium configurations and/or frequencies in the two electronic states. Overlap decreases sharply as the number of vibrational quanta of a mode increases. Thus only a few large frequency modes (CH stretches) are considered likely important contributors to F. Statistical factors increase as the energy gap (and number of vibrational quanta) increases. Robinson and Frosch[5] and Siebrand[8] have attempted to strike balances between these two factors, concluding that CH stretches are much more important to nonradiative decay than the lower frequency CD stretches. Siebrand finds values of F appropriate to τ by considering only CH oscillators and including anharmonicity.

The study reported here involves the partially deuterated benzenes. It is concerned with the role of the CH (and CD) modes in the decay process. Very reproducible lifetime measurements have uncovered effects due to position and degree of deuteration. Different relative efficiencies of vibrational modes on the observed rate constants have also been found. These data, together with Siebrand's findings about the possible role of anharmonicity, have led to an extension of this study into the near IR to see if anharmonicity and nonradiative decay are related.

II. EXPERIMENTAL

MATERIALS. The source and purity of the benzenes and solvents are described elsewhere.[10] m- and p-$C_6H_2D_4$ (Merck) were 97.8 and 96.2 mole % pure, respectively. The small amount of other deuterated benzenes did not adversely affect the lifetime measurements.

LIFETIME MEASUREMENTS. Solutions ($\sim 10^{-3}$ M) were cooled reproducibly to 77°K. A logarithmic converter simplified data processing and allowed the decay to be followed routinely for 2.5 orders (to base 10) of magnitude change in I. Only slowly cooled cyclohexane yielded strictly exponential decays. For the isopropanol (IPOH) and 3-methylpentane (3MP) solutions, the nonexponential decay was evaluated from the time interval between the intensity ratios I/I_o = 0.50 and 0.050. The standard deviation of all results for any solution was $\sim$1%. In cyclohexane, the standard error of the mean was < 0.1%.

NEAR IR MEASUREMENTS. Liquid samples of the benzenes were examined in cells of varying path (to 5 or 10 cm) lengths on the Cary 14 or the Perkin Elmer 421. The temperature was not controlled but did not affect peak positions (corrected to vacuum), which were reproducible to $\sim$2 cm^{-1}. (The weaker bands' positions are uncertain to $\sim$20 cm^{-1}). An analysis of the stronger bands in the $DCCl_3$ and $HCCl_3$ spectra was done to check the procedure, reproducibility, and isotope effects.

III. RESULTS AND INTERPRETATION

PHOSPHORESCENCE DECAY TIMES. The lifetime data (Table I) were obtained in three different solvents to preclude problems of interpretation arising from small differences that were solvent dependent. The data show clearly that there is a general trend of longer lifetimes with further deuteration, as is expected intuitively and derived by Lin and Bersohn.[3] However, the precision of the data also shows some further details: namely that the lifetimes of the two benzenes-d_4 are <u>not</u> equal and that τ for S3 is <u>longer</u> than that of P4.

This same nonlinear dependence of τ (or τ^{-1}) on the number of D (or H) atoms is also indicated by the data for H6, D1, D5, and D6. Data for these molecules are necessarily free of position effects and so overall trends can be discerned more easily.

If the radiative rate constant for benzene is independent of the isomer for a given solvent, as indicated by the few relevant studies extant,[2] then the change in the radiationless rate constant, per hydrogen ($\Delta\beta$/H), can be calculated. For example, $\Delta\beta$/H is 0.016, 0.022, and 0.033 $sec.^{-1}$ for the series H6, D1, D5, and D6 in annealed cyclohexane. Thus $\Delta\beta$/H (which is independent of the value assumed for b) varies with the degree of deuteration. This variation is well outside the propagated errors due to the lifetime measurements. As

TABLE I: τ^a (sec) for Deuterobenzenes at 77^oK

Benzene	Abbreviation	Solvent: Cyclohexane (monoclinic)	Solvent: 3MP (relaxed)	Solvent: IPOH (quickly frozen)
C_6H_6	H6	4.75	5.75	7.48
C_6H_5D	D1	5.15	6.05	7.95
1,3,5-$C_6H_3D_3$	S3	8.20	8.03	9.77
p-$C_6H_2D_4$	P4	7.65	7.61	9.54
m-$C_6H_2D_4$	M4	8.45	8.27	10.16
C_6HD_5	D5	9.60	8.90	10.80
C_6D_6	D6	14.10	12.02	13.69

[a] Corrected to 100 mole percent of the isomer.

suggested by the τ, the largest change in β occurs on passing from D6 to D5, an observation that further supports the belief the CH (stretching) vibrations are important to the radiationless decay of the triplet state. As more hydrogens are substituted for deuterium atoms, further increases in β are less. That this is certainly the case is shown by the rather smaller subsequent increases in β on passing from D5 to M4 and S3 (0.014 and 0.004 $sec.^{-1}$, respectively, in cyclohexane).

These results point to one effect arising from the relative position of the D (or H) atoms but there are too few data to determine the cause of this here. We therefore turn to the more general observation regarding the trend in $\Delta\beta/H$. As the number of H atoms increases so does the number of CH stretching modes. However, these modes cannot be equivalent contributors to β. Comprising these modes are the single, in-phase, totally symmetric CH stretch corresponding to $\nu_2(a_{1g})$ for H6 and the other CH stretches which are non-totally symmetric in H6. (The formally totally symmetric character of some of these modes in the various isomers does not appear to affect β at all significantly: compare τ for H6 (D_{6h}) and D1 (C_{2v})). This totally symmetric CH stretch first appears in D5, together with a large change in β. The substitution of further hydrogens (at least in some positions) affects β very little more (M4, S3, and P4). Therefore the in-phase CH stretch contributes more to β than at least some non-totally symmetric CH stretches and may be the major contributor to β. In terms of Franck-Condon considerations, this could be due to the fact that totally symmetric motions can be displaced in normal coordinate space (yielding non-zero overlap for all vibrational levels) and/or its frequency may be quite different in the two states, e.g., it may be associated with a large anharmonicity. This latter possibility was considered by examining the IR spectra of these molecules beyond the fundamental region.

CH(CD) STRETCHING ANHARMONICITY. In contrast to diatomic molecules, polyatomics have several normal modes each of which may exhibit some (diagonal) anharmonicity, X_{ii}. In addition, anharmonic coupling among the modes also occurs,[11] yielding nondiagonal anharmonic terms, X_{ij}. If the near IR spectra are sufficiently simple to permit assignments, appropriate X_{ij} can be evaluated. Since the X_{ij} show isotope effects,[11] the assignments can be checked by studying D6 as well as H6. In what follows the essential features of the near IR spectra of H6, D6, D1, and D5 are described, interpreted, and then analyzed to yield anharmonicity constants. Only the CH(CD) stretching bands are considered here and the language of normal modes is used throughout.

H6 displays a single strong series of bands decreasing relatively regularly (by ∿10) in intensity. After the third band (at ∿8700 cm^{-1}), the bands, observed out to eight CH stretching quanta,[12] appear to be single. (More rapidly decreasing multiple bands between these are CC-CH combinations.) Bands involving 2, 4,... quanta are necessarily combinations and not overtones since only bands of E_{1u} symmetry can be observed for the (planar) CH stretches.

Second differences (Δ^2, see Eq. (2) below) of the band positions become relatively constant. This observation, combined with the simplicity of the band system, suggests that the spectra may arise from a progression built upon $\nu_{20}(e_{1u})$. This is possible with either $\nu_2(a_{1g})$ or $\nu_2(e_{2g})$ modes. This requires that an X_{ij} be non-zero and says that only a few CH stretches are responsible for the near IR bands. A very similar, though shorter, series is found for D6, whose five bands successively decrease twenty-fold in intensity. The fourth and fifth bands appear single and all but the first Δ^2 are similar, as found for H6. The same is true for D1, a remarkable observation in view of the fact that all five CH stretching modes may combine or form overtones. Thus D1 would be expected to have a much more complex spectrum. Although the halfwidths of the bands appear to increase as the number of vibrational quanta increase (as observed for chloroform), the band maxima are 5/6 of those in the H6 spectrum and the spectrum is virtually the same as that of H6 (save of course, for the appearance of CD bands and a very weak (in coupling and intensity) CH-CD combination series). Therefore relatively few CH stretches appear to have sufficient anharmonicity to yield a near IR spectrum. The CD bands in D5 are very much like those in D6. D5 shows weak CH-CD combination bands like those in D1 and a strong overtone series due to the single CH stretching mode. The third member of this series has more intensity than the fourth CD band in D5, with which it overlaps.

In view of the above observations and using normal mode concepts, we have assumed that $\nu_{20} + n(\nu_2 \text{ or } \nu_7)$ describes the main band system for H6 and D6. In terms of observed fundamental frequencies (ν_i), the vibrational energy for such a combination-overtone, to first order and referred to the lowest level, is

$$G_o(n,1) = n\nu_1 + \nu_2 + nX_{12} + (n^2 - n)X_{11} \quad (1)$$

The first and second differences are then[10]

$$\Delta^1 G_o(n,1) = \nu_1 + X_{12} + 2X_{11}$$

and (2)

$$\Delta^2 G_o(n,1) = 2X_{11}$$

Here ν_2 represents the IR-active e_{1u} mode and ν_1 may be either the a_{1g} or the e_{2g} mode. The X_{11}

can be determined from the band positions for H6 and D6 and then X_{12} calculated, since the ν are well known.[13] These results appear in Table II. Also presented are the results of the application of the expression $X_{ij}/X_{ij}^D = \omega_i\omega_j/\omega_i^D\omega_j^D \simeq \nu_i\nu_j/\nu_i^D\nu_j^D$. This relation (due to Dennison) is unproved but is in good accord with experimental results.[10] These calculations show that if the progression is a combination-overtone, then it can be assigned as $n\nu_2(a_{1g}) + \nu_{20}(e_{1u})$. We can think of no special reason why only two or three CH stretching modes should have considerable anharmonicity. In particular, ν_2 appears to be one of these and this is puzzling because one expects a mode associated with simultaneous rupture of six CH bonds to have a very small anharmonicity. But the large anharmonicities are real and so the normal mode concept is inadequate when considering several CH stretching quanta. Siebrand has worked with local CH oscillators.[8] Such a local mode concept is consistent with many observations: The size of the X_{ii}, the dissociation energy of benzene into hydrogen and phenyl radicals, and the relative simplicity of the near IR spectra. In this context, we mean by ν_2 the (only) mode associated with an asymmetric potential function with motion along some displacement coordinate that approaches that of a single CH bond as the number of vibrational quanta increase. The interpretation of the progression as being associated with an asymmetric potential well is also consistent with the observation that the intensity falloff is fairly regular.

Obviously, the local/normal mode problem needs clarification. While we recognize the values of a local mode description however, we will use here the more familiar normal mode notation merely as a convenient (if inadequate) shorthand language.

The essential inferences drawn from both the lifetime and the near IR measurements indicate important contributions due to the CH stretching

TABLE II: Observed Fundamental Frequencies (ν, cm^{-1}) and Anharmonicity Constants (X_{ij}, cm^{-1}) Derived from Assignments of Overtone-Combination Bands for Liquid Benzene

	$\nu_{20}(e_{1u})$	$2X_{22}$ or ($2X_{77} + 2g_{77}$)	$\nu_2(a_{1g})$	X_{220}	$\nu_7(e_{2g})$	($X_{720} + g_{720}$)
H6	3057[a]	-116	3062	-150	3047	-135
D6	2276	- 63	2294	- 87	2267	- 57
Dennsion's Ratios	Obs.	1.84		1.74		2.37
	Calc.[b]	1.78		1.79		1.82
		(1.80)				

a ν (cm^{-1}) from Ref. 13.
b Assuming $\nu \sim \omega$.

mode associated with an asymmetric potential function and referred to here as υ_2. Theoretical considerations[8] regarding β suggest that this prominence found for υ_2 is related to its anharmonicity. This anharmonicity is found in the analysis of the near IR spectra. The virtually parallel behavior of these molecules with respect to β and the near IR spectra strongly suggests (but does not prove) that β depends upon anharmonicity, as proposed.[8]

We have therefore examined the spectra of M4 and P4, two molecules having equal numbers of hydrogens but with different lifetimes, to see if their anharmonicities are unequal and in the appropriate direction The results show their band positions and peak heights to be equal within experimental uncertainty. However, the X_{ii}^{CH} are very often similar in size[12] and so small differences are hard to establish experimentally. From Eq. (1) we see that X_{ii} is multiplied by n^2 where $n \sim 13$ for tunnelling in benzene. If a shift in levels affects β (see Discussion), then small changes in X_{ii} could affect β considerably. Here the β for M4 and P4 differ by only $\sim$15%.

The halfwidths for M4 are generally greater than those for P4 and the band contours for P4 appear more structured. This may arise because more CH bands are allowed to appear in the M4 spectrum. Thus the greater ($\sim$10-20%) halfwidths we have observed for D1 bands may be outside of experimental error. This suggests that some other CH mode(s), in addition to $\upsilon_{20} + n\upsilon_2$ may also contribute somewhat to the observed IR spectra, by virtue of anharmonicity associated with them. Now in the case of M4 it appears that such a mode contributes little more to β. On the other hand, P4, whose IR spectra hint at lesser contributions to anharmonicity, surely has a larger β. It therefore appears that either anharmonicity may not necessarily require that there be a contribution to β or that anharmonicity and β are not related. However these remarks are conjectural and further work (preferably resolved gas phase studies) is needed. Perhaps then the local/normal mode problem could also thereby be clarified.

IV DISCUSSION

The lifetime data show that CH stretching modes contribute unequally to β. The near IR data suggest that relatively few CH stretching modes have appreciable anharmonicity. Both kinds of data point to the CH stretch obeying an asymmetric potential function. It appears that the pronounced effect of this CH mode on β is derived from a considerable anharmonicity associated with it.

Not all CH stretching modes (whether local or normal) contribute equally to F, and thus β. F is composed of a statistical and an overlap factor, as noted above. The former, previously regarded as depending upon the number of CH stretches, must be reduced, in view of the conclusions based upon the lifetime measurements. Roughly then, the overlap factor needs to be increased. This is made possible by assuming greater anharmonicities since tunnelling takes place at nearly (~80%) the energy required for CH bond rupture. It may also be necessary to work with, e.g., Morse type asymmetric potential functions. Overlap is very sensitive to the nodal pattern of the wave functions and thus far all the calculations[6,8] have assumed symmetric (harmonic oscillator) potential functions.

Given then the observations noted at the outset of this section, we consider now the pathways of radiationless decay for the $^3B_{1u}$ state of benzene. Possible combination levels, to which tunnelling can occur, include (i) those not combined with the $\nu_{20} + \nu_2$ progression, (ii) those built on this progression, such as $\nu_{20} + \nu_2 + \nu_{CC}$, and (iii) the assigned combination-overtone itself. (i) probably contributes very weakly to the quasicontinuum and thus has little effect on β. As noted, (ii) and, to a lesser extent, (i) are the main contributors to the background quasicontinuum to which tunnelling takes place. The very prominent CH bands observed in the IR suggest that these main bands form a set of relatively discrete levels (of halfwidths < 400 cm^{-1}) superimposed upon the quasicontinuum. The Franck-Condon overlap factors for these bands would be especially large. Since such levels would be $\sim$1500 cm^{-1} apart near benzene's triplet level, overlap would normally be with levels (i) and (ii), the latter providing the more important (larger β) decay routes.

The presence of discrete levels might explain the unusual temperature dependence of the phosphorescence lifetime of benzene[14] (β increases at temperatures below 77°K while other aromatics exhibit changes in β above 150°K). If a discrete $\nu_{20} + \nu_2$ level lies near some low-frequency vibrational level of the triplet state, thermal excitation to this vibrational mode from the vibrationless level of the triplet would lead to a fast radiationless decay via this route. Similar ideas could also tentatively explain the observation that, in cyclohexane, β is greater for benzene in the cubic site than in the monoclinic site.[10,15] Phosphorescence from benzenes in cubic sites is shifted 59 cm^{-1} to higher energy.

Benzene's behavior in the $^3B_{1u}$ state can thus be considered unique. This uniqueness is probably a consequence of the much larger singlet-triplet energy gap (by $\sim$8000 cm^{-1}) in benzene, compared to those of other aromatic hydrocarbons. The smaller gap of the larger molecules means that fewer vibrational quanta are involved in the decay process. Thus overlap with the quasicontinuum would be relatively greater. Thus route (ii) would compete more favorably with (iii) for the larger aromatics; i.e., any discreteness would be less prominent. Moreover, the larger aromatics have many more normal modes which can add to the quasicontinua and perhaps further broaden half-widths of the postulated discrete bands.

For the present however, these remarks are confined to benzene whose behavior is, in many ways, fairly unique with respect to phosphorescence. We close with the comments that the deuterium effect is nonlinear; here only one aspect of this has been discussed. The rather large second order effect(s) observed in the τ for M4, S3, and P4 has not been treated. We hope to find the origin of this by examining the remaining deuterobenzenes.

ACKNOWLEDGEMENTS

We wish to thank G. A. Miller, P. J. Yound, P. O. Tchir, R. N. Swindlehurst, and A. I Budd for making some of the measurements and R. F. Kadlecz for technical help. Discussions with W. Siebrand and G. Nieman have been very stimulating.

REFERENCES

1. C. A Hutchinson Jr. and B. W. Mangum, J. Chem. Phys. 32, 1261 (1960); M. R. Wright, R. P. Frosch, and G. W. Robinson, J. Chem. Phys. 33, 934 (1960).
2. E. C Lim, J. Chem. Phys. 36, 3497 (1962); M. S. de Groot and J. H van der Waals, Mol. Phys. 4, 189 (1961); E. C. Lim and J. D Laposa, J. Chem. Phys. 41, 3257 (1964).
3. S. H Lin and R. Bersohn, J. Chem. Phys. 48, 2732 (1968); A. Heller, J. Am. Chem. Soc. 88, 2059 (1966).
4. T. E. Martin and A. H Kalantar, Chem. Phys. Letters 1, 623 (1968) and unpublished work; H. Offen (private communication); R Watts and S. Strickler (to be published).
5. G. W. Robinson and R P. Frosch, J. Chem. Phys. 38, 1187 (1963).
6. J. P. Byrne, E. F. McCoy, and I. G. Ross, Australian J. Chem. 15, 1589 (1965).
7. S. H. Lin, J. Chem. Phys. 44, 3759 (1966).
8. W. Siebrand, J. Chem. Phys. 47, 2411 (1967).
9. R. E. Kellogg and N. C. Wyeth, J. Chem. Phys. 45, 3156 (1966).
10. T. E. Martin and A. H. Kalantar, J. Phys. Chem. 72, 2265 (1968); J. Chem. Phys. 48, 3XXX (1968); J Chem. Phys. (to be published).
11. G. Herzberg, Infrared and Raman Spectra of Polyatomic Molecules (D. Van Nostrand Company, Inc., New York, 1945), pp. 201 ff.
12. J. W. Ellis, Trans. Faraday Soc. 25, 888 (1929).
13. S. Brodersen and A Langseth, Kgl. Danske Videnskab. Selskab, Mat.-fys. Skrifter, 1, no. 7 (1959).
14 G. F. Hatch, M. D. Erlitz, and G. C. Nieman (private communication).
15. J. D. Spangler and N. D. Kilmer, J. Chem. Phys. 48, 698 (1968).

INTERSYSTEM CROSSING FROM EXCITED TRIPLET STATES INTO THE SINGLET MANIFOLD

Richard A. Keller

National Bureau of Standards
Washington, D. C. 20234

INTRODUCTION

Intersystem crossing from excited singlet states, other than the lowest excited singlet state, into the triplet manifold must occur even in condensed media. Unfortunately the observation of these transitions is exceedingly difficult because such intersystem crossing processes must compete with the very rapid interval conversion. For this reason the crossing time ($1/k_{I.C.}$) must be of the order of magnitude of 10^{-11} sec. in order to be detected. If intersystem crossing from highly excited singlet states were an efficient process, the fluorescence quantum yield would decrease, and the phosphorescence quantum yield would increase upon excitation to electronic states higher than the first excited singlet state. Quantum yield measurements are very hard to make, and there are no reliable measurements which demonstrate intersystem crossing from excited singlet states other than the lowest excited singlet state.[2]

An equally interesting problem, and one that is easier to study experimentally, is intersystem crossing from excited triplet states into the singlet manifold. Intersystem crossing from the triplet manifold to the singlet manifold should be directly related to the reverse process discussed above. The experimental technique described below is based on a method in which no signal is observed unless triplet to singlet intersystem crossing occurs. This null technique is much more sensitive than the quantum yield measurements described above because those methods depend upon measuring small changes in large signals. In addition to contributing to the knowledge of intersystem crossing processes, this study increases our understanding of the fate of excited triplet molecules. Triplet-triplet absorption is well known[2-7] but triplet-triplet fluorescence has never been observed.[1] It has been postulated that a significant fraction of excited triplet molecules crosses over into the singlet system.[8] We will show below that this is not the case for the molecules that we studied. Another interesting question is the effect of $n-\pi^*$ excited states upon the intersystem crossing process.[1] It will be shown that the molecules quinoline and isoquinoline, which are isoelectronic with naphthalene, behave similarly to naphthalene with respect to triplet→singlet intersystem crossing. In these molecules, at least, there appears to be no enhancement of the intersystem crossing process by the presence of $n-\pi^*$ levels.

The method used to detect triplet→singlet intersystem crossing was to observe the fluorescence from the lowest excited singlet state which followed triplet-triplet absorption from a previously populated metastable triplet state. The only possible origin of this fluorescence is intersystem crossing from an excited triplet state. The adiabatic crossing need not occur from the terminal state of the optical absorption process, but can take place from any state of lower energy than the terminal state, but of higher total energy than the lowest excited singlet state. Again, the intersystem crossing process must compete with internal conversion in the triplet manifold. The intensity of this fluorescence is very weak and it was necessary to use sensitive detection techniques to observe it. Interference from normal fluorescence and delayed fluorescence[1] was eliminated by measuring the time dependence of the signal and the fluorescence intensity as a function of the intensity of visible radiation used to excite the triplet-triplet transition. Measurements were made at 77°K in a rigid glass matrix.

EXPERIMENTAL

The experimental apparatus is diagrammed in Figure 1. The sequence of steps in the experimental procedure is as follows:

(1) The monochromator was set to pass fluorescence radiation from the sample.

(2) With shutter 6 closed, the D.C. bias (11) was adjusted to cancel out the dark current from the photomultiplier tube.

(3) The sample was irradiated for several triplet lifetimes with shutter 3 and 4 open and shutter 6 closed.

(4) Shutter 4 was closed and shutter 6 opened rapidly. Any fluorescence at this point was due to delayed fluorescence[1] and this signal was subtracted from the final signal or, more typically, the concentration of the solute was decreased to eliminate the delayed fluorescence.

(5) Step 3 was repeated, but this time after irradiation shutter 3 was closed and shutter 6 opened rapidly. Shutter 3 filters out UV radiation but passes visible radiation which was absorbed by the metastable triplet molecules created

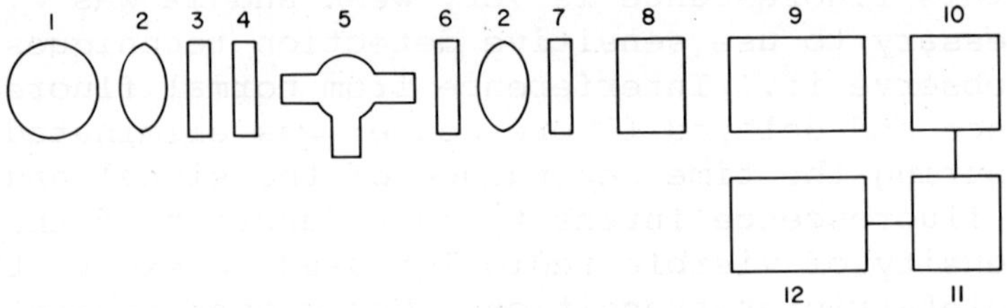

Figure 1 Arrangement of the Experimental Apparatus

1. 150 watt, high pressure mercury lamp. Approximately 2 x 10^{15} photons/sec cm^2 of UV radiation impinged upon the sample.
2. Quartz lens
3. UV blocking, visible transmitting shutter. (0-52 Corning[9] filter). The 0-52 filter transmits light of wavelength longer than 360 nm.
4. Opaque shutter.
5. Sample in liquid nitrogen dewar.
6. Opaque shutter.
7. UV transmitting, visible blocking filter (7-54 Corning[9] filter).
8. UV transmitting, visible blocking solution filter; 2.5 cm path length (90 gm $CoSO_4 \cdot 7H_2O$ and 500 gm $NiSO_4 \cdot 6H_2O$/liter of H_2O).
9. Low dispersion, wide aperture monochromator. (Baush and Lomb 33-66-02[9]).
10. Low noise, high sensitivity photomultiplier tube. (E.M.I.-6255S[9]).
11. D. S. bias supply.
12. High sensitivity oscilloscope. (100μ volt/cm).

in Step 3.

(6) The fluorescence signal was displayed on the oscilloscope and photographed. This signal decays with the lifetime of the triplet state.

(7) The monochromator was set to a different wavelength and the procedure was repeated to map out the fluorescence spectrum.

(8) Interference filters were combined with shutter 3 to verify that the Hg lines responsible for exciting the observed fluorescence were the ones absorbed by metastable triplet molecules.

The sample dewar contained the rigid glass in a copper cell which was in direct contact with liquid nitrogen. There was no liquid nitrogen in the light path. Quartz windows on the copper cell were made vacuum tight by the use of indium seals. Three-inch long stainless steel tubes extended from the windows into the vacuum jacket to reduce scattered light.

Other experimental arrangements, including some in which excitation and detection were perpendicular to each other, and other lamps were tried, but in all cases the above arrangement proved to be the most satisfactory.

The solvents used were fluorescence free. Naphthalene-d_8 and phenanthrene-d_{10} were obtained from Merck-Sharp and Dohme of Canada[9] and used without further purification. The remaining solutes were zone refined samples with the exception of quinoline and isoquinoline. These two materials were purified by vacuum distillation. Fluorene was treated by a Diels-Alder procedure to remove anthracene.

The fluorescence observed from a 10^{-4} molar solution of naphthalene-d_8 in 3 methyl pentane is shown in Figure 2 as an example of the data. The observed signal is well above the noise level but still very weak. The decay time of the signal agrees very well with the decay time of the triplet state of naphthalene-d_8.

The wavelength dependence of this signal is

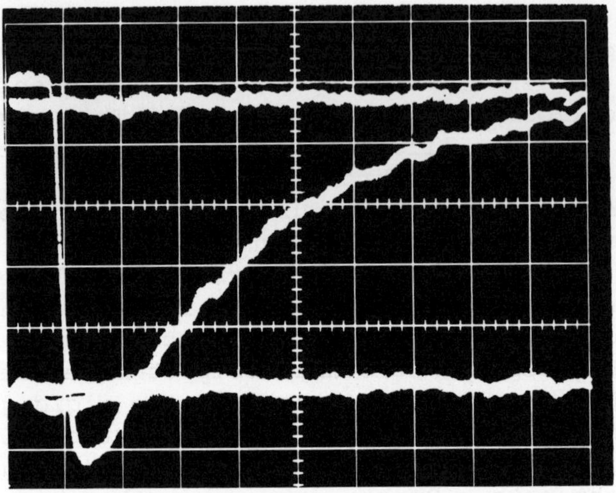

Figure 2 Naphthalene-d_8 Fluorescence Excited by Triplet ↔ Triplet Absorption

A. Measurement parameters
   1. Oscilloscope: vertical 5mv/cm; horizontal 5 sec/cm.
   2. Monochromator
      a. 320 nm
      b. entrance slit 1.8 mm; exit slit 1 mm
   3. Detection: 1 meg ohm input impedance paralleled by a 1 μf capacitor to give a one second response time.
   4. Photomultiplier
      a. 1500 V D.C.
      b. dark current 1×10^{-8} amp. (nulled by D.C. bias).
   5. Solution
      a. 10^{-4} M naphthalene-d_8 in 3-methyl pentane.
      b. 77°K

B. Data
   1. Upper traces represent signal and baseline for signal.
   2. Lower traces represent blank.

Shutter 4 is closed after population of metastable triplets, and no visible radiation is present to excite triplet-triplet transitions.

shown in Figure 3 and compared with normal fluorescence. The agreement is good.

It was possible to estimate the quantum yield of the fluorescence signal which results from the irradiation of metastable triplet molecules in their triplet-triplet absorption band [$\Phi_f(T \rightarrow T)$]. The method used was to compare the intensity of the triplet triplet induced fluorescence [$I_f(T \rightarrow T)$] to the intensity of normal fluorescence [$I_f(n)$]. When the geometrical factors remain unchanged, the desired quantum yield is given by the following expression:

$$\frac{\Phi_f(T \rightarrow T)}{\Phi_f(n)} = \frac{I_f(T \rightarrow T)}{I_f(n)} \alpha \frac{i_f(n)}{i_f(T \rightarrow T)} \beta \quad (1)$$

$i_f(n)$ is the intensity of UV light used to excite normal fluorescence; $i_f(T \rightarrow T)$ is the intensity of the visible light used to excite the triplet → triplet transition. α is a correction factor which results from the necessity to use different slit widths* to measure $I_f(T \rightarrow T)$ and $I_f(n)$. β is the fraction of the visible radiation which is absorbed by the solution. At the concentrations used, essentially all of the UV radiation was absorbed by the sample. The quantum yield was estimated for only 3 compounds: naphthalene-d_8, quinoline, and isoquinoline. For all 3 compounds the 404 nm Hg line was used to excite the triplet-triplet transition. This line was selected from the radiation of a high pressure Hg lamp by the use of an interference filter. An interference filter was also used to select 254 nm radiation from a low pressure Hg, pen lamp. This UV radiation was used to excite $I_f(n)$. The correction factor α was determined

*It was necessary to use narrow slits for the measurement of $I_f(n)$ to eliminate interference from the 313 nm Hg line. This slit width was too narrow to observe $I_f(T \rightarrow T)$.

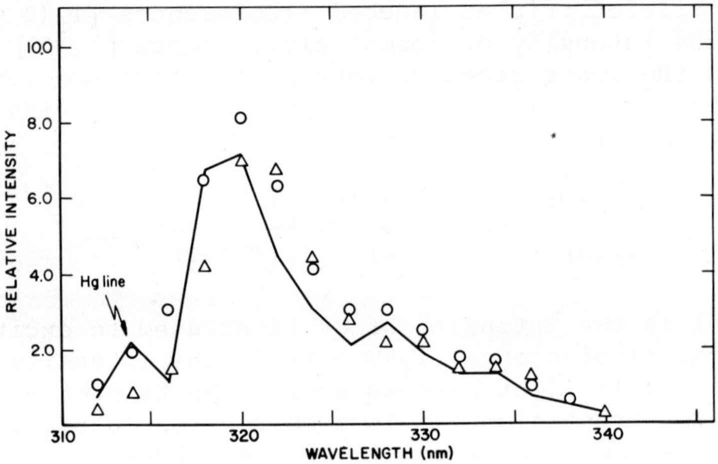

Figure 3 $I_f(T \leftrightarrow T)$ Compared With Normal Fluorescence; Naphthalene-d_8: Δ represents the maximum of the time dependent fluorescence signal which results from the irradiation of metastable triplet molecules with visible light. The wide slits (1 mm exit, 1.8 mm entrance) necessary to observe this signal resulted in rather low resolution. O represents normal fluorescence at the same slit widths used above. —— represents normal fluorescence at narrower slit widths (0.2 mm exit, 0.4 mm entrance) to increase resolution.

experimentally by measuring $I_f(n)$ as a function of slit width. β was determined by measuring the O.D. of the triplet-triplet transition at 404 nm. A quantum counter composed of 36 mg of rhodamine B in 10 ml of ethylene glycol was used to measure the ratio of $i_f(n)/i_f(T \rightarrow T)$.

RESULTS

NAPHTHALENE-d_8 AND NAPHTHALENE-h_8.

Relatively strong signals were obtained for both naphthalene-h_8 and naphthalene-d_8 dissolved in 3 methyl pentane and 3-7 solvent[108] (see Fig. 2). This signal was excited by the 404 nm Hg line in agreement with the $T \leftrightarrow T$ absorption spectra shown in Figure 4. The lifetime agreed with the lifetime of the triplet state of naphthalene.

A rough estimate of the emission intensities shows $I_f(T \leftrightarrow T)_{d_8}/I_f(T \rightarrow T)_{h_8}$ is approximately 3. This is less than what would be expected from the ratio of the triplet lifetimes (7) which governs the ratio of the steady state triplet concentrations. The conclusion which should be drawn from these measurements is that $\Phi_f(T \rightarrow T)_{d_8}$ is similar to $\Phi_f(T \rightarrow T)_{h_8}$. There is a slight indication that intersystem crossing is greater in the perhydro compound but not much credence can be put in that observation.

$\Phi_f(T \rightarrow T)$ for the perdeutero compound was estimated by the method described in the experimental section.

$$\Phi_{I.C.}(T \rightarrow S) = \Phi_f(T \rightarrow T) \cdot \Phi_f(n)^{-1} = \frac{I_f(T \rightarrow T)}{I_f(n)}\alpha \cdot$$

$$\cdot \frac{i_f(n)}{i_f(T \to T)}\beta = \frac{1}{350}(3.2)\frac{1}{6000}(3.6)$$

$$= 5 \times 10^{-7} \qquad (2)$$

$\Phi_{I.C.}(T \to S)$ is the quantum yield of the intersystem crossing process and is related to $\Phi_f(T \to T)$ of Eq. (1) by the factor $\Phi_f(n)^{-1}$. This factor results from the fact that only a fraction of the transitions back into the singlet system actually results in fluorescence emission.

QUINOLINE.

Quinoline is isoelectronic with naphthalene. The presence of the nitrogen in the ring introduces $n-\pi^*$ states into the naphthalene eigenstate system. A relatively strong signal was obtained from a 3.4×10^{-4} M solution in 3-7 solvent.[10] The fluorescence spectrum corresponds to the normal fluorescence spectrum of quinoline. $I_f(T \to T)$ was excited by both the 404 nm and the 436 nm Hg lines in agreement with the triplet $\leftrightarrow$ triplet absorption spectrum shown in Fig. 4. The lifetime agreed with the lifetime of the triplet state of quinoline (0.5 sec.).

The signal was too weak when excited through a 404 nm interference filter to determine the quantum yield as was done for naphthalene-d_8. Less than 5% of the visible light was absorbed by the metastable triplets. A rough comparison of the quantum yield of intersystem crossing between quinoline and naphthalene-h_8 was made by using the following expression:

$$\frac{\Phi_f(T \to S)_Q}{\Phi_f(T \to S)_{Nh_8}} = \frac{I_f(T \to T)_Q}{I_f(T \to T)_{Nd_8}} \cdot \frac{I_f(T \to T)_{Nd_8}}{I_f(T \to T)_{Nh_8}} \cdot$$

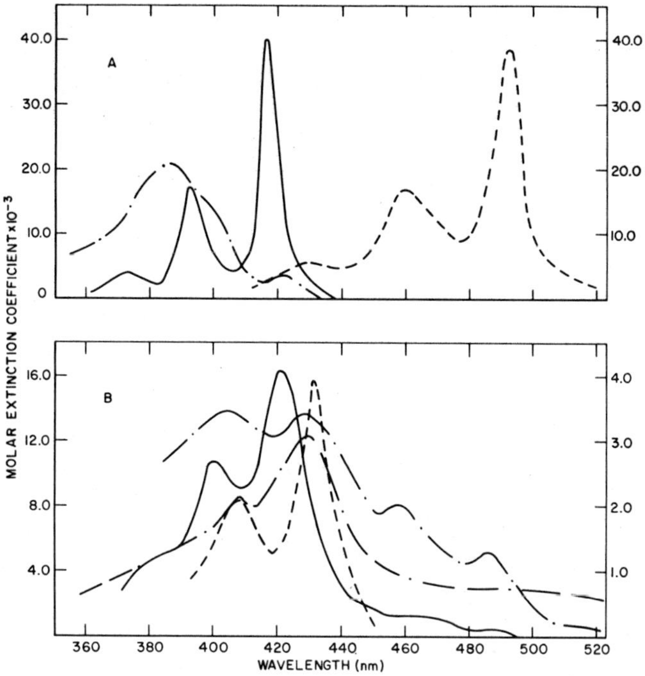

Figure 4 Triplet ↔ Triplet Absorption Spectra of the Molecules Studied: The spectra of naphthalene, fluorene, phenanthrene quinoline, and isoquinoline were taken from the work of Craig and Ross.[3] The spectrum of carbazole is from the work of Henry and Kasha.[6] The extinction coefficient of carbazole and fluorene were measured by Brian[7] and the remaining extinction coefficients were measured by Hadley and Keller.[5]
Key to the Spectra: Part A; — · — fluorene, —— naphthalene, — — — phenanthrene, Part B; — — · — — carbazole, — · — quinoline, —— isoquinoline, — — — — triphenylene.
The scale to the left refers to all compounds except quinoline. The scale for quinoline is to the right of Part B.

$$\cdot\ \alpha \frac{\varepsilon_{T \to T,N}(4040)}{\varepsilon_{T \to T,Q}(4040)} \cdot \frac{\tau_{N_{h_8}}}{\tau_Q} = \frac{3}{1} \cdot 3 \cdot \frac{1}{9}$$

$$\frac{3800}{3400} \cdot \frac{2.3}{0.5} = 5 \qquad (3)$$

The Q and N subscripts refer to quinoline and naphthalene. $\varepsilon_{T \to T}$ refers to the extinction coefficient for the triplet $\leftrightarrow$ triplet transition. These numbers have been recently measured by Hadley and Keller.[5] τ refers to the lifetime of the triplet state and the ratio represents the difference in the steady state triplet population of the two molecules. α again corrects for the different slit widths used in the two measurements. The I_f's are measured at the maximum of their emission curves. Eq. (3) assumes that the emission properties of the two molecules are the same. We are looking for large effects, and with this in mind the assumption is good. The second term in Eq. (3) was measured and the result is discussed in the preceding section. Although the estimates and approximations made in arriving at the answer for the ratio are crude, they are good enough to say that the introduction of $n\text{-}\pi^*$ excited states into the naphthalene energy system does not result in a very large increase in the rate of the triplet $\to$ singlet intersystem crossing process.

ISOQUINOLINE.

Isoquinoline is also isoelectronic with naphthalene. Relatively strong fluorescence was induced by excitation in the T $\leftrightarrow$ T bands of a 3.5×10^{-4} M solution of isoquinoline in 3-7 solvent.[10] The fluorescence spectrum corresponds to normal fluorescence, and the lifetime of the emission agrees with the lifetime of the triplet state of isoquinoline. The intensity of the emission is of the same order of magnitude as that observed for naphthalene and quinoline. The emission from isoquinoline is perhaps a factor of two more intense than the emission from quinoline under similar excitation intensities. This is in agreement with the larger $T \leftrightarrow T$ extinction coefficients at 404 nm and 436 nm for isoquinoline (see Fig. 4). Again, the introduction of a nitrogen atom into the naphthalene ring did not increase $\Phi_{I.C.}(T \rightarrow S)$ by a significant amount.

FLUORENE.

A signal of roughly the same order of magnitude as from naphthalene-h_8 was found from a 2.4×10^{-4} M solution of fluorene in 3-7 solvent.[10] The fluorescence corresponded to the normal fluorescence spectrum, and the lifetime of the emission corresponded to the lifetime of the triplet state of fluorene. No attempt was made to measure $\Phi_{I.C.}$ $(T \rightarrow S)$ for fluorene but it is roughly the same as for naphthalene.

BENZENE.

A very weak signal (signal/noise $\sim$ 2) with approximately the correct decay time was observed for a 4.5×10^{-3} M solution of benzene-d_6 in 3-7 solvent. A 1000 watt Hg-Xe lamp was used to populate the metastable triplet state and the high pressure Hg lamp was used to excite $T \leftrightarrow T$ transitions. The mercury lamp excitation was perpendicular to both the UV excitation and detection directions. The weak signal was probably the result of small excitation due to the weak absorption coefficient of ground state benzene and to little $T \leftrightarrow T$ absorption induced by the visible light. No estimates of $\Phi_{I.C.}(T \rightarrow S)$ were made.

PHENANTHRENE-d_{10}.

A 1.6×10^{-4} M solution of phenanthrene-d_{10} in 3-7 solvent[10] was carefully studied with several different experimental arrangements involving combinations of a 1000 watt high pressure Hg-Xe lamp, a high pressure Hg lamp; and a Tungsten iodine lamp. Both linear and perpendicular arrangements were tried. No signal was observed from any arrangement. Inspection of Fig. 4 shows that the 436 nm Hg line should excite the $T \leftrightarrow T$ transition. Failure to observe $I_f(T \leftrightarrow T)$ must mean that $\Phi_{I.C.}(T \rightarrow S)$ is at least a factor of 10 smaller than in naphthalene.

TRIPHENYLENE.

A 3.0×10^{-4} M solution of triphenylene in 3-7 solvent[10] was studied with the experimental arrangement shown in Fig. 1. No fluorescence signal which depended upon the $T \leftrightarrow T$ excitation was observed. An examination of the $T \leftrightarrow T$ absorption spectrum of triphenylene shown in Fig. 4 shows that both the 404 nm and the 436 nm Hg lines are in the correct region for strong $T \leftrightarrow T$ excitation. Failure to observe the signal must mean that $\Phi_{I.C.}(T \rightarrow S)$ is much smaller than for naphthalene.

CARBAZOLE.

A 2.6×10^{-4} M solution of carbazole in 3-7 solvent was carefully studied using several different combinations of lamps and experimental arrangements. In no case was any signal observed which depended upon $T \leftrightarrow T$ excitation. Inspection of Fig. 4 shows that the $T \leftrightarrow T$ absorption spectrum falls in the right region for excitation by both the 404 nm and the 436 nm Hg lines. Again, the failure to observe $I_f(T \leftrightarrow T)$ must mean that $\Phi_{I.C.}(T \rightarrow S)$ is much smaller than in naphthalene.

DISCUSSION

The measurements discussed above show that very few excited triplet molecules undergo intersystem crossing into the singlet system. Our measurements say nothing about the fate of the large majority of triplet molecules which do not cross into the singlet system. It is unlikely that a large fraction of these molecules undergoes photodissociation because many workers have irradiated their samples for much longer times than we did and noticed no photodissociation. It is probable that most excited triplet molecules undergo rapid internal conversion to the lowest excited triplet state.

It is difficult to relate the $T \rightarrow S$ intersystem crossing process to the $S \rightarrow T$ intersystem crossing process because a detailed knowledge of the density of states, the electronic energy levels, and the relaxation paths is necessary.[11] However, our results suggest that $S \rightarrow T$ intersystem crossing from electronic states higher in energy than the first excited electronic singlet state is not an important process.

Our failure to observe a larger $\Phi_{I.C.}(T \rightarrow S)$ in quinoline and isoquinoline than in naphthalene upon photoexcitation of the metastable triplets does not mean that $n\text{-}\pi^*$ states do not enhance intersystem crossing at lower energies as suggested by El-Sayed.[1]

REFERENCES

1. This point is discussed in a recent review article. See S. K. Lower and M. A. El-Sayed, Chem. Rev. 66, 199 (1966).
2. D. McClure, J. Chem. Phys. 19, 670 (1951); D. McClure and P. Hanst, J. Chem. Phys. 23, 1772 (1955).
3. D. Craig and I. Ross, J. Chem. Soc. 1589 (1954).
4. G. Porter and M. Windsor, Proc. Roy. Soc. (London) A245, 238 (1958).
5. R. Keller and S. Hadley, J. Chem. Phys. 42, 2382 (1965); S. Hadley and R. Keller (in preparation).
6. B. Henry and M. Kasha, J. Chem. Phys. 47, 3319 (1967).
7. J. Brinen, J. Chem. Phys. (in press).
8. B. Srinivasan, M. Kinoshita, J. Rabalais and S. McGlynn, J. Chem. Phys. 48, 1924 (1968).
9. Certain commercial materials and equipment are identified in this paper in order to adequately specify the experimental procedure. In no case does such identification imply recommendation or endorsement by the National Bureau of Standards, nor does it imply that the material or equipment identified is necessarily the best available for the purpose.
10. A mixture of 30% butyl alcohol and 70% isopentane.
11. D. Hanson and G. Robinson, J. Chem. Phys. 43, 4174 (1965); G. Robinson and R. Frosch, J. Chem. Phys. 37, 1962 (1962); 38, 1187 (1963); G. Nieman and G. Robinson, J. Chem. Phys. 39, 1298 (1963).

VIBRONIC INTERACTIONS AND RADIATIONLESS TRANSITIONS IN HETEROAROMATIC AND AROMATIC CARBONYL COMPOUNDS: I. GENERAL CONSIDERATIONS*

E. C. Lim**

Department of Chemistry
Loyola University
Chicago, Illinois

I. INTRODUCTION

Despite recent, rapid progress in the general understanding of radiationless transitions and luminescence behavior of organic molecules, the luminescence properties of many aza-aromatics and aromatic carbonyl compounds continue to be a subject which requires clarification. Of the various emission characteristics of heteroaromatic

*A portion of this work concerning the enhancement of $S_1 \rightarrow S_0$ radiationless transition by $n,\pi^*-\pi,\pi^*$ vibronic coupling was originally presented at the Symposium on Molecular Luminescence (organized by S. P. McGlynn for the Society of Applied Spectroscopy), Chicago, June, 1966.

**Address after November 1, 1968: Department of Chemistry, Wayne State University, Detroit, Michigan 48202.

molecules, the two which stand out the most are the "fluorescence activation" by hydroxyl solvents and the pronounced increase in fluorescence quantum yield with decreasing temperature. These phenomena are most likely associated with the dependence of $S_1 \rightarrow S_o$ (lowest excited singlet to ground) and $S_1 \rightarrow T$ (lowest excited singlet to triplet) radiationless transitions on the vibronic coupling between the low-lying n,π* and π,π* states, and they represent the topic of the present paper. The paper begins with a brief discussion of the mechanisms through which n,π*-π,π* vibronic coupling can enhance $S_1 \rightarrow S_o$ and $S_1 \rightarrow T$ radiationless transitions. A brief survey of the evidence for the occurrence of the n,π*-π,π* vibronic coupling is then discussed. Finally, probable environmental (solvent and temperature) effects on the vibronic coupling are described and compared with the environmental effects on the fluorescence of isoquinoline.

II. VIBRONIC INTERACTION BETWEEN ^{1}n,π* AND ^{1}π,π* STATES AND $S_1 \rightarrow S_o$ and $S_1 \rightarrow T$ RADIATIONLESS TRANSITIONS

It is now generally recognized that the major factor determining the rate of radiationless transition is the Franck-Condon factor for the associated transition.[1] The magnitude of the Franck-Condon factor for a particular vibrational mode is larger the greater is the relative displacement of the two electronic states along the vibration coordinate. To examine the effect of vibronic interaction between n,π* and π,π* states on the Franck-Condon factor, we consider the energy level diagram of Fig. 1 which may be regarded to be appropriate for many polycyclic monoazines. The vibronic coupling between the lowest energy ^{1}π,π* state and the higher-lying ^{1}n,π* state requires out-of-plane modes as

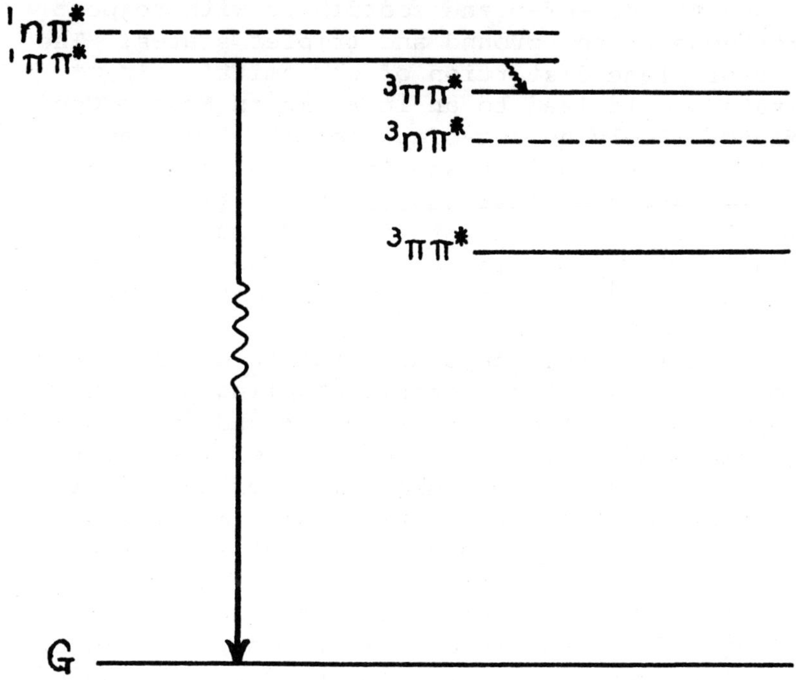

Figure 1 A hypothetical energy level diagram.

perturbing vibrations, and it has the effect of displacing the nuclei of $^1\pi,\pi^*$ and $^1n,\pi^*$ states along the out-of-plane coordinate with respect to those of the ground and triplet states. The out-of-plane distortion of the emitting $^1\pi,\pi^*$ state should lead to an increase in Franck-Condon factor involving out-of-plane vibrations and therefore to an increase in $S_1 \rightarrow S_o$ and $S_1 \rightarrow T$ radiationless transitions. The $n,\pi^*-\pi,\pi^*$ vibronic coupling in the triplet manifold would have a qualitatively similar effect on the intersystem crossing originating from the lowest π,π^* singlet and triplet states.

Aside from the consideration of the Franck-Condon factor, the vibronic coupling between $^1n,\pi^*$ and $^1\pi,\pi^*$ or between $^3n,\pi^*$ and $^3\pi,\pi^*$ states is expected to increase the rate of intersystem crossing through the enhancement of the matrix elements of the perturbation which mix the singlet π,π^* states with triplet π,π^* states. The Franck-Condon factor, important in radiationless transitions, increases rapidly with the decreasing energy gap. Because of this reason, the higher triplet state(s) lying near the first excited singlet state is expected to be important in the $S_1 \rightarrow T$ radiationless transitions. For many polycyclic monoazines and certain aromatic carbonyl compounds, one expects a π,π^* triplet state to lie very near the emitting $^1\pi,\pi^*$ state, and the intersystem crossing between the emitting $^1\pi,\pi^*$ state and the nearly degenerate $^3\pi,\pi^*$ state is thought to be an important path of radiationless transition.[2] Within the framework of the Born-Oppenheimer approximation, the matrix elements of the perturbation which mix $^1\pi,\pi^*$ and $^3\pi,\pi^*$ states are vanishingly small.[3] In the case of heteroaromatic molecules possessing nearly degenerate n,π^* and π,π^* states, it is expected that the Born-Oppenheimer approximation will fail. When significant deviation from the Born-Oppenheimer approximation occurs as a result of vibronic interaction, the selection rule forbidding $^1\pi,\pi^* \leftrightarrow {}^3\pi,\pi^*$ radiationless coupling becomes invalid, and the radiationless transitions are expected to be generally increased. At the very least, vibronic interaction within the singlet or triplet manifold is expected to enhance the intersystem crossing to π,π^* triplet states through the following vibronic spin-orbit coupling mechanisms:[4]

$$^1\pi,\pi^* \overset{\text{vib}}{\leftrightarrow} {}^1n,\pi^* \overset{\text{SO}}{\leftrightarrow} {}^3\pi,\pi^* \quad (1)$$

$$^1\pi,\pi^* \overset{\text{SO}}{\leftrightarrow} {}^3n,\pi^* \overset{\text{vib}}{\leftrightarrow} {}^3\pi,\pi^* \quad (2)$$

The possible consequence of the deviation from Born-Oppenheimer approximation was also considered by El-Sayed,[5] while the vibronic spin-orbit mechanism was emphasized in several recent publications from this laboratory.[4,6,7]

There are therefore several reasons why the vibronic interaction between π,π^* and the nearly degenerate n,π^* state may enhance $S_1 \rightarrow S_0$, $S_1 \rightarrow T$, and $T_1 \rightarrow S_0$ radiationless transitions in heteroaromatic and aromatic carbonyl compounds.

III. EVIDENCE FOR THE OCCURRENCE OF n,π^*-π,π^* VIBRONIC INTERACTIONS

The occurrence of a strong vibronic coupling in the singlet manifold can be recognized in principle, by the appearance of an out-of-plane vibration in fluorescence or, when the vibronic coupling within the triplet manifold can be distinguished, by the appearance of in-plane polarized vibronic bands of relevant out-of-plane vibrations in the phosphorescence spectra.

In rigid glass at 77°K, the resolution of fluorescence spectra is not normally good enough to allow an unequivocal demonstration of the former effect,[+] and emphasis has been placed, in this laboratory, on the observation of the latter effect.

Vibronic interaction between n,π* and π,π* states can introduce dipole-allowed character to π* → π phosphorescence through the mechanisms (1) and (2) of the previous section. Both of these vibronic spin-orbit mechanisms introduce in-plane polarized intensity (or vibronic bands, in some cases) outside the 0,0 band of phosphorescence.[4] When the energy of an n,π* state is sensitive to hydrogen bonding, as is frequently the case, it is sometimes possible to distinguish mechanisms (1) and (2) through the solvent effect on spectral distribution and polarization of phosphorescence.[7] Studies along these lines indicate that the important vibronic spin-orbit route is very probably mechanism (1) for most polycyclic monoazines[6] (e.g., aza-naphthalenes and aza-phenanthrenes) and mechanism (2) for many aromatic carbonyl compounds[7] (e.g., certain derivatives of acetophenone and benzaldehyde). Vibrational analysis of phosphorescence spectra of several polycyclic diazines lead to an interesting conclusion that hydrogen bending modes are more important than the skeletal modes when there is a C-H bond in close proximity to the non-bonding electrons of the heteroatom.[8] This conclusion is supported by the observation of an important deuterium isotope effect on the vibronic spin-orbit coupling[6] and n → π* absorption band[8] of quinoxaline.

[+]See, however, the paper by Hochstrasser and Marzzacco in these proceedings.

IV. ENVIRONMENTAL EFFECTS ON $n,\pi^*-\pi,\pi^*$ VIBRONIC COUPLING AND FLUORESCENCE OF HETEROAROMATIC MOLECULES

Since the efficiency of vibronic interaction between n,π^* and π,π^* states is dependent on the vibrational overlap integral as well as the energy gap between the two states, temperature and the nature of solvent (hydroxyl or non-hydroxyl) are expected to have considerable effect on $n,\pi^*-\pi,\pi^*$ vibronic interactions. The temperature effect on vibronic coupling has been discussed by Robinson[9] and it has been experimentally verified, for example, for $n \rightarrow \pi^*$ absorption of quinoxaline[8] (whose oscillator strength decreases with decreasing temperature). The hydrogen bonding by hydroxyl solvents can affect the vibronic coupling via the decrease in the charge density of the non-bonding electrons, which decreases the overlap integral,[6,7] or through its effect on the energy gap between n,π^* and π,π^* states.[4,6,7] For vibronic interaction between the lowest excited singlet state of π,π^* character and higher-lying n,π^* singlet state, the effect of hydrogen bonding is therefore to decrease vibronic coupling through both of these mechanisms.

From the above considerations, it can be expected that the radiationless deactivation via $n,\pi^*-\pi,\pi^*$ vibronic coupling should be sensitive to solvent and temperature. Furthermore, if the perturbing vibrations which mix the π,π^* and n,π^* states are out-of-plane hydrogen bending motions, as they appear to be in many cases, one would also expect a significant deuterium effect on radiationless transitions (including $S_1 \rightarrow T$ intersystem crossing). A good example of these expectations is afforded by the fluorescent behavior of isoquinoline which shows:[10]

(1) Fluorescence quantum yield is considerably greater in hydroxyl solvents than in hydrocarbon solvents (e.g., $\Phi = 0.034$ in ethanol vs

$\Phi = 0.004$ in isooctane at $310^{o}K$);

(2) There is a pronounced increase in fluorescence quantum yield with decreasing temperature (e.g., $\Phi = 0.343$ in ethanol at $195^{o}K$ vs ca. 0.034 at $310^{o}K$);

(3) Fluorescence yield is greater for isoquinoline-d_7 than for isoquinoline-h_7; and

(4) The deuterium effect on fluorescence yield is larger in hydrocarbon solvents than in hydroxyl solvents and at higher temperatures than at lower temperatures (e.g., Φ_D/Φ_H of ca. 2.75 in isooctane at $310^{o}K$ vs Φ_D/Φ_H of ca. 1.24 and ca. 1.09 in ethanol at $310^{o}K$ and $195^{o}K$, respectively).

These results establish the occurrence of radiationless transitions whose rate is dependent on factors affecting n,π^*-π,π^* vibronic coupling. That the $S_1 \rightarrow S_o$ internal conversion represents a considerable portion of these radiationless transitions is indicated by the sum of the quantum yields of fluorescence and intersystem crossing, which is considerably less than unity (particularly in hydrocarbon matrices).[10] It should be mentioned that the enhancement of fluorescence with decreasing temperature is not unique to heteroaromatic molecules, and it is theoretically expected[11] and observed for a variety of compounds, including aromatic hydrocarbons.[12] The effect is, however, considerably smaller than what is observed for isoquinoline and related molecules, where a higher energy but nearly degenerate n,π^* singlet state lie above the lowest energy π,π^* states. Evidently, thermal excitation of out-of-plane vibrations, which can mix n,π^* and π,π^* states, is responsible for the very small fluorescence yield of many heteroaromatic molecules at higher temperature. Although these data, as well as those in the literature, do not lend experimental proof for the proposed radiationless deactivation via vibronic coupling, they are at least consistent with the proposed model. A more systematic and quantitative effort now being made in this laboratory should be of value in clarifying the role of $n,\pi^*-\pi,\pi^*$ vibronic interactions in radiationless transitions of heteroaromatic and aromatic carbonyl compounds.

ACKNOWLEDGEMENT

This work was supported by the National Science Foundation.

REFERENCES

1. G. W. Robinson and R. P. Frosch, J. Chem. Phys. 37, 1962 (1962); 38, 1187 (1963); J. P. Byrne, E. F. McCoy, and I. G. Ross, Aust. J. Chem. 18, 1589 (1965).
2. E. C. Lim and J. M. H. Yu, J. Chem. Phys. 45, 4742 (1966).
3. D. S. McClure, J. Chem. Phys. 20, 632 (1952).
4. E. C. Lim and J. M. H. Yu, J. Chem. Phys. 47, 3270 (1967); E. C. Lim, Ber. Bunsenges Phys. Chem. 72, 273 (1968).
5. M. A. El-Sayed, Accounts of Chemical Research 1, 8 (1968).
6. E. C. Lim and J. M. H. Yu, J. Chem. Phys. (in press).
7. E. C. Lim, Y. Kanda, and J. Stanislaus (to be published).
8. E. C. Lim and Y. H. Li (to be published).
9. G. W. Robinson, in Molecular Physics, D. Williams, Ed. (Academic Press, New York, 1962), p. 253.
10. R. Li and E. C. Lim (unpublished results).
11. S. H. Lin, J. Chem. Phys. 44, 3759 (1966); D. L. Dexter and W. B. Fowler, ibid. 47, 1379 (1968); M. Bixon and J. Jortner, ibid. 48, 715 (1968).
12. See, for example, J. Sahu, J. Ind. Chem. Soc. 37, 411 (1960).

ENERGY TRANSFER IN CHEMILUMINESCENCE

Emil H. White, David R. Roberts and David F. Roswell

Department of Chemistry
Johns Hopkins University
Balitmore, Maryland

INTRODUCTION

In chemiluminescent reactions, excited states of molecules are produced by chemical energy.[1-4] Once formed, the excited molecules behave in an identical manner to those produced by irradiation. Thus internal conversion, intersystem crossing, radiationless transitions and, in particular, energy transfer can all occur. However the fact that an irradiating source is not necessary ensures that all the energy is originally located in one species, thus allowing the possibility of observing some of the more subtle interactions. At the same time some flexibility is lost since the reactions must take place in fluid solutions and (usually) in the presence of oxygen. Thus triplet states are usually assumed to be efficiently quenched and consequently to play no significant role in chemiluminescence emission.

Energy transfer in chemiluminescence is a relatively recently discovered phenomenon. The most outstanding example of this process is the reaction of oxalyl chloride or oxalic esters with hydrogen peroxide in the presence of fluorescent compounds.[5-7] The reaction of bis(2,4-dinitrophenyl) oxalate with hydrogen peroxide in the presence of rubrene has a quantum yield of 0.23, the highest yet reported for a chemiluminescent reaction.[6] The proposed reaction scheme involves an active intermediate which transfers its energy to the fluorescer. Other examples include the decomposition of dicyclohexylperoxycarbonate in the presence of acceptors,[8] the autoxidation of tetralin in the presence of 9,10-diphenylanthracene,[9] and the decomposition of tetralin peroxide in the presence of porphyrins.[10] Recently there has also been a report[11] of triplet-triplet energy transfer in the chemiluminescent oxidation of methyl ethyl ketone, in which the donor was excited biacetyl and acceptors were various derivatives of anthracene. Energy transfer is also involved in the chemiluminescence involving singlet oxygen as a donor and eosin or zinc tetraphenylporphin as acceptors.[12]

INTERMOLECULAR TRANSFER

The substituted phthalic hydrazides form a well known[1,4,13,14] group of chemiluminescent molecules, with luminol I (5-amino-2,3-dihydrophthalazine-1,4-dione) by far the most widely studied member. The classical researches of Drew[15-17] and his coworkers established that an unblocked six-membered heterocyclic ring was necessary for chemiluminescence in this series. Drew also formulated empirical rules correlating the chemiluminescence efficiency of 3- and 4- substituted phthalic hydrazides with the electronic properties of the substituent: electron donors enhance chemiluminescence; electron withdrawing groups diminish it.[16,17] The chemiluminescent reaction of phthalic hydrazides is usually carried out in basic aqueous solution containing hydrogen peroxide and hemin or some other catalyst. However, White and his co-workers showed that in solutions containing high molar percentages of dimethyl sulfoxide, dimethyl formamide or hexamethylphosphoramide only a strong base and oxygen are necessary for chemiluminescence.[4,13] Utilizing this simpler system, it was shown that the stoichiometry of the luminol chemiluminescent reaction was as shown in I and II of the diagram. From a comparison of the fluorescence emission spectrum of 3-aminophthalate dianion and the chemiluminescence emission, together with the determination of II as the sole organic product, excited II was identified as the emitter. The work of Bursey[18] and Zafiriou[19] on other substituted phthalic hydrazides confirmed that this scheme was a general one, and that in every case the emission was that of the corresponding phthalic acid dianion. Their data also served to verify the rough rule that chemiluminescence efficiency follows the fluorescence efficiency of the product diacid. The only known exceptions to the above scheme are the parent compound, phthalic hydrazide, and the 3- and 4-methyl substituted derivatives. While in the aqueous system these compounds show an extremely weak blue chemiluminescence,[20,21] in aprotic solvents an easily detectable yellow emission is produced.[19] Since phthalate dianion is non-fluorescent in either solution it cannot be the emitter. Zafiriou demonstrated,[19] however, that the anion of phthalic hydrazide is weakly yellow fluorescent ($\Phi_f = 0.002 \pm 0.001$ in hexamethylphosphoramide[22]) and that the fluorescence spectrum corresponded to the chemiluminescence emission. As will be seen below, phthalic hydrazide, when joined to an acridone moiety, does give light, showing that excited phthalate is produced and can participate in energy transfer. This observation, coupled with the fact that the product of the phthalic hydrazide chemiluminescent reaction is phthalate dianion, strongly supports the hypothesis that intermolecular energy transfer is occuring in this system. Further support is given by the effect of concentration on the light yield of the phthalic hydrazide chemiluminescence.

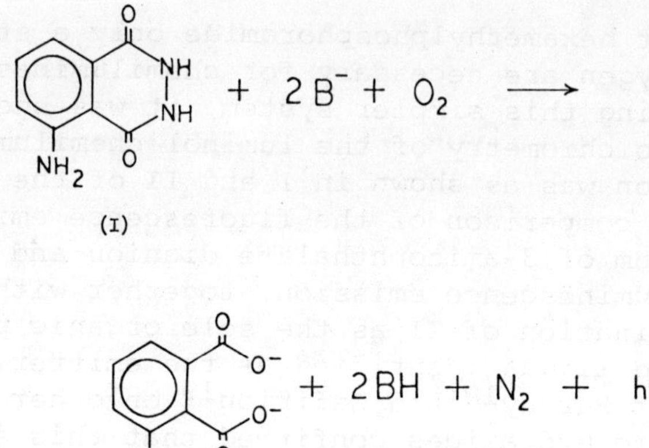

(I) → (II)

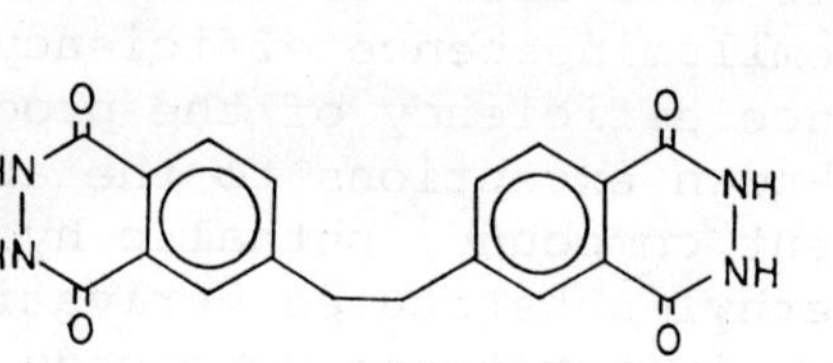

(III)

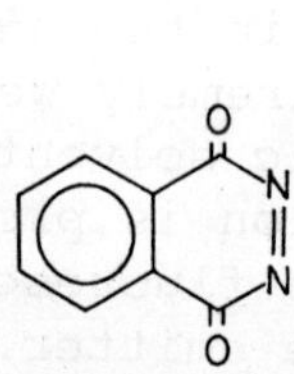

(IV)

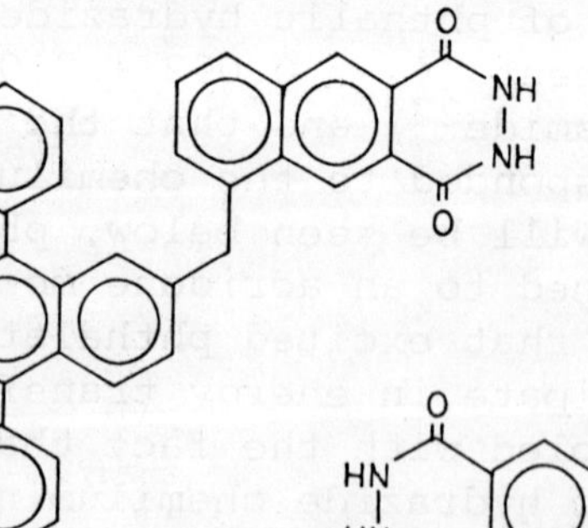

(V)

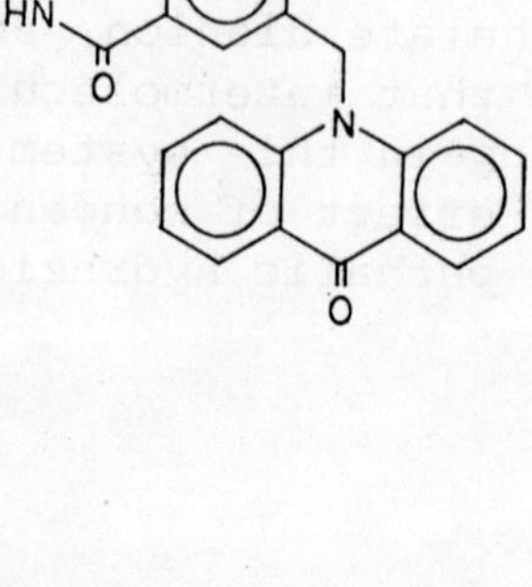

(VI)

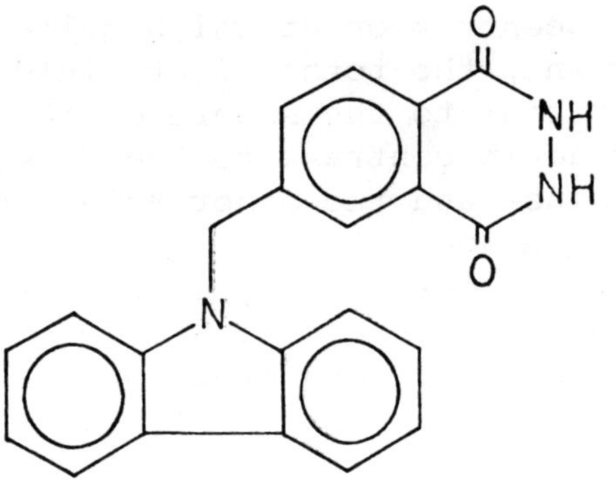

(VII)

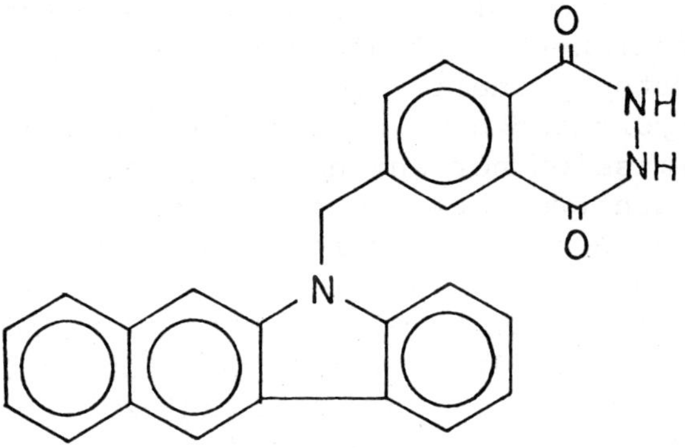

(VIII)

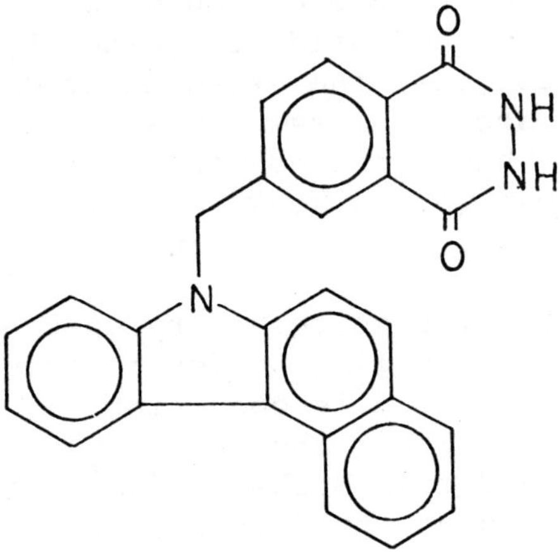

(IX)

Below 5×10^{-4} M, the concentration at which self-quenching becomes important, the total light yield of the system is proportional to the square of the concentration of hydrazide in contrast to the first order dependence for luminol and the other relatively efficient phthalic hydrazides.

The foregoing observations of themselves are consistent with an energy transfer mechanism for chemiluminescence. However there are other observations which are difficult to explain without additional restrictions. Firstly it has not proved possible so far to observe intermolecular energy transfer from phthalate to other acceptors. Thus addition of 9,10-diphenyl anthracene, 8-aminonaphthalene-2-sulfonic acid, anthranilic acid and N-methylphthalic hydrazide to solutions of phthalic hydrazide gave no intensification of the light emission nor any new emission maxima. Furthermore, when two phthalic hydrazide moieties were joined by an ethylene bridge the chemiluminescence emission was no more intense than that of an equivalent concentration of phthalic hydrazide itself. Thus the chemiluminescent reaction of 1,2-bis (6'-(2',3'-dihydro-1',4'-diketophthalazyl))-ethane III would be expected tc give initially a molecule in which an excited phthalate moiety would be joined to a phthalic hydrazide molecule capable of emitting a photon. However by analogy to the compound to be described in which phthalic hydrazide is joined by a methylene bridge to acridone, the expected quantum yield of chemiluminescence emission via intramolecular transfer would have been no more than 5×10^{-6}, whereas the observed value for phthalic hydrazide itself is 3.6×10^{-5} at a concentration of 5×10^{-4} M.

The above observations require a very specific type of intermolecular energy transfer to occur in this system if this mechanism is operating. It seems inherently unlikely that the chemistry of phthalic hydrazide should differ markedly from all its substituted derivatives as would be required by a mechanism such as that of Kautsky and Kaiser.[23] This mechanism requires that the key intermediate be phthalazine-1,4-dione IV and that this gives di-imide on reaction with base. The reaction of di-imide with a further molecule of IV then gives excited phthalic hydrazide and nitrogen. IV has been prepared however and on reaction with base in dimethyl sulfoxide is not chemiluminescent, even in the presence of a small amount of t-butanol as a proton source.[24]

The chemiluminescence of phthalic hydrazide is very sensitive to the presence of water in the dimethyl sulfoxide. Furthermore dimethyl sulfoxide is known not to solvate anions well. It therefore seems possible that hydrogen bonding between excited phthalate and the anion of phthalic hydrazide could account for the relatively efficient transfer of energy in this system. Further investigation is necessary, however, before the true nature of the chemiluminescence of phthalic hydrazide is understood.

INTRAMOLECULAR TRANSFER

As outlined above, for a high chemiluminescence quantum yield, the product must be highly fluorescent. In order to achieve this aim certain bifunctional compounds A-C in which the energy generating part A (an aromatic hydrazide) is different, and separated, from the emitting part C, which is a highly fluorescent group, have been studied.

$$\text{A-C} \rightarrow \text{B}^*\text{-C} \rightarrow \text{B-C}^* \rightarrow \text{B-C} + h\nu$$

Thus 5-(9,10-diphenyl-2-anthrylmethyl)-2,3-naphthalic hydrazide V was synthesized and shown to have a quantum yield of chemiluminescence of 0.26 relative to luminol, whereas 2,3-naphthalic hydrazide itself is only 0.06 times as efficient as luminol. As is well known, for efficient energy transfer the emission spectrum of the donor should have a large degree of overlap with an absorption band of the acceptor.[25] This is the situation in V since the emission spectrum of 2,3-naphthalate dianion has a maximum at 358 nm, while the first absorption band of 9,10-diphenylanthracene has maxima at 392, 373, 353, 337 and 319 nm. The chemiluminescence emission from a basic aqueous solution shows maxima at 355, 425 and 440 (s) nm, while in dimethyl sulfoxide the maximum at 355 nm disappears leaving only those at longer wavelength. The fluorescence spectrum of 9,10-diphenylanthracene has maxima at 425 and 440 (s) nm in both water and dimethyl sulfoxide, while the fluorescence of 2,3-naphthalate is quenched markedly in the aprotic solvent. It is apparent therefore that partitioning of the excited 2,3-naphthalate ions takes place. Some of the excited states decay either by emitting a photon, leading to emission from the naphthalate portion of the molecule in the aqueous system, or by some radiationless process in dimethyl sulfoxide. Some of the excited states transfer their energy to the diphenylanthracene moiety which leads to the long wavelength emission. The ratio of the emission at 355 nm to that near 430 nm is 0.099 showing that the majority of the excitation is transferred rather than emitted directly. The total light yield is linearly related to the concentration of V over the range 1.1-5.5 x 10^{-6} M, and an equimolar mixture of 2,3-naphthalic hydrazide and 9,10-diphenylanthracene (10^{-4} M each) gave no more light than a 10^{-4} M solution of the hydrazide itself, indicating the energy transfer to be intramolecular. Measurement of the relative light efficiencies of 2,3-naphthalic hydrazide and V showed the former to be 6% and the latter 26% relative to luminol at 100%. Thus it is seen that energy transfer is important in increasing the efficiency of chemiluminescence in V.

While 2,3-naphthalic hydrazide is chemiluminescent of itself, phthalhydrazide in the aqueous solution is not, as outlined above. Thus the fact that 4-(acridonylmethyl)-phthalic hydrazide VI is moderately efficient, 8% compared to luminol, indicates further that energy transfer can be an important factor in chemiluminescence, and that excited phthalate ions are formed in this reaction. As in V the energy transfer from VI was shown to be intramolecular since the total light yield is linear with concentration. Similarly a mixture of 4-methylphthalic hydrazide and N-methylacridone (10^{-4} M each) gave no measureable light under conditions where VI emitted strongly. The emission spectrum of the chemiluminescence corresponds to the fluorescence spectrum of N-methylacridone.

Since energy transfer occurs from excited phthalate ions in VI it was of interest to determine whether transfer could occur to other acceptors, for example carbazole. Carbazole is structurally similar to acridone and also fluoresces quite efficiently. However electronically they differ markedly since the first absorption band of N-methylacridone is at 405 nm while that of N-methylcarbazole is at 345 nm. Now dipotassium phthalate is non-fluorescent, even in carefully degassed solution, but it is to be expected that since the first absorption band of phthalate peaks near 280 nm the absent fluorescence would be expected to have a maximum near 310 nm, by analogy with 2,3-naphthalate; overlap with an absorption band in carbazole would then be ensured. It is therefore very surprising to find that 4-(carbazolylmethyl)-phthalic hydrazide VII is virtually non-chemiluminescent having an efficiency differing from that of VI by a factor of about two hundred.

The reason for the absence of fluorescence in dipotassium phthalate is unknown, but it has been suggested[26] that in phthalic anhydride and phthalimide at least, the lowest singlet excited state is $n-\pi^*$, conjugation of the carboxylate groups with the aromatic ring having lowered the energy of the π^* orbital. Though no separate band can be identified as $n-\pi^*$, the ultraviolet absorption spectrum of dipotassium phthalate does show a shoulder on the long wavelength edge of the first absorption band. If this hypothesis is correct it would explain the absence of fluorescence because of the high rate of intersystem crossing characteristic of $n-\pi^*$ singlet excited states. To explain the chemiluminescence of VI therefore either it must be hypothesized that energy transfer is occurring at a rate faster than the efficient intersystem crossing, which would need to be greater than ca. 10^{10} sec^{-1},[27] or the triplet state of phthalate is involved. A third possibility is that some precursor to the phthalate dianion provides the required energy, but again this requires a different reaction mechanism from that of the majority of phthalic hydrazides.

Dipotassium phthalate shows an intense phosphorescence centered at 410 nm which would overlap well with the first absorption band of acridone but only to a minute extent with that of carbazole. Thus if triplet-singlet energy transfer of the dipole-dipole type proposed by Förster[25] is operative the chemiluminescence properties of VI and VII would be explained. This type of transfer has been observed intermolecularly in rigid glasses by four independent groups of workers.[8,28-30] However to date no observation of triplet-singlet transfer in fluid solutions has been reported. The systems under discussion are particularly favorable for its direct observation since all the excitation is initially localized in the phthalate moiety. Thus even very weak fluorescence can be observed from the acceptor portion with the certain knowledge that it was not due to direct absorption and emission. Furthermore since the two components of the molecules are separated only by a methylene bridge the concentrations can be very low while the transfer distances are also very small. However since the process is forbidden and the excited phthalate dianions must therefore have relatively long lifetimes it is to be expected that oxygen quenching would be important. While this is true there are two reasons why this need not necessarily rule out this mechanism. It should first be noted that intermolecular triplet-triplet energy transfer has been observed[31] in the presence of oxygen in fluid solution at room temperature. While this should occur at a faster rate via a collisional mechanism the fact that molecules must diffuse together before transfer obviates some of this advantage. Furthermore, assuming about 10% of the phthalate moieties are excited (about the fraction excited in luminol) then from the observed quantum yield of chemiluminescence of (VI) of 8×10^{-4} and an estimated quantum yield of fluorescence for the acridone moiety of 2×10^{-1}, only about 4% of the excited molecules need transfer.

If the triplet-singlet transfer mechanism is correct, it would be predicted that the light yields of chemiluminescence of 4-(2',3'-benzocarbazolylmethyl)-phthalic hydrazide VIII and 4-(3',4'-benzocarbazolylmethyl)-phthalic hydrazide IX should be approximately in proportion to the overlap of the phosphorescence emission of phthalate with their first absorption bands. Thus VIII should have a quantum yield less than, but of the same order as, that of VI while that of IV should be about an order of magnitude less. The preliminary results are shown in Table I and fully confirm the predictions. Work is continuing to correlate the relative values predicted by the Förster equation[25] with those observed, in a quantitative manner.

While the interpretation that triplet phthalate is involved in the chemiluminescence of phthalic hydrazide does not explain the specific type of intermolecular energy transfer described above, it does not create any more difficulties than the assumption that a singlet excited state is involved. It does however provide an explanation for the chemiluminescence properties of compounds V-IX within the framework of the current knowledge of energy transfer mechanisms, where that based on singlet-singlet transfer fails.

TABLE I

Compound	Relative Light Yields[a]
VI	100
VIII	55
IX	7
VII	0.4

[a] 1P21 Phototube used, values uncorrected for phototube frequency response.

REFERENCES

1. F. McCapra, Quart. Rev. (London), 20, 485 (1966).
2. J. W. Haas, Jr., J. Chem. Educ., 44, 396 (1967).
3. K. D. Gundermann, Angew. Chem. Internal. Edn., 4, 566 (1965).
4. E. H. White in "Light and Life," W. D. McElroy and B. Glass, Eds., Johns Hopkins Press, Baltimore, Md., 1961, p. 183.
5. M. M. Rauhut, B. G. Roberts and L. M. Semsel, J. Am. Chem. Soc., 88, 3604 (1966).
6. M. M. Rauhut, L. J. Bollyky, B. G. Roberts, M. Lay, R. H. Whitman, A. V. Iannotta, A. M. Semsel and R. A. Clarke, ibid., 89, 6515 (1967).
7. L. J. Bollyky, R. H. Whitman, B. G. Roberts and M. M. Rauhut, ibid., 89, 6523 (1967).
8. D. Phillips, V. Anissimov, O. Karpukhin and V. Shiliapintokh, Nature, 215, 1163 (1967).
9. G. Lunden and R. Livingston, Photochem. Photobiol., 4, 1085 (1965).
10. H. Linschitz in "Light and Life," W. D. McElroy and B. Glass, Eds., Johns Hopkins Press, Baltimore, Md., 1961, 0. 173.
11. V. A. Belyakov and R. F. Vasil'ev, Dokl. Akad. Nauk. SSSR., 176, 862 (1967); English transl. Doklady Physical Chemistry, 176, 731 (1967).
12. A. U. Khan and M. Kasha, J. Am. Chem. Soc., 88, 1574 (1966).
13. E. H. White, O. C. Zafiriou, H. M. Kägi and J. H. M. Hill, ibid., 86, 940 (1964).
14. E. H. White and M. M. Bursey, ibid., 86, 941 (1964).
15. H. D. K. Drew and R. F. Garwood, J. Chem. Soc., 1841 (1937).
16. H. D. K. Drew and R. F. Garwood, ibid., 836 (1939).
17. H. D. K. Drew and T. H. Pearman, ibid., 586 (1937).
18. M. M. Bursey, Ph.D. thesis, the Johns Hopkins University, Baltimore, Md., 1963.

19. O. C. Zafiriou, Ph.D. thesis, the Johns Hopkins University, Baltimore, Md., 1966.
20. W. V. Mayneord, W. Anderson, H. D. Evans and D. Rosen, Radiat. Res., 3, 379 (1955).
21. J. Stauff and G. Hartmann, Ber. Bunsenges. Phys. Chem., 69, 145 (1965).
22. D. F. Roswell, Ph.D. thesis, the Johns Hopkins University, Baltimore, Md., 1968.
23. H. Kautsky and K. H. Kaiser, Z. Naturforsch., B, 5, 353 (1950).
24. O. C. Zafiriou, the Johns Hopkins University, Baltimore, Md., unpublished work.
25. Th. Förster, Disc. Faraday Soc., 27, 7 (1959).
26. R. N. Nurmukhametov, I. L. Belaits and D. N. Shigorin, Zh. Fiz. Khim., 41, 1928 (1967); English transl. Russ. J. Phys. Chem., 41, 1032 (1967).
27. F. Wilkinson, Advan. Photochem., 3, 241 (1964).
28. V. Korsunskii and A. Faidysh, Dokl. Akad. Nauk. SSSR., 150, 771 (1963); English transl. Soviet Phys. Doklady, 8, 564 (1963).
29. V. Ermolaev and E. Sveshnikova, Dokl. Akad. Nauk. SSSR., 149, 1295 (1963); English transl. Soviet Phys. Doklady, 8, 373 (1963).
30. R. G. Bennett, R. P. Schwenker and R. E. Kellogg, J. Chem. Phys., 41, 3040 (1964).
31. M. El-Sayed and M. Bhaumik, ibid., 39, 2391 (1963).

MOLECULAR CHEMILUMINESCENCE IN DIFFUSION FLAMES OF HALOGENS AND HALIDES BURNING IN ALKALI METAL VAPORS*

H. B. Palmer, A. Tewarson, D. W. Naegeli,**
and C. M. Pathak***

Fuel Science Section
Department of Materials Science
Pennsylvania State University
University Park, Pennsylvani 16802

INTRODUCTION

Very rapid gas-phase reactions occur between potassium or sodium vapor and a large number of halogens or gaseous halides, as explored first by M. Polanyi and his collaborators.[1] The result may frequently be the creation of large nonthermal populations of molecules or radicals in excited electronic states, yielding strong chemiluminescent emission. During the past few years, spectroscopic

---

*Work supported by a grant from the National Science Foundation.
**Present address: Research Laboratories, United Aircraft Corp., East Hartford, Connecticut.
***Postdoctoral scholar. Permanent address: Department of Spectroscopy, Banaras Hindu University, Varanasi 5, India.

studies of such reaction systems have yielded much new information, including extensions of known band systems, discovery of new electronic states of known chemical species, observation of emission from previously unobserved chemical species, measurements of population inversions, elucidation of predissociation behavior, and construction of potential curves for excited states. In some instances, it has been possible to use the spectroscopic data to describe the energy partitioning in products of elementary chemical reactions. In other cases, the observed excitation allows one to use arguments from the available energetics to identify the elementary process responsible for the excitation of the particular species in question.

The reaction system used in all of this work is a low-pressure diffusion flame operating at pressures from about 1 to 10 torr. The apparatus[2] is basically a 1-liter spherical flask with a potassium (or sodium) reservoir attached to the bottom. A sidearm with a quartz window permits observation of emission spectra. The halogen or halide, with or without carrier gas, is admitted to the center of the reactor from a tube entering either from the top or the bottom. A resistance furnace surrounds the entire reactor. The line to the vacuum pump is equipped with condensers and traps for possible product analysis and for protection of the pump.

Upon heating the alkali metal-containing reactor to 300-350°C and subsequently commencing to admit halide in a slow, controlled stream, an essentially spherical flame forms spontaneously at the halide inlet. The flame can be maintained for periods up to several hours without undue difficulty. For some of the more weakly emitting flames, the required exposure times for spectra may be as long as 3 or 4 hours. Spectra are taken with a Jarrell-Ash f/6.3 plane grating instrument blazed for 5000 Å in the first order. Its focal length is 0.75 m and its reciprocal linear dispersion is about 20 Å/mm in the first order. Slit widths have ranged from 30 to 150 microns but have normally been 50 to 100. We have used Kodak plates of types 103aF for the visible spectrum and 103aO for the ultraviolet.

The temperature in the most intensely emitting region of the diffusion flames has been measured with a fine chromel-alumel thermocouple and found to be typically about 700°C. Thus the visible and ultraviolet emission from the reactions is exclusively chemiluminescent in origin.

RESULTS AND DISCUSSION

In order to illustrate the kinds of information available in the molecular chemiluminescence from Polanyi-type diffusion flames, we outline here the recent results from studies of a variety of such flames.

EXTENSIONS OF KNOWN BAND SYSTEMS.

C_2. Flames of carbon tetrahalides burning in potassium vapor yield a plethora of C_2 bands.[3] Several dozen new transitions of the Swan system have been found, about twenty new Phillips bands, and a comparable number of new bands of the Ballik-Ramsay system, and about fifty bands due to forbidden transitions. Rotational structure associated with some of the bands is very extensive and presents some interesting possibilities for high resolution work. Although some excitation occurs as a direct result of chemical reaction, it appears that the strength and extensiveness of the C_2 emission from these flames is largely due to production of a very large concentration of carbon atoms, which upon association populate many excited states of C_2 up to high vibrational levels.

<u>CS</u>. In potassim-supported flames of several carbon- and sulfur-containing molecules or mixtures of molecules (e.g. $CSCl_2$, Cl_3CSCl, $SCl_2 + CCl_4$, $SOCl_2 + CHCl_3$), bands of the main (A-X) system of CS are observed in emission along with K lines, C_2 bands, and usually S_2 bands. We have observed 17 new bands of the main system of CS in these flames.[4]

<u>Tin halide molecules</u>. The reaction of $SnCl_4$ with potassium produces emission from bands attributed to $SnCl_2$ and SnCl. The scanty data on the former has been extended by the flame studies and a Deslandres scheme for a triatomic molecule has been successful.[5] The known bands of SnCl have not actually been extended, but rather the species responsible for the red system of SnCl has been clarified; it is neutral SnCl, not the ion. This is established by the absence of sufficient energy to produce $SnCl^+$. The same argument applies to the red bands of SnBr, which have been tentatively identified in emission from the K-$SnBr_4$ flame.

<u>GeO and GeS</u>. Addition of oxygen to the K-$GeCl_4$ flame, or of SCl_2 to the same flame, produces emission of GeO and GeS bands, respectively. The principal emission is from the main A-X system in both cases. Forty-three new bands of the A-X system of GeO have been identified,[6] and 10 of the A-X system of GeS.

<u>Na_2</u>. Emission from reactions of sodium vapor with halogens includes many new bands[7] of the red system of Na_2. The green system of Na_2 is absent. The reaction of potassium with halogens yields the red system of K_2, but no new bands have been seen in it. The bands are relatively few in number and are partially obscured by an underlying continuum.

K halides. Flames of halogens burning in potassium emit the visible-ultraviolet systems of potassium halide molecules. Bands of KBr have also been observed in emission from the K-HBr flame. Numerous new bands of the visible-ultraviolet systems of KCl, KBr, and KI have been identified,[7] up to very high vibrational levels of the ground state: v' = 61, 80, and 60 for the three molecules, respectively. It is interesting that flames of halogens burning in sodium apparently do not emit sodium halide bands.

NEW ELECTRONIC STATES.

CS. In the flames that emit the main system of CS, previously mentioned, we also see a new system of what is almost certainly CS that appears in the near ultraviolet. A Deslandres scheme for the 14 bands observed is successful[4] and identifies them, with considerable certainty, as the triplet-singlet (ground state) system analogous to the Cameron bands of CO. The triplet state lies 79 kcal above the ground state.

$GeCl_2$. The flame spectrum of $GeCl_4$ burning in potassium contains a large group of closely-spaced, diffuse bands in the blue-green region which fit nicely into a Deslandres scheme for a triatomic molecule[8] and thus are quite certainly due to $GeCl_2$. The excited state lies 64 kcal above the (presumed) ground state.

GeO. A weak and diffuse system of new red bands has been seen[6] in the emission from the $GeCl_4$-O_2-K flame. They are difficult to measure, and although 20 bands have been tabulated, a Deslandres scheme is not free from ambiguity. They are tentatively ascribed to GeO because the vibration frequency of the lower state appears to be close to that of the upper state of the main GeO system. The upper state is weakly bound. If the assignment is correct, the energetics are such that the upper state is probably populated by association of an O atom and an excited Ge atom. The latter can be produced in the reaction of K with GeCl, while the O atom may result from the reaction, $K_2 + O_2 = K_2O + O$ or from $Ge + O_2 = GeO + O$. The bands are under further study.

NEW SPECIES.

Phosphorus oxyhalide radicals. The emission from flames of $POCl_3$ and $POBr_3$ burning in potassium vapor contains diffuse systems of previously unobserved bands that are too complex to be due to diatomic species. Measurements of heads have been carried out and it is found[9] that Deslandres schemes can be successfully constructed using two frequencies in the upper state and two in the lower. The frequencies are appropriate to a stretch and a bend in each state. Available energetics are such that it is highly improbable that the bands are due to the parent molecules. The systems are different for the two halides, so the emitter must contain at least one halogen atom. Thus the emitter is surely either a POX radical or a POX_2 radical. Because the bands are double-headed, we are tentatively ascribing them to $POCl_2$ and $POBr_2$.

POPULATION INVERSIONS.

C_2. The intensity distribution in the C_2 Swan bands as seen in emission from flames of haloforms (CHX_3) or carbon tetrahalides (CX_4) with potassium or sodium is obviously very non-thermal and suggests a partial inversion of the population in the $A^3\Pi_g$ state. We have made densitometric tracings of the plates and have calculated the relative populations of vibrational levels in the A state up to v' = 7. The populations differ for the four flames examined ($CHCl_3$, CI_4, CBr_4, and CCl_4). We attribute the differences to differences in the character and contributions of the chemical reactions that produce the excited C_2. Partial inversions are indeed observed.[10] The CCl_4-K flame is outstanding in this regard; populations increase almost exponentially as v increases from 0 to 6.

Other species. The reaction of sodium vapor with chlorine produces emission from Na_2 with an intensity distribution such[7] that there is a probable inversion of some populations of vibrational levels in the upper state. Likewise the flame of a mixture of boron halides and oxygen burning in potassium vapor yields the alpha bands of BO with an unusual intensity distribution[11] and we suspect that there may be at least a partial inversion of populations in the upper state. In neither of these cases has it been possible, so far, to carry out population measurements.

PREDISSOCIATION.

OH and OD. Addition of a little oxygen to the flame of a haloform burning in potassium vapor at low pressure produces OH emission in which rotational cutoffs can be observed with unusual clarity.[12] By using CHX_3 and CDX_3 molecules, it has been possible to obtain a limiting curve of dissociation that includes the results for both OH and OD,[13] showing that the difference in tunneling effects between the two is insignificant. The limiting curve is nearly straight. It defines a crossing on the potential of the upper ($A^2\Sigma^+$) state lying at an energy of about 40,300 cm^{-1} (relative to the minimum of the ground state) and an internuclear distance of 1.35 Å.

Other species. Flames of a number of sulfur-containing compounds burning in potassium exhibit emission from S_2 in which predissociation can be observed.[7] The S_2 spectrum is very extensive and complicated and it is difficult to analyze, but it is hoped that some useful new information on predissociation of S_2 can be extracted from the plates.

EXCITED STATE POTENTIAL CURVES.

OH and OD. The crossing point of the potential of the $A^2\Sigma^+$ state of OH and the state that predissociates the A state is at a location (see above) such that the latter state must be essentially pure-repulsive in character. One can sketch a reasonable approximation to the shape of the repulsive state, but we are not yet confident as to the proper designation of the state.

KCl, KBr, and KI. Polanyi-type flames of Cl_2, Br_2, HBr, and I_2 burning in potassium vapor emit bands of the corresponding potassium halides. Although the bands have been observed before, our observations have extended the spectra considerably and permit determination of improved potentials[7] of the upper states. All three are weakly stable. The depths of the minima are respectively about 1000, 1100, and 1400 cm^{-1} for KCl, KBr, and KI.

IDENTIFICATION OF ELEMENTARY PROCESSES LEADING TO ELECTRONICALLY EXCITED STATES. Although flames are generally complicated reaction systems, and flames of halides burning in alkali metals are no exception, it is possible in some cases to use the observations to draw conclusions as to the probable elementary reaction step in which a particular excited species is produced. The conclusions are possible only because the possibility of appreciable thermal excitation of the excited species is nil. A few examples follow.

OH*. Excited OH is observed in the K-CHX_3 flame with added oxygen. The excitation exhibited by the OH is as high as 136 kcal above the ground state, or 35 kcal above the dissociation limit. The latter figure rules out atom association, and leaves as the only plausible excitation reaction, CH + O_2 = CO + OH, which is 159 kcal exothermic. Although there has long been acceptance[14] of this reaction as the likely step for production of OH in hydrocarbon flames, our observations of the energetics provide useful quantitative support for it.

C_2^*. In flames of alkalis with CHX_3 or CX_4 molecules, there are several ways by which excited C_2 might be generated: (a) atom association; (b) C + CX = C_2 + X; (c) C + CH = C_2 + H; (d) C + CK = C_2 + K; (e) 2CX = C_2 + X_2; or (f) 2CH = C_2 + H_2.

Consider the K-CHX_3 reaction first. There is logic and some experimental evidence to indicate that CH radicals, which will be abundant in the system, disproportionate to produce CH_2 and C. The disproportionation reaction should be preferred over reaction (f). Both are exothermic, but (f) is a four-center reaction and probably also has a higher activation energy. The experimental evidence[15] consists of the observation that methane and ethylene are the principal gaseous products of the flame reaction. Both are to be expected if CH_2 is produced in quantity. Thus (f) seems to contribute little. Atom association will surely occur, but is not favored by the low pressure in the system. This leaves reactions (c) and (d). The exothermicity of (c) corresponds very closely to the energy at which the maximum population of excited C_2 is observed.[10] However, some C_2 is observed at still higher energies, which presumably means that either (d) is making some contribution, or there is some contribution from excited carbon atoms participating in (c). In any event, it is quite certain that reaction (c) is the most important source of excited C_2 in the system.

In the K-CX_4 flames, C_2 emission is much stronger than with CHX_3, and the populations of excited C_2 are a function of the halogen to some extent. The maximum observed excitation of C_2 is as high as about 120 kcal above the ground state, which means that much of the energy available in atom association (145 kcal) must be contributing in some fashion. Since reaction (a), a three-body process, is not favored, we think that (d) is probably moderately important. It is essentially the association of carbon atoms catalyzed by potassium. The species CK can be produced via the reaction, $C + K_2 = CK + K$, with most of the exothermicity of this step retained in vibration of CK. Reaction (d) then can leave the product C_2 in the high energy states. However, most of the C_2 emission is from $v' = 7$ and below. These states are probably populated by other mechanisms.

The thermochemical features of reactions involving the species CX are not well defined because the bond energies D(C-X) are not well known, for the most part. Using the best available estimates, it is very improbable that reaction (e) can produce excited C_2. Reaction (b) can yield excited C_2 only when X is Br or I. Experimentally, we observe maxima in the populations[10] of excited C_2 that are plausibly attributed to contributions of (b) in these two cases. In all three of the K-CX_4 systems (CF_4 does not give a flame), population maxima are observed at $v' = 6$ to 7 of the A state of the Swan system. This peak gives rise to the so-called high pressure bands of C_2. It is quite clear[16] from our work plus that from two other laboratories that the peak is a consequence of C_2 molecules crossing from another state (the $A'^3\Sigma_g^-$ state) into the $A^3\Pi_g$ state of the Swan system.

Thus the processes that can produce excited C_2 are numerous, but some reasonable conclusions can be drawn from the flame studies.

ENERGY PARTITIONING IN PRODUCTS OF ELEMENTARY REACTIONS. Because all of our observations are of electronic band emission, the experiments yield information only on elementary reactions in which one or more products or reactants are in excited electronic states. This is a severe enough limitation, but furthermore there are few of the systems in which the chemistry is sufficiently well defined to permit one to identify the pertinent reaction and proceed to study the details of its energetics. The reactions producing electronically excited C_2, just discussed, illustrate the complexities as well as the potential for obtaining useful information. Thus in the K-CHX_3 systems, we conclude from the excited state populations[10] that in reaction (c), the majority of reaction events that produce electronically excited C_2 leave essentially all of the exothermicity of the reaction in vibration of the C_2.

In the K-CX_4 flames, if one uses the excited C_2 population distribution from the CCl_4 case[10] to subtract out the contribution of the high pressure band mechanism from the populations observed[10] for CBr_4 and CI_4, one is left essentially with the distribution characteristic of reaction (b) in the two cases (ignoring the small contribution of (d) at the lower energies). One finds a distribution that apparently extends up to the total available exothermicity, but the most probable state for the product C_2^* lies at an energy corresponding to about 25% to 35% of the exothermicity.

It should be pointed out that, for all the complexities, there is an inherent power in this method of studying energy distributions in that the radiative lifetime of a species such as $C_2(A^3\Pi_g)$ is so short (ca. 10^{-6} sec) that the observed radiation should correspond quite well to the condition of the C_2^* as it is produced in the elementary reaction events. At pressures of a few torr, an excited C_2 will undergo only a few collisions before radiating.

Further information on energy partitioning in the present work has come from the classical Polanyi-type reactions between alkali metals and halogens. We have observed potassium atom emission in the reaction of potassium vapor with chlorine.[7] The emission extends with substantial strength all the way up to 0.99-0.995 of the energy available in the reaction, $Cl + K_2 = KCl + K$. This is not a new observation, but its implications with regard to the excitation mechanism have not been previously noted.

Two principal possibilities exist for exciting alkali metal emission in the system: the two-step sequence, (1) $Cl + K_2 = KCl^\dagger + K$ followed by (2) $KCl^\dagger + K = KCl + K^*$ (the dagger represents vibrational excitation), and the single-step process, (3) $Cl + K_2 = KCl + K^*$. The third possibility, successive transfers of energy in (2), with K^* being raised to higher and higher electronic states, is very improbable because the radiative lifetime of K^* is about one percent of the time between collisions. Molecular beam studies[17] imply that the probability that the KCl formed in (1) will contain a large fraction of the exothermicity of the reaction as vibration is large, <u>but</u> the probability that it will contain more than 99 percent of it is very small. Since the probability of perfectly efficient transfer of energy in (2) will also be very small, the sequence, (1)-(2) does not offer an effectual route to production of the very highly excited potassium atoms observed. The direct-production route (3) is much more probable. This has been predicted theoretically.[18] For producing potassium in lower states of excitation, no doubt both mechanisms contribute, as suggested by earlier experiments.[19]

SUMMARY

The luminescence of molecules, radicals, and atoms created in excited states by the exothermic chemical processes occurring in low-temperature, low-pressure diffusion flames of alkali metals with halogens or halides has been used to derive a variety of new information on electronic spectra, new chemical species, populations, potential energy curves, identifiaction of elementary reactions, and energy distributions in elementary reactions.

REFERENCES

1. M. Polanyi, Atomic Reactions (Williams and Norgate, Ltd., London, 1932).
2. D. W. Naegeli and H. B. Palmer, Eleventh International Symposium on Combustion (Combustion Institute, Pittsburgh, Pa., 1967), p. 1161.
3. A. Tewarson, D. W. Naegeli, and H. B. Palmer, Twelfth International Symposium on Combustion (Combustion Institute, Pittsburgh, Pa., to be published).
4. A. Tewarson and H. B. Palmer, J. Mol. Spectry. (in press).
5. D. W. Naegeli and H. B. Palmer, J. Mol. Spectry. 21, 325 (1966).
6. C. M. Pathak and H. B. Palmer (work to be published).
7. A. Tewarson and H. B. Palmer (work to be published).
8. A. Tewarson and H. B. Palmer, J. Mol. Spectry. 22, 117 (1967).
9. D. W. Naegeli and H. B. Palmer, J. Mol. Spectry. (in press).
10. D. W. Naegeli and H. B. Palmer, J. Chem. Phys. 48, 2372 (1968).
11. D. W. Naegeli, Ph.D. thesis, Pennsylvania State University (1967).
12. D. W. Naegeli and H. B. Palmer, J. Mol. Spectry. 23, 44 (1967).
13. H. B. Palmer and D. W. Naegeli, J. Mol. Spectry. (in press).
14. A. G. Gaydon, The Spectroscopy of Flames, (Chapman and Hall, Ltd., London, 1957).
15. W. J. Miller and H. B. Palmer, J. Chem. Phys. 40, 3701 (1964).
16. D. W. Naegeli and H. B. Palmer, J. Mol. Spectry. (in press).
17. J. H. Birely and D. R. Herschbach, J. Chem. Phys. 44, 1700 (1966).
18. P. Pechukas, J. C. Light, and C. Rankin, J.

Chem. Phys. 44, 794 (1966).
19. M. Polanyi and G. Schay, Z. Physik. Chem. 1, 46 (1928).

THE CO* AND OH* CHEMILUMINESCENCE IN HYDROCARBON ATOM FLAMES

K. H. Becker, D. Kley and R. J. Norstrom*

Institut für Physikalische Chemie
der Universität Bonn
Bonn, Germany

INTRODUCTION

Chemiluminescence and chemi-ionization in hydrocarbon-oxygen flames are objects of many investigations, but the knowledge about radical mechanisms leading to these phenomena is still rather weak. Previous work has shown that only few radicals are possible precursors for the chemiluminescence[1-11] and the chemi-ionization.[3,4,11-16]

Acetylene plays a major role among these hydrocarbon flames, because acetylene flames produce the most intensive emissions, and, on the other hand, it has been found,[17,18] that most

*N. R. C. C. Fellow, present address: Department of Physical Chemistry, University of Cambridge, England.

hydrocarbons decompose to acetylene and acetylene-type products in hot flames.

Recently it was shown that the same radical mechanism[5,10] producing CO^* chemiluminescence in a carbon suboxide oxygen atom reaction, is also responsible for the CO^* chemiluminescence in the reaction of acetylene with atomic oxygen and in many other hydrocarbon flames.[7]

Reaction (1) has been proposed[5,10] for the formation of electronically excited CO^* in these flames.

$$C_2O + O \rightarrow CO + CO^* \qquad (1)$$

In the presence of atomic hydrogen, the carbon suboxide atom flame produces also other acetylene-type emitters,[11] such as CH^*, OH^*, and C_2^*. Therefore the reaction $C_3O_2 + O + H$ was thought to be an interesting hydrocarbon-like flame which might give more information about chemiluminescence and chemi-ionization than hydrocarbon flames do directly.

The chemiluminescence and the total chemi-ionization of the carbon suboxide reaction were compared with those of the reactions $C_2H_2 + O + H$, $C_2H_4 + O + H$, and $CH_2CO + O + H$ under most identical conditions. In this paper the results about the CO^* and OH^* chemiluminescence are presented, and their relation to the chemi-ionization and the CH^* emission will be discussed.

EXPERIMENTAL

The experiments were carried out in a flow-tube which was similar to that used for previous work.[10,11,19] Atomic oxygen and hydrogen were produced by two separated microwave discharges in molecular oxygen and hydrogen, highly diluted by argon (more than 95% argon). The total pressure in the reaction tube was always kept at 2 torr with a flow rate of about 17 torr ltr/sec at a linear flow rate of 430 cm/sec. Through calibrated capillaries hydrocarbons or carbon suboxide were added to the flow with a partial pressure of 10^{-3} to 10^{-2} torr. Downstream from the mixing point the reaction was followed by a photomultiplier which was sensitive only for the 4th positive bands of CO^* below 2000 Å. The emissions above 2000 Å were photoelectrically recorded by a low resolution (10 Å) monochromator. For more highly resolved spectra (0.12 Å) the flow-tube was mounted before the entrance slit of a 3.4 m Ebert-monochromator. In previous experiments the spectra in the vacuum-uv between 1200 and 2000 Å were recorded by a 1 m monochromator. The relative ion concentration in the reaction tube was measured by two collecting wires. The concentrations of the oxygen and hydrogen atom concentration was measured by the isothermal calorimeter technique just before the inlet of H atoms into the reaction zone.

RESULTS

CO^* chemiluminescence was observed in the reactions C_3O_2 + O, C_2H_2 + O, CH_2CO + O, and C_2H_4 + O. Fig. (1)* shows that the 4th positive bands of CO^* emitted from the reactions C_3O_2 + O and C_2H_2 + O have an identical vibrational distribution. Also ketene shows this distribution. In the C_2H_4 + O reaction the CO^* chemiluminescence has been observed with much lower intensity. As it can be seen in Fig. (2)*, together with the 4th positive bands CO^* ($A^1\Pi \rightarrow X^1\Sigma^+$) CO^* bands from the triplet transitions $d^3\Delta \rightarrow a^3\Pi$ and $e^3\Sigma^- \rightarrow a^3\Pi$ occurred in the visible spectrum. In the reaction C_2H_2 + O the triplet bands were partly hidden by the much stronger C_2^* and CH^* bands. It was found that upon

The CO spectra were taken from previous work.[10]

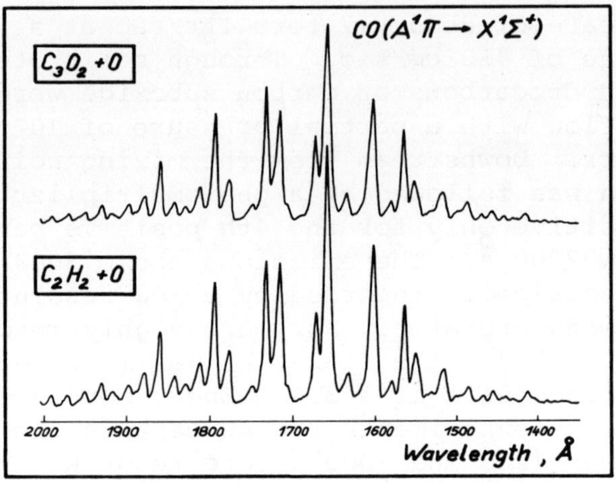

Figure 1 A comparison of the CO* emission bands in the vacuum-uv for the C_3O_2 + O and C_2H_2 + O reactions.

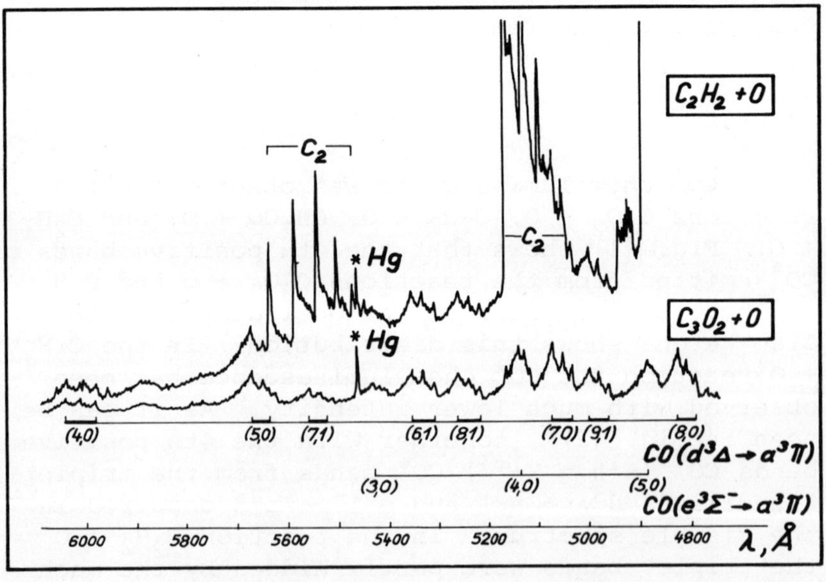

Figure 2 A comparison of the visible CO* emission bands from the C_3O_2 + O and C_2H_2 reactions. The asterisk indicates a mercury line.

any change of conditions in the reaction system, such as changing the O atom concentration, the partial pressure of C_3O_2 or hydrocarbons, or addition of O_2 or NO, and addition of H atoms, the intensities of the CO^* triplet and singlet bands were affected in the same way, seen in Fig. (3) for C_3O_2 + O. Fig. (4) shows that the intensity of the CO^* emission I_{CO^*} was increased by the addition of atomic hydrogen to the C_3O_2 + O reaction. A similar dependence was found for the C_2H_2 flame. In the C_3O_2 + O + H reaction chemi-ions were observed in about the same concentrations as in the C_2H_2 + O reaction. The ion concentration I_{ion} and the emission intensity I_{CO^*} have shown a very similar dependence upon addition of molecular oxygen in the reaction C_3O_2 + O + H, Fig. (5). Similar results were obtained by the addition of nitric oxide.

Two types of $OH^*(A^2\Sigma^+ \rightarrow X^2\Pi)$ bands were observed as it can be seen in Fig. (6). The reactions C_3O_2 + H + O_2, C_2H_2 + O, and CH_2CO + H + O_2 were found to emit a so called "hot" OH^* emission with a "hot" rotational energy distribution of the 0,0 and 1,0 bands, Fig. (7).

From the reaction C_2H_4 + O a so called "cold" OH^* 0,0 band with a "cold" rotational energy distribution was analyzed, Fig. (6) and Fig. (7). Contrary to the "cold" 0,0 band in the C_2H_4 + O reaction, a "hot" 1,0 band was observed, Fig. (6). When oxygen atoms were added to the reaction CH_2CO + H + O_2 a "cold" OH^* 0,0 band, superimposed on the "hot" band was observed. In all cases, the intensity I_{OH^*} of the "hot" OH^* emission was increased by the addition of molecular oxygen and atomic hydrogen. In the C_3O_2 + H + O_2 and CH_2CO + H + O_2 reactions oxygen atoms were found to be unnecessary for the formation of "hot" OH^*. Fig. (8) shows for C_3O_2 + H + O_2 that atomic oxygen caused even an inhibition of the "hot" OH^*. In Fig. (5) and Fig. (9) the dependence of I_{OH^*}("hot") on the O_2 and H concentration is

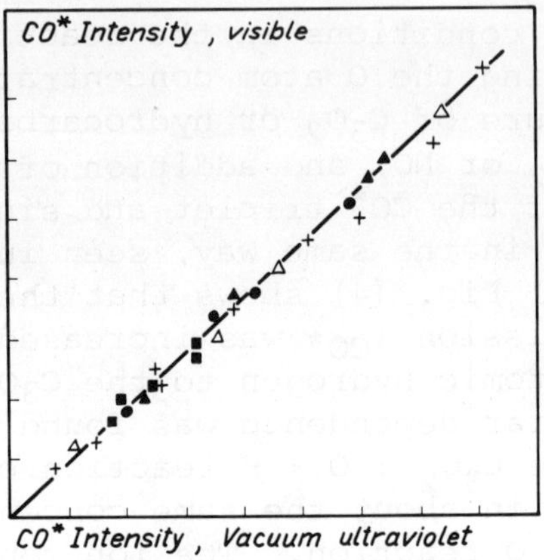

Figure 3 Variation of the undispersed CO* emission in the vacuum-uv with the (7,0) band of the "triplet" system for various conditions: (+) vary C_3O_2 concentration, (▲) vary oxygen atom concentration, (■) addition of O_2, (●) addition of NO, (△) addition of H atoms.

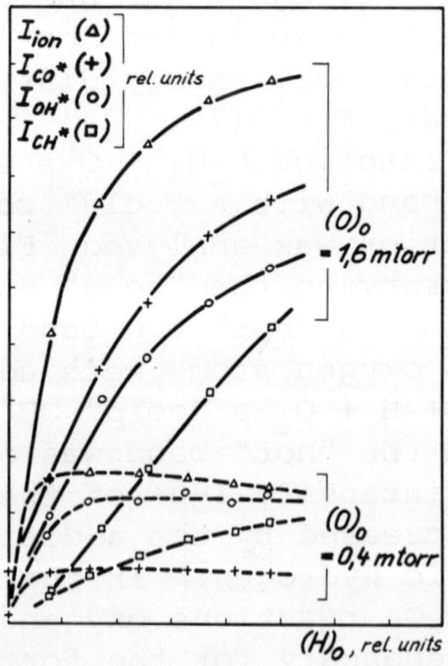

Figure 4 Dependence of I_{ion}, I_{CO^*}, I_{OH^*} and I_{CH^*} on relative H atom concentration $(H)_o$ added to C_3O_2 + O for two different O atom concentrations. $(C_3O_2)_o$ = 0.5 mtorr.

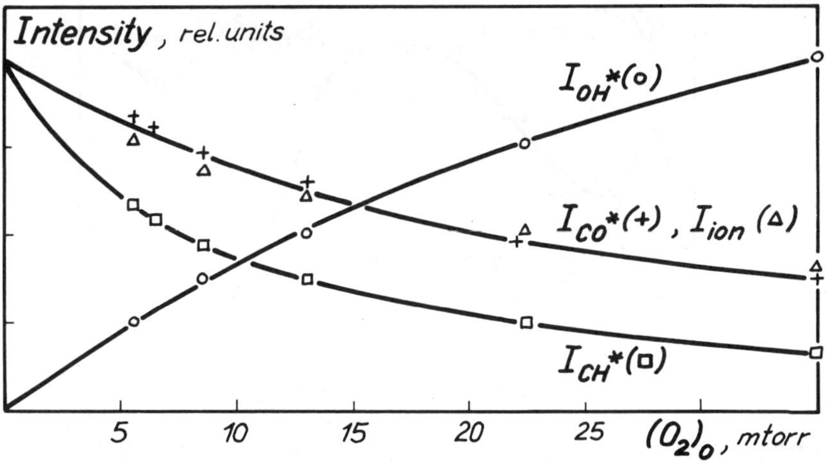

Figure 5 Dependence of I_{ion}, I_{CO*}, I_{OH*} and I_{CH*} on O_2 added to C_3O_2 + O + H. $(C_3O_2)_o$ = 0.5 mtorr.

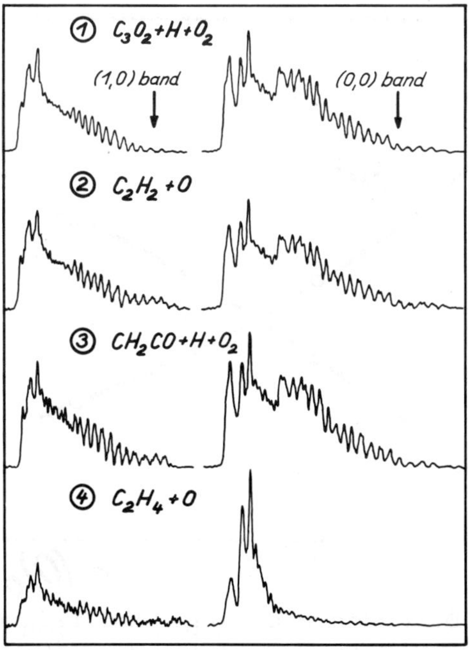

Figure 6 Spectra of the OH* (0,0) band at 3064 Å and the (1,0) band at 2811 Å for several reactions.

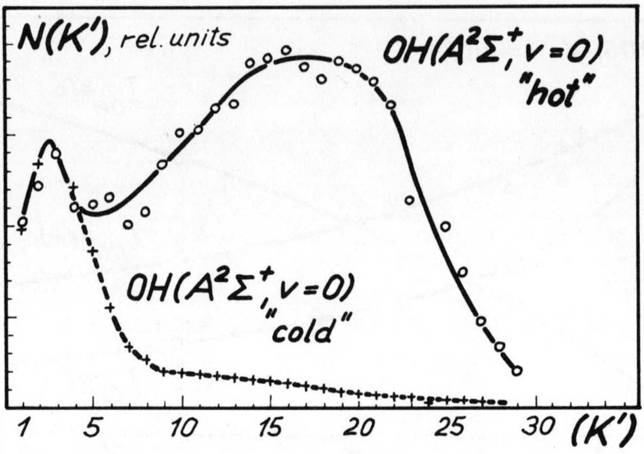

Figure 7 Relative rotational population N(K') of "hot" and "cold" OH* radicals at 2 torr total pressure of argon (transition probabilities from reference 32).

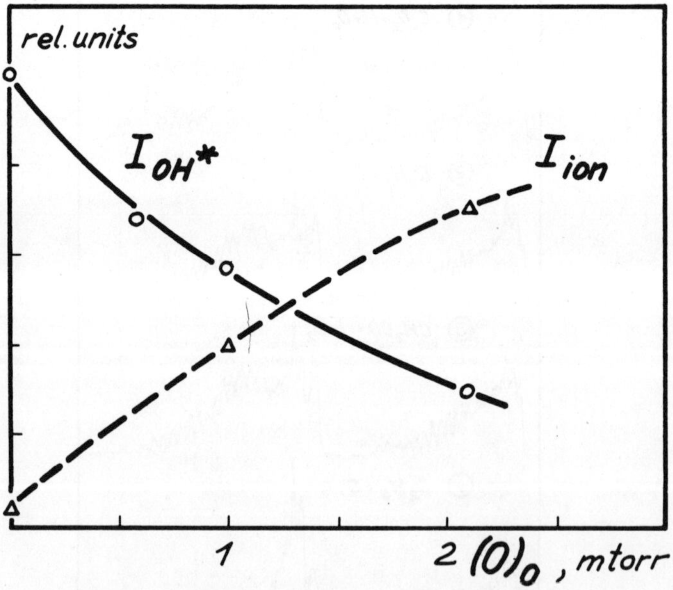

Figure 8 Dependence of I_{OH*} and I_{ion} on O atoms added to C_3O_2 + H + O. $(C_3O_2)_o$ = 1.2 mtorr, $(O_2)_o$ = 5.4 mtorr, $(H)_o$ = 1.2 (see Figure 9).

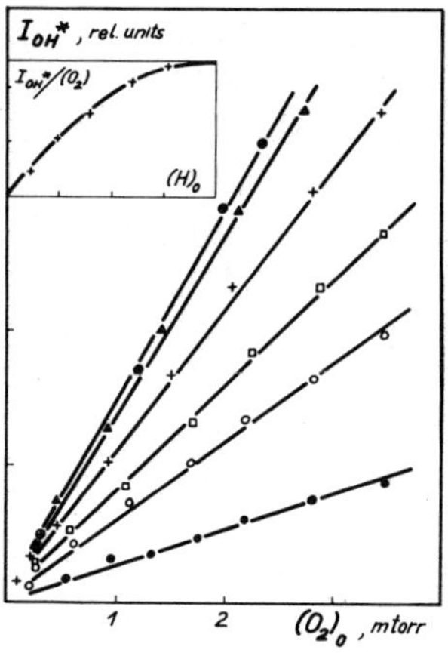

Figure 9 Dependence of I_{OH^*} on O_2 added to C_3O_2 + H for several relative H atom concentrations $(H)_o$: (●) 0.35, (○) 0.74, (□) 1.18, (+) 1.79, (▲) 2.3, (⊕) 3.0 $(C_3O_2)_o$ = 1.8 mtorr. Slopes $I_{OH^*}/(O_2)$ vs $(H)_o$.

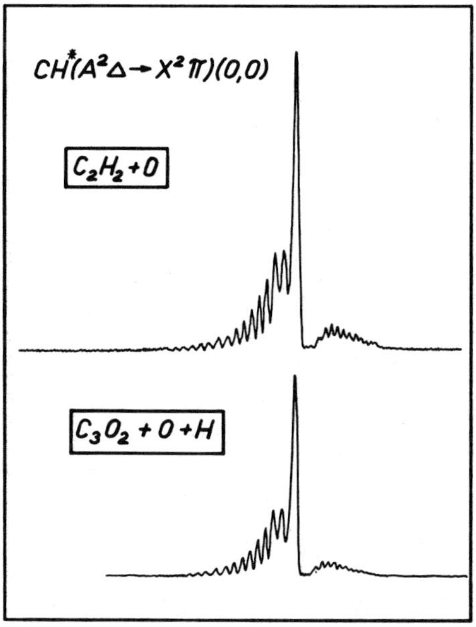

Figure 10 A comparison of the CH* (0,0) band at 4314 Å for the C_3O_2 + H + O and C_2H_2 + O reactions.

shown for the C_3O_2 flame, without oxygen atoms.

The CH^* 0,0 band at 4312 Å observed in the reactions $C_3O_2 + O + H$ and $C_2H_2 + O$ is seen in Fig. (10). More highly resolved spectra have shown that the rotational energy distribution of the CH^* band is identical for both reactions and also for $CH_2CO + O$. Besides the $A^2\Delta \rightarrow X^2\Pi$ transition, also $B^2\Sigma^- \rightarrow X^2\Pi$ at 3889 Å, but not $C^2\Sigma^+ \rightarrow X^2\Pi$ at 3145 Å have been observed in the flame spectra. The dependence of the emission intensity I_{CH^*}(4312 Å) on the H atom concentration is shown in Fig. (4) for the $C_3O_2 + O + H$ reaction.

In the $C_2H_4 + O$ or $C_2H_4 + O + H$ reaction I_{CO^*} was found to be 200 times, I_{ion} 20 times, and I_{CH^*} about 2000 times smaller than in the comparable $C_2H_2 + O + H$ and $C_3O_2 + O + H$ reactions.

When traces of mercury or nitric oxide were added to these flames, in the flame spectra the Hg-2537 Å line or the NO-β bands (with lower intensities also the NO-γ bands) were found. For not too high O and H atom concentrations, the Hg* or NO* emissions were found to follow linearly the emission intensity I_{CO^*}.

DISCUSSION

The CO* chemiluminescence in hydrocarbon oxygen flames very likely is produced by reaction (1) as it was shown recently.[5,10] Reaction (1) was first suggested[20] to explain the visible CO* emission bands of the reaction $C_3O_2 + O$. The reaction $C_2O + O \rightarrow 2CO$ is exothermic by 204.4 kcal/M (8.86 eV), and <u>all</u> observed CO* states show this excitation limit.[10] On the other hand, the observed inhibition of CO* by O_2 and even stronger by NO addition cannot be explained by electronic quenching, but the findings that $C_2O(^3\Sigma)$ reacts fast with O_2 and even faster with NO explains the CO* inhibition and supports reaction (1). The ratio k_{O_2}/k_{NO} was found to be about 1/100 in flames[10] and in a system where C_2O was formed by the C_3O_2 photolysis.[21]

Reaction (2) being the source of C_2O in the C_3O_2 + O reaction was found to be

$$C_3O_2 + O \rightarrow C_2O + CO_2 \qquad \Delta H = -38 \text{ kcal/M} \qquad (2)$$

rather slow with $K = 1.6 \times 10^{-14}$ cm^3/molec. sec.[21,22] The observed strong increase of the CO* emission intensity by H atoms which were added to the reaction C_3O_2 + O, Fig. (4), (similar results were obtained for the C_2H_2 flame) leads to the conclusion that reaction (2) and the previous suggested[5,10] reaction (3) are not as much important as reaction (4) which involves ketyl radicals. The involvement of HC_2O will be discussed later in connection with

$$C_2H_2 + O \rightarrow C_2O + H_2 \qquad \Delta H = -22 \text{ kcal/M} \qquad (3)$$

$$HC_2O + H \rightarrow C_2O + H_2 \qquad \Delta H \sim 0 \text{ kcal/M} \qquad (4)$$

the OH* emission. According to recent findings,[23] the ketyl radical is thought to be a major primary product of the reaction C_2H_2 + O. The "hot" OH* radicals, Fig. (6) and Fig. (7) are formed by H atoms and O_2 molecules in the C_3O_2 and CH_2CO flames, Fig. (5) and Fig. (9). The addition of O atoms to these flames, shown in Fig. (8) for C_3O_2 + H + O_2, even inhibits the OH* formation. In the C_2H_2 flame the precursor of the "hot" OH* is only formed in the presence of atomic oxygen. The maximal rotational population N(K') of "hot" OH* for v' = 0 appears at K' = 17, Fig. (7). K' = 17 represents an excitation energy of 107 kcal/M. Within 10% of the maximal population rotational levels up to K' = 29 were observed. The excitation energy at K' = 29 is about 130 kcal/M. This energy has to be supplied by the formation of a chemical bond if an energy transfer is not considered. Very likely only the strength of a C-O bond is high enough. A direct H atom-radical reaction forming "hot" OH* can therefore be excluded.

Among the radicals CH, CH_2, CH_3, C_2H, HC_2O, and HCO* only the reaction of CH with molecular oxygen would be sufficiently exothermic to produce "hot" OH*. Our results strongly support the previously[1,2] proposed reaction (5) as the source

$$CH + O_2 \rightarrow CO + OH \qquad \Delta H = -158 \text{ kcal/M} \qquad (5)$$

of "hot" OH*. Recently this has already been discussed in more details elsewhere.[11] Our results evidently show that the reaction-path forming "hot" OH* does not involve necessarily atomic oxygen but oxygen molecules. This is contrary to the formation of "cold" OH*, Fig. (6) and Fig. (7), which involves oxygen atoms. The addition of O_2 to the C_2H_4 + O reaction decreased the emission intensity from "cold" OH*. Previous work[1,2] had not made a distinction between two types of OH* observed in hydrocarbon flames, and it had not been found that O atoms were not necessary for the reaction-path producing "hot" OH*. Very recent results[25] have shown that a very similar, if not identical, "cold" OH* which has been observed in the C_2H_4 + O reaction occurred also in a system containing no hydrocarbons, but H and O atoms.

Recent work on the H + O reaction has explained the OH* chemiluminescence by a two-body recombination mechanism.[26] However, preliminary experiments[25] indicate that "cold" OH* might be formed by vibrationally excited OH radicals and not by a

*Taking D(H-CHCO) = 105 kcal/M[24], as in the ethylene bond, and using $\Delta H_f(CH_2CO)$ = -14.5 kcal/M[24], the heat of formation $H_f(HC_2O)$ = 38.4 kcal/M can be calculated. With $\Delta H_f(C_2O)$ = 92 kcal/M[10] $D(H\text{-}C_2O)$ = 105.7 kcal/M is calculated. The other heats of formation, except $\Delta H_f(CH_2)$, were also taken from Reference 24.

two-body recombination of H and O. In the C_2H_4 + O flame the primarily formed HCO[27,28] could give vibrationally excited OH by the reaction HCO + O → OH + CO $\Delta H = -79$ kcal/M.

At higher temperatures C_2H_4 decomposes into acetylene and acetylene-type products[17,18] which would cause an increase of the "hot" OH* chemiluminescence. Fig. (6) shows that even in a low-temperature atom flame of C_2H_4 a little amount of "hot" OH* was observed, which was hidden in the 0,0 band, but which appeared in the 1,0 band for which the "cold" OH* emission was found to be weak.

The previously proposed[4,12-16] reaction (6) as source of the ions is connected with the formation of "hot" OH* by the CH radicals.

$$CH + O \rightarrow CHO^+ + e \qquad \Delta H \sim 0 \text{ kcal/M} \qquad (6)$$

$$C_2O + H \rightarrow CH + CO \qquad \Delta H = -29.5 \text{ kcal/M} \qquad (7)$$

Reaction (6) is most consistent with our results. The formation of the ions by the proposed reaction[4,16] $C_2H_2 + CH^* \rightarrow C_3H_3^+ + e$ is not supported kinetically. It has been previously suggested[11] that the likely precursor of CH is C_2O where CH is formed by the reaction (7). The discussed reactions (1), (5), (6) and (7) explain satisfactorily the similar kinetic behavior of I_{CO^*}, $I_{OH^*(hot)}$, and I_{ion}, shown for the C_3O_2 reaction in Fig. (4), Fig. (5), Fig. (8), Fig. (9), and Fig. (11). In this reaction scheme C_2O is thought to be formed mainly by reaction (1). In the case of acetylene the ketyl radicals as the precursors of C_2O are formed by oxygen atoms, probably in the primary step by reaction (8), whereas in the case of carbon suboxide and ketene the ketyl radicals are thought to be formed by hydrogen atoms in reaction (9) and (10).

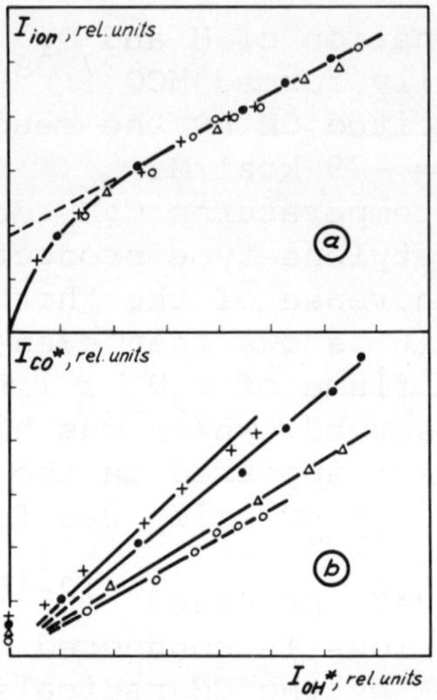

Figure 11 (a) I_{ion} vs I_{OH*} of C_3O_2 + O + H for several relative H atom concentrations at different O atom concentrations. $(O)_o$: (O) 1.1 mtorr, (△) 1.6 mtorr, (●) 2.6 mtorr, (+) 3.6 mtorr $(C_3O_2)_o$ = 0.5 mtorr
(b) I_{CO*} vs I_{OH*} under conditions of (a).

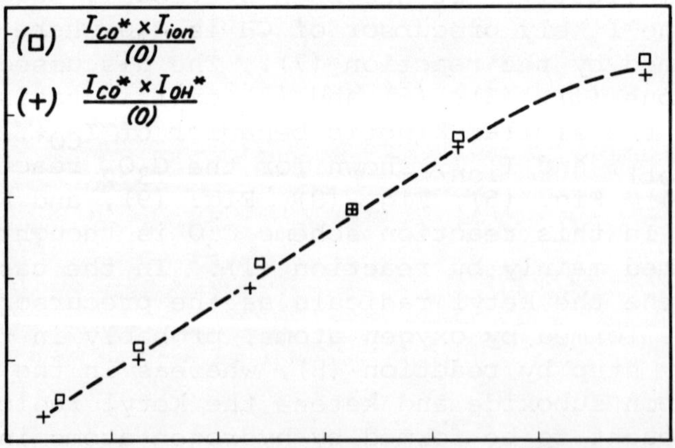

Figure 12 $(I_{CO*} \times I_{ion})/(O)$ vs I_{CH*} and $(I_{CO*} \times I_{OH*})/(O)$ vs I_{CH*} from C_3O_2 + O + H for different H and O atom concentrations. $(C_3O_2)_o$ = 0.5 mtorr.

$$C_2H_2 + O \rightarrow HC_2O + H \qquad \Delta H = -23.3 \text{ kcal/M} \quad (8)$$

$$C_3O_2 + H \rightarrow HC_2O + CO \qquad \Delta H = -16.6 \text{ kcal/M} \quad (9)$$

$$CH_2CO + H \rightarrow HC_2O + OH \qquad \Delta H \sim 0 \text{ kcal/M} \quad (10)$$

In flames producing CO* chemiluminescence, chemi-ions, and "hot" OH*, always strong CH* emission from $A^2\Delta$ and with weaker intensity from $B^2\Sigma^-$ state has been observed. The dependence of the emission intensity I_{CH^*} on H atoms, Fig. (4), and on O_2 addition, Fig. (5), shows that I_{CH^*} does not follow the similar kinetic behavior of I_{CO^*}, I_{ion}, and I_{OH^*}. In Fig. (12) $(I_{CO^*} \times I_{ion})/(O)$ and $(I_{CO^*} \times I_{OH^*})/(O)$ were plotted against I_{CH^*} for different O and H atom concentrations of the $C_3O_2 + H + O$ reaction. (Without addition of O_2 the O_2 concentration in the reaction tube was about proportional to (O). The ratio $(O)/(O_2)$ was determined mainly by $(O)/(O_2)$ coming out of the discharge). Fig. (12) shows a linear dependence for not limiting conditions of too high or too low atom concentrations. The ratios $I_{OH^*}/(O)$ and $I_{ion}/(O)$ are proportional to (CH), according to the discussed reaction scheme. By that a linear dependence $I_{CH^*} \propto (CO^*) \times (CH)$ follows from Fig. (12). An energy transfer reaction between CO* and CH forming electronically excited CH* would be consistent with these results. A likely energy carrier in a flame producing CO* emission is the metastable $CO^*(a^3\Pi)$ molecule. The excitation energy of $CO^*(a^3\Pi)$ is at least 140 kcal/M (6 eV), and its lifetime is longer than 10^{-3} sec[29]. The metastable CO* is formed by the observed radiative deactivation of the $d^3\Delta$ and $e^3\Sigma^-$ states of CO*. Probably reaction (1) forms also $CO^*(a^3\Pi)$ in relative high concentrations because the energy distribution of all observed radiative CO* states has shown a strongly increasing population with decreasing excitation energy.[10] Evidence for the metastable CO* might also come from the NO* and the Hg* emission which occurred when nitric oxide or mercury was added to the flames. These emissions can be explained by an energy transfer from $CO^*(a^3\Pi)$ to NO or Hg, in analogy to the energy transfer reactions from $N_2(A^3\Sigma_u^+)$ to NO or Hg.[19,30,31]

It seems therefore reasonable to explain the CH* formation tentatively by an energy transfer mechanism as an alternative reaction to the previously proposed reaction[1] $C_2 + OH \rightarrow CH^* + CO$ for which there exist some doubts.[3,8]

SUMMARY

(1) The following reaction scheme producing CO* chemiluminescence, emission from rotational "hot" $OH^*(A^2\Sigma^+)$, and chemi-ions in hydrocarbon flames is most consistent with our results:

$$HC_2O + H \rightarrow C_2O + H_2$$

$$C_2O + H \rightarrow CH + CO$$

$$C_2O + O \rightarrow CO^* + CO$$

$$C_2O + O_2 \rightarrow \text{products}$$

$$CH + O_2 \rightarrow OH^* + CO$$

$$CH + O \rightarrow HCO^+ + e$$

The HC_2O is mainly formed by H atoms:

$$C_3O_2 + H \rightarrow HC_2O + CO$$

$$CH_2CO + H \rightarrow HC_2O + H_2$$

In the acetylene flame oxygen atoms are necessary for the formation of HC_2O:

$$C_2H_2 + O \rightarrow HC_2O + H$$

(2) The mechanism which produces rotational "cold" $OH^*(A^2\Sigma^+)$ cannot be explained at the moment. Preliminary results indicate that vibrational excited OH radicals might be involved.

(3) Energy transfer to NO and Hg which were added to the flame is explained by metastable $CO(a^3\Pi)$ in analogy to a similar reaction of $N_2(A^2\Sigma_u^+)$ with Hg and NO. The $CO^*(a^3\Pi)$ are formed by radiation from $CO^*(d^3\Delta)$ and $CO^*(e^3\Sigma^-)$, but $CO^*(a^3\Pi)$ with higher concentrations is probably formed by reaction (1) directly.

(4) The kinetic benavior of the CH* chemiluminescence compared with CO* and OH* or the ions is tentatively explained by an energy transfer process from $CO^*(a^3\Pi)$ to CH, forming electronically excited $CH^*(A^2\Delta)$ and $CH^*(B^2\Sigma^-)$ in hydrocarbon flames.

ACKNOWLEDGEMENT

The authors wish to thank Professor Groth for his interest in this work. The financial support by the "Deutsche Forschungsgemeinschaft" is gratefully acknowledged.

REFERENCES

1. A. G. Gaydon, The Spectroscopy of Flames (Chapman and Hall, London 1957).
2. S. L. N. G. Krishnamachari and H. P. Broida, J. Chem. Phys. 34, 1709 (1961).
3. C. A. Arrington, W. Brennen, G. P. Glass, J. V. Michael, and H. Niki, J. Chem. Phys. 43, 1489 (1965).
4. A. Fontijn, W. J. Miller, and J. M. Hogan, Tenth Symposium on Combustion (The Combustion Institute, 1965), p. 545.
5. K. H. Becker and K. D. Bayes, J. Chem. Phys. 45, 396 (1966).
6. A. Fontijn, J. Chem. Phys. 44, 1702 (1966).
7. P. H. Kydd and W. I. Foss, Eleventh Symposium on Combustion, Berkeley 1966, 1167 (1967).
8. W. Brennen and T. Carrington, J. Chem. Phys. 46, 1 (1967).
9. F. F. Marmo, J. P. Padur, and P. Warneck, J. Chem. Phys. 47, 1438 (1967).
10. K. H. Becker, D. Kley, and R. J. Norstrom, Twelfth Symposium on Combustion, Poitiers 1968.
11. K. H. Becker, D. Kley, and R. J. Norstrom, Twelfth Symposium on Combustion, Poitiers 1968.
12. A. Fontijn and G. L. Baughman, J. Chem. Phys. 38, 1784 (1963).
13. J. A. Green and T. M. Sudgen, Ninth Symposium on Combustion (Academic Press, 1963), p. 607.
14. H. F. Calcote, ibid, p. 81.
15. E. M. Bulewicz and P. J. Padley, ibid, p. 622.
16. H. F. Calcote, S. C. Kurzius, and W. J. Miller, Tenth Symposium on Combustion, (The Combustion Institute, 1965), p. 545.
17. J. B. Homer and G. B. Kistiakowsky, J. Chem. Phys. 47, 5290 (1967); I. D. Gay, G. P. Glass, R. D. Kern, and G. B. Kistiakowsky, J. Chem. Phys. 47, 313 (1967).

18. K. H. Homann, M. Mochizuki, and H. Gg. Wagner, Z. Physik. Chem. 37, 299 (1963).
19. K. H. Becker and K. D. Bayes, J. Phys. Chem. 71, 371 (1967).
20. H. von Wayssenhoff, S. Dondes, and P. Harteck, J. Am. Chem. Soc. 84, 1526 (1962).
21. D. G. Williamson and K. D. Bayes, J. Am. Chem. Soc. 89, 3390 (1967).
22. G. Liuti, C. Kunz, and S. Dondes, J. Am. Chem. Soc. 89, 5542 (1967).
23. D. G. Williamson and K. D. Bayes, (to be published).
24. J. G. Calvert and J. N. Pitts, Jr., Photochemistry (Wiley, New York 1966).
25. K. H. Becker and D. Kley (to be published).
26. G. B. Spindler, S. Ticktin, and H. I. Schiff, Nature 214, 1006 (1967); S. Ticktin, G. Spindler, and H. I. Schiff, Discussions Faraday Soc. 44, 218 (1967).
27. R. J. Cvetanovic. J. Chem. Phys. 23, 1375 (1955).
28. J. M. Brown and B. A. Thrush, Transact. Faraday Soc. 63, 630 (1967).
29. R. J. Donovan and D. Husain, Transact. Faraday Soc. 63, 2879 (1967).
30. K. H. Welge, J. Chem. Phys. 45, 166 (1966).
31. R. A. Young and G. A. St. John, J. Chem. Phys. 48, 898 (1968).
32. R. C. M. Learner, Proc. Roy. Soc. (London) A269, 311 (1962).

ELECTRONIC ENERGY TRANSFER IN OLIGOMERS AND POLYMERS OF L-TYROSINE*

J. W. Longworth, J. J. ten Bosch,** J. A. Knopp and R. O. Rahn

Biology Division
Oak Ridge National Laboratory
Oak Ridge, Tennessee

INTRODUCTION

Several authors,[1-5] using the absorption[6] and fluorescence spectra[7] of the aromatic amino acids, have determined a theoretical value for the rate of transfer of electronic energy from one amino acid to another. They used the quantum mechanical theory of dipole-dipole resonance, developed by Förster,[8-11] in a very weak coupling approximation. The values found for the Förster critical distances, assuming a random orientation

*Research jointly sponsored by the National Cancer Institute and the United States Atomic Energy Commission under contract with the Union Carbide Corporation.

**On leave of absence from the University of Utrecht, the Netherlands.

of the residues, were comparable to the molecular volume of proteins.[5] In particular, tyrosyl-to-tryptophanyl transfers, as well as intramolecular transfers in proteins between tyrosyl residues and between tryptophanyl residues, are expected. In our laboratory we have concentrated on intramolecular transfers of electronic energy in oligo-[12] and poly-L-tyrosines[12-16] in an attempt to delineate the techniques that are necessary to observe transfer, and to define some of the characteristic spectroscopic features associated with the phenomenon of transfer. Polymers of tyrosine are suitable for this study, since the singlet[6,13] and triplet states of the phenoxyl ionized form of tyrosine (tyrosinate)[15] have a lower energy than the corresponding un-ionized tyrosyl residues. The critical distance for singlet tyrosine-to-tyrosine transfers was estimated to be 0.8 nm,[4] and for tyrosine-to-tyrosinate transfers the estimate was 1.3 nm.[2] These values were obtained by using a tyrosine fluorescence quantum yield that was 0.2 of the natural lifetime; the residues were assumed to be randomly oriented. Inspection of space-filling molecular models showed that the ring-ring separations in oligotyrosines were approximately 1.2 nm,[1] and in the polymer, which has a helical structure, there was a near distance of 0.6 nm. Thus, electronic energy transfers between tyrosyl residues and from tyrosyl-to-tyrosinate residues are expected in oligotyrosines.[1,17] The ratio of donor tyrosine to acceptor tyrosinate can be altered by varying the pH of the solution, and the fractional ionization can be easily determined from absorption spectrophotometry.[6,13] An added feature of the polymer poly-L-tyrosine is that its molecular conformation in solution is established.[18-22] Therefore, an explicit theoretical calculation of the transfer rates can be made for this molecule, though account has to be taken of both homotransfers between tyrosyl residues, and of heterotransfer between tyrosyl and tyrosinate residues.[23] We have also used polarized fluorescence measurements to demonstrate tyrosyl-to-tyrosyl transfer,[16] and have investigated the role of transfers at the triplet level in poly-L-tyrosine, using electron spin resonance to observe the photoinduced triplets states.[14]

METHODS

Although detailed accounts of the materials, methods, and instrumentation used for the experiments described in this paper are given in earlier papers,[12-16] we will mention some of the important points of the methods.

(a) To obtain neutral poly-L-tyrosine in solution, it is necessary to dissolve the polymer first into dimethylsulphoxide, and then combine this solution with glass-forming glycol and aqueous salt or base to form a glaning solvent.

(b) Samples were measured in 3 mm quartz tubes, held in a fingertip Dewar that fitted all the instruments, so that absorption, emission spectra, and ESR of the photoexcited triplet states were determined on the same samples at 77°K.

(c) Absorption spectra at 77°K were obtained by using a condensing lens microbeam assembly, so that it was possible to reduce the complications from partial cracking of the glasses and from the bubbling of the liquid nitrogen. In this way, the fractional ionization was determined at the same temperature as used for the luminescence measurements.

(d) Titrations were performed by using the Job procedure of continuous variations, and the spectra that were measured at 298 and 77°K (absorption and emission) had intersection points (isosbestos and isoemissive) that were clearly defined.

(e) Monochromatic light was always used to either excite emission or to form triplet states in the microwave cavity of the ESR instrument. Two wavelength regions were used: (i) the isosbestos, so that a constant fraction of light would be absorbed by a sample throughout a titration and the signal intensities from individual species would be proportional to the concentration of that species in the absence of transfer, and (ii) 300 to 305 nm light for exciting only the ionized tyrosyl residues, since the neutral residues have no appreciable absorption at these wavelengths.

EXPERIMENTAL RESULTS AND DISCUSSION

Since the absorption and emission spectra of the tyrosine oligomers and the polymer poly-L-tyrosine are very similar to the spectra found with the monomer N-acetyl-L-tyrosine amide, nearest neighbor interactions between the aromatic rings of tyrosyl residues do not affect absorption and emission. The ionized phenoxyl form of tyrosine both absorbs and emits to longer wavelengths than does the neutral form. In a base titration, isosbestos and isoemissive points are found at 298 and 77°K. Hence, the monomer, the oligomers, and the polymer can be treated as a two-component equilibrium, and the fractional ionization of the tyrosyl residues can be measured from the absorption of the ionized form. The presence of the isoemissive points and a constant spectral profile at both 298 and 77°K also eliminates the possibilities of nonspecific quenching by hydroxyl ions, and of an excited-state protolysis.

The behavior of hexa-L-tyrosine is typical of all the tyrosine oligomers we have investigated. The absorption and emission spectra for the neutral and ionized forms in an equal volume mixture of ethylene glycol and water (EGW) at 298°K are given in Figure 1, together with the spectra for a sample that was 25% ionized. Isosbestos points are found in the absorption at 267 nm and 279 nm and an isoemissive point in the fluorescence was at 365 nm. The emission from the sample ionized to 25% has a considerable contribution from the ionized molecule, with the neutral fluorescence being 80% quenched, yet the absorption spectrum is dominated by the neutral spectral profile.

A quantitative analysis of the dependence of the neutral fluorescence on the fractional ionization[24] is presented in Figure 2; this time the solvent is dimethylsulphoxide, ethylene glycol, and water 4:5:1 by volume (DEW), so that the results obtained for the oligomers and poly-L-tyrosine can be compared in the same solvent because the polymer is not soluble in EGW. The neutral fluorescence intensity, normalized to unity, was observed at 305 nm for excitation at 284 nm isosbestos in DEW at 298°K. Tyrosinate formation in an oligomer of tyrosine leads to a quenching of the neutral tyrosyl residue fluorescence, but no quenching is found with the monomer N-acetyl-L-tyrosine amide (NATA). The effectiveness of tyrosinate as a quencher increases as the number of tyrosyl residues in the molecule increases. The data points for the dependence of the fractional ionization are fitted by the term $(1 - I)^{n}$, the binomial function which represents the concentration of the completely neutral molecules and which is given as the solid line in Figure 2. Here I is the fractional ionization and n the number of tyrosyl residues in the oligomer. The analysis is based on there being (a) complete transfer of one or more residues to an ionized residue and (b) equivalent probabilities of ionization for every residue in the molecule, for all the different degrees of ionization. This latter approximation is not valid for the dimer, because there is a small electrostatic interaction between the two ionizing sites when one site is ionized. If one

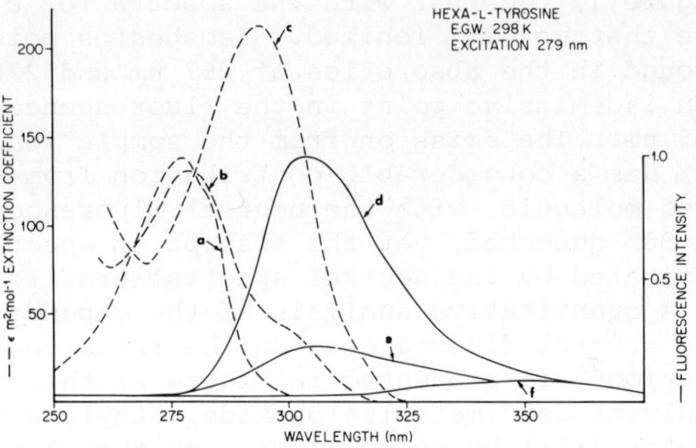

Figure 1 Absorption and emission of L-hexatyrosine. Solvent, E.G.W.; temperature, 298°K; wavelength of emission excitation, 279 nm. Absorption spectra: (a) neutral, (b) 25% ionized, (c) ionized. Emission spectra: (d) neutral, (e) 25% ionized, (f) ionized.

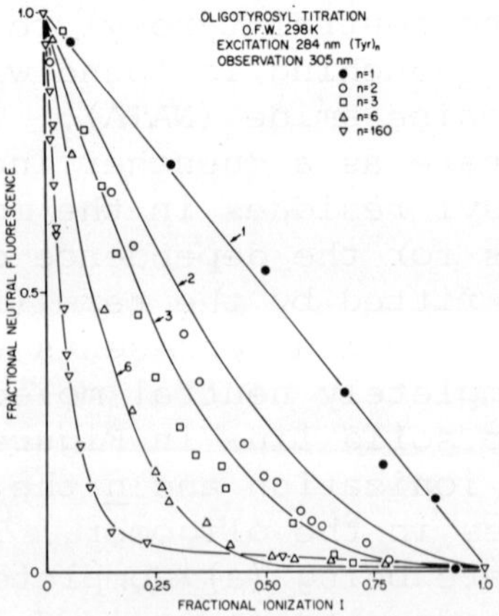

Figure 2 Oligotyrosine titration. Solvent, D.E.W.; temperature, 298°K; excitation, 284 nm; observation, 305 nm. Concentration: O.D. 10/280 nm = 0.2 (neutral). ●, N-acetyl-L-tyrosine amide; ○, L-tyrosyl-L-tyrosine; □, L-tyrosyl-L-tyrosyl-L-tyrosine; △, L-hexatyrosine; ▽, poly-L-tyrosine.

takes into account the electrostatic interactions between neighboring sites of ionization, it is possible[12] to interpret the fluorescence data on the basis that the fluorescence is only from the neutral molecules. Hence, with all of the oligomers, a single tyrosinate residue is sufficient to quench the fluorescence of all the remaining tyrosyl residues for oligomers at least as large as the hexamer (i.e., up to five tyrosyl residues)

To eliminate complications from additional quenching mechanisms, and to increase the quantum yield of the tyrosyl fluorescence, a titration of hexatyrosine was repeated in EGW glass solutions at 77°K. The viscosity of these solutions at 77°K is several orders of magnitude greater than at 298°K, so diffusional processes such as hydroxyl ion quenching and excited state protolysis are effectively eliminated. The fluorescence and phosphorescence in EGW at 77°K spectra are given in Figure 3, and the absorption spectra are similar to the spectra found at 298°K, though the ionized absorption shifts 5 nm to shorter wavelengths. Isosbestos points are found in the absorption at 255 and 278 nm; the fluorescence isoemissive is at 342 nm al, and the phosphorescence isoemissive at 405 nm. The fractional ionization of a sample is considerably greater at 77°K than at 298°K, so that the fractional ionization must be determined from the absorption spectrum measured at 77°K. Accordingly, the absorption spectra, after correction for small variations in the base line from scattering, were normalized at the isosbestos wavelength 279 nmol. The emission measurements were also corrected for variations caused by the scattering in these partially cracked glasses. Emission spectra were first obtained for isosbestos excitation, and then normalized by using the isoemissive for the phosphorescence spectra. This normalization, obtained in phosphorescence, was then applied to both fluorescence and total emission spectral data. The fractional neutral

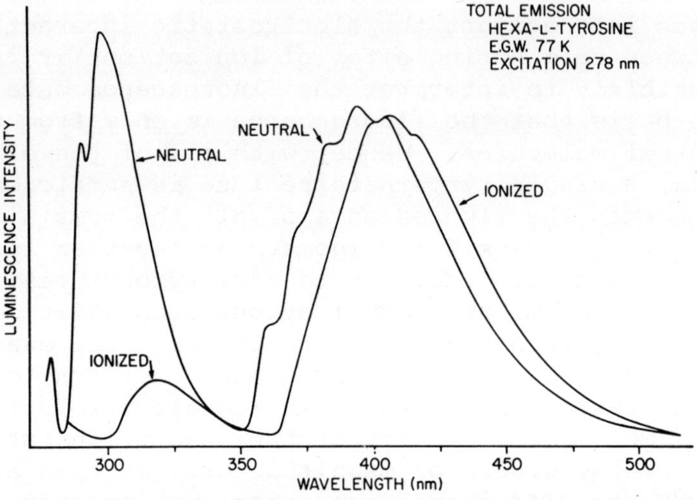

Figure 3 Total emission L-hexatyrosine. Solvent, E.G.W.; temperature, 77°K; excitation, 278 nm. (a) neutral; (b) ionized. Concentration: O.D. 10/280 mm = 0.6.

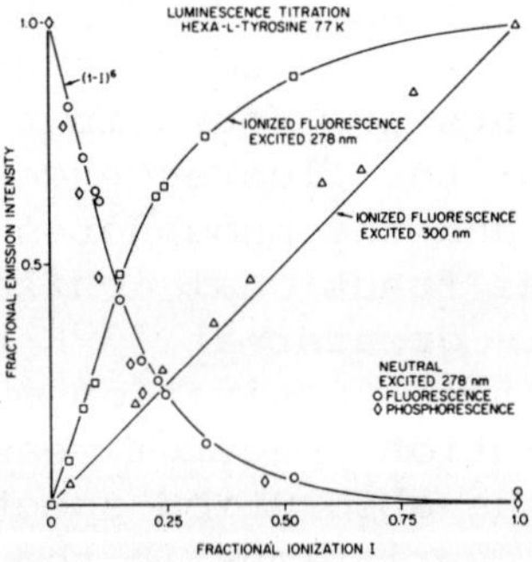

Figure 4 Luminescence titration L-hexatyrosine. Solvent, E.G.W.; temperature, 77°K; concentration, O.D. 10/280 mm = 0.6 (neutral). ○, observation 305 nm; excitation 278 nm—neutral fluorescence. ◇, observation 365 nm; excitation 278 nm—neutral phosphorescence. □, observation 330 nm; excitation 278 nm—intensity corrected for neutral contribution—ionized fluorescence; △, observation 330 nm; excitation 300 nm—ionized fluorescence.

emission was determined from the fluorescence intensity at 305 nm and the phosphorescence intensity at 365 nm (see Fig. 3); the fractional emission intensities were plotted against the fractional ionization (Fig. 4), which had been previously determined from the absorption at 300 nm measured at 77°K. No difference was found between the ability of tyrosinate to quench fluorescence and to quench phosphorescence. The fluorescence quenching was identical to that observed at 298°K (Fig. 2). In figure 4, there is also a plot of the fluorescence intensity of the ionized residues measured at 325 nmol. This curve actually reflects the fact that the intensity remains largely constant at this wavelength, and it is the neutral intensity measurement that determined the values given. Included in Figure 4 is a plot of the ionized fluorescence intensity for the excitation at 300 nm, where the absorption is only due to the ionized residues. This plot shows that the quantum yield of the ionized residues remained constant throughout the titration.

The polymer poly-L-tyrosine neutral fluorescence is efficiently quenched by tyrosinate residues; $3 \pm 1\%$ is sufficient to quench by half the neutral fluorescence (Figs. 2 and 7) at both 298 and 77°K. The fluorescence of the neutral and ionized polymer at 77°K is given in Figure 5a, together with the emission from a sample that is ionized to 13%. The emission from this partially ionized sample is predominantly from the ionized residues, even though the absorption is largely due to the neutral species. The excitation spectra of the ionized and the neutral species are given in Figure 5b, together with that obtained from the sample ionized to 13%, which was observed at the isoemissive point. The excitation spectrum of the 13% ionized sample is dominated by the neutral absorption spectral profile, though the emission is essentially only from the ionized species at the wavelength of observation; the

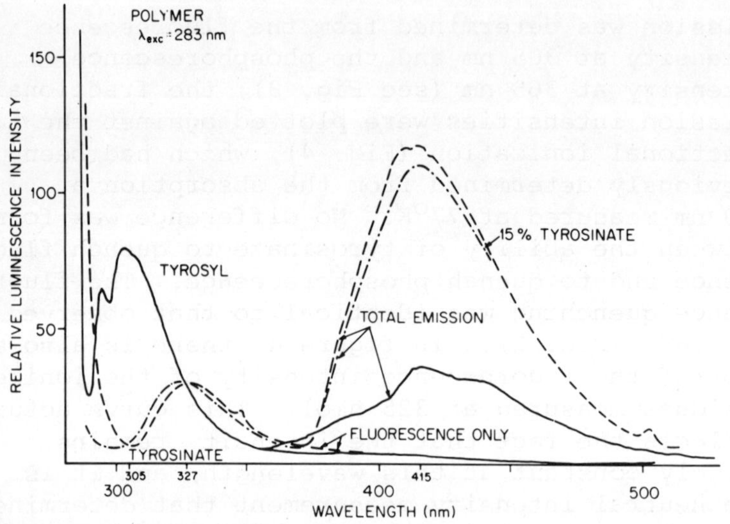

Figure 5a Luminescence of poly-L-tyrosine. Solvent, D.E.W.; temperature, 77°K; concentration, O.D. 10/280 mm - 0.6 0.3 mg/ml. Excitation, 283 nm. (a) neutral; (b) 15% ionized; (c) ionized.

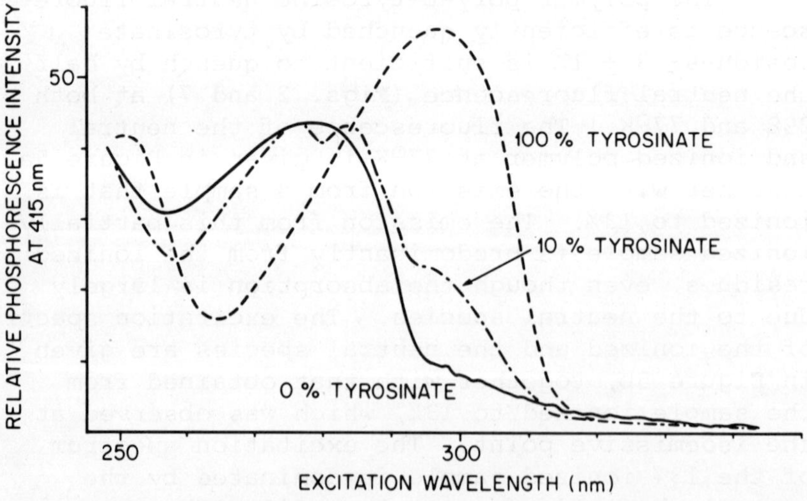

Figure 5b Fluorescence excitation spectra. Solvent, D.E.W.; temperature 77°K; observation, 325 nm.

excitation spectra is identical to the absorption spectrum. This behavior has been found with all the oligomers, as well as for the phosphorescence excitation spectra, provided the intensity is observed at the phosphorescence isoemissive.

The triplet state of the ionized residues in the polymer is lower in energy than the triplet of the neutral residues, and the neutral species has a lifetime of 1.8 sec at 77°K.[25-27] Hence, the possibility of transfers at the triplet level must be considered for the polymer—though not for the hexamer, where complete transfer takes place already at the singlet level. However, the triplet transfers would have to be comparable in rate to the transfer rates at the singlet level to be detectable. The quenching efficiency of tyrosinate was compared at the singlet and triplet levels to indicate the presence of triplet transfers. It was not possible to measure any reduction in the neutral residue phosphorescence quantum yield on tyrosinate formation because the phosphorescence spectra of the neutral and ionized forms overlap each other considerably in the polymer, in contrast to the hexamer. However, there were different values for the magnetic field strength at which there was an electron spin resonance of the photoexcited triplet states of the neutral and ionized residue in the polymer.[14] It was possible with ESR amplitude studies to determine the steady-state triplet concentration of both the neutral and ionized species in the same sample. The triplets were excited by illuminating the sample in the microwave cavity with monochromatic light at the isosbestos wavelength. The concentration at which the steady-state neutral triplet resonance amplitude was reduced to half was 3 $\pm$ 1%. Consecutive fluorescence intensity measurements were performed by measuring the fluorescence intensity at 305 nm and the fractional ionization was obtained from the 300 nm absorption at 77°K. The same ionization, 3 $\pm$ 1%, reduced the fluorescence quantum yield by half. Thus, we are not able to detect the presence of any triplet transfers, and we consider that the majority of the energy is transferred at the singlet level and triplet transfers are neglible in comparison.

The transfer of electronic energy from an excited donor to an acceptor in its ground state has been treated quantum mechanically by Förster. We have applied this well-known theory to the transfer of singlet electronic energy in poly-L-tyrosine, using the very weak coupling and dipole-dipole approximations. We consider these approximations to be justified for the polymers, since no appreciable differences were found between the absorption and emission spectra of the polymer and those of a monomer. Furthermore, the polymer extinction coefficients were similar to those of the monomer. Förster[11] has suggested that with polymers only two theoretical limits need be considered, the strong coupling and the very weak case; and since strong coupling causes the appearance of new absorptions, which is not the behavior observed for poly-L-tyrosine, we have used the very weak coupling approximation. The oscillator strengths of the transitions are small, and the nearest distance of approach of two residues in the polymer is 0.6 nm, so that the dipole-dipole approximation is considered valid. Further support for the validity of the approximation comes from an internal consistency. The values for the transfer rates calculated with these approximations are about 10^{11} sec^{-1} at the maximum, and this is considerably longer than the estimated vibronic relaxation rate of 10^{12} sec^{-1} to 10^{13} sec^{-1}.

Förster's[8-11] final equation, which relates the absorption and emission spectra to the rate of transfer in sec^{-1}, is:

$$\underline{K}_{\underline{d}\to\underline{a}} = \frac{9(\ell n10)}{128\pi^5 \underline{n}^4 \underline{N}} \frac{1}{\tau_{\underline{i}}} \frac{\underline{K}^2}{\underline{R}^6_{\underline{da}}} \underline{f}_{\underline{d}}(\bar{\underline{v}})\,\varepsilon_{\underline{a}}(\bar{\underline{v}}) \frac{d\bar{v}}{\underline{v}^{-4}} \qquad (1)$$

where the terms have the meanings: $\underline{n}$, refractive index of the medium; $\underline{N}$, Avogadro's number; $\tau_{\underline{i}}$, the intrinsic lifetime of tyrosyl fluorescence; $\underline{\bar{R}}_{da}$, the distance between donor and acceptor in nanometers; $\underline{K}$, the orientation dependent factor of products of the dipole transition moments; $\underline{f}_{d}(\bar{\nu})$, the normalized fluorescence intensity plotted against a wave-number scale; $\varepsilon_{\underline{a}}(\bar{\nu})$, the acceptor extinction coefficient (in Briggsian logs, $m^2 mol^{-1}$), where $\bar{\nu}$, the wave number, is in m^{-1}. The lifetime of the donor, in the absence of any processes other than fluorescence is $\tau_{\underline{a}}$, and this is related to the intrinsic lifetime by the quantum yield of the fluorescence Φ, where

$$\tau_{\underline{i}} = \tau_{\underline{a}}/\Phi \qquad (2)$$

The number of transfers that occur within the lifetime of the fluorescence is simply obtained by multiplying equation (1) by $\tau_{\underline{a}}$.

The overlap integrals were obtained from the absorption and emission data given in an earlier paper. The neutral absorption of the polymer has a small shoulder at 300 nm that is not found in the spectra of monomers or in the excitation spectrum of the polymer neutral fluorescence. This shoulder has been neglected in these calculations, with the long wavelength profile being obtained from the excitation spectrum. Because there are only small differences in the absorption and emission spectra of polymer, monomer, and oligomers, we have used the same overlap integrals for calculations on all of the oligomers. The quantum yield of the polymers at 298°K was found to be 0.10 ± 0.01, and the oligomers all have similar quantum yields which are greater (0.23 ± 0.03).

To determine the transfer rates it is necessary to know both the orientation of the transition moments and the distance between them for the pair of molecules involved in a transfer step.

It is possible to obtain this information explicitly for the polymer for all possible transfer pairs. The amide chain of poly-L-tyrosine forms a right-handed helix in solution,[18,19] and the aromatic rings form a 3·7-helix around the amide backbone helix.[20] Molecular models[21] and theoretical calculations[22] of the conformational energies based on estimates for the intramolecular forces are in agreement, and both indicate that in the lowest energy conformation for the polymer, the short axis of aromatic rings is perpendicular to the amide helix axis. We have used the direction and position coordinates of the aromatic electronic transition moment vectors in this conformation, as given by Pao and coworkers,[21] who obtained these values from a space-filling molecular model. The fluorescence transition moment is known to lie in the molecular plane from fluorescence absorption polarization studies,[16] and this moment forms an angle of $\pm$ 0.444 radians to the short axis absorption moment (which is the lowest energy aromatic ring transition). From these coordinates, and with the overlap integrals, substitution into equation (1) gives the rates of transfer per tyrosyl lifetime for two types of transfer, the homotransfer steps between tyrosyl residues and the heterotransfer from tyrosyl residues to tyrosinate residues. The overlap integrals from equation (1), at 298°K in DEW, are 2.3×10^{-26} mol^{-1} m^{6} for homotransfer and 68×10^{-26} mol^{-1} m^{6} for heterotransfer. The other numerical constants of equation (1) have a value of 0.13×10^{-20} mol at 298°K. The maximum rate of transfer for the heterotransfer is found to be 1.5×10^{3} greater than the fluorescence lifetime and for homotransfer, the rate is 50 times greater. A complete description of the transfer rates and the orientation terms is given elsewhere.[23]

To compare the theoretical effectiveness of tyrosinate quenching of tyrosine, it is necessary to adopt a simple model and consider that each tyrosinate acts independently of all other tyrosinates in the molecule. That the number of residues quenched per tyrosinate is additive is reasonalbe, since only a small fractional ionization is required to produce a large tyrosyl quenching. In Figure 6, the probability that an excitation on a tyrosyl residue, number i, will transfer to the tyrosinate residue number 0 is given for residues on either side in the primary sequence from the tyrosinate. All of these probabilities for each of the residue sites were then summed; they had a value of 10.3, excluding the tyrosinate trap center. It is also possible to consider that the tyrosinate acts as either a completely effective trap, or else causes no quenching. Then from the probability summation we conclude that 10.3 residues are completely quenched by a single tyrosinate. To derive an experimental figure that is equivalent to the above model, the initial slope of the quenching curve for the dependence of the fractional fluorescence intensity on fractional ionization was determined, and its intercept on the fractional ionization coordinate is then equivalent to a completely quenched polymer in which there is no interaction between each tyrosinate quenching site, i.e., where their effectiveness is additive and complete. This point is found to be at 0.07 fractional ionization, which implies that 14 tyrosyl residues are quenched by one tyrosinate (Fig. 7), including the single tyrosinate. Clearly the theoretical value is significantly greater than the experimental value in Figure 7, which suggests that tyrosyl-to-tyrosyl transfer occurs and increases the quenching efficiency of tyrosinate.

Electronic energy transfers between like molecules is usually determined from luminescence polarization measurements.[28-32] Since it is unlikely that any two neighboring molecules would have identical coordinates, then absorption of polarized light by one molecule and emission by another must cause a depolarization, as opposed

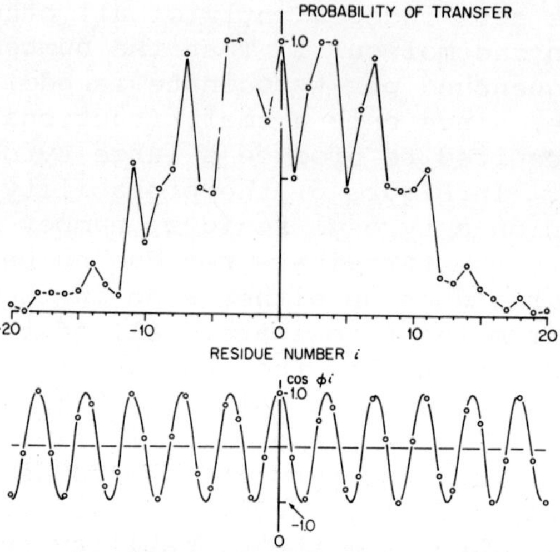

Figure 6 Probability of transfer from tyrosine to tyrosinate for residues in the primary response of poly-L-tyrosine helix.

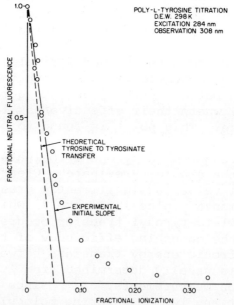

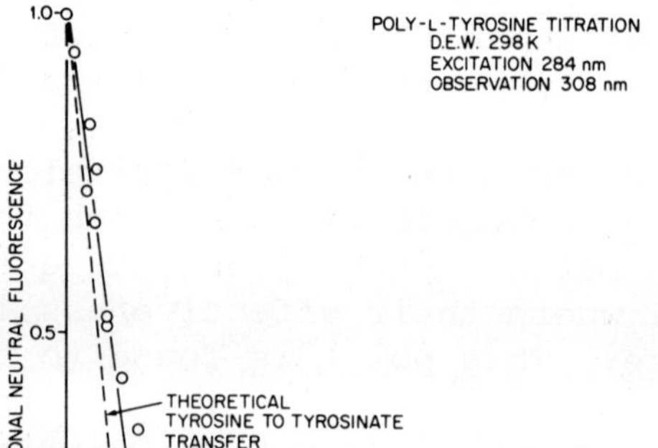

Figure 7 Fluorescence titration of poly-L-tyrosine. Solvent, D.E.W.; temperature 298°K; observation, 708 nm; excitation, 284 nm.

to absorption and emission by the same molecule. Tyrosyl-to-tyrosyl transfer has been detected from fluorescence absorption polarization spectra[31,32] of neutral poly-L-tyrosine. Since the residues of poly-L-tyrosine form a helix, transfer among the aromatic rings would also cause a depolarization of fluorescence of the polymer compared to values obtained from a monomer. The polarization spectra of N-acetyl-L-tyrosine amide and poly-L-tyrosine are shown in Figure 8, and it is clear that the polymer is considerably more depolarized than the monomer. At wavelengths longer than 285 nm, the depolarization decreases, and at 295 nm none is found. We have no explanation for this phenomenon and are currently investigating the fluorescence and phosphorescence emission polarization for several excitation wavelengths. G. Weber informs us[33] that he has observed a similar phenomenon in concentrated dye solution and in dye-protein complexes.

By following the previously described procedure used in the calculation of the heterotransfer, the transfer rates between pairs of tyrosyl residues were calculated for the different residues in the primary sequence. The individual rates were found to be 30-fold smaller than the heterotransfer rates. The probability that a given residue will emit is determined by a competition between two rates, that of emission and that of transfer. The distribution of the excited state population among the residues in the primary sequence of the α-helical polymer was calculated as a function of time after the initial act of excitation. A simplified polymer model was used, in which there are 101 residues, and the site of the initial excitation is the central residue, number 51. Initially, the total population of the excitation was normalized to unity, and the time dependence of the spatial distribution for a given residue was obtained from a numerical integration of the diffusion-type equation:

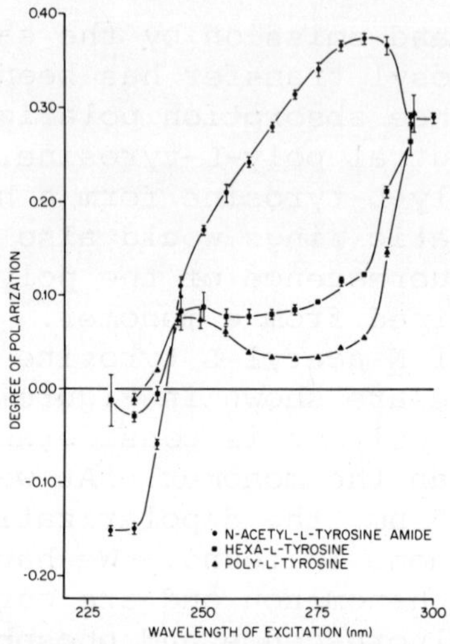

Figure 8 Fluorescence absorption polarization. Solvent, propane-1:2-diol; temperature, 210°K; concentration, O.D. 10/280 mm = 0.6. Fluorescence isolated by Cornning CS-54 Color Filter. (a) N-acetyl-L-tyrosine amide; (b) L-hexatyrosine; (c) poly-L-tyrosine.

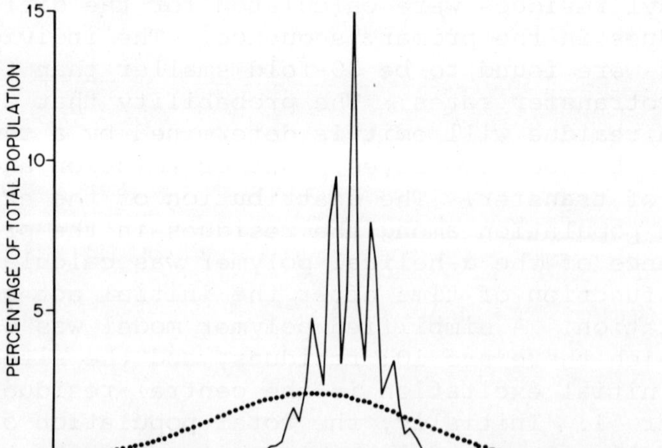

Figure 9 Energy distribution among neutral residues as a function of time after excitation.

$$\frac{dX_i}{d(t/\tau)} = -X_i \left(\sum_{j=i-7}^{i+7} K_{i \to j} \right) + \sum_{j=i-7}^{i+7} (K_{i \to j} X_j) \quad j \neq i \tag{3}$$

where t/τ is time after excitation/fluorescence decay time and X_i and X_j are the respective populations of the ith and j^{th} residues. The values for the rate constants $K_{i \to j}$ are obtained from Förster's theory calculations. To determine polarization of the fluorescence from the polymer, we first determine the polarization expected from an absorption at residue 51, followed by emission at residue *n*. We then weighed each particular value by the time dependence of the fractional population for this site; the population calculated by equation (3) was corrected for fluorescence decay. The polarization of the polymer is then the sum of all these time-dependent sums. The population density time dependence was carried out to 4 tyrosyl fluorescence lifetimes, though the final value was effectively attained after only 0.2 of the lifetime (Fig. 9). The final value found for the limiting polarization was 0.12, and the experimental value was 0.05. The lower polarization experimentally found with the polymer could be a result of the polymer not having a helix of length of up to 100 residues.

Since there is both theoretical and experimental support for the homotransfers between tyrosyl residues, the effectiveness of tyrosinate in quenching tyrosine was recalculated by using both tyrosine-to-tyrosine transfers and tyrosine-to-tyrosinate transfers. This was accomplished by including a single tyrosinate into a model polymer of 101 residues and varying the number of residues between the site of excitation of the tyrosinate. The total amount of energy transferred to tyrosinate is then the average of all these individual polymers. The final sum of all the tyrosyl residues which completely transfer their energy to the tyrosinate was found to be 2.6 ± 3. This number is in reasonable agreement with the experimental observations (see Fig. 7).

The magnitude of the quenching calculated theoretically depends on the values for the individual rates for each transfer step, and is not strongly dependent on the orientation between the residues. In contrast, the theoretical calculation of the extent of depolarization is dependent largely on the orientation terms used, and is effectively insensitive to the magnitude of the rates of transfer. As good agreement is found between the experimental and theoretical values for quenching and depolarization, we consider that the use of very weak coupling is a valid approximation of and that Forster's theory accounts adequately for the amount of homo- and heterotransfer observed in poly-L-tyrosine. We also find that the molecular conformation on which these calculations were based is satisfactory.

In summation, poly-L-tyrosine has provided a molecular system which exhibits two kinds of transfer of electronic energy, tyrosyl-to-tyrosyl and tyrosyl-to-tyrosinate. A good agreement has been found between the experimentally determined extent of transfer and the extent calculated by use of Förster's theory. Thus, we are encouraged to apply this theory to the more complicated transfers which occur in proteins.

REFERENCES

1. G. Karreman, R. H. Steele and A. Sent-Gyorgyi, Proc. Natl. Acad. Sci. U. S. 44, 140 (1958).
2. F. W. J. Teale and G. Weber, Biochem. J. 67, 15P (1959).
3. Yu. A. Vladimirov, Invest. Akad. Nauk. USSR 23, 89 (1959).
4. L. Stryer, Radiation Res., Suppl. 2, 432 (1960).
5. F. W. J. Teale, Biochem. J. 76, 18 (1960).
6. G. H. Beaven and E. R. Holiday, Advan. Protein Chem. 7, 319 (1952).
7. F. W. J. Teale and G. Weber, Biochem. J. 65, 476 (1957).
8. Th. Förster, Ann. Physik 2, 55 (1948).
9. Th. Förster, Z. Naturforsch 4a, 321 (1949).
10. Th. Förster, Z. Elecktrochem. 53, 93 (1949).
11. Th. Förster, in Modern Quantum Chemistry, O. Sinanoglu, Ed. (Academic Press, New York 1966), Istanbul Lectures, Vol. 3, p. 93.
12. J. A. Knopp and J. W. Longworth, Biochem. Biophys. Acta, 154, 436 (1968).
13. J. W. Longworth and R. O. Rahn, Biochem. Biophys. Acta 147, 526 (1967).
14. J. J. ten Bosch, R. O. Rahn, J. W. Longworth and R. G. Shulman, Proc. Natl. Acad. Sci. U. S. 59, 1003, (1968).
15. J. J. ten Boxch, J. W. Longworth and R. O. Rahn, Biochem. Biophys. Acta (submitted for publication).
16. J. A. Knopp, J. J. ten Bosch and J. W. Longworth, Biochem. Biophys. Acta (in preparation).
17. R. W. Cowgill, Biochem. Biophys. Acta 112, 550 (1966).
18. G. D. Fasman, E. Bodenheimer and C. Lindblow, Biochemistry 3, 1665 (1964).
19. S. Beychok and G. D. Fasman, Biochemistry 3, 1675 (1964).
20. G. Brady, R. Salovey, and J. M. Reddy, Biopolymers 3, 573 (1965).

21. Y. H. Pao, R. Longworth and R. L. Kornegay, Biopolymers 3, 419 (1965).
22. T. Ooi, R. A. Scott, G. Vanderkooi and H. A. Scheraga, J. Chem. Phys. 46, 4410 (1967).
23. J. J. ten Bosch and J. A. Knopp, Biochem. Biophys. Acta (in preparation).
24. R. F. Steine, Biochem. Biophys. Res. Commun. 30, 502 (1968).
25. A. Terenin and V. Ermolaev, Trans. Faraday Soc. 52, 1042 (1956).
26. G. Porter and F. Wilkinson, Proc. Roy. Soc., Ser. A, 264A, 1 (1961).
27. R. G. Bennett and R. E. Kellogg, Photochem. Photobiol. 7, (1968).
28. E. Gaviola and P. Pringsheim, Z. Physik 24, 24 (1924).
29. F. Weigert and G. Kappler, Z. Physik 25, 99 (1924).
30. V. L. Levschin, Z. Physik. 26, 274 (1924).
31. G. Weber, Biochem. J. 75, 345 (1960).
32. J. Lynn and G. D. Fasman, Biopolymers 6, 159 (1968).
33. G. Weber, in Molecular Associations in Biology, B. Pullman, Ed. (Academic Press, New York, 1968) p. 499.

PHOSPHORESCENCE FROM TYROSINE AND TRYPTOPHAN IN DIFFERENT MICROENVIRONMENTS*

Eloise Kuntz, Robert Canada, Richard Wagner and Leroy Augenstein

Biophysics Department
Michigan State University
East Lansing, Michigan

It is normally accepted that the amino acid side chains in protein molecules exist in a range of microenvironments varying in their chemical and physical characteristics. These can include regions which are characterized according to parameters such as hydrophilic, hydrophobic, thermal stability, etc.[1] The biological function of proteins can be markedly changed by factors which modify either their structure or the behavior of individual critical residues. Thus, it is essential that a variety of experimental approaches be used to characterize as extensively as possible the properties of the microenvironments which surround

*This research supported in part by grant AEC(11-1) 1155 from the United States Atomic Energy Commission

constituent residues and which may influence their behavior.

This report compares the nature of the phosphorescence from tyrosine and tryptophan in different solvent systems and films with that emitted from proteins. These experiments were undertaken as a means of trying to characterize some ofthe properties of the microenvironment surrounding those tyrosines and tryptophans which emit phosphorescence in proteins such as trypsin and hyaluronidase. In particular, we have utilized earlier observations[2,3] which showed that the quenching of phosphorescence as a function of temperature is very sensitive to the type of matrix in which these aromatic residues are embedded. This temperature-dependent quenching seems to be a function of the rigidity of the matrix: presumably whether the microenvironment is "frozen" or "melted" determines the ability of immediately adjacent solvent molecules to reorient and interact with excited states.

We have adapted the earlier techniques in order to get some crude estimates of the rigidity of the microenvironments surrounding the aromatic residues in these two proteins, and also to investigate whether the emitting tyrosines are on the "inside" or "outside" of these proteins. In addition, we have also explored in preliminary experiments, the similarities and dissimilarities in the quenching caused by adjacent amino acid residues to that caused by interaction of an excited chromophore with a surrounding solvent matrix.

MATERIALS AND METHODS

L-tyrosine and l-tryptophan, grade A from Calbiochem (Los Angeles), the dipeptide tryptophyl-tyrosine produced by Yeda and distributed by New England Nuclear (Boston) and the enzymes hyaluronidase highly purified grade and trypsin 2x crystallized from Worthington (Freehold, N. J.) were used without further purification.

The aqueous solutions were prepared using glass-distilled water and reagent-grade glucose. The pH was adjusted with dilute HCl or NaOH.

Relatively thick layers of protein were adsorbed onto quartz plates or onto prewashed Visking membrane stretched in a circular frame. The protein was applied by adding a thin layer of solution onto these materials and then allowing the water to evaporate off.

The polyvinyl alcohol preparations were made by incorporating the amino acid or protein into a 5% solution of PVA (DuPont 73-125) and evaporating the H_2O from a 1 mm layer of this mixture. The films were dried at room temperature with final drying conducted in a dessicator overnight.

To facilitate the estimation of room-temperature quantum yields of the peptides and proteins, an appropriate dilution of the amino acids was made which had an optical density matching that portion of the optical density at 265 nm due to the amino acid constituents of the protein or peptide. The emission intensities of these two samples were then compared in a "front face sample holder"[4] in an Aminco spectrophosphorimeter. The quantum yields of tryptophyl tyrosine and the tryptophan yields from trypsin are based upon those photons absorbed in the constituent tryptophans. Emission from the films was compared with that from 1 mm thick samples of amino acids having the same OD. This procedure was employed to minimize geometrical errors. Low temperature quantum yields were obtained by a comparison of the room-temperature and low-temperature intensities with appropriate corrections for wavelength shifts and light scattering according to a method developed by us previously.[5]

For the low-temperature measurements an iron-constantan thermocouple was embedded in the liquid samples contained in a quartz capillary placed in a vacuum dewar. The films were positioned directly in the dewar at an angle slightly off 45° to the incident light so as to minimize reflections. The thermocouple was positioned in contact with the surfaces of the films. The changes in emission intensity with changing temperature were recorded as the samples slowly warmed up after the liquid nitrogen had boiled off.

RESULTS AND DISCUSSION

GENERAL ANALYSIS. Typical plots of the effect of temperature on phosphorescence intensity are seen in Figures (1)-(4). It can be seen in these plots of log intensity vs. 1/T that there are normally three main regions (designated as MQ, Tr, EQ).

<u>MQ.</u> At the lowest temperatures the line is almost completely flat indicating a constant intensity of phosphorescence. It was reported previously that the total quantum yield of fluorescence plus phosphorescence in this temperature range is essentially unity (see Fig. (1)). This indicates that for sufficiently low temperatures the matrix must be so rigid that the individual solvent molecules do not interact with the excited state of the aromatic chromophore and thus minimal quenching occurs, during even the long lifetime of the triplet state.[2] By comparing the differences in Figure (1) between the quenching of fluorescence and phosphorescence for either tyrosine or tryptophan, it can be seen that the quenching of phosphorescence begins at a lower temperature than is the case for fluorescence: it is to be expected that the matrix should begin to interact with the longer-lived triplet states at a lower temperature than with the shorter-lived singlets.

If there are essentially no excited state-matrix interactions at the lowest temperatures then there should be essentially no wavelength shifts

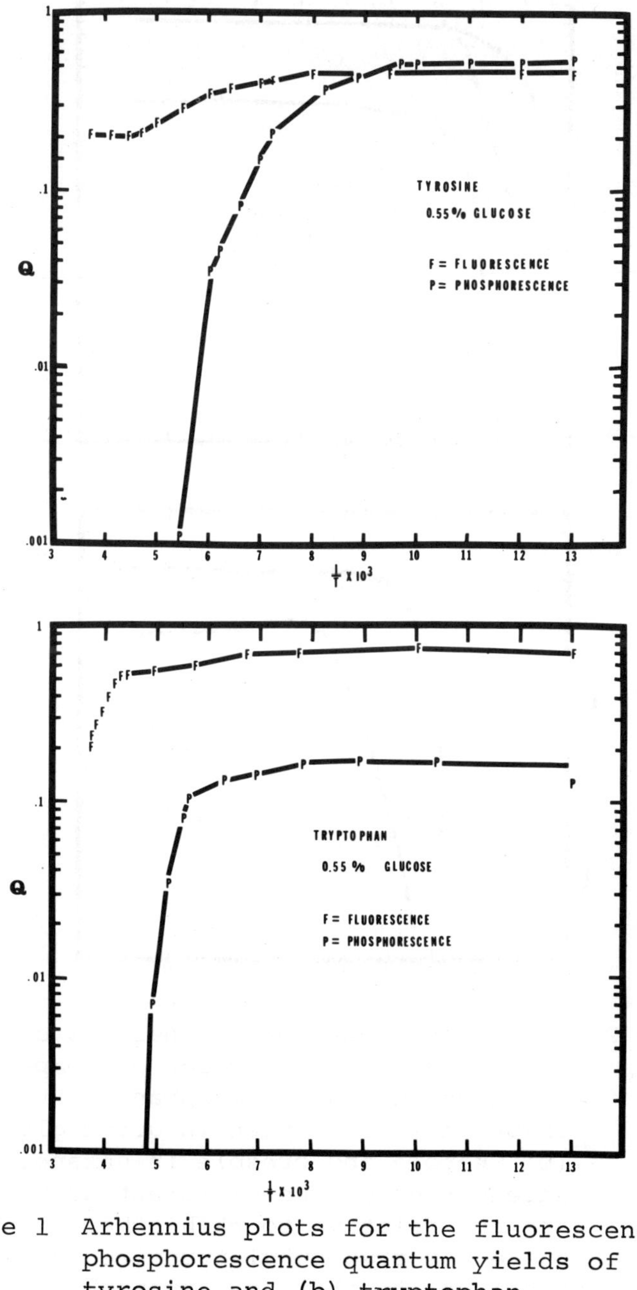

Figure 1 Arhennius plots for the fluorescence and phosphorescence quantum yields of (a) tyrosine and (b) tryptophan.

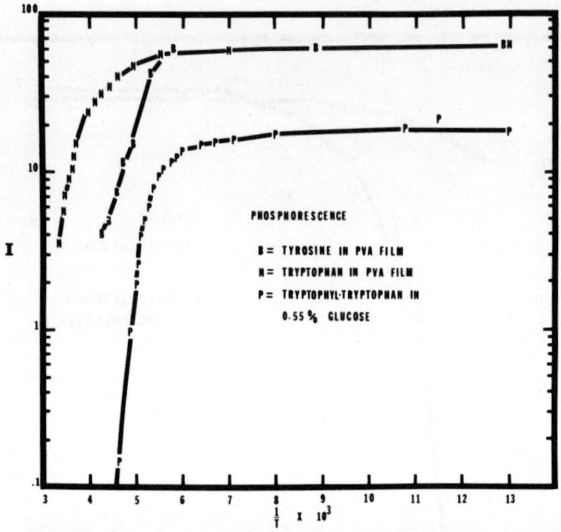

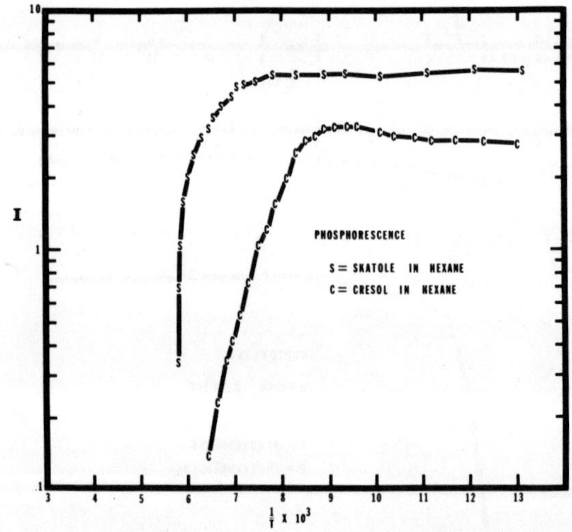

Figure 2 Arhennius plots for intensities of phosphorescence as a function of temperature: (a) tyrosine and tryptophan in PVA and tryptophyl tryptophan in 0.55% glucose. (b) Skatole and cresole in hexane. The intensities of the different compounds are not relative to each other. The curve for tryptophyl-tyrosine is almost identical to that for tryptophyl-tryptophan.

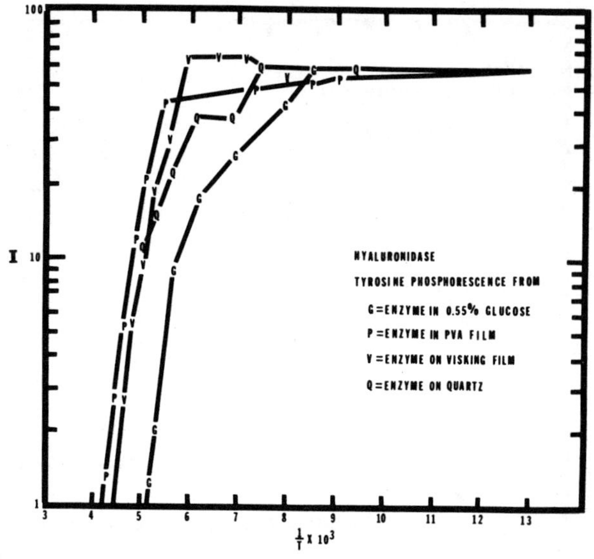

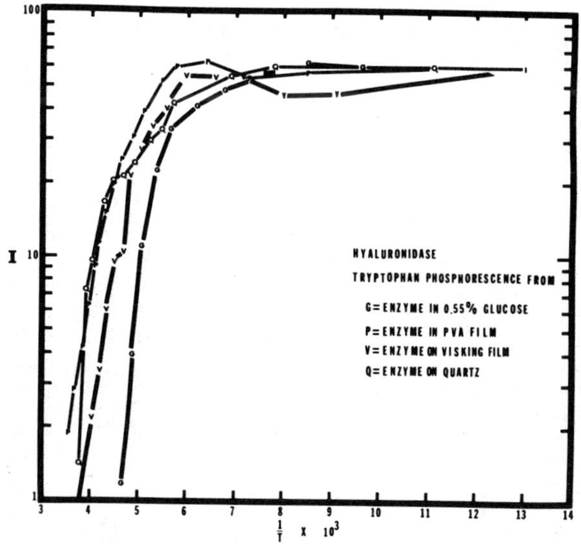

Figure 3 Arhennius plots for the phosphorescence from hyaluronidase. (a) the tyrosine component measured at 390 nm and (b) the tryptophan component measured at 425 nm. The 77°K values were all normalized to the same intensity.

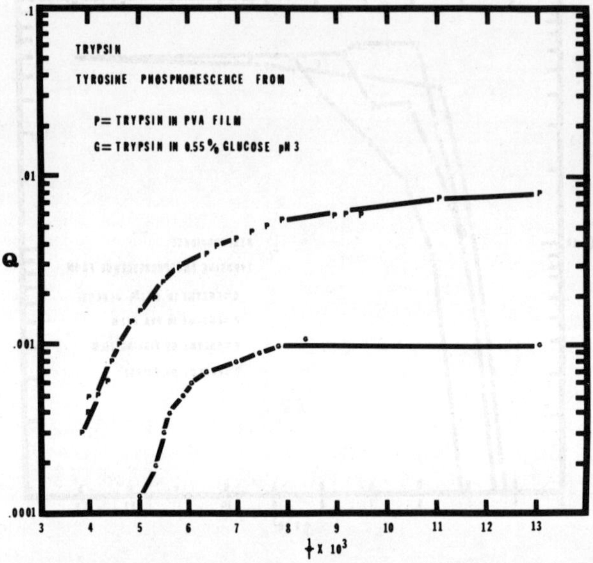

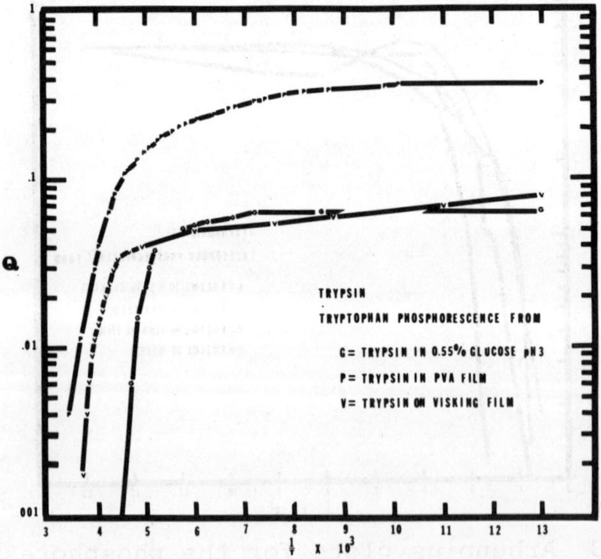

Figure 4 Arhennius plots for the phosphorescence quantum yields from trypsin. (a) the tyrosine component measured at 390 nm and (b) the tryptophan component measured at 425 nm.

due to solvent perturbations.[6] Consistent with this the wavelength of maximum fluorescence from skatole (3-methyl indole is the tryptophan side chain and is soluble in hydrocarbons as well as water) is at 326 nm for solutions in both hexane and water measured at $77^{o}K$ and λ_F for tryptophan in water at $77^{o}K$ is 325 nm. The same general behavior is observed for cresol (p-methyl phenol is the tyrosine side chain which is soluble in hydrocarbons as well as water) which has $\lambda_F = 303$ nm in both hexane and water at $77^{o}K$; however, at $77^{o}K$ tyrosine in water has a $\lambda_F = 295$ nm.

EQ. At the highest temperatures the slopes of the lines become much greater indicating that there is efficient quenching of the excited states--presumably due to the fact that the matrix has "melted" sufficiently so that there are a variety of interactions of the excited states with vibrational and rotational modes. Reference to Fig. (1) again indicates that as would be anticipated, the increase in quenching of long-lived triplet states can be as much as 10 times greater per temperature interval than that for the singlet state in the same matrix (see also Ref. (3)).

Tr. Finally, there is a transition region between the temperatures where the matrix is so rigid that there is essentially no quenching (region MQ) and where the plots become essentially linear (region EQ), indicating that quenching is quite extensive. This Tr region presumably reflects those temperatures within which there is "melting" of the matrix adjacent to the excited states.

It is important to emphasize that all three of these regions occur at temperatures considerably below those at which gross melting can be demonstrated. Thus, these features must be ascribed to the localized conditions associated with the microenvironments immediately surrounding individual aromatic residues.

TYROSINE AND TRYPTOPHAN IN VARIOUS MATRICES. The data in Figure (2) show that the microenvironments surrounding either tyrosine or tryptophan are quite different in the various matrices tested. For example, region Tr begins at about 110°K for tyrosine in water or cresol in hexane and about 130°K for tryptophan in water or skatole in hexane. In PVA this is delayed to 170°K for the two amino acids.

The different matrices also can produce a differential effect on singlet and triplet excited states. As mentioned above, the data in Figure (1) illustrate that "melting" sufficient to allow significant quenching occurs at different temperatures for singlet and triplet states. Furthermore, the different matrices have an important influence on intersystem crossing: the P/F ratios are almost twice as great in PVA as they are in the completely frozen aqueous media. This large difference arises because ϕ_P in PVA is slightly more than 50% greater than ϕ_P in the aqueous-glucose mixture. Since this differential effect is produced without significant quenching, presumably the different matrices must impose different configurations on the solute molecules, <u>but</u> without enhancing vibronic coupling either intramolecular or between solute and solvent molecules.

It appears that the sharpness of the melting (i.e., the extent of region Tr) may be quite different for tyrosine and tryptophan in a given solvent: e.g. for tyrosine in PVA it is 30-40°K in its extent, whereas for tryptophan region Tr extends over almost 100°K and in water-glucose the corresponding values are 40° and 90°K. Presumably this reflects differences in the specific arrangement or configuration of the matrix immediately surrounding these residues. Such differences are not unexpected since these two molecules have quite different shapes, and thus presumably quite different distortions must be produced in a solvent in order to accommodate these two molecules.

Even so, it seems fairly clear from these data that most of the quenching is not an intramolecular phenomenon, but rather the result of interactions between solvent and solute molecules. In particular, if most of the quenching reflected intramolecular conversions, we would anticipate that the slope of the quenching curve in region EQ should not depend greatly upon the external matrix. However the data in Figs. (1) and (2) indicate that the similarities in the slope for the quenching of tyrosine and tryptophan in water and the same two values in PVA are greater than the similarities between tyrosine in the two media and tryptophan in the two media.

QUENCHING OF AROMATIC EMISSION IN PEPTIDES. In both the dipeptides tryptophyl-tryptophan and tryptophyl-tyrosine, only tryptophan phosphorescence is observed. Further, both the total yield of ϕ_F and ϕ_P and the yield of phosphorescence, ϕ_P, for these dipeptides are much smaller than for the individual amino acids in solution alone (see also Ref. (8)). However, the phosphorescence decay times and the plots of log intensity vs. 1/T (Fig. (2)) are almost identical for the individual amino acids and the dipeptides.

These results indicate that phosphorescence is observed only from tryptophan residues--either there is complete energy transfer from tyrosine to tryptophan or else tyrosine triplets are quenched. Further, those tryptophan residues which do emit must be in a microenvironment similar to that surrounding tryptophan alone in H_2O-glucose. This suggests that most of the dipeptides have a configuration in which neighbor-neighbor quenching is very efficient, and in only a small fraction are the tryptophans solvated similar to tryptophan in solution alone.

THE NATURE OF THE MICROENVIRONMENTS SURROUNDING EMITTING TYROSINES AND TRYPTOPHANS IN TWO PROTEINS. The results in Figure (3) show that the quenching of the phosphorescence emitted by constituent tyrosines and constituent tryptophans is greatly affected by changing the external environment of hyaluronidase. Particularly, the differences between the preparations adsorbed onto quartz and Visking membranes indicate that some of the effects reflect conformation changes since extensive external solvents are not involved--we did not, however, go to great lengths to remove all bound water. Nevertheless, in terms of the extent of both regions MQ and Tr and also the slope of the plots in region EQ, the tyrosine and the tryptophan phosphorescence from hyaluronidase in H_2O-glucose is very similar to that from the corresponding amino acid in H_2O-glucose, and similarly for the PVA preparations. This suggests that the emitting residues must be fairly accessible to external solvent molecules.

In this regard, the data in Fig. (3) suggest particularly that water can get to the tryptophans responsible for the emission with relative ease. If so, however, the nature of the solvation must be different than that for tryptophan alone in H_2O-glucose: i.e., although the temperature quenching pattern is very similar the λ_F at room temperature is 340 nm in hyaluronidase compared to 348 nm in water alone. Nevertheless, in most proteins there is even less environmental perturbation, since the most common values for tryptophan λ_F are 330-335 nm.[7] Thus, presumably a microenvironment dominated by water or glucose surrounds the tryptophans, but the actual configuration of the matrix is different than that in a regular frozen aqueous solution: perhaps some arrangement analogous to that suggested by Yanari and Bovey[9] and Kronman[10] may be pertinent.

The correspondence between the quenching of tryptophan phosphorescence in hyaluronidase embedded in PVA and the phosphorescence from tryptophan alone in PVA is not so great as with the H_2O-glucose preparations. Presumably, this means that the tryptophans are in the interior of this protein in such an arrangement that they are less accessible to the high-molecular weight PVA than to H_2O-glucose. Surprisingly, the transition from the completely rigid state (MQ) to the extensive quenching situation is very abrupt for tryptophan emission from hyaluronidase embedded in PVA. In fact, there is almost no Tr region under this condition, whereas region Tr occupies about 100^oK for tryptophan alone in PVA. However, again, once extensive quenching does predominate, the slope of the two lines for the two PVA preparations are almost identical in region EQ.

In the absence of external solvent, the emitting tryptophans must exist in differing microenvironments within the protein. Hyaluronidase adsorbed onto Visking film must assume a conformation such that the emitting tryptophans are in environments whose temperature characteristics resemble those of PVA. By contrast, when hyaluronidase is adsorbed onto quartz, region Tr is quite complex, indicating that there must be some of the tryptophans which are in a region of the protein which "melts" almost like an aqueous medium, whereas at least 1/3 of the emission comes from residues which are in almost a PVA-like environment.

The emitting tyrosine residues in hyaluronidase also appear to occur in different microenvironments. A major fraction of them appear to be readily available to external aqueous medium, since the onset of quenching occurs at about 110^oK in the plots for tyrosine alone in H_2O-glucose and tyrosine emission from the hyaluronidase dissolved in the H_2O-glucose mixture. However, the nature of the microenvironment of these tyrosines must be modified somewhat from that in the general aqueous matrix since there are obvious differences in the Tr and EQ regions between these two conditions. In particular, the interaction of tyrosine with surrounding water appears to be less in the hyaluronidase than it is in the aqueous matrix in general since the whole curve for hyaluronidase is shifted to temperatures between those for tyrosine in glucose solution and those for PVA. This interaction also seems to be borne out when similar comparisons are made for tyrosine in PVA and tyrosine in hyaluronidase embedded in PVA. In particular, although the onset of region EQ is about the same, it can be noted that for tyrosine emission from hyaluronidase in PVA, there is a continuous positive slope of the line which persists even down to 77°K. This seems to indicate that although there is rather intimate interaction of external water and the emitting tyrosines, the PVA cannot completely solvate all the tyrosines. Furthermore, under these conditions, the tyrosine microenvironment in hyaluronidase never becomes completely rigid with the consequence that significant interactions continue even at 77°K.

The plots of phosphorescence from tryptophan in trypsin in H_2O-glucose (Fig. (4)) are almost identical to those for either of the tryptophan dipeptides. This suggests that H_2O or perhaps glucose can reach and interact with the tryptophans which emit. However, the tryptophans must not be solvated completely since there are shifts of about 10-15°K in the onset of region Tr. Further, once melting is fairly complete there are remarkable similarities between the slopes in region EQ for tryptophan alone in H_2O-glucose and for tryptophan in trypsin dissolved in the aqueous-glucose mixture. In addition, it is to be emphasized that most of the tryptophan emission is quenched inside the protein since the total quantum yields are only 0.3, whereas for tryptophan alone in H_2O-glucose the total quantum yield is almost unity.

The plot of tryptophan phosphorescence from trypsin embedded in PVA exhibits an onset of Tr at 100°K--a temperature normally characteristic of H_2O-glucose. Yet the onset of region EQ is at about 225°K which is most characteristic of a PVA environment. This may mean that only one or two of the tryptophans are accessible to PVA and the others are in a H_2O-like microenvironment in the interior; however, the breadth of region Tr and the shape of the curve might also be consistent with some of the tryptophans being in an environment which has a transition region resembling that of skatole in hexane. If so, then adsorption onto Visking must change trypsin's configuration such that some of the tryptophans are in a microenvironment which behaves in the EQ region approximately the same as does the PVA surrounding tryptophan in a PVA preparation: as a result, phosphorescence is observed in both preparations at room temperature. Furthermore, the general temperature range in which "melting is essentially complete" is pretty nearly the same. Thus, in terms of the temperature at which melting occurs and the ability of the neighboring environment to interact in a solvent-solute type relation, portions of the interior of trypsin appear to be affected by temperature somewhat comparable to polyvinyl alcohol. However, for tryptophan emission from trypsin adsorbed onto the Visking membrane, the slope is not zero even at the lowest temperatures studied. This seems to imply that in the absence of an external solvent, the microenvironment surrounding the majority of the emitting tryptophans in trypsin never completely freezes. Extrapolating this slope until it meets the normal curve for tryptophan alone in PVA, gives an intersection at 25°K. Accordingly, we are now preparing for experiments in which we will extend this type of measurement down into this lower temperature range.

Since the absolute yield of tyrosine in trypsin is very small, either most of the tyrosine residues are completely quenched, or else there is extensive transfer of tyrosine excitation via a Förster mechanism to the tryptophan.[11,12] This low intensity makes it difficult to assess the results for tyrosine phosphorescence accurately. Nevertheless, it appears that like the tryptophans, the emitting tyrosines exist in various microenvironments. In H_2O-glucose the onset of quenching occurs at a temperature characteristic of tyrosine alone in H_2O-glucose. For trypsin in PVA the EQ region occurs at a comparable temperature to that for tyrosine alone in PVA, but there is a greatly extended Tr region and the slope doesn't become flat at the lowest temperatures. Presumably, one or at most a very few emitting tyrosines are on or near the exterior so that they can be readily solvated by either H_2O-glucose or PVA, while others are in an interior which does not completely "freeze."

REFERENCES

1. S. N. Timasheff and M. J. Gorbunoff, Ann. Rev. of Biochem. 36, 13 (1967).
2. F. Bishai, E. Kuntz and L. Augenstein, Biochem. Biophys. Acta 140, 381 (1967).
3. E. Kuntz, Nature 217, 845 (1968).
4. J. Drobnik and L. Augenstein, Photochem. and Photobiol. 5, 83 (1966).
5. E. Kuntz, F. Bishai and L. Augenstein, Nature 212, 980 (1966).
6. R. S. Becker and M. Kasha, The Luminescence of Biological Systems, F. H. Johnson, Ed. (Am. Assoc. for the Advancement of Sci, 1955), p. 25.
7. S. V. Konev, Fluorescence and Phosphorescence of Proteins and Nucleic Acid, trans. by S. Udenfriend (Plenum Press, 1967), p. 100-101.
8. R. W. Cowgill, Biochem. Biophys. Acta 133, 6 (1967).
9. S. Yanari and F. A. Bovey, J. Biol. Chem. 235, 2818 (1960).
10. M. Kronman, Biochem. Biophys. Acta 133, 19 (1967).
11. S. V. Konev, Fluorescence and Phosphorescence of Proteins and Nucleic Acid, trans. by S. Udenfriend (Plenum Press, 1967), Chapter 3.
12. R. F. Chen, in Fluorescence, Theory, Instrumentation and Practice, G. G. Guilbault, Ed. (Marcel Decker, Inc., 1967), pp. 487-488.

REFERENCES

1. S. N. Timasheff and M. J. Gorbunoff, Ann. Rev. of Biochem. 36, 13 (1967).
2. F. Bishai, E. Kuntz and L. Augenstein, Biochem. Biophys. Acta 140, 381 (1967).
3. E. Kuntz, Nature 217, 845 (1968).
4. J. Drobnik and L. Augenstein, Photochem. and Photobiol. 5, 83 (1966).
5. E. Kuntz, F. Bishai and L. Augenstein, Nature 212, 980 (1966).
6. R. S. Becker and M. Kasha, The Luminescence of Biological Systems, F. H. Johnson, Ed. (Am. Assoc. for the Advancement of Sci., 1955), p. 25[illegible].
7. S. V. Konev, Fluorescence and Phosphorescence of Proteins and Nucleic Acid, trans. by S. Udenfriend (Plenum Press, 1967), p. 100-101.
8. R. W. Cowgill, Biochem. Biophys. Acta 133, 6 (1967).
9. S. Yamane and E. A. Bovey, J. Biol. Chem. 235, 2816 (1960).
10. [illegible] Biochem. Biophys. Acta 123, 19 (1967).
11. S. V. Konev, Fluorescence and Phosphorescence of Proteins and Nucleic Acid, trans. by S. [illegible] Udenfriend (Plenum Press, 1967), Chapter [illegible].
12. R. F. Chen, in Fluorescence, Theory, Instrumentation [illegible] G. G. Guilbault, Ed. (Marcel Dekker, Inc., 1967), pp. 487-488.

THE NATURE OF THE FLAVIN TRIPLET AND A MODEL FOR BIOLOGICAL QUANTUM CONVERSION*

William E. Kurtin, Thomas A. Moore, and Pill-Soon Song*

Department of Chemistry
Texas Technological College
Lubbock, Texas 79409

INTRODUCTION

We have studied the following riboflavin (RF)-sensitized photoreaction as a model for bioquantum conversion:[1]

*Supported by the Robert A. Welch Foundation (Grant No. D-182).

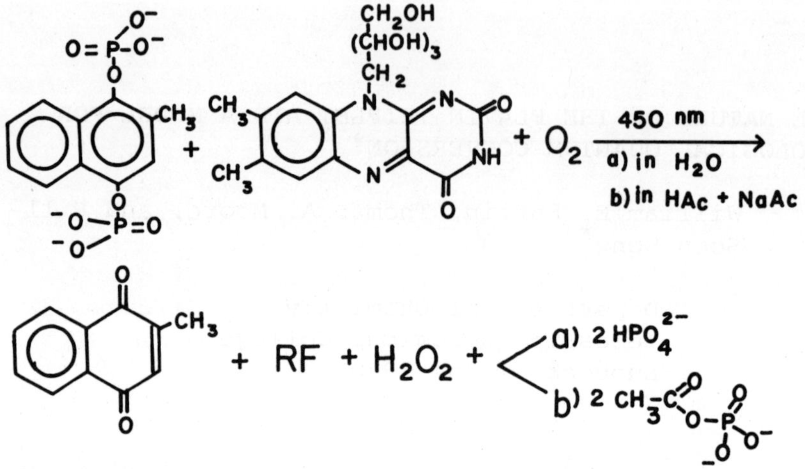

While this photodephosphorylation of menadiol diphosphate in the presence of oxygen is an interesting model for the conversion of light energy into chemical potential ("high energy" phosphates), its mechanism has not been elucidated due to the lack of definite information on the nature of the flavin excited states, particularly the phosphorescent triplet state. A direct oxidation and dephosphorylation of menadiol diphosphate by the triplet riboflavin, followed by regeneration of the oxidized flavin by O_2 was ruled out. The next possibility was the so-called "quantum ladder"[2] type mechanism for generating the flavin triplet and singlet oxygen ($^1\Delta_g$) as the reactive species. The "quantum ladder" was proposed on the basis of the claim that the phosphorescence emission of riboflavin at the 600 nm region requires the presence of oxygen. In turn, we re-examined the phosphorescence properties of flavins, and studied the details of the kinetics of the above photoreaction to correlate the spectroscopic results with photochemical data.

Flavins are complicated molecules. They are nitrogen-heteropolycyclic compounds with two carbonyl groups. In general, the lowest triplet of nitrogen-heteropolycyclics is of the $^3(\pi,\pi^*)$

type, while carbonyl compounds have $^3(n,\pi^*)$ character.[3] Thus, our aim is two-fold. First, we hope to establish the singlet-triplet intervals in riboflavin and alloxazine, since the reported emission values varied from 600-660 nm. Furthermore, the question of the oxygen requirement and the quantum ladder mechanism in the riboflavin phosphorescence process is to be resolved. The second aim is to determine whether the lowest triplet configurations of the flavin molecules are of the $^3(n,\pi^*)$ or $^3(\pi,\pi^*)$ type. A study of this type is important, since the two types of the lowest triplet configurations will give rise to different photochemical reactivities. Results from these studies will then be applied to the above model for bio-quantum conversion in order to elucidate the mechanism of the reaction involving the riboflavin triplet and oxygen.

EXPERIMENTAL

PHOSPHORESCENCE SPECTRA. The phosphorescence excitation and emission spectra were obtained on an Aminco-Bowman spectrophoto-fluorometer using the Aminco-Keirs phosphoroscope attachment. The mean lifetime was estimated from the emission decay curve traced on a time-based X-Y recorder.

PHOSPHORESCENCE POLARIZATION SPECTRA. The spectra are recorded as a function of the four different orientations of the Glan-Thompson polarizers at the exciting and emitting slits. The polarization at each wavelength may be calculated from the well-known formula of Azumi and McGlynn:[4]

$$P = \frac{I_{EE} - I_{EB}(I_{BE}/I_{BB})}{I_{EE} + I_{EB}(I_{BE}/I_{BB})}$$

where E and B refer to orientations of the polarizer in the vertical and horizontal direction, respectively. The first and second subscripts, e.g., in I_{EB}, refer to the exciting and emitting polarizers, respectively. Because of the weakness of the signal, it was necessary to repeat these measurements at least 10-15 times in order to insure reproducibility.

RESULTS AND DISCUSSION

The HMO, P-P-P SCF MO, and CNDO methods all predict the lowest singlet state of the riboflavin ring (isoalloxazine) to be a $^{1}(\pi,\pi^*)$ type.[5,6,7] A recent semiempirical calculation[8] and circular dichroism measurements[9] predict the $n \rightarrow \pi^*$ singlet to be 3.342 ev and 3.6 ev, respectively, above the ground state, which would place it above the long wavelength absorption band (2.783 ev, 445 nm) of riboflavin and within the $\pi \rightarrow \pi^*$ envelope.

The P-P-P SCF MO calculation, which includes only the π-electron system, predicted the lowest triplet state to be 1.6-1.8 ev above the ground state, depending on which model is chosen for the treatments of the 6,7-methyl groups.[11] The CNDO method yields a value greater than 2 ev for the particular geometric species of the triplet configuration.[7] It was found that the wavefunctions of the lowest triplet of the riboflavin nucleus are of π-symmetry.[7] If we take the calculated lowest $^{1}(\pi,\pi^*)$ state of 2.783 ev[6] and the lowest triplet state of 1.811 ev,[10] then, the value of the exchange integral (K_{ij}) will be 0.49 ev[+]. This

[+]The exchange integral is defined as follows: For the orbital excitation $\psi_j \leftarrow \psi_i$:

$$K_{ij} = \int\int \psi_i^*(1)\psi_j^*(2)\psi_i(2)\psi_j(1)(e^2/r_{12})d\tau_1 d\tau_2 \text{ and } {}^1E - {}^3E = 2K_{ij}:$$

value is certainly of a magnitude more characteristic of a $^1(\pi,\pi^*)$-$^3(\pi,\pi^*)$ or $^1(n,\pi^*)$-$^3(\pi,\pi^*)$ energy split than of a $^1(\pi,\pi^*)$-$^3(n,\pi^*)$ energy interval for nitrogen heterocyclics, in which the $^1(\pi,\pi^*)$ is the lowest state. Both in terms of theory[11] and experiment[12] it is well known that the former type of the singlet-triplet interval is considerably larger than the latter type. All these considerations suggest that the lowest configuration of riboflavin is a $^3(\pi,\pi^*)$ state, and the predicted triplet energies are in semi-quantitative agreement with the experimental results which are to follow. How pure is this triplet and how devoid it is of any intermixing with the $^3(n,\pi^*)$ state is open for question. It is generally known that the $^3(n,\pi^*)$ is photochemically reactive toward hydrogen abstraction and photoreduction.[13,14] Since riboflavin undergoes similar hydrogen abstractions intramolecularly,[15-18] more rigorous theoretical treatments of the flavin triplet will be helpful in determining the extent of the intermixing. An attempt in this direction is being made in our laboratory.

The singlet and triplet transition energies for alloxazine have also been calculated using the molecular orbital methods. The π-electron calculations by the P-P-P SCF MO method have been reported.[5,10] The lowest triplet state of alloxazine was predicted to be above that of riboflavin, at approximately 2.548,[10] 2.465,[10] or 2.125 ev[6] depending on the model used. This agrees reasonably with the observed value of 2.343 ev reported in this work.

Table 1 compares the results of the CNDO calculations on iso-alloxazine (riboflavin nucleus) and alloxazine.

TABLE 1: Comparison of the Lowest Triplet Configurations of Isoalloxazine and Alloxazine, as Calculated by the CNDO MO Method

Properties	Isoalloxazine	Alloxazine
Lowest singlet excited state	$^1(\pi,\pi^*)$	$^1(\pi,\pi^*)$
Symmetry of the lowest triplet wavefunctions	$^3(\pi,\pi^*)$	$^3(\pi,\pi^*)$
K (exchange integral)	∿0.49 eV (∿3,930 cm^{-1})[a]	∿0.58 eV (∿4,680 cm^{-1})[a]
Dipole moment:		
ground state	5.50 D	1.79 D
triplet state	6.08 D	2.73 D
Energy of the triplet:		
electronic	-18,335.792 eV	-18,244.505 eV
total	- 4,289.662 eV	- 4,292.008 eV

[a] From P-P-P SCF MO calculations.

The phosphorescence excitation and emission spectra of riboflavin in an ethylene glycol-water matrix (1:1, EGW) are presented in Fig. 1. One sample contained 0.05 M KI because, as will be discussed later, the emission was significantly enhanced upon addition of KI. This allowed a much more accurate spectrum to be recorded. The excitation spectrum is identical in shape with the fluorescence excitation spectrum of riboflavin, with maxima at 460, 365, and 275 nm. These values correspond very closely to those in the absorption maxima of riboflavin, even though the former values were uncorrected. The absorption maximum of riboflavin is at 445-450 nm, and the excitation maximum is obtained at 460 nm due to the fact that the maximum output of the xenon light source occurs at about this wavelength. The emission maximum occurs at 595 nm (uncorrected) or 605 nm (corrected). Both the uncorrected and corrected maxima are in complete agreement with the values obtained by Steele.[19] It was repeatedly observed that O_2 (at atmospheric pressure) did not affect the phosphorescence emission frequency or intensity significantly. Thus, it appears that O_2 has very little effect, if any, at atmospheric pressure. However, it is possible that O_2 may enhance the phosphorescence intensity at high pressures[20] since the lowest triplet of riboflavin is of $^3(\pi,\pi^*)$ character on the basis of the theoretical considerations given above and the experimental results to be discussed in this section. In any case, it is now unlikely that the "quantum ladder"[2] is in operation for the riboflavin phosphorescence emission.

The emission enhancement and decrease in the mean lifetime caused by externally added heavy atoms have been well established,[21] and are due to an increase of spin-orbit coupling. It can be seen, from Fig. 1, that the enhancement by KI is also seen in the excitation spectrum, indicating that the emission is not due to impurities. The

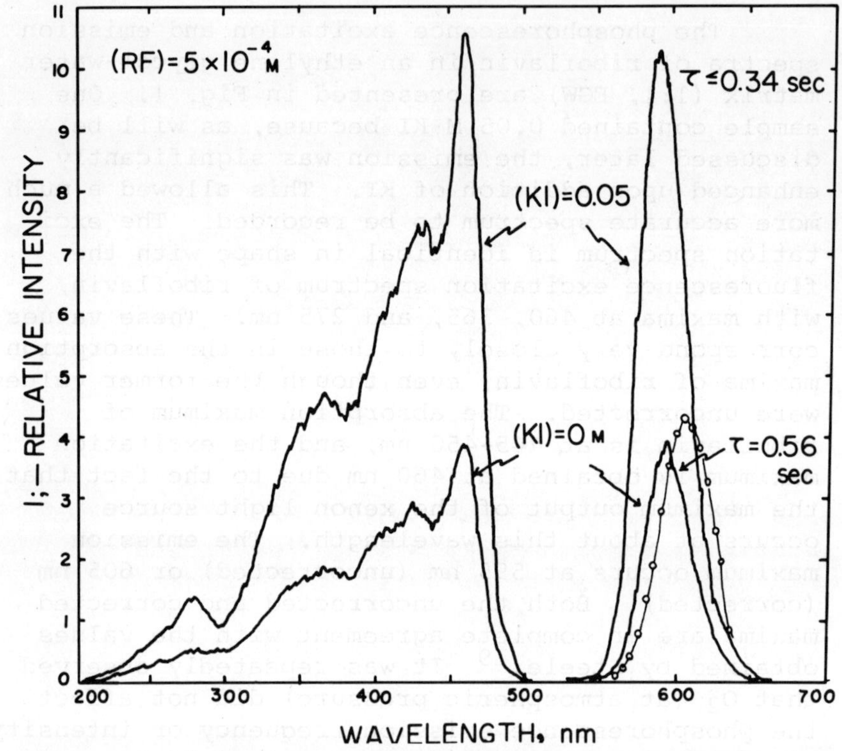

Figure 1 The phosphorescence excitation (left) and emission (right) spectra of riboflavin in an ethylene glycol-water matrix. The more intense spectra were obtained in the presence of 0.05 M KI. The corrected spectrum (-o-) is also shown.

enhancement of the emission also has practical value. As will be shown later, a somewhat improved resolution in the polarization spectra can be obtained under such conditions, since the intensified emission allows a greater purity of the monochromatic light with narrower slits.

Table 2 lists the emission maxima (corrected) in different environments. Note a gradual red shift in going from EPA (non-polar) to EGW and 1% glucose-water (polar) media. The blue shift of the emission in phosphoric acid can be explained by the protonation of riboflavin (at N_1). The Pariser-Parr-Pople MO calculations of the protonated flavin predict the hypsochromic shifts of both the absorption and phosphorescence emission bands (unpublished results). However, the diprotonated species shows a red shift with respect to the neutral flavin. It would be interesting to investigate whether the molecule in phosphoric acid (85%) at 77°K is mono- or diprotonated. In all media including 35% phosphoric acid, the emission was strongest in EGW. In general, this type of weak and structureless emission as well as the red shift is characteristic of a $^3(\pi,\pi^*)$, due to the weak spin-orbit interaction between the lowest $^1(\pi,\pi^*)$ and $^3(\pi,\pi^*)$ states. Apparently, the vibronic coupling between $^1(n,\pi^*)$ and $^1(\pi,\pi^*)$ is also not appreciable enough to induce additional spin-orbit coupling between the vibronically coupled lowest singlet with a $^3(\pi,\pi^*)$ state.

The relatively long lifetimes observed here (Fig. 1) are also characteristic of a triplet state of (π,π^*) type. However, it is possible that the $^3(\pi,\pi^*)$ and $^3(n,\pi^*)$ states of riboflavin may intermix, especially when they are closely spaced. In this case, the magnitude of the measured lifetime would not be a good indication of the true nature of the lowest triplet state. The decay of the riboflavin phosphorescence was found to be exponential. Somewhat similar spectral characteristics are observed for alloxazine; the

TABLE 2: The Emission Maxima (corrected) of Flavins in Different Matrices

Flavin	EPA	EtOH	EGW (4:1)	EGW (1:1)	Glucose (1%)	H_3PO_4
Riboflavin	600 nm (2.07 eV)	600 nm (2.07 eV)	600 nm (2.07 eV)	605 nm (2.05 eV)	610 nm (2.03 eV)	595 nm (2.08 eV)
Alloxazine	530 (2.34)	530 (2.34)	532 (2.33)	535 (2.32)		505 (2.45)
	565[a] (2.19)	560 (2.21)	560 (2.21)	565 (2.19)		520 (2.38)

[a] A shoulder at the 560-570 nm region can be seen. This shoulder becomes an apparent peak in certain matrices after spectral corrections are made.

similarity of the emission properties of riboflavin (an isoalloxazine) and alloxazine is to be expected from the comparison of the data shown in Table 1. However, the comparison of both flavins is not clear-cut, as will be discussed later.

The phosphorescence polarization spectrum of riboflavin in EGW at 77°K is presented in Fig. 2, which has been obtained from a large number of measurements of the spectra as a function of the polarizer orientation. Due to the weakness of the phosphorescence, an accurate polarization spectrum was difficult to obtain. The large number of measurements seem to confirm the reproducibility however. There was a particularly thorough examination of the negative polarization below the 575 nm region. To check this, a sample with KI was measured. The enhanced emission made it possible to use narrower slits behind the excitation monochromator and in front of the emission monochromator, increasing the accuracy and resolution of the polarization measurement. Approximately the same results were obtained. However, more negative polarization is obtained in the presence of KI. The negative polarization at 565 nm may be assigned to the 0-0 band. The polarization spectrum in the presence of 0.05 M KI was obtained from only two measurements. Currently, we are measuring the polarization spectrum at higher concentrations of KI (0.125 or 0.15 M). The results from approximately ten measurements indicate that the degree of polarization is most negative (-0.124) at 565 nm. Occasionally, more negative values have been obtained, as was the case with the spectrum in the presence of 0.05 M KI (Fig. 2). No apparent depolarization was noticed in the presence of KI (0.05 ~ 0.125 M).

Theoretically, one could expect constant polarization if only one transition is being excited. However, the non-uniform polarization is probably the result of (a) impure monochromatic excitations (b) effects of Rayleigh and Raman

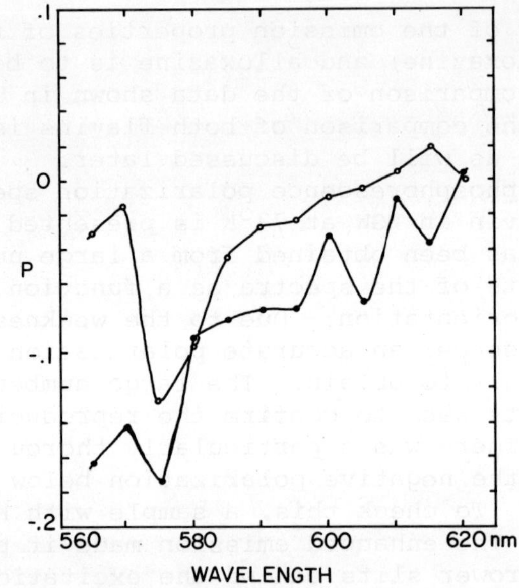

Figure 2 The phosphorescence emission polarization of riboflavin in EGW glasses in the absence (-o-) and presence (-o-) of KI (0.05 M).

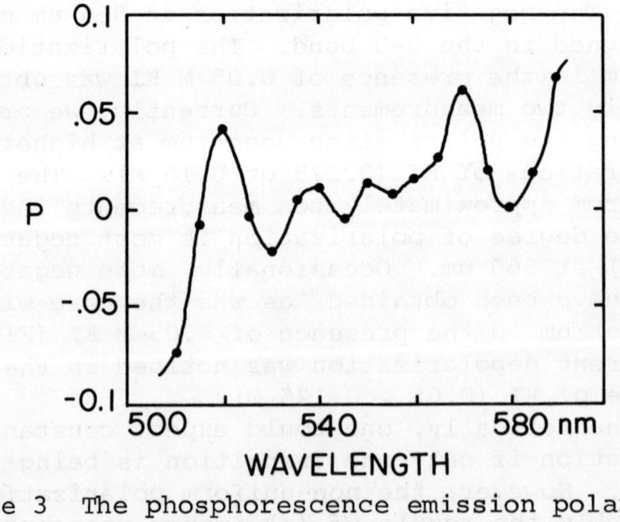

Figure 3 The phosphorescence emission polarization spectrum of alloxazine in an EGW glass in the presence of KI (0.12 M).

scattering,[22] and (c) the vibrational structure and vibronic components of the emission oscillators, as was postulated for the singlet-singlet emission.[5] Further work is needed to obtain much higher resolution of the polarization spectrum in order to carry out a vibrational analysis. This may be done in the presence of a very high concentration of KI or in an ethyl iodide matrix. Since mixing the guest (σ,π) states with as little as 4% of host states leads to phosphorescence which is predominantly borrowed from the solvent transitions,[23] the effects of different solvents on the phosphorescence polarization should also be thoroughly investigated.

The polarization, although close to zero at longer wavelengths, is negative throughout the spectrum. This result is also in keeping with the suggestion that the lowest triplet of riboflavin is a $^3(\pi,\pi^*)$ type. The transition moment for the triplet-singlet emission from a $^3(\pi,\pi^*)$ in nitrogen heterocyclics is usually oriented perpendicular to the molecular plane. This is because of the fact that in nitrogen heterocyclics the mixing singlet might be of the (n,π^*), (σ,π^*) and/or perpendicularly polarized Rydberg state, when the emitting triplet is of (π,π^*) type.[23] In the case of polyacenes the $\pi \rightarrow \pi^*$ triplet-singlet transition probability is due to spin-orbit coupling involving (σ,π) configurations. The interaction of the (π,π^*) singlets with (π,π^*) triplets contributes only 10% of the total singlet-triplet transition probability.[24] For riboflavin and probably for alloxazine, the weak emission from the lowest flavin triplets of $^3(\pi,\pi^*)$ character may be described in terms of the square of the spin-orbit matrix element, $\beta_{jj'}$:

$$\beta_{jj'} = \langle {}^1\Psi_j | H_o | {}^3\Psi_{j'} \rangle \langle {}^1\Omega | H_s | {}^3\Omega \rangle$$

where $^1\Psi$ and $^3\Psi$ are the singlet and triplet space wavefunctions, respectively, and Ω's are the corresponding spin wavefunctions. H_o and H_s represent the orbital and spin parts of the spin-orbit Hamiltonian. It turns out that the magnitude of the square of the matrix element is roughly 10^2 cm^{-1} for $(n,\pi^*)-(\pi,\pi^*)$ coupling, while $(n,\pi^*)-(n,\pi^*)$ or $(\pi,\pi^*)-(\pi,\pi^*)$ coupling is of the order of 1 cm^{-1}.[25] Since riboflavin and alloxazine correspond to the last coupling case, the weak emission as well as the ou-of-plane polarization of the emission are to be expected.

Fig. 3 shows the phosphorescence emission polarization of alloxazine, which was obtained from an average of a large number of measurements. On the basis of the negative polarization at the shorter wavelength region, the 0-0 band appears to be at about 500-505 nm. The general shape of the spectrum is quite similar to that of riboflavin. However, there definitely seems to be a more positively polarized band at 560 ~ 570 nm in alloxazine as compared to riboflavin. It is probably meaningful to note that alloxazine has a shoulder (or second peak, Table 2) at this wavelength, while riboflavin does not show any recognizable sign of a shoulder beyond 610 nm. However, riboflavin emits appreciably even beyond the 650 nm region in a 1% glucose-water cracked matrix. No polarization of the spectrum in the cracked matrix was obtained due to probable depolarizations by scattering. On the basis of the polarization data, solvent effects (Table 2), and theoretical results given above, one can propose that the lowest triplet of alloxazine has also a (π,π^*) character. Since alloxazine has both $^1(\pi,\pi^*)$ and $^1(n,\pi^*)$ states spaced closely (theoretical result shown in Fig. 5 and Ref. 8), unlike in riboflavin, there is a possibility that the alloxazine phosphorescence peaks represent structure arising from vibronic interaction between the lowest $^3(\pi,\pi^*)$ and $^3(n,\pi^*)$ states, unique in alloxazine, but not in riboflavin. Vibronic interaction between (n,π^*) and (π,π^*) states is well known.[26] In other words, such speculation is not unreasonable in view of the possibility that a $^3(n,\pi^*)$ triplet level is located between the lowest singlet (π,π^*) and triplet (π,π^*) states. However, further work is needed to analyze the alloxazine phosphorescence. The phosphorescence polarizations, decay time, and phosphorescence quantum yield of alloxazine relative to riboflavin will be determined in different solvents, and results will be reported in the future.

Preliminary results indicate that the phosphorescence quantum yield of alloxazine in EGW (2:1) matrix is approximately 12 times higher than that of riboflavin; $\phi^P_{alloxazine}/\phi^P_{riboflavin} = 11.9$. On the other hand, the fluorescence yield of riboflavin is higher than that of alloxazine; $\phi^F_{riboflavin}/\phi^F_{alloxazine} = 4.2$ at room temperature. It is suggested that the quantum yield for inter-system crossing is relatively higher in alloxazine than in riboflavin. Therefore, vibronic interactions between $^{1,3}(\pi,\pi^*)$ and $^{1,3}(n,\pi^*)$ states appear to be rather important in alloxazine. Experiments suggested above will provide further information. It may even be possible that the polarization shown in Fig. 3 is either close to zero or positive. The polarization measurements in the presence of high concentrations of KI (0.12-0.15 M) are in progress in order to check on this point.

To summarize the results given in this paper Figs. 4 and 5 contain Jablonski-type diagrams of the experimental and calculated electronic energy levels and polarizations of riboflavin and alloxazine, respectively. As can be seen, there is excellent agreement between the experimental and calculated values.

On the basis of the present work and additional kinetic data to be presented shortly,[27] we are now able to elucidate the mechanism for the photodephosphorylation of menadiol diphosphate (M) by riboflavin and oxygen.[1] The following scheme is consistent with all the data available

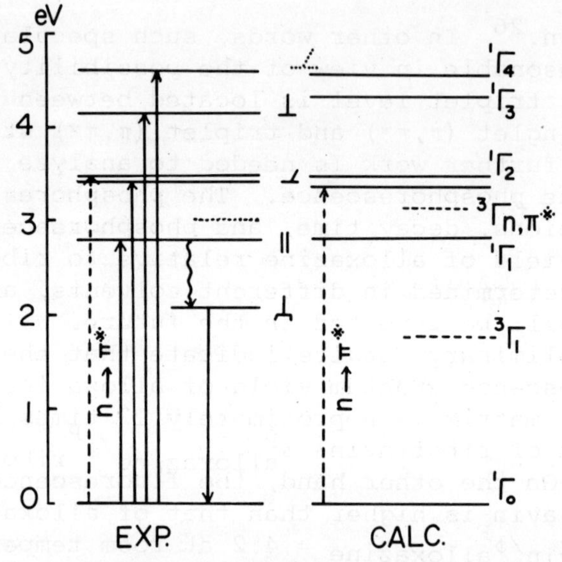

Figure 4 A Jablonski diagram for riboflavin based on available experimental data and calculations. See various sources (cited in the text) from which this diagram has been constructed. Dotted state lines represent uncertainty in the energy assignment due to lack of data. Polarizations are also indicated with the following notations: ⊥; polarized perpendicular to the molecular plane. || ; polarized along the long axis (x-axis) of the molecule. ∠; polarized along an axis between the long and short axes of the molecule. ⊥ ; polarized along the short axis of the molecule. ∠; polarized along an axis between the long and short axes, but experimental confirmation lacking. All the other polarizations above are at least qualitatively in agreement between the theoretical (absolute) and experimental emission polarizations (relative). The term values are in eV, as commonly used in spectroscopy, but dividing 1,239.81 by eV will give energies in nm.

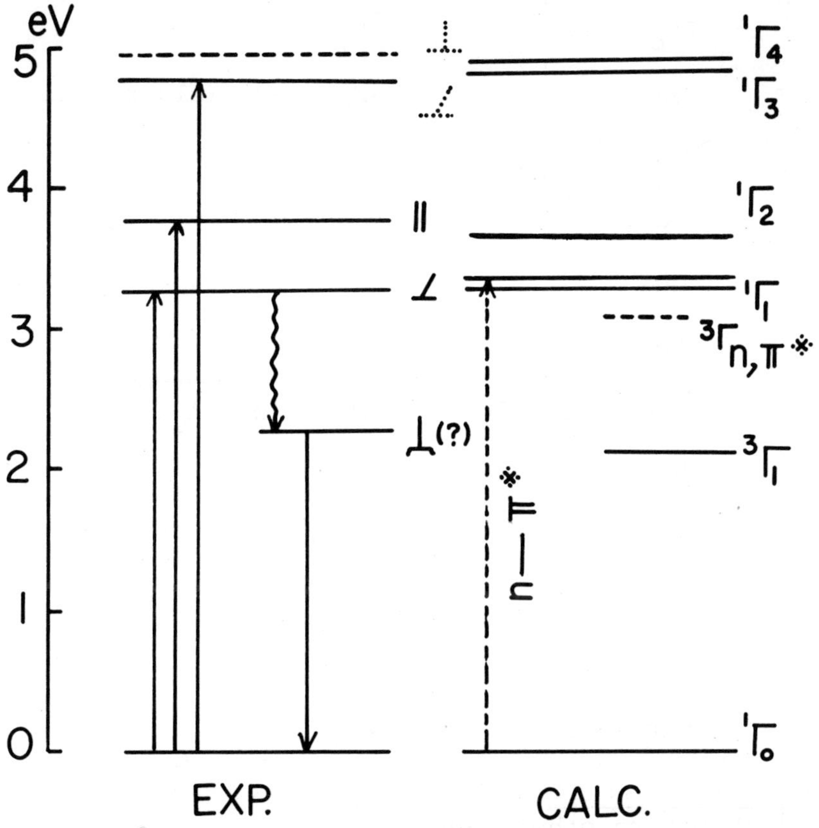

Figure 5 A Jablonski diagram (tentative) for alloxazine based on available experimental data and calculations. See the caption for Fig. 4 for notations.

in our laboratory.

$RF_o + h\nu$	$\rightarrow$	^1RF
^1RF	$\rightarrow$	$RF_o + h\nu'$ (fluorescence)
^1RF	$\rightarrow$	RF_o + heat
$^1RF + M$	$\rightarrow$	$RF_o + M$
^1RF	$\rightarrow$	^3RF (intersystem crossover)
^3RF	$\rightarrow$	RF_o + heat
$^3RF + O_2(^3\Sigma_g^-)$	$\rightarrow$	$RF_o + {}^1O_2(^1\Delta_g)$
$^1O_2 + M$	$\rightarrow$	MO_2
MO_2	$\xrightarrow[2H_2O]{}$	Products(1)
$^1O_2$	$\rightarrow$	O_2 + heat and $h\nu''$
$^1O_2 + I_n^*$	$\rightarrow$	$In \cdot O_2$
$^3RF + KI$	$\rightarrow$	$RF_o + KI$

*Inhibitors other than KI.

REFERENCES

1. P. S. Song and T. A. Moore, Photochem. Photobiol. 7, 113 (1968).
2. R. H. Steele and L. C. Cusachs, Nature 213, 800 (1967).
3. S. K. Lower and M. A. El-Sayed, Chem. Rev. 66, 199 (1966).
4. T. Azumi and S. P. McGlynn, J. Chem. Phys. 37, 2413 (1962).
5. W. E. Kurtin and P. S. Song, Photochem. Photobiol. 7, 263 (1968).
6. P. S. Song, Abstracts of Papers, Paper No. S-150, 155th American Chemical Society meeting, San Francisco, April, 1968.
7. P. S. Song, J. Phys. Chem. 72, 563 (1968).
8. P. S. Song, J. Phys. Chem. (submitted for publication).
9. D. W. Miles and D. W. Urry (to be published). The authors are grateful to Dr. Urry for making the preprint available to us prior to publication.
10. P. S. Song and W. E. Kurtin, J. Am. Chem. Soc. 89, 4248 (1967).
11. S. P. McGlynn and F. J. Smith, in Modern Quantum Chemistry, O. Sinanoglu, Ed. (Academic Press, New York, 1965), Part III, pp. 67-80.
12. R. N. Nurmukhavetov, V. G. Plotnikov, and D. N. Shigorin, Zh. Fiz. Khim (in Russian) 40, 1154 (1966).
13. A. Beckett and G. Porter, Trans. Farad. Soc. 59, 2051 (1963).
14. N. C. Yang and J. L. Murov, J. Chem. Phys. 45, 4358 (1966).
15. P. S. Song and D. E. Metzler, Photochem. Photobiol. 6, 691 (1967).
16. B. Holmström and G. Oster, J. Am. Chem. Soc. 83, 1867 (1961).
17. W. E. Kurtin, M. A. Latino, and P. S. Song, Photochem. Photobiol. 6, 247 (1967).

18. G. R. Penzer and G. K. Radda, Quart. Rev. (London), 21, 43 (1967).
19. R. H. Steele, Biochemistry 2, 529 (1963).
20. D. W. Warwick and C. H. J. Wells, Spectrochim. Acta 24A, 589 (1968).
21. S. P. McGlynn, M. J. Reynolds, G. W. Daigre, and N. D. Christodoyleas, J. Phys. Chem. 66, 2499 (1962), and references therein.
22. J. M. Price, M. Kaihara, and H. K. Howerton, Appl. Optics 1, 521 (1962).
23. (a) M. A. El-Sayed and R. G. Brewer, J. Chem. Phys. 39, 1623 (1963).
(b) S. K. Lower and M. A. El-Sayed, Chem. Rev. 66, 199 (1966).
(c) M. A. El-Sayed, Accounts Chem. Res. 1, 8 (1968).
24. V. G. Krishna and L. Goodman, J. Chem. Phys. 37, 912 (1962).
25. V. G. Plotnikov, Opt. i Spektroskopia (in Russian) 20, 735 (1966).
26. For example, see E. C. Lim and J. M. H. Yu, J. Chem. Phys. 45, 4742 (1966).
27. P. S. Song and T. A. Moore (in preparation). To be presented at the 156th American Chemical Society meeting, Atlantic City, September, 1968.

THE NATURAL FLUORESCENCE OF PROTEINS*

Robert W. Cowgill

Bowman Gray School of Medicine
Wake Forest University
Winston-Salem, North Carolina

The natural fluorescence of simple proteins in aqueous solution arises from the indole ring of tryptophan and the phenolic ring of tyrosine. Because the fluorescence yield is exquisitely sensitive to the micro-environments of these Trp and Tyr residues within or upon the surface of the protein, fluorescence is now extensively employed as an empirical measure of conformational changes. As our knowledge of these environmental effects develops, fluorescence should become an even more valuable technique for determination of the precise nature of these conformational changes. Even now a number of structural and environmental conditions are known to enhance or quench tryptophan and tyrosine fluorescence. For example, the peptide carbonyl group quenches as illustrated in Figure I for peptides of tyrosine. The fluorescence output of Tyr residues is compared to that of tyrosine itself at pH 7.0 by the ratio R_{tyr}. (An analogous term R_{trp} will be employed to compare Trp residues with the fluorescence of tryptophan at pH 7.0). Inspection of Figure I will show that the fluorescence decreased with increase in the number of peptide groups but seemed to approach a limiting range of R_{tyr} = 0.25-0.35 for most peptides larger

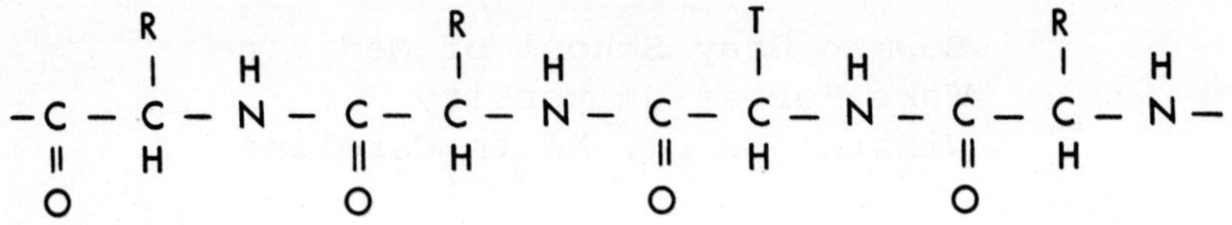

R_{tyr} = 0.3 0.4 1.0 0.55

Insulin	0.17
RNase	.07
Panc. T.I.	.08

Figure 1 Fluorescence of peptides and proteins containing tyrosine but no tryptophan.

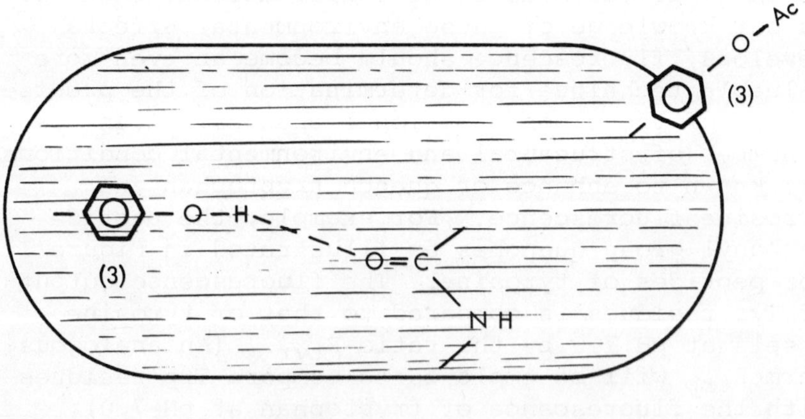

Figure 2 Schematic distribution of the exposed and buried Tyr residues of RNase A.

than a tri-peptide.[1,2] That is, fluorescence of Tyr residues was only 1/3-1/4 of that for free tyrosine because of partial quenching by the peptide carbonyl groups.

This peptide carbonyl quenching did not occur if the peptide group was in a non-polar environment[2] as would be the case for regions of a peptide chain buried within the protein interior. Also, this quenching was lost if the peptide group engaged in the hydrogen-bonding of the α-helix. These latter environmental and bonding conditions could account for fluorescence greater than the values indicated in Fig. I. However, the fluorescence often is less than would be expected solely on the basis of quenching by the peptide groups; for example, compare the low values in Fig. I for three proteins that contain tyrosine but no tryptophan. Observations such as these suggest that interactions between the fluorescence centers and specific side-chains of other amino acid residues also can quench. A number of these interactions are known, and the mechanisms of some, such as static hydrogen-bonding of phenolic groups[3] and collisional quenching by carboxylate ions,[4] are relatively clear. The mechanisms of others, such as the quenching by peptide carbonyl groups[2] and by disulfide groups,[5] are still uncertain. Despite these uncertainties, the existence of the quenching effects has been demonstrated in a sufficient number of laboratories so as to justify the provisional classification of protein Trp and Tyr residues given in Table I.

Most of these values or ranges of values of R_{trp} and R_{tyr} came from studies on peptides and simpler indole or phenol derivatives, and for several types the values have been rather arbitrarily selected.[2,12] Certainly this classification scheme is still in a preliminary stage and modifications or refinements will undoubtedly arise from its increased application to structural studies of peptides and proteins. Even in its present form

TABLE I: Classification in Terms of Fluorescence of Trp and Tyr Residues in Proteins and Polypeptides

Classification of Trp Residues:

I. Non-quenched*
   A. Buried in a hydrophobic environment (R_{trp} = 2.5 - 3.5)
   B. Exposed to an aqueous environment[7] (R_{trp} = 2.0 - 3.0)

II. Quenched by hydrated peptide carbonyl groups (R_{trp} = 0.50 - 0.75)[2]

III. Quenched by disulfide groups**[5]

IV. Quenched by ionized Tyr residues**[4,8,9]

V. Quenched by charge-transfer interaction with the basic amino acid residues.[10,11]

Classification of Tyr Residues:

I. Exposed*** and non-quenched* (R_{tyr} ∿ 1.0)[6]

II. Quenched by <u>hydrated</u> peptide carbonyl groups (R_{tyr} = 0.25 - 0.35)[2]

III. Quenched by disulfide groups**[5]

IV. Quenched by ionized Tyr residues**[4,8,9]

V. Buried in a <u>hydrophobic</u> environment and hydrogen-bonded to peptide carbonyl groups (R_{tyr} = 0.00)[3]

VI. Quenched by collision with ionized carboxylate groups**[4]

VII. Quenched by Tyr residues of type V and VI**[3]

VIII. Quenched by Trp residues**[4]

---

*Quenching by the peptide carbonyl groups being abolished by the helical conformation[4,6] or location of the peptide linkage in a hydrophobic environment.[2]

**Degree of quenching depends upon spatial location of the groups.

***Buried Tyr that have been studied are all of types V and VII.

the classification has been of help in interpretation of fluorescence changes accompanying denaturation of helical muscle proteins and globular proteins such as ribonuclease A.

Ribonuclease A (RNase A) is a small protein of known amino acid sequence. It contains six Tyr residues but no tryptophan. Therefore, we shall be concerned with the average fluorescence yield of these Tyr residues. It may be noted that two Tyr residues at positions #25 and # 73 on the peptide chain are adjacent to disulfide groups. Also, a variety of studies indicate that Tyr residues #25, #92, and #97 are buried in the interior of the protein. Solvent perturbation of the fluorescence of the exposed Tyr residues[12] or rendering these exposed residues non-fluorescent by acetylation[3] has demonstrated that all fluorescence of native RNase A came from these exposed Tyr residues. (Fig 2). To account for the non-fluorescence of the three buried Tyr residues, it was proposed that they were hydrogen-bonded to carbonyl groups. Thus the buried residues would be of the non-fluorescent type V. This approach to the study of RNase A structure was extended further by systematic denaturation and interpretation of the fluorescence changes in terms of probable alterations of the environments or bondings of the various Tyr residues. A summary of some of these findings is presented in Table II. The values calculated for quantum yield (Q), as originally published,[12] were based on a value for tyrosine (Q = 0.21)[4] that is probably too high.[13] The unambiguous values for the fluorescence ratio R_{tyr} are readily calculated from these values of Q and are valid regardless of the ultimate quantum yield of the reference compound tyrosine. Fluorescence of RNase A in 8M urea was greatly enhanced. This is consistent with the extensive loss of native structure and the exposure of all six Tyr residues to the aqueous urea. This eliminated residues of type V from further consideration. Fluorometric titration data

TABLE II: Average Fluorescence Output of the Six Tyr Residues of Ribonuclease A

State of the Ribonuclease	Calc. Q ÷ 0.21 = R	Tyr	Tentative Classification of Tyr Residues
Native	0.014	0.067	2-3 of V; 3-4 of II/III/VII
Denatured in 8M urea	0.033	0.16	3-4 of II; 2-3 of III
Denatured and the S-S bonds reduced	0.058	0.28	All 6 of type II

and the lack of a significant amount of helical structure permitted us also to eliminate all other types of residues except types II and III. The number of residues assigned to each of these two types was based in part on the observed value of R_{tyr} and those values expected for residues of these two types. (It was also based on the foreknowledge that two Tyr residues were adjacent to disulfide bonds in the peptide sequence). Reduction of the disulfide bonds gave the expected increase in R_{tyr} to 0.28 that was within the range expected if all six Tyr residues were now of type II in a completely denatured and randomly coiled structure.

This classification scheme and the measurements in terms of quantum yield or R_{tyr} provide a convenient method for following the kinetics of protein denaturation to predetermined stages. The method also has been of value for detection of unexpected stages of denaturation. For example, the denaturation of RNase A by the detergent cetyldimethylethylammonium bromide increased the ratio R_{tyr} to 0.20 rather than the value of 0.16 in solutions of urea. A number of environmental or conformation changes might have accounted for this significant difference but one, suggested by the enhanced fluorescence, was a disulfide interchange in the denatured state and a lessening of the disulfide quenching of type III residues. Experiments were designed and did confirm this supposition.[12]

The helical muscle proteins present a somewhat simpler situation than do the globular proteins. For simplicity, let us first consider rabbit muscle tropomyosin; a protein which also contains tyrosine but no tryptophan. This protein is believed to be 80-90% α-helical and to occur as a rod (20° x 450°A) formed by the spiralling of two α-helical coils about one another. Diagram I illustrates one possible arrangement of side-chains for a segment of one of the helical coils. In the

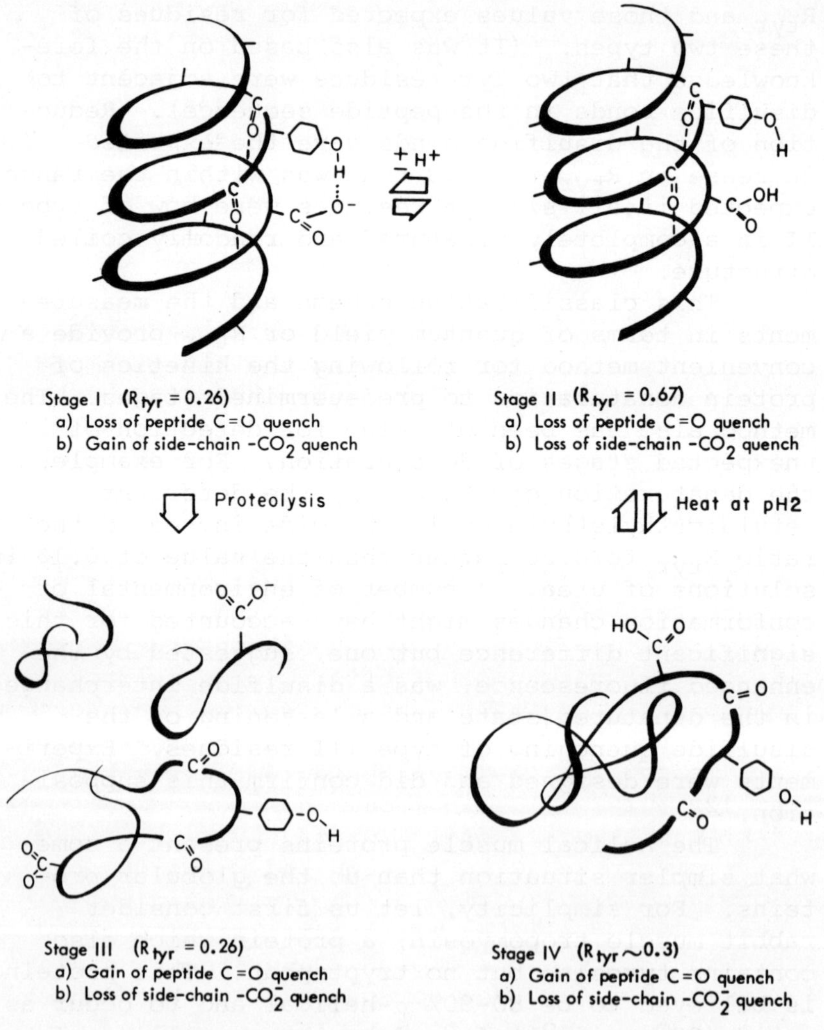

Diagram I Stages of denaturation of tropomyosin.

absence of any detectable quenching by disulfide groups (type III) and absence of buried Tyr residues that might be of non-fluorescent type V, the Tyr were essentially reduced to three types. The non-quenched (type I), those partially quenched by peptide carbonyl groups (type II), and those quenched by ionized carboxylate side-chains of Asp and Glu residues (type VI). The observed fluorescence and changes in fluorescence under various conditions all seem accountable in terms of variations in amounts of these three types of Tyr residues. Consider first the increased fluorescence from R_{tyr} = 0.26 at neutral pH (Stage I) to R_{tyr} = 0.67 at pH 2 (Stage II). This apparently does not reflect a change in conformation for ORD measurements[14] indicate that the α-helical conformation remains intact at pH 2. Instead, the lower fluorescence at neutral pH would suggest quenching by ionized carboxylate groups of Asp and Glu residues. To test this supposition, the carboxyl groups were blocked by esterification with methanol; then, the fluorescence at neutral pH rose to the same value as in acid solution. Models built with Corey-Pauling-Koltun atoms show that proteins in the helical conformation would retain Tyr and Asp or Glu residues in favorable positions for repetitive collisions and hence effective quenching if the Asp or Glu residue were one helical turn above or below the Tyr residue as depicted for Stage I. If it is assumed that Tyr residues favorably situated for this collisional quenching are non-fluorescent, then approximately 40% of the Tyr residues of tropomysin would be so situated. This is not an unreasonable fraction of the Tyr residues, for roughly 35% of all the amino acid residues of tropomyosin are Asp and Glu. Quenching by these carboxylate groups was not observed in the random coil; that is, values of R_{tyr} for the random coils in Stage III were the same at pH 2 and pH 7. This would be expected if carboxylate quenching was effective only when the interacting residues were held in fixed and favorable positions.

Consider now the effect on fluorescence by loss of the helical structure. Proteolysis with trypsin gave extensive degradation. However, the average fluorescence ratio for the mixture of randomly coiled fragments (Stage III) was the same as for Stage I. This apparently occurred because of a fortuitous counter-balancing of gain of peptide carbonyl quenching and loss of side-chain carboxylate ion quenching on transition from Stage I to Stage III. A loss of fluorescence was observed when the helical conformation was disrupted by elevated temperature, that is, by Stage II→Stage IV. Denaturation at high temperature is shown in Fig. 3. The decrease in fluorescence with increase of temperature shown by slopes of -0.8%/^{o}C or -1.0%/^{o}C is typical for peptides of tyrosine. The solid dots represent the fluorescence output as tropomyosin was heated at pH 2. The fluorescence dropped sharply above 60°, and this compares well with the transition temperature of 61° for marked loss of helical conformation by ORD measurements.[14] At 75° and higher, the slope of fluorescence change with increased temperature seemed to return to the value of -0.8%/^{o}C. If we accept these values at 75-85° as fluorescence from the randomly coiled form, a hypothetical extrapolation back to 20° with a slope of -0.8%/^{o}C would yield a value indicated by Θ. The fluorescence of Θ, which is 43% of that for helical tropomyosin at pH 2, would correspond to a value of R_{tyr} = 0.43 x 0.67 = 0.29. The latter value is well within the range of the fluorescence ratio (R_{tyr} = 0.25-0.35) for Tyr residues of type II and is consistent with a change from helix to random coil at 60-70°. The plot of similar data for paramyosin from the adductor muscle of the clam is shown in the upper portion of Fig 3. By contrast with tropomyosin, no break in the linear decrease in fluorescence with increase of temperature was noted for paramyosin. This would suggest greater stability of paramyosin and

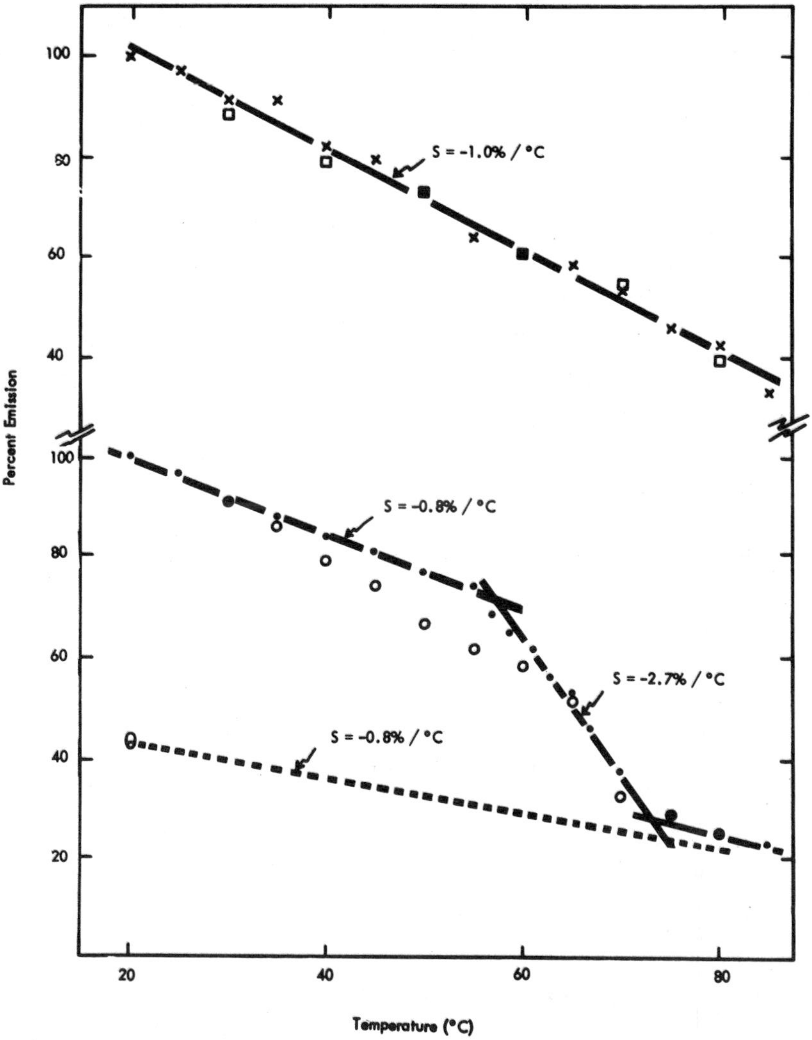

Figure 3 Effect of temperature on fluorescence of tropomyosin and paramyosin at pH 2. (See text for conditions).

retention of the helical conformation even at 85°C. The reversal of the thermal denaturation of tropomyosin by rapid decrease of temperature showed an interesting hysteresis (open circles in Fig. 3). Both this hystersis and the broad temperature range for denaturation and its reversal would suggest distinct stages in the denaturation and reformation of the helical conformation as though there were several helical segments of varying stability.

Another muscle protein, myosin, may be split by trypsin to yield as one of the products a homogeneous fraction termed light meromyosin (LMM).[15] LMM also consists of a rod formed by the intertwining of two α-helical coils. However, it differs from tropomyosin and paramyosin in composition, for it contains tryptophan as well as tyrosine (6 tryptophan and 12 tyrosine per 10^5 gm protein).[15] Despite the predominance of tyrosine over tryptophan, the observed fluorescence of LMM appeared to come entirely from the Trp residues. This is demonstrated in Fig. 4 for a comparison of emission spectra of LMM and model peptides excited by 275 mμ light that should be absorbed by and excite both Trp and Tyr residues to fluoresce; and by 295 mμ light that should be absorbed by and excite only Trp residues to fluoresce. The peaks at 275 and 295 mμ were from scatter of excitation light and may be ignored for these comparisons. Comparison of the emission spectra clearly showed a component of tyrosine fluorescence at 305 mμ in the 2:1 molar mixture of Gly-Tyr and tryptophanamide (Fig. 4e) upon excitation with 275 mμ light but the absence of the tyrosine fluorescence component for Trp-Tyr (Fig. 4c) and LMM (Fig. 4d). Similarly, activation spectra (not shown) of LMM and tryptophanamide were identical. These observations indicate that Tyr residues in LMM were not contributing to the fluorescence either directly by emission of fluorescence characteristic of Tyr residues nor indirectly by passage of energy to Trp residues for emission. This

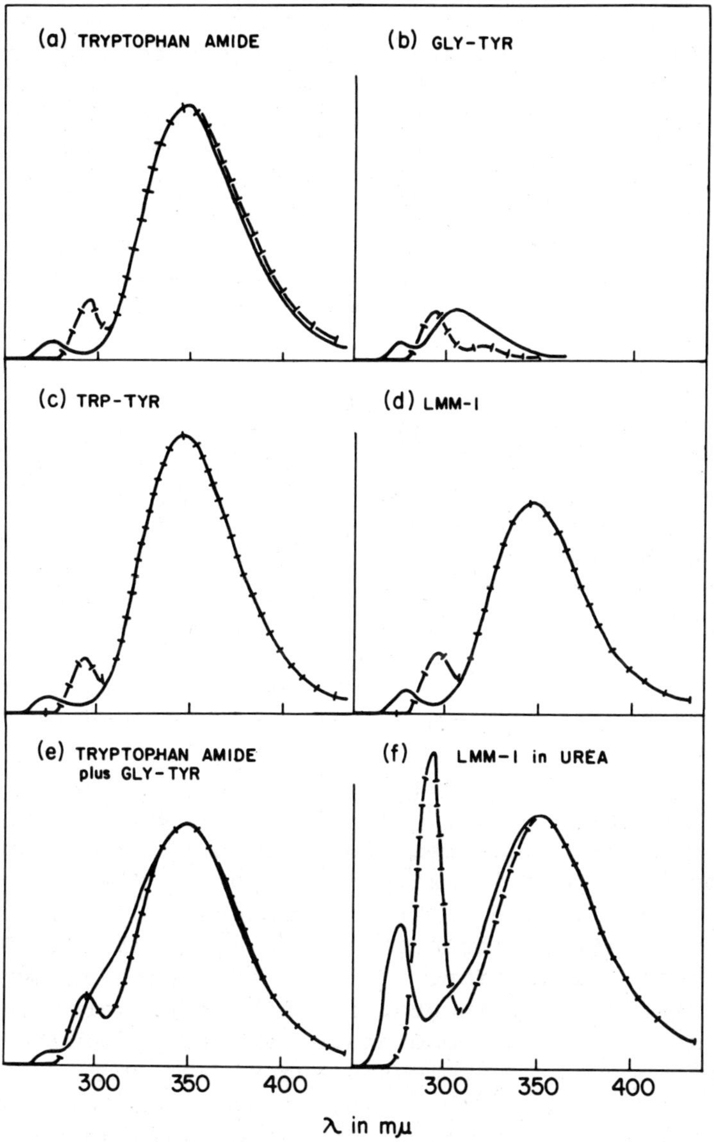

Figure 4 Emission spectra upon activation at 275 mμ (——) or 295 mμ (⊢— ⊢—) normalized to the same peak heights. All spectra were measured in aqueous solution at pH 7 and 25°C. Peaks below 300 mμ were scatter of excitation light.

peculiar lack of Tyr fluorescence is a common phenomenon in proteins that contain both tyrosine and tryptophan[4] but the fate of light absorbed by the Tyr residues (classified as type VIII) is obscure. Even though Tyr residues were non-fluorescent in LMM it seemed unsafe to assign a measured value of total fluorescence of LMM solely to Trp residues without assurance there was no energy transfer from Tyr to Trp. As a precaution, the values of R_{trp} were measured with activation by 295 mμ light that was absorbed to only an insignificant extent by Tyr residues. The situation for LMM is illustrated in Diagram II. The value of R_{trp} = 1.70 for LMM is intermediate between values of R_{trp} = 0.50-0.75 for Trp residues in randomly-coiled polypeptides (Type II) and those of R_{trp} = 2.0-3.0 for residues not quenched by peptide carbonyl groups (type IA). Because of the present uncertainty regarding these latter values, we can merely conclude that most of the Trp residues are of Type IA in helical regions but that 1-2 Trp residues must be of type II in a non-helical region and partially quenched by the peptide carbonyl groups. (No evidence could be found for disulfide quenching, i.e., type III. Also, the invariance of LMM fluorescence over the range pH 2-9 indicates no quenching occurred from its residues or carboxyl groups, either ionized or un-ionized,i.e., type V).

A decrease in Trp fluorescence by disruption of the helical structure was a critical test for this classification. Helical structure of LMM can be disrupted by incubation in neutral solutions of 5M urea at room temperature, and the products are heterogeneous protomyosin subunits[16] that exist as random coils.[17] The value of R_{trp} for the average of the Trp residues on the protomyosin subunits was 0.55. This value is just within the range selected for Trp residues of type II that are partially quenched by hydrated peptide carbonyl groups. This three-fold decrease in R_{trp} from 1.70 to 0.55 was accompanied by a small shift of the emission peak

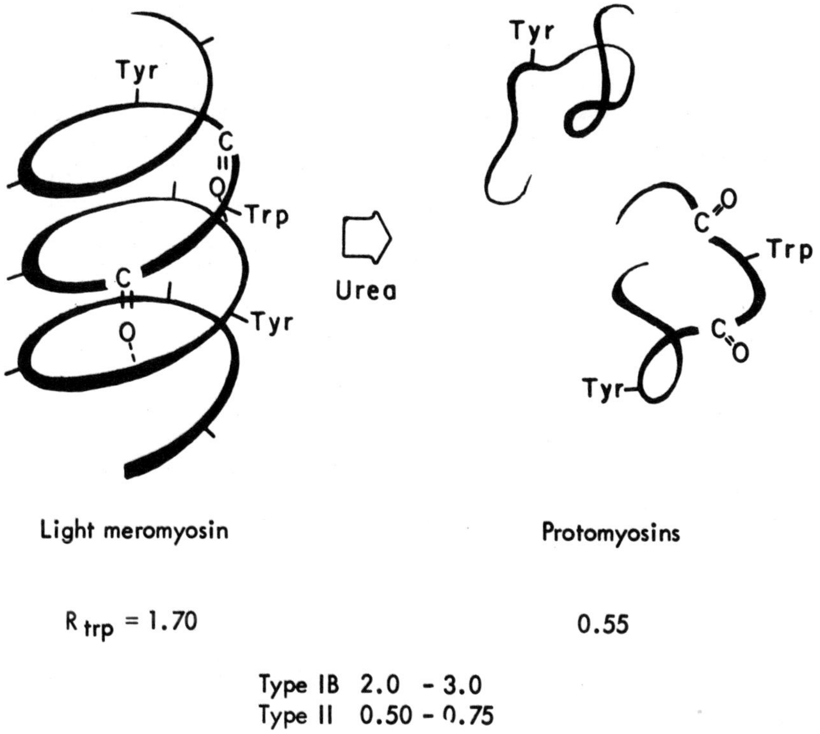

Diagram II Disruption of the helical conformation of LMM.

from 340mμ to 350 mμ and by the appearance of a shoulder on the emission peak at 305 mμ (see Fig. 4f). The appearance of fluorescence characteristic of Tyr residues probably reflects the heterogenenity of the protomyosins, some of which (as illustrated in Diagram II) may possess Tyr but no Trp residues and thus are able to emit fluorescence characteristic of tyrosine. The slight shift of the emission maximum from 340 mμ for LMM to 350 mμ for the mixture of protomyosins would suggest some Trp residues of LMM were not completely exposed to the aqueous environment. That is, a shift of the emission maximum from 350 mμ toward 300 mμ has been attributed to decreased polarity of the environment,[2,4] or change in solvation.[7]

In conclusion, this approach to the study of natural fluorescence of proteins by quantitative measurement of fluorescence output and consideration of the data in terms of the classification scheme in Table I has proved fruitful in our laboratory. In the future, the classification scheme will undoubtedly be modified and refined but even now this approach could be applied to a wide spectrum of structural studies on polypeptides and proteins.

ACKNOWLEDGEMENT

This research was supported by a U. S. Public Health Service research grant from the National Institute of General Medical Sciences.

REFERENCES

1. R. W. Cowgill, Arch. Biochem. Biophy. 100, 36 (1963).
2. R. W. Cowgill, Biochim. Biophys. Acta. 133, 6 (1967).
3. R. W. Cowgill, Biochim. Biophys. Acta. 122, 550 (1966).
4. G. Weber and F. W. J. Teale, in The Proteins, H. Neurath, Ed. (John Wiley & Sons, New York, 1965), Vol. III, Chapt. 17.
5. R. W. Cowgill, Biochim. Biophys. Actac. 140, 37 (1967).
6. R. W. Cowgill, Biochim. Biophys. Acta. (in press).
7. M. S. Walker, T. W. Bednar and R. Lumry, J. Chem. Phys. 47, 1020 (1967).
8. R. W. Cowgill, Biochim. Biophys. Acta. 94, 81 (1965).
9. H. Edelhoch, L. Brand and M. Wilchek, Biochemistry 6, 547 (1967).
10. G. D. Fasman, E. Bodenheimer and A. Pesce, J. Biol. Chem. 241, 916 (1966).
11. M. Shinitzky and R. Goldman, Europ. J. Biochem. 3, 139 (1967).
12. R. W. Cowgill, Biochim. Biophys. Acta. 120, 196 (1966).
13. R. F. Chen, Anal. Letters 1, 35 (1967).
14. C. E. Bodwell, D. M. Kominz and B. J. Duntley, Biochem, Biophys. Res. Comm. 21, 210 (1965).
15. S. Lowey and C. Cohen, J. Mol. Biol. 4, 293 (1962).
16. A. Szent-Gyorgyi and M. Borbiro, Arch. Biochem. Biophys. 60, 180 (1956).
17. D. J. Hartshorne and A. Stracher, Biochemistry 4, 1917 (1965).

DEPENDENCE OF FLUORESCENCE LIFETIMES UPON THE EXCITATION AND FLUORESCENCE SPECTRA

Richard D. Spencer, William M. Vaughan and Gregorio Weber

Department of Chemistry and Chemical Engineering
University of Illinois
Urbana, Illinois 61801

INTRODUCTION

The methods for measuring lifetimes of the excited state utilized in the past did not permit the spectral resolution of both excitation and emission. Usually a broad band of emission selected by a low-pass filter was collected. Such data as are available indicate the independence of the lifetime from the excitation wavelength, within the rather large limits of error of the methods employed. We have begun the detailed examination of the dependence of lifetime upon the excitation and fluorescence spectra using bandwidths of 6 nm for both excitation and emission. Under these

---

*This research was supported by USPH Grant GM 11223 and by a grant from the Graduate College, University of Illinois.

conditions the absolute precision of the lifetime determinations has been ± 0.05 nsec for lifetimes of 0.2 to about 5 nsec and ± 0.1 nsec for lifetimes of 5 to 20 nsec, so that in general a change of 10% in the value of the measured lifetime may be deemed significant. Our aim has been to detect the presence of ground state tautomeric forms, either intrinsic to the fluorescent molecule, or resulting from specific interactions with the solvent. It is evident that these tautomeric forms may be expected to be excited with greater probability if their own absorption spectrum exceeds the spectrum of the more prevalent species at the long wave edge of the absorption spectrum. We have therefore examined the effects of excitation in this region with particular care. Contaminating impurities would also be expected to reveal themselves with increased weight under the same circumstances, as we learned during the progress of the observation.

LIFETIME MEASUREMENTS

Fluorescence lifetimes were measured by two methods: Laser excitation at 3471 Å and use of a phase fluorometer where the wavelength of exciting light provided by a 150 watt xenon arc could be varied at will from 240 to 1,000 nm.

LASER METHOD. Fluorescence was excited by the frequency doubled output (3417 Å) of a Q-switched ruby laser (KORAD K-1QP). The fluorescence emitted at right angles to the laser path was observed by a 56-UVP photomultiplier tube after selecting a band of 1.67 nm by means of a Jarrell-Ash monochromator. The output voltage was displayed on a Fairchild 766 H/F oscilloscope and photographed with polaroid 410 film. The signal input was delayed some 200 nsec with respect to the oscilloscope triggering pulse by a length of coaxial cable between the 56-UVP and oscilloscope. The triggering pulse was provided by a second photomultiplier (RCA 1P28) which monitored the scatter of the laser light by air. (Figure 1)

The oscilloscope was calibrated to ± 1% using a 10 MHz signal prior to a series of photographs, using for the calibrating signal the same conditions used for data photographs. The photographs were analyzed for deflection versus time by means of plots on semilog paper. In this way lifetime values could be reproduced to ± 5-7%.

PHASE AND MODULATION METHOD: THEORY. The excitation of a population of fluorescent molecules at time t by sinusoidally modulated light of frequency f is described by the relation

$$I(t) = a + b\cos 2\pi ft$$

The degree of modulation of the excitation is b/a. The fluorescence emission by a homogeneous excited species with exponential decay τ is given by (Dushinsky, 1933)

$$F(t) = a + b\cos\phi\cos(2\pi ft - \phi) \qquad (1)$$

where,

$$\tan\phi = 2\pi f\tau \qquad (2)$$

The degree of modulation of the emission relative to that of the excitation is

$$M = \left(\frac{b\cos\phi}{a}\right) / \left(\frac{b}{a}\right) = \cos\phi = (1 + 4\pi^2 f^2 \tau^2)^{-\frac{1}{2}} \qquad (3)$$

Thus τ may be calculated either by measurements of the phase or of the relative modulation of the emission.

Figure 1
EQUIPMENT FOR MEASURING FLUORESCENCE DECAY BY LASER EXCITATION

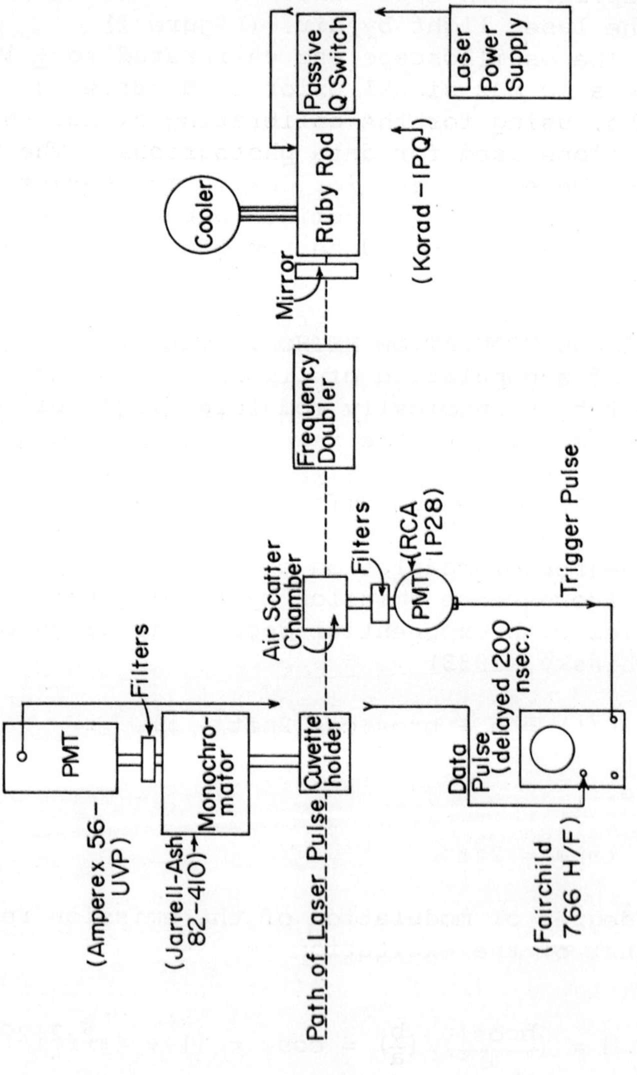

Figure 1 Block diagram of instrumentation measuring fluorescence lifetimes by laser photolysis.

Unfortunately, one cannot always assume a homogeneous emitting population. If the population is heterogeneous with respect to τ, the average value of the phase shift and the relative modulation observed are given by,

$$\overline{\tan\phi} = (\Sigma A_i \sin\phi_i \cos\phi_i)/(\Sigma A_i \cos^2\phi_i) \qquad (4)$$

$$\overline{m}^2 = (\Sigma A_i \cos^2\phi_i)^2 + (\Sigma A_i \cos\phi_i \sin\phi_i)^2 \qquad (5)$$

$$\overline{\tau}_p = \overline{\tan\phi}/2\pi f; \quad \overline{\tau}_m = \frac{1}{2\pi f}(\sqrt{(i/\overline{m}^2) - 1}) \qquad (6)$$

In the above equations ϕ_i is the phase-lag by species i and A_i is the fractional intensity. The equations show that the lifetime of a heterogeneous population measured by phase-lag is always shorter than the weighted average of the component lifetimes, whereas the lifetime measured by modulation is usually longer than the weighted average.

CROSS CORRELATION FLUOROMETER

The fluorescence lifetimes were measured on the modified Cross-correlation Phase and Modulation fluorometer previously described (Spencer and Weber, 1967). The three main features of the fluorometer are the ultrasonics light modulation technique, the cross-correlation electronics, and the phase and modulation measuring devices. A simplified block diagram of the optics and electronics is shown in Figure 2.

The ultrasonics light modulator is similar to the systems described by Debye and Sears (1932) and Bailey and Rollefson (1953). With this technique, a light beam is modulated as it passes through and perpendicular to an ultrasonic standing wave in an aqueous alcohol solution. An ultrasonic standing wave of frequency 7.1 MHz (or 14.2) modulates the light at twice the frequency, 14.2 MHz

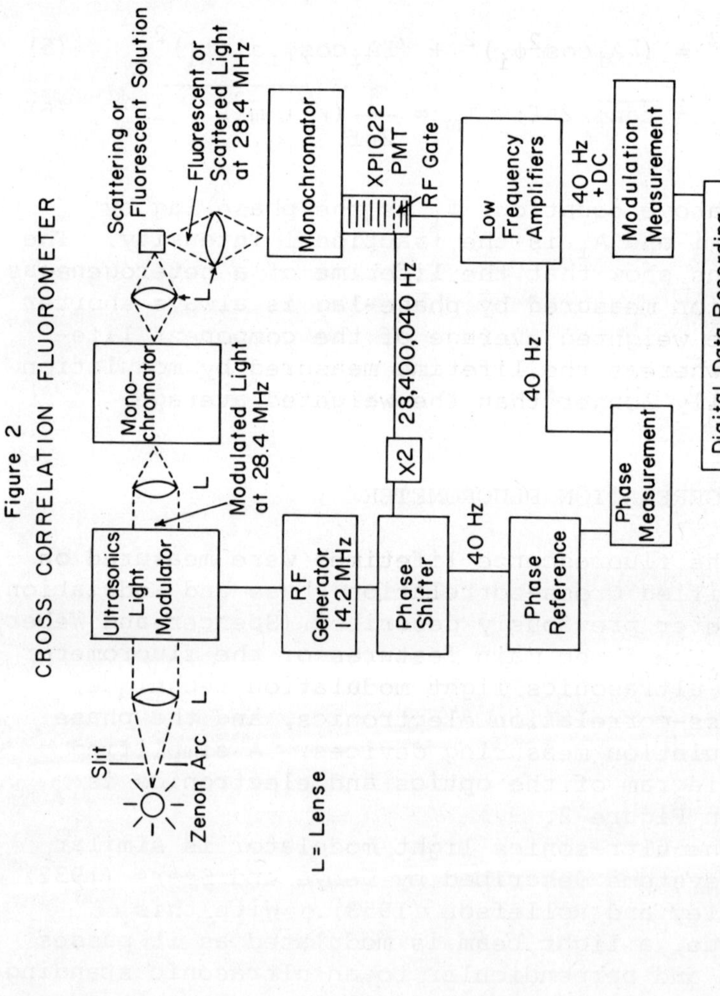

Figure 2 Simplified diagram of the Phase-Modulation Cross-Correlation Fluorometer.

(or 28.4 MHz). Two monochromators (0.25 M Jarrell-Ash, Model 82-410) select a band of exciting or fluorescent light with 6 nm bandwidth.

The modulated fluorescent emission is detected by a fast Amperex photomultiplier tube (XP1022) which has a 1.7 nsec rise time. A cross correlation technique derived from that of Birks and Little (1953) is used to transform the high frequency signal into a low frequency signal while preserving in the latter the phase and relative modulation of the former. This is accomplished by modulating the gain of the photomultiplier tube with an RF signal of 14,200,020 Hz (or 28,400,040). The unique addition of the audio signal (20 Hz) to the RF frequency (14.2 MHz) is accomplished by a Variogon Phase Shifting Transducer (Nilson Mfg. Co., Haines City, Fla.). The sum, 14,200,020 Hz is absolutely locked in frequency and in phase to the reference (Morrison (1937) and Holmes (1949)). Only the DC and the low frequency (20 Hz or 40 Hz) components of the mixing process are detected at the anode by the low frequency selective amplifier.

PHASE AND MODULATION MEASUREMENTS

Since the phase information is contained in a low frequency signal, numerical time-interval counting may be used to determine the phase difference between the exciting and the fluorescence light. We used a two channel frequency counter (Hewlett-Packard Model 5223L) which can measure time intervals to 0.01 msec. The counter is turned on by the rise of a phase reference square wave from the phase shifting transducer, and turned off by the passage through zero of the audio signal from the photomultiplier tube.

Phase measurements are made of both the light scattered by a water suspension of glycogen and the fluorescence of the sample. The phase shift in milliseconds, α, due to the fluorescence is therefore,

$$\alpha = \alpha_{fluorescence} - \alpha_{scatter}$$

or in degrees,

$$\phi = \frac{\alpha}{\text{period}} \times 360^{\circ}$$

The degree of modulation of the fluorescence is simply measured with a Ratio Digital Voltmeter (dana 5400). The DC voltage from the anode of the photomultiplier provides the denominator for the ratio DVM, and the demodulated low frequency component of the signal the numerator. Thereby, the degree of modulation of an anode signal is measured directly as,

$$\text{RATIO} = \frac{\text{AC VOLTAGE}}{\text{DC VOLTAGE}}$$

Since both the glycogen scattering solution and the fluorescent sample are measured, the degree of modulation of the fluorescence is,

$$M = \frac{\text{RATIO}_{fluorescence}}{\text{RATIO}_{scatter}}$$

The BCD (Binary Coded Decimal) output of the frequency counter and ratio voltmeter are punched on paper tape. Calculation of the average values and standard deviations of $\overline{\tau}_p$ and $\overline{\tau}_m$ are carried out from the tape by means of an IBM 1800 computer. Digital data processing by the computer greatly increases the sensitivity of the instruments by averaging a large number of observations, as well as decreasing the time required for measurement.

PERFORMANCE

The two frequencies (14.2 and 28.4 MHz) used for modulating the exciting light have enabled us to measure actual lifetimes over the range of 0.2 to 200 nanoseconds with a high degree of accuracy. We have previously shown (Spencer and Weber, 1967) by optical delay techniques and collisional quenching experiments that lifetimes measured by the phase-lag determination are accurate to $\pm$ 0.03 nanoseconds in the range of 0 to 5 nanoseconds. A 1% standard deviation for phase measurements is typical for lifetimes greater than 5 nanosec. However, the lifetimes as measured by phase become increasingly inaccurate as τ lengthens because the modulated component of the fluorescence emission decreases rapidly as the lifetimes become large compared to $1/(2\pi f)$. For example, a fluorescence emission with a lifetime of 150 nanoseconds will have only 3% modulation when excited by light sinusoidally modulated with a frequency of 28.4 MHz.

Nevertheless, by accurate measurements of the degree of modulation of the emission (equation 3) fluorescence lifetimes of 200 nanoseconds have been recorded with 1 to 2% standard deviations. The values for these long lifetimes agree within a few percent with those obtained by the single-flash laser technique described before. The agreement of the lifetime measured by phase and modulation in cases with seemingly a single fluorescent component, with $0.5 < \tau < 50$ nsec. is of the order of 1 to 3%.

RESULTS

We have examined in detail the behavior of three substances in solution: a) Flavin mononucleotide (FMN) in aqueous buffer solutions of neutral pH, b) solutions of 1-anilinonaphthalenesulfonate (ANS) in dry propanol and in 1,2-propanediol, c) pyrene butyric acid (PBA) in water or propanediol solutions.

OBSERVATIONS UPON THE FLUORESCENCE OF FMN. The observations are summarized in Tables I and II. Table I shows the constancy of the lifetime of the fluorescence emitted at 560 nm for different wavelengths of excitation. Notice that the same value is observed when the excitation falls upon the maximum of the first absorption band (450 nm) and the maximum of the second absorption band (370 nm). Thus the decay from the latter to the former preceding the emission can be no longer than two or three times the standard deviation of the observations (5.10^{-11} sec). A very slight trend towards shorter lifetimes as measured by phase τ_p and slightly longer lifetimes as measured by modulation τ_m is seen on excitation at the long wave edge of the absorption spectrum ($\lambda > 490$ nm). This is still within possible experimental errors and in any case very small. Table II shows the constancy of the lifetime within the whole of the fluorescence band when excitation is at 450 nm.

OBSERVATIONS ON 1-ANILINO-8-NAPHTHALENESULFONATE. Observations on the fluorescence lifetime of ANS in dry propanol excited at 370 nm are given in Table III, for several emission wavelengths. At a light modulation frequency of 14.2 MHz $\tau_p = 10.4$ nsec, $\tau_M = 10.8$ nsec, a difference which can hardly be considered significant. At a light modulation frequency of 28.4 MHz a very slight decrease in τ_p without apparent change in τ_M takes place. The drop in τ_p is again in the limit of significance. By contrast excitation at 436 nm (Table IV) reveals a considerable decrease in the absolute value of τ_p or τ_M as compared to the values observed on excitation at 370 nm (10.3 nsec). Moreover the

TABLE I: Lifetimes of FMN Across Absorption Bands (Fluorescence Wavelength = 560 nm)

Excitation Wavelength (nm)	Lifetimes (nsec) f = 28.4 MHz	
	Phase	Mod
370	4.64	4.74
390	4.71	-
410	4.74	-
430	4.74	-
450	4.65	4.70
470	4.64	-
490	4.56	4.67
500	4.48	4.97
510	4.50	4.98

Solvent = 0.1 M Phosphate Buffer, pH 7.
Temperature = 20°C.
Concentration = 5×10^{-5} M.

TABLE II: Lifetimes of FMN Across the Fluorescence Band (Excitation Wavelength = 450 nm)

Fluorescence Wavelength	Lifetimes (nsec) f = 28.4 MHz		f = 14.2 MNz
	Phase	Mod	Phase
470	4.45	4.94	-
490	4.59	4.80	-
500	4.72	4.70	4.69
520	4.80	4.70	4.76
540	4.81	-	-
560	4.65	4.70	-
570	4.78	4.75	4.69
590	4.69	4.87	-
610	4.95	4.98	-

Solvent = 0.1 M Phosphate Buffer, pH 7.0.
Temperature = 20°C.
Concentration = 4×10^{-5} M.

TABLE III: Lifetimes of ANS in Dry Propanol (Concentration = 1 x 10^{-4} M; Excitation Wavelength = 370 nm)

Fluorescence Wavelength	Lifetimes (nsec) f = 14.2 MHz		f = 28.4 MHz	
	Phase	Mod	Phase	Mod
420	10.3	10.9	9.7	11.4
470	10.6	10.9	10.0	11.5
560	10.3	10.9	10.3	11.3
570	10.2	10.1	9.5	10.8

TABLE IV
Excitation Wavelength = 436
Concentration = 8 x 10^{-4}

460	8.4	10.0	7.3	9.7
470	8.4	9.9	7.0	9.7
480	8.5	10.0	6.9	9.5
540	8.0	9.5	6.9	9.7
560	7.6	9.0	6.6	8.3

lifetime ($\overline{\tau}_p$) decreases steadily across the fluorescent band from 7.3 nsec (at 460 nm) to 6.6 nsec at 560 nm. In the same interval $\overline{\tau}_M$ decreases from 9.7 to 8.3 nsec. The discrepancy of the values obtained by phase and modulation reveals a significant heterogeneity in the emission. This is further confirmed by comparing the values obtained on excitation at 28.4 and 14.2 MHz modulation. In a heterogeneous system the longest lifetime would be expected to be $\overline{\tau}_M$ at 14.2 MHz and the shortest $\overline{\tau}_p$ at 28.4 in agreement with the observations.

Similar observations were carried out in solutions of ANS in 1:2 propanediol. These are summarized in Figures 3 and 4. On excitation at 370 nm the blue edge of the emission shows a significant splitting in $\overline{\tau}_p$ and $\overline{\tau}_M$, which is absent or nearly absent in propanol solutions. This finding would be consistent with the presence of two overlapping emissions, one much less intense of very short lifetime, blue shifted with respect to the predominant, longer lived emission at the longer wavelengths. On 436 nm excitation the phenomena are quite similar to those observed in dry propanol.

It is to be noticed that 1,2 propanediol cannot be freed from water with the same ease as propanol so that part of the differences between the two solvents on excitation at 370 nm could conceivably be due to the presence of residual amounts of water.

We have confirmed the heterogeneous character of the emission of ANS in propanol by measurements of the dependence of the fluorescence spectrum and the overall quantum yield upon the excitation wavelengths. In the former investigation application of the rank analysis method (Weber, 1961, Wallace and Katz, 1964) showed unmistakeably the existence of more than one component in absorption. The absolute quantum yield of the fluorescence was found to be constant with exciting wavelengths

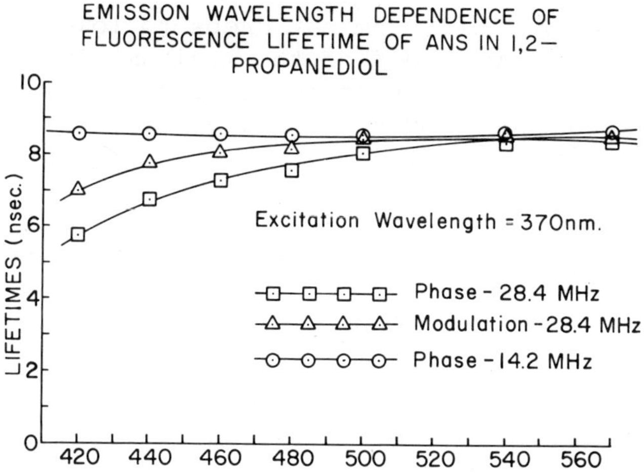

Figure 3 Dependence of lifetime of ANS in 1,2-propanediol across the fluorescence band, exciting at 370 nm.

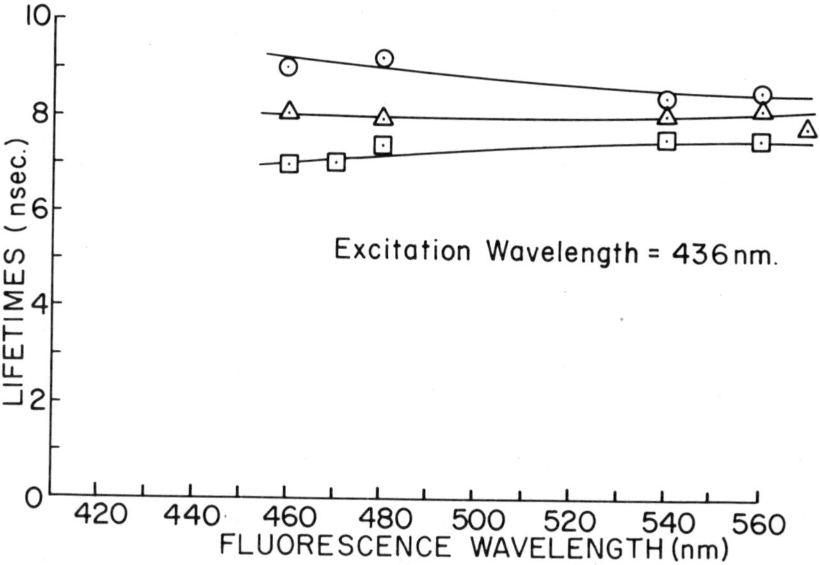

Figure 4 Dependence of lifetime of ANS in 1,2-propanediol across the fluorescence band, exciting at 436 nm.

in the region 300-400 nm but drops to lower values (at least as low as 0.5 of the maximum) in the region 400-430. It is at these wavelengths that the emission spectrum undergoes a very slight shift toward the red.

OBSERVATIONS ON PYRENE BUTYRIC ACID. The lifetime of pyrene butyric acid and of some carboxyamide derivatives is known to be on the order of 100 nsec (Knopp and Weber, 1967), while values for pyrene are several hundred nanoseconds (Birks and Dyson, 1963). These values stand in sharp contrast to the short lifetimes of 10-20 nsec observed (Knopp, 1967) when substitution in the pyrene ring is by a group capable of conjugation with the π electron system, as in the case of hydroxy-pyrene, amino pyrene and pyrene sulfonate. The long lifetime derivatives of pyrene are particularly suitable for a study by the flash excitation at 3471 Å generated by means of a ruby laser and ADP frequency doubler. The light pulse employed by us had a half width of 15-20 nsec and an energy in the neighborhood of 0.1 Joule. Because of the high fluorescence intensity the fluorescence decay over as narrow a band as desired within the emission spectrum could be followed.

When lifetimes of pyrene butyric acid in water or propanediol solutions were studied by means of either the cross correlation method or the single flash 3471 Å technique, it was evident that two decays differing in order of magnitude (approximately 200 nsec, and 10 nsec) could be observed. The laser experiments indicated that the short lived component had preferential emission at the longer wavelengths (λ > 430 nm) and was undetectable in the emission at 390 nm, while the phase shift fluorometer indicated that preferential excitation of short lived fluorescence was achieved at the long wave edge of the spectrum (approximately 365 nm). Freshly prepared solutions of pyrene butyric acid appeared free from impurities when examined by absorption spectroscopy, fluorescence spectra excited at different wavelengths and thin layer chromatography. It was concluded at first that the two emissions observed were an intrinsic property of the pyrene butyric molecule, but the observation that repeated laser flashing, moderate heating of the solutions, or simple long term standing produced an evident increase in short lived component lead us to reevaluate the possibility that the very high sensitivity of the methods used was sufficient to reveal a small amount of contamination: Consider the case of activation at 365 nm and observation at 430 nm. If an impurity of 1% of total exists having an absorption and emission spectrum displaced 10 nm to the red with respect to that of PBA, it may be calculated that when excited at 365 nm it would contribute 50% to the total emission at 430 nm if its fluorescence yield is the same as that of PBA. If the lifetime is measured by the degree of modulation, a small amount of component with $\tau \sim (1/2\pi f)$ in the presence of the bulk with $\tau >> (1/2\pi f)$ will produce a conspicuous decrease in the lifetime. Table V gives the values of $\overline{\tau}_M$ calculated when a fraction of the total intensity is due to an 8 nsec component and the complement is due to a component with τ = 195 nsec. With the expected fractional contribution of 50%, the value of $\overline{\tau}_M$ measured would be 18 or 24 nsec. This range contains the value shown in Fig. 5 for the emission at 430 nm. Since the measurements of long lifetime by $\overline{\tau}_M$ could be duplicated with $\pm$ 2 nsec, it is seen that a contribution of 1% to the total emission by the short lived compound could in principle be demonstrated. This would correspond to an impurity present as 1/50 of 1%, or 1/5,000 of the main component.

Consider on the other hand the laser measurements. The contribution of the short lived component will all appear in the first few nanoseconds

TABLE V: Calculated Effect of 8 nsec Component on Measurements of PBA Lifetimes; By Degree of Modulation

% Fractional Intensity of 8 nsec	Lifetimes 14.2 MHz	28.4 MHz
0	195	195
1	180	168
2	165	146
5	130	104
10	92	70
20	56	41
50	24	18

TABLE VI: Lifetimes of Pyrene Butyric Acid in 1,2-propanediol

Fluorescence Wavelength (nm)	Lifetimes (nsec) Laser	Modulation f = 14.2 MHz
380	197	196
390	205	195
440	193	189
460	-	179
480	188	-

Temperature = 20°C.

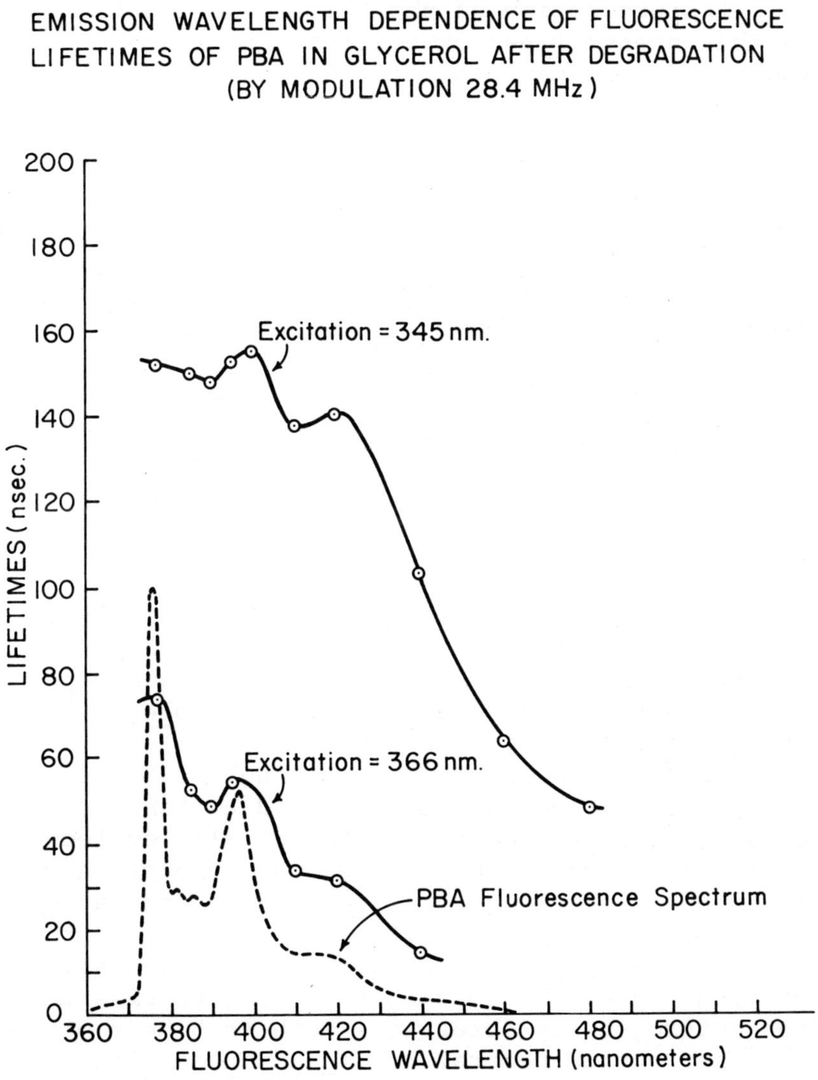

Figure 5 Dependence of lifetime of degraded PBA in glycerol across the fluorescence band, exciting at 345 nm and 366 nm.

after the flash, and a logarithmic plot of intensity against time will reveal its presence even if it is only a few percent of the total. In our case the production of short lived derivatives by the intense flash excitation contributed to the artifact because a solution was sometimes subjected to repeated flashes to adjust the amplitude of the display on the oscilloscope screen after setting a new wavelength of observation.

The above considerations indicate that very stringent criteria must be met before ascribing an observed short decay to the emission of pyrene butyric acid rather than to a small amount of ring substituted product. To decide this we systematically avoided exposure of the solutions to excessive temperature and discarded the use of solvents like glycerol in which an increase of the short lived component with time could be observed. In the use of laser flashes, exposure of the solution was limited to a single flash. In cases in which several flashes were required for intensification of the oscilloscopic traces an unexposed solution was used for each individual flash. Solutions were used immediately after preparation and discarded. By rigidly adhering to these precautions we found it possible to obtain the data shown in Fig. 6 and Table VI. These show conclusively that a single fluorescence decay time of 190 nsec is observed across the emission spectrum by excitation at all wavelengths including those at the edge of the absorption band. We have presented in detail the cause and nature of the artifact because it was not immediate to us that a new fluorescent compound created after preparation of the solutions could give rise to the heterogeneity observed. Both the laser method and the double spectral resolution used with the phase fluorometer turned out to be able to reveal amounts of impurity far smaller than expected from the usual spectroscopic techniques. Since the use of these types of method is becoming

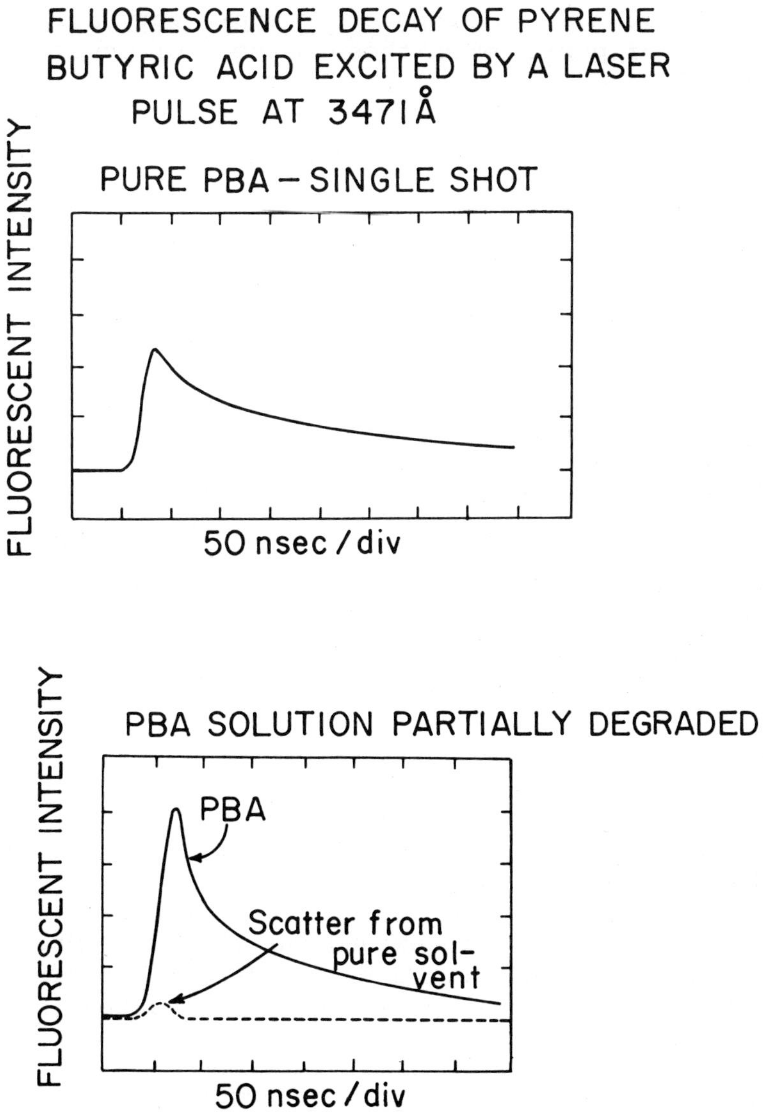

Figure 6 Sample traces of photograph obtained by laser photolysis. Notice the obvious double decay in the lower sample containing the degradation product. Extreme care in preparation yields the upper trace showing only one long decay.

general, we must be prepared to apply very strict criteria of purity when these methods of observation are used.

CONCLUSIONS

The findings in solutions of flavin mononucleotide and pyrene butyric acid show that the fluorescence lifetime is constant within a few percent across the fluorescence emission, independently of the wavelength of excitation, so that to a first approximation the emission has the simple, homogeneous character attributed to it in the past. The findings in the case of anilino naphthalene sulfonate show that considerable heterogeneity in the emission may be observed under the same circumstances. Because of the high sensitivity of the methods used to the presence of contaminants, either of a solvent or fluorophor nature, a final decision on the origin of this evident heterogeneity must await the exhaustive use of other methods to define as completely as possible the components present in the solutions.

ACKNOWLEDGEMENT

We would like to extend our thanks to Mr. Earl N. Hudson and Mr. Terry L. Pasby for their participation in the initial studies leading to this paper.

REFERENCES

1. E. A. Bailey and G. K. Rollefson, J. Chem. Phys. 21, 1315, (1953).
2. J. B. Birks, D. J. Dyson and I. H. Munro, Proc. Roy. Soc. (London), Ser. A275, 575 (1963).
3. J. B. Birks and W. A. Little, Proc. Phys. Soc. (London) A66, 921 (1953).
4. P. Debeye and F. W. Sears, Proc. Nat. Acad. Sci. 18, 409 (1932).
5. F. Dushinsky, Z. Physik. 81, 7 (1933).
6. E. A. Holmes, M. I. T. Radiation Laboratory Series Vol. 17 (Components Handbook), 288 (1949).
7. J. A. Knopp, Thesis, Dept. of Chem. and Chem. Engr., University of Illinois (1967).
8. J. A. Knopp and G. Weber, J. Biol. Chem., 239, 1415 (1967).
9. J. F. Morrison, Proc. I. R. E. 25, 1310 (1937).
10. R. D. Spencer and G. Weber, New York Acad. Sciences (in press) 1967.
11. R. M. Wallace and S. M. Katz, J. Phys. Chem., 68, 3890 (1964).
12. G. Weber, Nature 190, 27 (1961).

ELECTRONIC SPECTRA OF MOLECULES WITH NEARBY ELECTRONIC STATES*

Robin M. Hochstrasser and C. A. Marzzacco**

Department of Chemistry and Laboratory for Research on the structure of Matter
University of Pennsylvania
Philadelphia, Pennsylvania 19104

INTRODUCTION

The spectroscopy of molecules having nearby electronic states is assuming an increased importance as experimental emphasis changes from aromatic hydrocarbons to heteroaromatics and organic ketones. The presence of both $\pi\pi^*$ and $n\pi^*$ states introduces the possibility of nearby states and in order to understand the spectra one must investigate the perturbations of nearby states on one another.

---

*This research was supported by the Advanced Research Projects Agency and by a U.S. Department of Health Grant GM-12 592-03.
**Present Address: Frick Chemical Laboratories, Princeton University, Princeton, New Jersey 08541

Customarily in the molecular spectroscopy of large systems the Born-Oppenheimer approximation is assumed and apart from Herzberg-Teller vibronic coupling[1] each successive observed level in a given energy region is usually characterized by a single, and constant, electronic quantum number and a changing vibrational quantum number. This is no longer a good description when there are two or more nearby states. There is a considerable literature dealing with the case when two electronic states are formally degenerate in the fixed nucleus approximation—the Jahn-Teller effect[2]—but the experimental features that might arise if the two states are nearby have not been outlined in any simple manner.[3] The purpose of this article is to present a simplified, yet useful description of vibronic states when the electronic states are known to be relatively close. In addition we have tried to outline the more likely experimental manifestations of the vibronic interactions between the nearby states, and we have presented a summary of some new experimental results that appear to exemplify a number of these features.

THE ADIABATIC APPROXIMATION

We choose to describe the molecule in terms of the so-called[4] crude adiabatic approximation, in which the electronic eigenfunctions are first chosen at a single nuclear configuration Q_1, and are not functions of Q. By Q_1 we mean a particular set of values for the totality of vibrational coordinates $Q_a, Q_b, \ldots$. etc. With the nuclear <u>motion</u> set at zero, the zero-order eigenfunctions are given by:

$$\varepsilon_i^{(1)}|i\rangle = H_o(Q_1)\,\phi_i^{(1)}(x) = \varepsilon_i^{(1)}\phi_i^{(1)}(x) \qquad (1)$$

The complete Hamiltonian for the fixed nuclear configuration Q_1, is written as $H_o(Q_1)$. The functions $\phi_i^{(1)}(x)$ (the electronic coordinates are represented by x) are not eigenfunctions of the Hamiltonian for any fixed nuclear configuration, but we can find such a set of adiabatic functions by diagonalizing the matrix of:

$$\langle i|H_o(Q)|j\rangle \tag{2}$$

$H_o(Q)$ is the nuclear position dependent, but nuclear motion independent, Hamiltonian. The evaluation of the matrix elements can proceed by first expanding $H_o(Q)$ about the configuration Q_1, and for small displacements, ΔQ, we need only consider terms up to ΔQ^2:

$$H_o^{(1)}(Q) = H_o(Q_1) + \sum_a H_o'(Q_1)\Delta Q_a + \tfrac{1}{2}\sum_{a,b} H_o''(Q_1)\Delta Q_a \Delta Q_b \tag{3}$$

with ΔQ_a the displacement from Q_1 along the ath normal mode. We now introduce the following simplifying assumptions:

(i) There are only two electronic states that need be considered.

(ii) The two electronic wavefunctions have different symmetry.

(iii) The normal coordinates are identical in the two electronic states.

Diagonalization of the 2 x 2 matrix[2] yields for the adiabatic functions and their eigenvalues:

$$\begin{aligned}\phi_1^{(1)}(Q,x) &= \alpha(Q)|1\rangle + \beta(Q)|2\rangle \\ \phi_2^{(1)}(Q,x) &= -\beta(Q)|1\rangle + \alpha(Q)|2\rangle\end{aligned} \tag{4}$$

$$\varepsilon^{(1)}_{1,2}(Q) = \varepsilon^{(1)}_{av}(Q) \pm \tfrac{1}{2}\{\Delta\varepsilon^2_{12} + 4\left[\Sigma V_{12}(n)\Delta Q_n + \tfrac{1}{2}\Sigma V_{12}(a,b)\Delta Q_a \Delta Q_b\right]^2\}^{\frac{1}{2}}$$

$$\equiv \varepsilon^{(1)}_{av}(Q) \pm \tfrac{1}{2}|u| \qquad (5)$$

In setting down these results we have made the following definitions:

$$\Delta\varepsilon_{12} = \varepsilon_1(Q) - \varepsilon_2(Q) \qquad (6)$$

$$\sum_n V_{12}(n)\Delta Q_n = \sum_n \langle 1| \left(\frac{\partial H_o(Q)}{\partial Q_n}\right)_{Q_1} |2\rangle \Delta Q_n \qquad (7)$$

$$\sum_{s,n} V_{12}(s,n)\Delta Q_s \Delta Q_n = \sum_{s,n} \langle 1| \left(\frac{\partial^2 H_o(Q)}{\partial Q_s \partial Q_n}\right)_{Q_1} |2\rangle \Delta Q_s \Delta Q_n \qquad (8)$$

Equations (7) and (8) are the electronic integrals defining the first and second order vibronic coupling energies. The average of the diagonal energies is written as $\varepsilon^{(1)}_{av}(Q)$, and each is given by:

$$\varepsilon_i(Q) = \varepsilon^{(1)}_i + \sum_s V_{ii}(s)\Delta Q_s + \tfrac{1}{2}\sum_{a,b} V_{ii}(a,b)\Delta Q_a \Delta Q_b \qquad (9)$$

The symbols s and n are used to denote symmetric and antisymmetric nuclear displacements respectively, the symmetry being defined by the point group of the nuclear framework at Q_1. The terms $\alpha(Q)$ and $\beta(Q)$ are the eigenvectors of the matrix (2). The functions (4) and energies (5) satisfy, for small displacements from Q_1, the Schrodinger equation:

$$H_o^{(1)}(Q)\,\phi_i^{(1)}(Q,x) = \varepsilon_i^{(1)}(Q)\,\phi_i^{(1)}(Q,x) \qquad (10)$$

THE VIBRATIONAL EIGENFUNCTIONS

The vibronic states are assumed to be of the type:

$$\Psi(Q,x) = \phi_1^{(1)}(Q,x)F_\mu(Q) + \phi_2^{(1)}(Q,x)F_{\mu'}(Q) \qquad (11)$$

The functions $F_\mu(Q)$ and $F_{\mu'}(Q)$ satisfy the conventional[5] coupled equations, which in this case assume the form:

$$0 = \begin{bmatrix} \varepsilon_1^{(1)}(Q) + T_Q + \beta(Q)\sum_k \gamma_{12}(k)\nabla_k - E, & -\sum_k \gamma_{12}(k)\nabla_k \\ \sum_k \gamma_{12}(k)\nabla_k, & \varepsilon_2^{(1)}(Q) + T_Q + \beta(Q)\sum_k \gamma_{12}(k)\nabla_k - E \end{bmatrix} \begin{bmatrix} F_\mu \\ F_{\mu'} \end{bmatrix} \qquad (12)$$

The nuclear kinetic energy is written as T_Q. We have neglected second order coupling in writing equation (12) and for convenience $\Delta\varepsilon_{12}$ has been considered independent of Q, and large. This results in the vanishing of all displacement derivatives of $\alpha(Q)$ and of the 2nd derivative of $\beta(Q)$. It is not difficult to include these and higher order effects if necessary but in the present context we are most interested in the results for $\Delta\varepsilon_{12}$ larger than $\gamma_{12}(k)\Delta Q_k$ at small ΔQ_k. The vibronic coefficients are written as:

$$\gamma_{12}(k) = (\hbar^2/\Delta\varepsilon_{12})V_{12}(k) \qquad (13)$$

In this approximation $\alpha(Q) \approx 1$, $\beta(Q) \approx \Delta\varepsilon_{12}^{-1} \cdot \sum_a V_{12}(a)\Delta Q_a$.

THE POTENTIAL ENERGY SURFACES

The manner in which the electronic energy varies with the vibrational coordinates is contained in equation (5). It is convenient to choose Q_1 as the equilibrium configuration that is the same in both states. Under these conditions the $V_{ii}(k)$ terms vanish and the potential energy is harmonic except for the terms in $|\mu|$. That is

$$0 = V_{11}(k) = \langle 1| \left(\frac{\partial H_o(Q)}{\partial Q_k}\right)_{Q_o} |1\rangle$$

$$= \left[\frac{\partial}{\partial Q_k}\langle 1|H_o(Q)|1\rangle\right]_{Q_o} \tag{14}$$

$$V_{11}(a,b) = \left[\frac{\partial^2}{\partial Q_a \partial Q_b}\langle 1|H_o(Q)|1\rangle\right]_{Q_o} = f_{ab}$$

$$= \delta_{ab} f_{aa} \tag{15}$$

where f_{aa} is the harmonic force constant, and the coordinates are chosen such that f_{ab} is zero in both states unless a and b represent the same vibrational coordinate. Differentiation of equation (5) with respect to Q_k leads to the following results for each mode k.

$$\Delta Q_k \{f_{kk} \pm \frac{2V_{12}^2(k)}{|\mu|}\} = 0 \tag{16}$$

Apart from the minimum at $\Delta Q_k = 0$ we find other turning points. The <u>plus</u> state (corresponding to state 1 in equation (4)) has no other minima since the bracketted term is always positive. The <u>minus</u> state (lower energy) has symmetrically disposed minima given by equation (16), and more specifically, using equation (5), as:

$$\Delta Q_k{}^2 = \frac{V_{12}^2(k)}{f_{kk}^2} - \frac{\Delta\varepsilon_{12}^2}{4V_{12}^2(k)} \tag{17}$$

This double minimum disappears from the potential for the lower energy state whenever the following inequality holds:

$$(f_{kk}\Delta\varepsilon_{12})^{\frac{1}{2}} > 2^{-\frac{1}{2}}V_{12}(k) \tag{18}$$

INFLUENCE OF VIBRONIC COUPLING ON THE POTENTIAL ENERGY CURVES

The foregoing relationships demonstrate that two nearby electronic states, considered identical in the absence of vibronic coupling, become quite dissimilar when nuclear motions occur. The lower state adopts a double minimum potential in modes for which equation (18) is satisfied: The force constants of the lower state are decreased while those of the upper state are increased, and this occurs regardless of the inequality (18). Indeed, as anticipated, these results are just a special case of the Jahn-Teller effect, but for non-degenerate states: The two nearby states become strongly mixed as the nuclei move around the point Q_o at which we chose to define them as independent in the fixed nucleus approximation.

The force constants for low frequency vibrations of aromatic type molecules are usually about 10^5 cm^{-1} (Å)$^{-2}$. The vibronic coupling energies could be considered known from Herzberg-Teller band intensities to be in the range 10^3-10^4 cm^{-1} (Å)$^{-1}$. Thus a double minimum is expected in all molecules having states as nearby as up to ca. 1000 cm^{-1}. Some representative potential energy curves for two vibronically mixing states are shown in Figure 1.

If we consider a molecule that has only one mode (n) that may mix effectively the two electronic states, then the potentials for the two

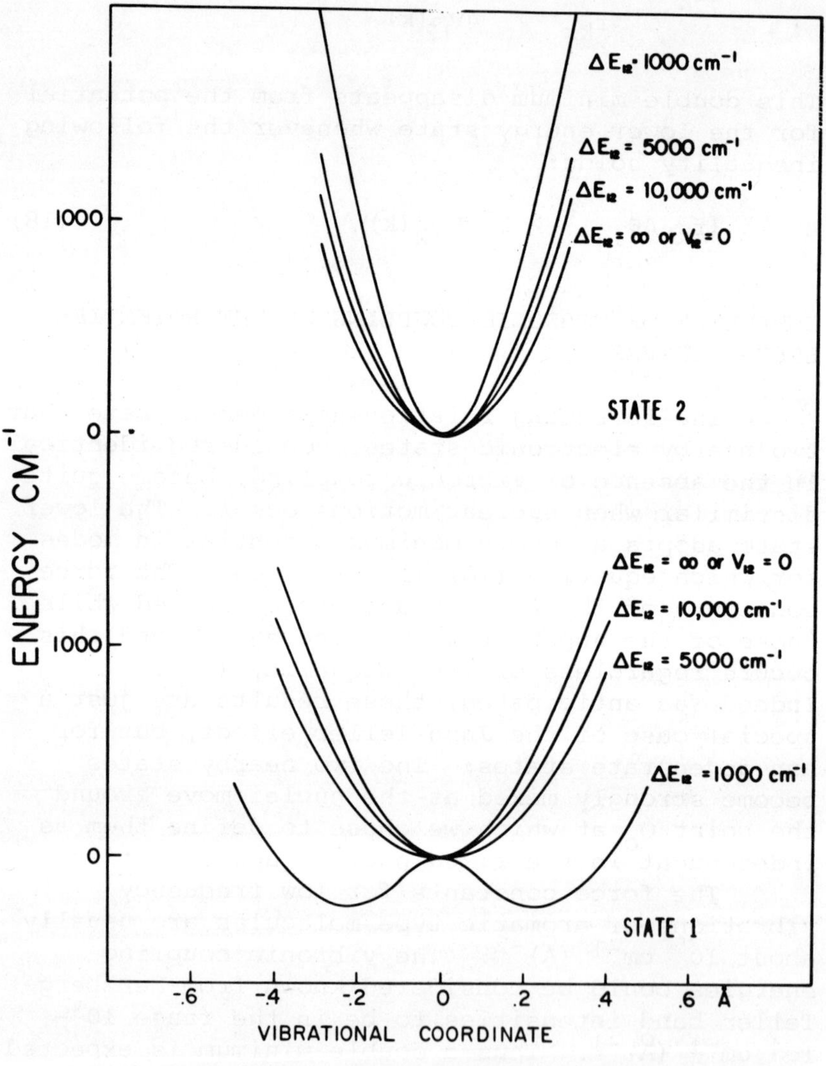

Figure 1 Calculated potential energy curves for two states having different symmetry that are coupled by non-totally symmetric nuclear displacements. The curves are drawn for a fixed vibronic interaction V_{12} (n) of 5×10^3 cm^{-1}(Å)$^{-1}$ and at various energy gaps.

states, at large $\Delta\varepsilon_{12}$, take the form:

$$\Delta\varepsilon_{12}^{(o)}(Q) = \varepsilon_{1,2}^{(o)} + \tfrac{1}{2}\sum_k{}' f_{kk}\Delta Q_k^2 + \tfrac{1}{2}\{f_{nn} \pm \frac{2V_{12}^2(n)}{\Delta\varepsilon_{12}}\}\Delta Q_n^2 \qquad (19)$$

With $\Delta\varepsilon_{12} = 10^3 \mathrm{cm}^{-1}$ and $V_{12}(n) = 3 \times 10^3 \mathrm{cm}^{-1}$ $(\text{Å})^{-1}$ the ratio of the modified force constants for the mode n is found to be 1.5:1. The corresponding effect on the vibrational frequency is smaller ($\sim$1.23:1). Thus the simplified model predicts substantial reductions in the frequencies of these vibrations on excitation to the lower energy partner of a pair of nearby states. It is hardly necessary to point out that these numerical considerations are quite approximate from a number of standpoints.

THE VIBRONIC STATES

Rather than directly solving the coupled equations (12) we chose to start with a zero-order set of vibronic functions $\Psi_{i\mu}(Q,x)$ at energies $E_{i\mu}$, for each electronic state i and vibrational quantum number μ, defined as:

$$\Psi_{i\mu}(Q,x) = \phi_i^{(1)}(Q,x)F_{i\mu}(Q) \equiv |i\mu\rangle \qquad (20)$$

where the $F_{i\mu}(Q)$ are harmonic oscillators, and are eigenfunctions of the Hamiltonian $T_Q + \langle i|H_o^{(o)}(Q)|i\rangle$ when only one electronic state is considered (i.e., $V_{12}(k) = 0$) and when an equilibrium condition is defined. The introduction of another electronic state introduces into the vibronic matrix off-diagonal elements of $H_o^{(o)}(Q)$ between states having the same and between those having different electronic quantum numbers.

INTERACTIONS BETWEEN STATES HAVING THE SAME ELECTRONIC QUANTUM NUMBER.

$$<1\mu|T_Q + H_o^{(o)}(Q)|1\nu> = E_{1\nu}\delta_{1\nu;1\mu} + \sum_{i,j}\frac{V_{12}(i)V_{12}(j)}{\Delta\varepsilon_{12}}\{<Q_iQ_j>_{\mu\nu} + \frac{\hbar}{i\Delta\varepsilon_{12}}<Q_iP_j>_{\mu\nu}\} \quad (21)$$

P_j is the momentum associated with the jth mode. Accordingly we find in the second term that vibrational levels having quantum numbers that differ by 2 units ($\mu = \nu \pm 2$) are mixed by the vibronic interaction. Again, for simplicity but not by mathematical necessity, we have assumed that there is no double minimum in the potential energy, or that:

$$|\mu| = \Delta\varepsilon_{12} + \frac{\{\sum_n V_{12}(n)\Delta Q_n\}^2}{\Delta\varepsilon_{12}} \quad (22)$$

The coupling terms in equation (21) are presumably important when there are two unsymmetric motions (i and j) that can mix the two electronic states. These cross-terms can mix vibronic states consisting of combinations of non-totally symmetric vibrations.

INTERACTIONS BETWEEN STATES HAVING DIFFERENT ELECTRONIC QUANTUM NUMBERS.

$$<1\mu|T_Q + H_o^{(o)}(Q)|2\nu> = \sum_k \frac{\hbar}{i}\left(\frac{V_{12}(k)}{\Delta\varepsilon_{12}}\right)<F_{1\mu}|P_k|F_{2\nu}> \quad (23)$$

This is the ordinary first order Herzberg-Teller coupling,[1] that mixes vibronic levels that differ in just one non-totally symmetric quantum ($\mu = \nu \pm 1$); the nth order term mixes μ with $\mu \pm 1, \ldots, \mu \pm n$.

For a specific problem one can readily diagonalize the vibronic matrix if one knows the vibronic coupling energy, and the energies of the zero-order states—neither of which are extractable from experiment by any obvious technique.

An alternative, and more direct manner of producing the vibronic eigenfunctions of the two state system would be to start in the basis (20) with the functions $F_{i\mu}(Q)$ being eigenfunctions of $T_Q + \varepsilon_i^{(o)}(Q)$. This procedure produces two zero-order sets of harmonic oscillators $F_{1\mu}(Q)$ and $F_{2\mu}(Q)$ with the different force constants given by equation (19). The matrix elements in equation (23) then have to be taken over vibrational wavefunctions having different force constants, while the integrals equation (21) assume different values in each electronic block.

It should also be remarked that the Herzberg-Teller effect is already implicit in the adiabatic functions in equation (4), and when viewed in this manner vibronic coupling—the presence of spectral false origins—does not appear to be a deviation from the zero-order Born-Oppenheimer approximation: But this depends on the choice of the adiabatic functions and on the choice of a fixed nuclear configuration, Q_1, at which vibronic transitions might be observed. It is also to be remembered that while admitting the presence of, and interactions with, another electronic state in equation (4), it becomes incorrect to assume later, say in equation (12), that the other state does not influence the results. The corrections for adiabaticity in equation (4) are in the same order of approximation as the first order deviations from Born-Oppenheimer behavior, and the two effects should be considered inseparable. It therefore seems reasonable to regard a Born-Oppenheimer condition as one in which an electronic state does not in any way experience the presence of other electronic states.

LUMINESCENCE SPECTRA

At low temperatures in condensed media the luminescence originates at the vibrationless level of the emitting (usually the lowest) state. The vibronic interactions with a nearby state modify the wavefunction for the zero-point level such that it becomes of the form:

$$\Psi_{10} = \alpha_{10;10}|10> + \sum_{\substack{\text{even}\\ n}} \beta_{10;1n}|1n> + \sum_{\substack{\text{odd}\\ n}} \gamma_{10;2n}|2n> \qquad (24)$$

Where α, β and γ are various eigenvectors of the vibronic matrix partly described above. Accordingly the emission will form progressions of non-totally symmetric vibrations, most generally displaying an intensity alternation between even and odd quanta. If the vibronic interaction becomes very strong these progressions will become longer, as should also occur if the two states become very close together. When the double minimum situation exists we expect a long progression of odd quanta (strong), and even quanta (weak). Although we have not developed the double minimum situation in detail it is relatively simple to estimate the relative intensities of $0 \rightarrow 1$, $0 \rightarrow 2$, $0 \rightarrow 3$ etc. using the adiabatic functions developed here. In the limit when the perturbations on the potential exceed the zero-point energy we have a truly bent excited state, and now the zero-point vibronic levels have a different form to those in equation (24). An important, and already well-known point about vibronic progressions is that the observation of an emission transition involving three quanta of a non-totally symmetric mode is already evidence that the potential curve along that coordinate is quite distorted: Normally we would conclude that the molecule is bent unsymmetrically in its excited state.

THE INFLUENCE OF CRYSTAL FIELDS

A molecule occupies a particular position in a crystal lattice because the intermolecular potential is minimized for that position and orientation. If the excited state of the molecule has a different electronic distribution to the ground state or if the equilibrium nuclear coordinates are not precisely the same in the two states, then there is no reason to assume that the excited molecule will assume the same position or orientation as in the ground state. This applies to mixed crystals as well as to pure crystals.

When there is a distortion (double minimum) in the electronic potential energy for the excited state then the details of the intermolecular potential may favor one configuration of the nuclei over the other. Indeed the intermolecular potential will modify the electronic potential energy variations with ΔQ, and in general will influence the double minima. In addition to this effect the crystal field will cause nearby states to shift relative to one-another, thereby lessening or increasing the vibronic interaction.

The former effect resembles the static Jahn-Teller situation, and both effects suggest that the luminescence of molecules having nearby states may be quite different in the condensed and vapor phases, and furthermore that the luminescence spectrum may vary from medium to medium in terms of its non-totally symmetric vibrational content. Possible examples of this are dibromobenzene[9] and pyrazine.

SOLVENT EFFECTS ON LUMINESCENCE SPECTRA

It is known that π,π^* states and n,π^* states frequently shift quite differently under the influence of polar solvents.[6] These solvent effects (or substituent effects for that matter) thereby introduce the possibility of bringing π,π^* and n,π^* states extremely close to one-another, and indeed much closer in a zeroth approximation than the extent of the vibronic interaction between them. It follows that the lowest state, which will be an intimate mixture of the π,π^* and n,π^* states at small values of ΔQ, should be strongly distorted in out-of-plane coordinates. This distortion will have the effect of causing long progressions of out-of-plane modes in the emission spectrum and it will also seriously influence the relative importance of radiationless transitions which are known to depend on the overlap of the vibrational wavefunctions of the combining or intercombining states.

INFLUENCE OF OTHER VIBRATIONAL MODES

In most of the foregoing we have conveniently assumed that $V_{12}(n)$ is zero for all modes except one—the vibronically active vibration. This assumption is very often realized since one mode usually dominates in the Herzberg-Teller interactions that occur in most simple aromatics. When a molecule has reasonable symmetry there are seldom more than a few modes in each symmetry type. The interactions we are discussing here have the effect of modifying the normal coordinates from our assumed zero-order forms.

If there are two or more vibrational modes for which $V_{12}(n)$ is non-zero then the results presented here are only correct at $\Delta Q = 0$, for either of the modes. The form of the potential energy curve for either of the modes is dependent on the magnitude of the displacement along the other coordinate. It follows that the set Q, assumed the same in both states as in the ground state, are not in fact normal coordinates for either of the two excited states. Equations (12) and (17)-(18) have to be modified to include interference terms between the two displacement amplitudes. If the new vibronically modified normal coordinates were obtained explicitly then the transitions between these excited states and the ground state, involving first-order non-totally symmetric modes, could once again be described in terms of a conventional Franck-Condon analysis: Such would automatically arise if the functions $F_\mu(Q)$ and $F_{\mu'}(Q)$ from equation (12) could be obtained explicitely.

An interesting application of the coupling of the motions corresponding to two non-totally symmetric modes is found through equations (21) and (23) which can be used to estimate the relative strengths of progression members to combinations. For example if $V_{12}(i)$ and $V_{12}(j)$ are both finite, the cross-terms of equation (21) give the contribution of a combination state; specifically if $|1\mu\rangle = |10\rangle$; $|1\nu\rangle = |1i_1j_1\rangle$ (i.e., one quantum each of i and j) we find:

$$\langle 10|T_Q + H_o^{(o)}(Q)|1i_1j_1\rangle =$$

$$\frac{2V_{12}(i)V_{12}(j)}{\Delta\varepsilon_{12}}\langle\overline{Q}\rangle_{01}^{2}\{1 - \frac{h\overline{\nu}_{ij}}{\Delta\varepsilon_{12}}\} \qquad (25)$$

where $\overline{\nu}_{ij}$ is a geometric mean of ith and j^{th} vibrational frequencies. The mixing of $|10\rangle$ with $|1i_2\rangle$ or $|1j_2\rangle$ (that is, two i or j quanta) includes, instead, the term $<Q^2>_{02}$. The combination bands are expected in emission from $|10>$ roughly in accordance with the Franck-Condon principle in conventional progressions, but in this case the controlling feature is the vibronic interaction.

VIBRONIC COUPLING IN THE SINGLET AND TRIPLET MANIFOLDS

To choose a set of zero-order electronic states $\phi_i^{(l)}(x)$ is by no means a clear-cut procedure. The observed vibronic energies are not usually a suitable set of zero-order energies. The wavefunctions from approximate fixed nucleus theories are not necessarily good zero-order eigenfunctions unless all the terms in the approximate Hamiltonian dominate the vibronic interactions. A particularly interesting feature of this difficulty concerns the relative magnitudes of the vibronic interactions and of the electron exchange interactions (Pauli energies) that determine the term splittings. If the vibronic interactions are included in the term scheme rather than in the level scheme the resulting vibronic states can be considerably different. In general the effect of overlooking this effect is to make the vibronic effects in singlets and triplets from the same term, more similar than would be expected from the observed $\Delta\varepsilon_{12}$ values in each manifold. In the limit of large vibronic coupling one can readily calculate almost identical vibronic effects in the singlet and triplet notwithstanding that the S_1-S_2 and T_1-T_2 separations may be observed to be quite different.

ABSORPTION SPECTRA

There are many examples from absorption spectra which illustrate the effect of a perturbation between electronic states. A comparison of the low resolution vapor spectra of pyridine and 2,6-dichloropyridine is shown in Figure 2. In pyridine the lowest $^1\pi,\pi^*$ state lies 3600 cm^{-1} above the lowest $^1n,\pi^*$ state.[7] Vibronic transitions to the $^1n,\pi^*$ state are sharp and show rotational fine structure under high resolution. The π,π^* state on the other hand exhibits a rather diffuse spectrum. Upon 2,6-dichloro substitution, the $^1\pi,\pi^*$ state red shifts by 2200 cm^{-1}, an amount similar to the 1900 cm^{-1} red shift observed for the $^1\pi,\pi^*$ state of 1,3-dichlorobenzene relative to benzene. Since the $^1n,\pi^*$ state of 2,6-dichloropyridine is expected to be blue shifted relative to that of pyridine, it is likely that the ordering of the $^1n,\pi^*$ and $^1\pi,\pi^*$ states in 2,6-dichloropyridine is opposite to that in pyridine.

We believe that the broadness of the $\pi^* \leftarrow \pi$ transition in pyridine results from a vibronic perturbation of the π,π^* state with the vibrational electronic levels of the n,π^* state. The appearance of the sharp π,π^* state in the 2,6-dichloropyridine is an experimental verification that there is no n,π^* state below the π,π^* state.

A second example of an n,π^* - π,π^* perturbation is the singlet-triplet spectra of substituted pyrazine crystals. In pyrazine the lowest triplet state has been assigned $^3B_{3u}(n,\pi^*)$.[2] A $^3B_{1u}(\pi,\pi^*)$ state, the benzene analogue, is expected to be located in the same energy region. The $\pi^* \leftarrow n$ transition begins at 3800 Å with sharp bands of about 1 cm^{-1} width and the spectrum shows a sudden broadening at 3600 Å. We believe that this broadening is due to a perturbation between the vibronic levels of the $^3n,\pi^*$ state and those of a $^3\pi,\pi^*$ state which lie in this energy region. The spectra are shown in Figure 3.[9,10]

In 2,6-dimethylpyrazine the $^3n,\pi^*$ state is seen to blue shift relative to benzene. The π,π^* states of dimethylpyrazine are expected to be red shifted relative to pyrazine. Therefore the

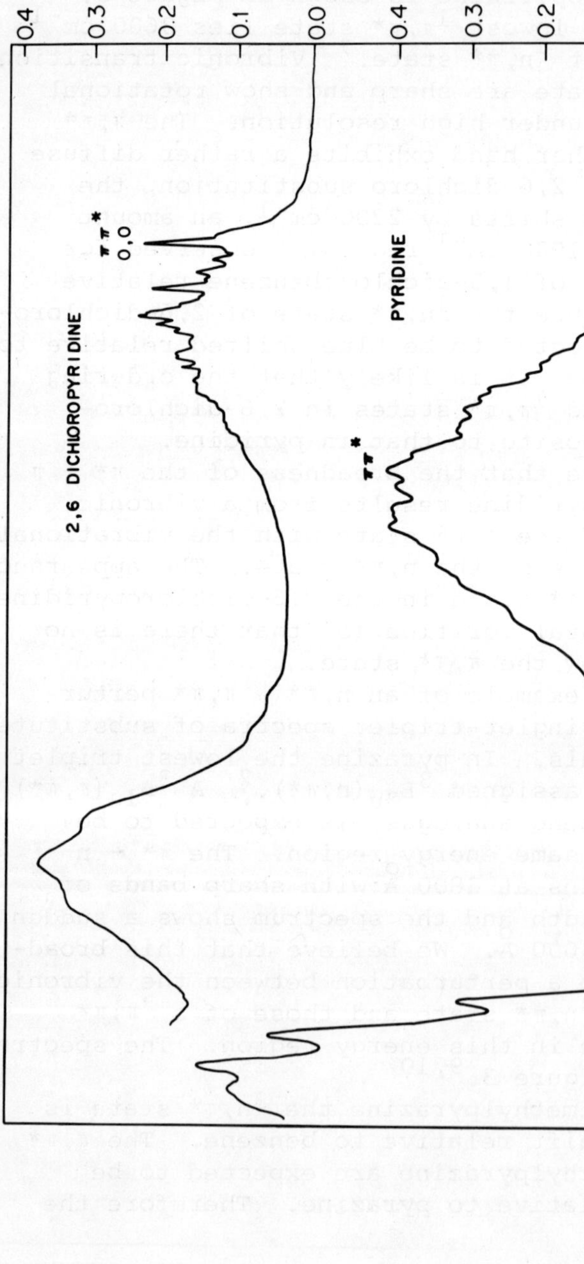

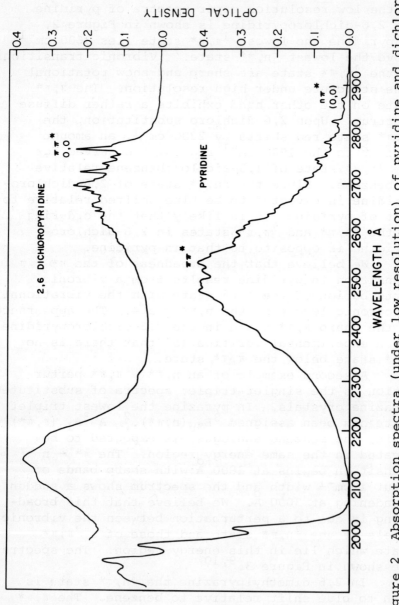

Figure 2 Absorption spectra (under low resolution) of pyridine and dichloro-pyridine vapors.

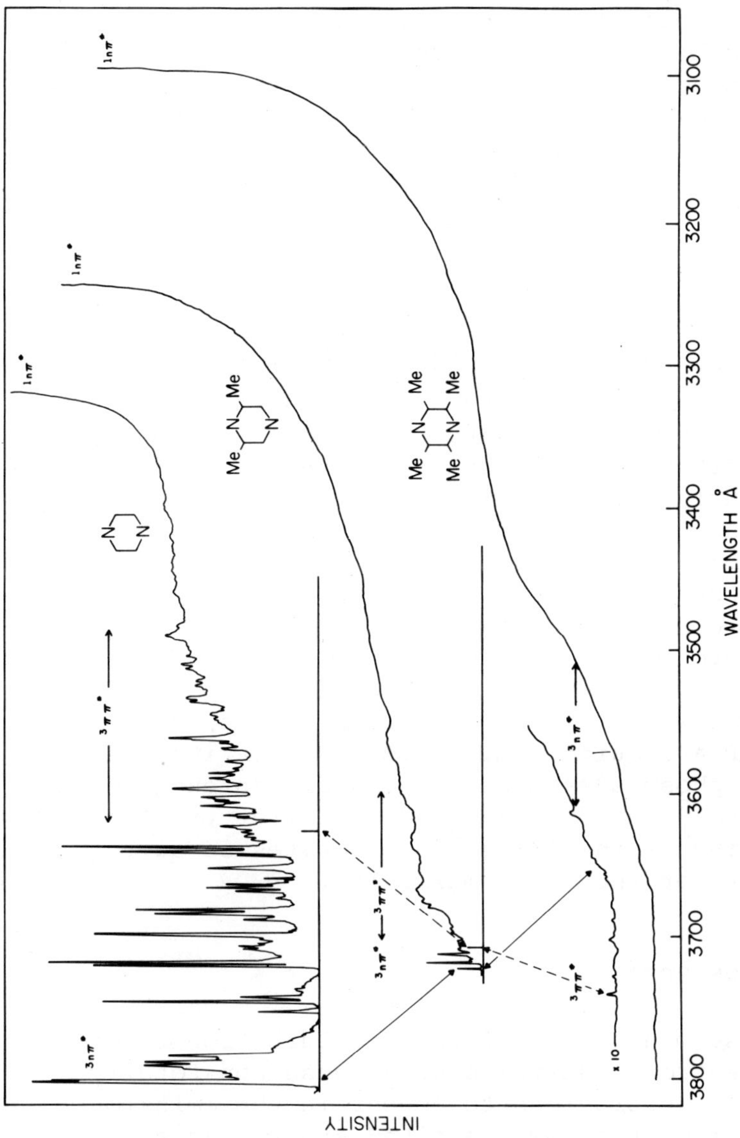

Figure 3 Absorption spectra (crystals at 4.2^{o}K) of pyrazine, dimethylpyrazine and tetramethylpyrazine. The suspected positions of states identified by perturbations are shown by arrows.

$^3n,\pi^*$ and $^3\pi,\pi^*$ states of 2,6-dimethylpyrazine should be much closer together than in pyrazine. The singlet-triplet $\pi^* \leftarrow n$ transition of dimethylpyrazine begins with very sharp bands that severely broaden beyond 50 cm^{-1} from the origin. The broadening is so drastic that it is difficult to discern even the Franck-Condon pattern of vibronic levels in the transition. Again the loss of structure in the higher energy portion of the spectrum is attributed to a perturbation on the $^3n,\pi^*$ state by a $^3\pi,\pi^*$ state.

Tetramethylpyrazine (T.M.P.) crystals of comparable thickness to those above show only a diffuse spectrum i.e., one that is essentially devoid of vibrational structure. With much thicker samples a new weak sharp absorption system is observed. This sharp transition is two orders of magnitude weaker than the transition and is apparently due to a $\pi^* \leftarrow \pi$ transition. Thus the $^3n,\pi^*$ and $^3\pi,\pi^*$ states have inverted due to the tetramethyl substitution. This result is in agreement with recent E.S.R. work by Vincent[11] and is consistent with the considerably longer phosphorescence lifetime observed for T.M.P. compared with pyrazine. The relative positions of the lowest $^3\pi,\pi^*$ states of pyrazine, 2,6-DMP and TMP are quite similar to the relative positions of the phosphorescence origins of benzene[12], m-xylene[13] and durene.[14] The singlet triplet splitting of the lowest $^3n,\pi^*$ states is quite similar for the three molecules.

EMISSION SPECTRA

As mentioned before a perturbation between two electronic states should cause non-totally symmetric vibrations to appear in the emission spectrum of the lower excited state. As an illustration of this we present the emission spectrum of pyrazine. The complete emission spectrum of pyrazine in benzene is shown in Figure 4. Since these spectra were taken at 4.2°K, the emission must be occurring from the vibrationless level of the singlet and triplet n,π* states.

The gross features of the fluorescence and phosphorescence spectra are similar. The totally symmetric modes ν_{6a} and ν_{9a} are most prominent in both spectra.[15] In the fluorescence spectrum one quantum of the 930 cm^{-1} b_{1g}, ν_{10a}[16] mode appears with considerable intensity. This mode is probably short axis polarized and due to a vibronic mixing of the $^1B_{3u}(n,\pi^*)$ state and the $^1B_{2u}(\pi,\pi^*)$ state. It does not appear in the phosphorescence spectrum because the $^3B_{2u}(\pi,\pi^*) \leftarrow {}^1A_g$ transition has little intensity relative to $^3B_{3u}(n,\pi^*) \leftarrow {}^1A_g$. Twice this frequency, however, appears in both the fluorescence and phosphorescence spectra. We believe that this observation is a result of the vibronic perturbation of the $B_{3u}(n,\pi^*)$ state by the $B_{2u}(\pi,\pi^*)$ state as described in the beginning of this paper. It is important to remember that the appearance of 2 x 930 cm^{-1} is not the result of a vibronic borrowing. It appears because the interaction between the $^3B_{3u}(n,\pi^*)$ and $^3B_{2u}(\pi,\pi^*)$ states causes the potential energy surfaces along b_{1g} normal coordinates to distort. This distortion results in a redistribution of the Franck-Condon intensity into these non-totally symmetric modes: i.e. the force constant of the lower state is modified.

There is another prominent non-totally symmetric mode present in the phosphorescence spectrum. This is the 752 cm^{-1} ν_5, b_{2g}[16] mode which mixes the $^3B_{3u}(n,\pi^*)$ state with the $^3B_{1u}(\pi,\pi^*)$ state. The 752 cm^{-1} band is weaker than the 2 x 752 cm^{-1} band in the phosphorescence spectrum. In the fluorescence spectrum the 752 cm^{-1} band is very weak and 2 x 752 cm^{-1} is absent. Since the appearance of 2 x 752 cm^{-1} is due to a vibronic perturbation between the B_{3u} and B_{1u} states one would expect such a perturbation to be stronger

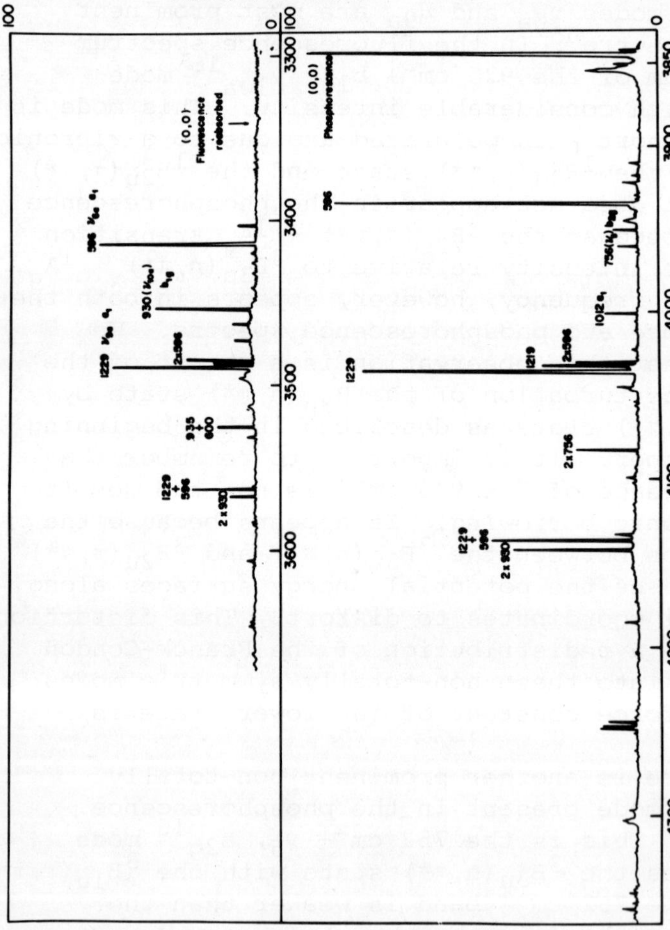

Figure 4 Total emission spectrum (upper, fluorescence; lower, phosphorescence) of pyrazine in benzene at 4.2°K.

in the triplet manifold than in the singlet manifold. This is because these states are much closer in energy in the triplet manifold.

If the above interpretation is correct, one would expect a solvent effect on the luminescence spectrum of pyrazine. It is known that n,π^* and π,π^* states often shift differently in halogenated solvent. We have taken the phosphorescence spectrum of pyrazine in p-dichlorobenzene and found that the $^3n,\pi^*$ state shows a 600 cm^{-1} blue shift relative to the benzene host. The $^3\pi,\pi^*$ states of pyrazine are expected to be shifted in the opposite direction. It is therefore likely that the gaps between the n,π^* state and the two lowest $^3\pi,\pi^*$ states are considerably reduced in dichlorobenzene. The emission spectrum of pyrazine in p-dichlorobenzene (Figure 5) shows considerably more intensity in the b_{1g} and b_{2g} modes which are responsible for the mixing of the n,π^* state with the low energy π,π^* states. There is an intensity alternation in these modes with the even quanta being stronger. It is therefore likely that in this solvent the potential energy has a double minimum along these two normal coordinates.

We have measured the phosphorescence lifetime of pyrazine in benzene and in dichlorobenzene and have found no difference. This is consistent with the interpretation of this effect as a vibronic perturbation but not an intensity borrowing process.

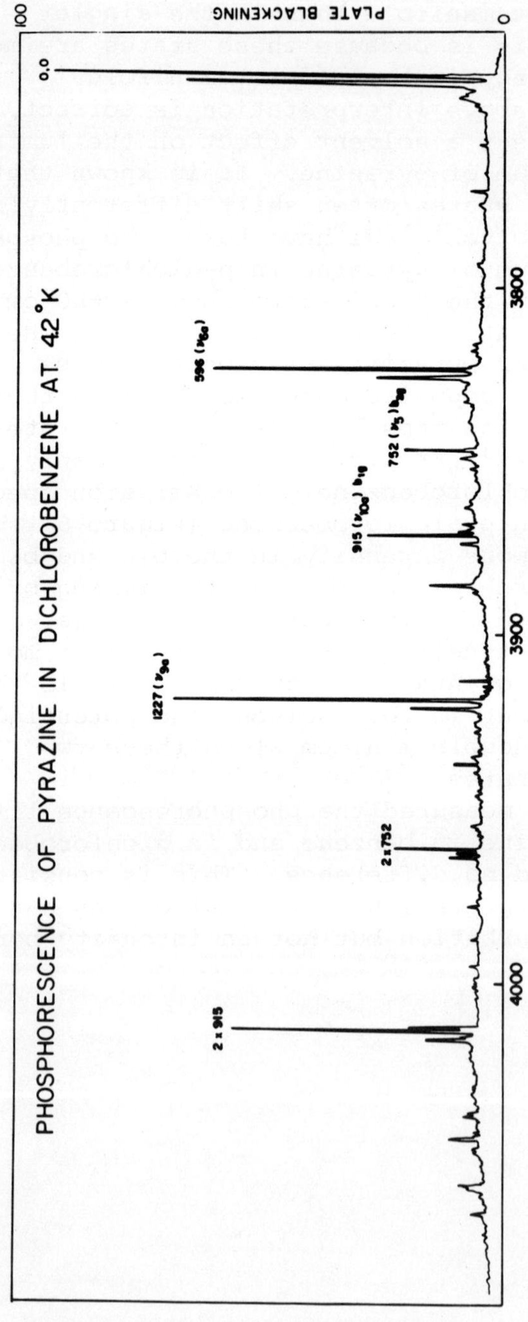

Figure 5 Phosphorescence spectrum of pyrazine in dichlorobenzene at 4.2°K.

REFERENCES

1. G. Herzberg and E. Teller, Z. Physik. Chem. B21, 410 (1933).
2. (a) H. A. Jahn and E. Teller, Proc. Roy. Soc. 161A, 220 (1937).
   (b) W. Moffitt and A. D. Liehr, Phys. Rev. 106, 1195 (1957).
   (c) W. Moffitt and W. Thorson, Phys. Rev. 108, 1251 (1957).
   (d) A. D. Liehr, J. Phys. Chem. 67, 389 (1963).
   (e) H. C. Longuet-Higgins, U. Opik, M. H. L. Pryce, and R. A. Sack, Proc. Roy. Soc. 244A, 1 (1958).
   (f) G. Herzberg, Electronic Spectra of Polyatomic Molecules (D. Van Nostrand Co. Inc., 1966), Chapt. 1, and references therein.
3. The vibronic interactions, via e_{2g} modes, between the E_{1u} and B_{2u} states of benzene provides a theoretical example of pseudo-Jahn-Teller coupling that has been treated in the literature: A. D. Liehr, Z. Naturfor. 16, 641 (1961); J. H. van der Waals, A. M. D. Berghuis, and M. S. de Groot, Mol. Phys. 13, 301 (1967).
4. H. C. Longuet-Higgins, Advances in Spectroscopy, 2, 429 (1961).
5. M. Born and K. Huang, Dynamical Theory of Crystal Lattices (Oxford University Press, 1966), Appendix VIII, p. 406.
6. M. Kasha, Disc. Farad. Soc. 9, 14 (1950).
7. K. K. Innes, J. P. Byrne and I. G. Ross, J. Mol. Spectry. 22, 125 (1967).
8. L. Goodman and M. Kasha, J. Mol. Spectry. 2, 58 (1958).
9. R. M. Hochstrasser and C. Marzzacco, J. Chem. Phys. 49, 000 (1968).
10. R. M. Hochstrasser, Accounts of Chemical Research 1, August (1968).

11. J. S. Vincent, J. Chem. Phys. 47, 1830 (1967).
12. G. N. Lewis and M. Kasha, J. Amer. Chem. Soc. 66, 2100 (1944).
13. L. A. Blackwell, Y. Kanda and H. Sponer, J. Chem. Phys. 32, 1465 (1960).
14. Y. Kanda and H. Sponer, J. Chem. Phys. 40, 778 (1964).
15. R. C. Lord, A. L. Marston and J. A. Miller, Spectrochim. Acta, 9, 113 (1957).
16. E. F. Zalewski, Ph.D. thesis, University of Chicago, 1968. (We are indebted to Dr. Zalewski and Professor D. S. McClure for discussions of this work prior to its publication).

BORN-OPPENHEIMER APPROACH TO THE STUDY OF THE VIBRONIC STRUCTURE OF DIMERS

R. Lefebvre and M. Garcia-Sucre*

Laboratoire de Photophysique Moléculaire
Faculté des Sciences
Orsay, France

I. INTRODUCTION

A molecular dimer is a system with two equivalent parts interacting weakly enough for their electronic excitations to retain some signification. The near degeneracy of the electronic levels which may result from this situation is an indication that a Born-Oppenheimer product wave-function[1] (that is to say an electronic wave-function depending parametrically on the nuclear positions times a vibrational factor) may be unable to provide an accurate description of the system. The usual approach[2,3,4] to describe the excited

*Present Address: Instituto Venezolano de Investigaciones Cientificas, Caracas, Venezuela.

vibronic states of a dimer has therefore consisted in writing for the total wave-function:

$$\Psi(q,Q) = \phi_{A^*B}\xi_1(Q) + \phi_{AB^*}\xi_2(Q) \tag{1}$$

where q and Q denote the electronic and nuclear coordinates respectively, and ϕ_{A^*B} and ϕ_{AB^*} two product electronic wave-functions localizing the electronic excitation on either A or B (the two molecules making up the dimer). $\xi_1(Q)$ and $\xi_2(Q)$ are two nuclear functions to be determined variationally. This is the so-called vibronic treatment.

The function (1) is a sum of two product wave-functions. It is not to be confused, however, with the sum of product wave-functions which results from a systematic application of the Born-Oppenheimer (B.O.) approach to this system. In the B.O. procedure there is first of all to solve the electronic wave-equation which determines the eigenfunctions of $H-T_N$, H being the total Hamiltonian and T_N the nuclear kinetic energy operator. In the present case this produces two electronic functions having the form[5,6]

$$\phi^{\pm}(q,Q) = C_1^{\pm}(Q)\phi_{A^*B} + C_2^{\pm}(Q)\phi_{AB^*} \tag{2}$$

and two electronic energies $E^{\pm}(Q)$. A given dimer will fall in one of the two following cases:

(a) The zeroth order B.O. approximation is valid. The electronic energies $E^-(Q)$ and $E^+(Q)$ can be used as potential energies to describe the motion of the nuclei in the lower (ϕ^-) and upper (ϕ^+) electronic states. The vibronic wave-functions of the dimer assume the form $\phi^-(q,Q)X_i^-(Q)$ or $\phi^+(q,Q)X_j^+(Q)$. For sufficiently high values of the quantum number i, accidental degeneracies or quasi-degeneracies may arise between the vibronic levels belonging to the two different electronic energy levels. A two by two secular equation has to be solved, T_N being the mixing operator.

Such a departure from the zeroth order B.O. approximation has been called[5] a case of weak break down.

(b) The zeroth order B.O. approximation is not valid because of many appreciable off-diagonal matrix elements of T_N between the vibronic functions of both electronic states. This occurs when the electronic splitting $E^+(Q) - E^-(Q)$ may be small for some value of Q which is accessible to the nuclei. In such a case the vibronic states are best described by functions of the form:

$$\Psi(q,Q) = \phi^+(q,Q)X_1(Q) + \phi^-(q,Q)X_2(Q) \tag{3}$$

The variational principle applied to (3) produces two coupled equations to determine $\chi_1(Q)$ and $\chi_2(Q)$, which are related to $\xi_1(Q)$ and $\xi_2(Q)$ appearing in (1) according to:

$$\begin{aligned} X_1(Q) &= C_1^+(Q)\xi_1(Q) + C_2^+(Q)\xi_2(Q) \\ X_2(Q) &= C_1^-(Q)\xi_1(Q) + C_2^-(Q)\xi_2(Q) \end{aligned} \tag{4}$$

This case has been called[5] that of strong break down of the zeroth order B.O. approximation.

II. THE SOLUBLE MODEL

A number of simplifying assumptions leading to an exact solution in both the vibronic[3,4] and the B.O.[5,6] approaches make it possible to build model dimers falling under the above categories (a) and (b).

Some of these assumptions concern the monomers: (1) the electronic spectrum of a monomer involves only one progression, due to a single normal coordinate Q. (2) the potential energy for this normal coordinate is harmonic in both the ground and excited electronic state, with the same force constant k and a change λ in the equilibrium value. McCoy and Ross have shown[7] that with the use of such assumptions one may account for the gross features in the distribution of intensity within the lowest electronic transitions of aromatic hydrocarbons.

The other assumptions concern the dimer. The two quantities:

$$W = \langle \phi_{A^*B} | V_{AB} | \phi_{A^*B} \rangle_q$$

and $$v = \langle \phi_{A^*B} | V_{AB} | \phi_{AB^*} \rangle_q$$

where V_{AB} is the intermolecular electronic interaction, do not depend on Q_A and Q_B, the two intramolecular normal modes belonging respectively to A and B. This amounts physically to assuming that the intermolecular motion is not involved in the transfer of excitation.[8]

We summarize briefly the results obtained from a comparison of the vibronic and B.O. treatments[5,6] for a variety of cases.

(a) The zeroth order B.O. treatment has a wider validity than generally appreciated. It may produce accurately the lowest vibronic energies and wave-functions even in a case of weak coupling,[9] that is to say when v is much smaller than $h\nu$, a vibrational quantum associated with the normal mode Q. In such a case $E^-(Q)$ is a double-well potential and the region of small electronic splitting corresponds to the top of the barrier separating the two wells. If these wells are shallow enough, in the lowest vibrational levels the nuclei do not penetrate in the region where $E^+(Q) - E^-(Q)$ is small. As the vibrational energy increases, however, some penetration occurs and this treatment looses progressively its validity.

(b) Whenever applicable, the zeroth order B.O. treatment makes it possible to interpret the progressions in the spectra in terms of Franck-Condon factors associated with the $Q^+ = 2^{-\frac{1}{2}}(Q_A + Q_B)$ and the $Q^- = 2^{-\frac{1}{2}}(Q_A - Q_B)$ modes, vibrationally induced bands and vibronic mixing between B.O. product wave-functions.

III. AN EXAMPLE OF A DIMER ABSORPTION SPECTRUM

To illustrate the usefulness of the B.O. approach when only a weak break down of the zeroth order approximation is occuring, Figure 1 gives the absorption spectra of a model dimer with $\frac{1}{2}k\lambda^2/h\nu = 1$ and $\upsilon/h\nu = 1.35$ (a case of intermediate coupling according to the traditional interia). Three different procedures have been used.

NON ADIABATIC B.O. The mixing coefficients $C_1^{\pm}(Q)$ and $C_2^{\pm}(Q)$ of (1) are given the values they take in the simple exciton theory[10] (for instance $C_2^{\pm}(Q) = \pm 2^{-\frac{1}{2}}$). Any change in the quantum number of the Q^+ (symmetric) mode is allowed. The quantum numbers for the Q^- (non-symmetric) mode must be both even or both odd. Thus if one starts from the zero-point level of the ground state, only states with even quanta of Q^- can be reached. The patterns shown in (1a) illustrate this for the case where the electronic transition moments $\vec{M}_A$ and $\vec{M}_B$ of the two monomers are at right angles. All bands above the base line correspond to transition moments having the factor $(\vec{M}_A + \vec{M}_B)$, all below the factor $(\vec{M}_A - \vec{M}_B)$. In the vibronic theory[4] they are called the plus and minus systems respectively. For a sandwich dimer only the plus system, corresponding to the upper electronic state, remains, while for a head to tail dimer, the spectrum is given by the minus system, corresponding to the lower electronic state. The interpretation of the various bands is as follows:

<u>Minus system</u>. The series of bands marked A_1, A_2, A_3, A_4,....and A_1', A_2', A_3',.... represent Franck-Condon progressions of the Q^+ mode originating

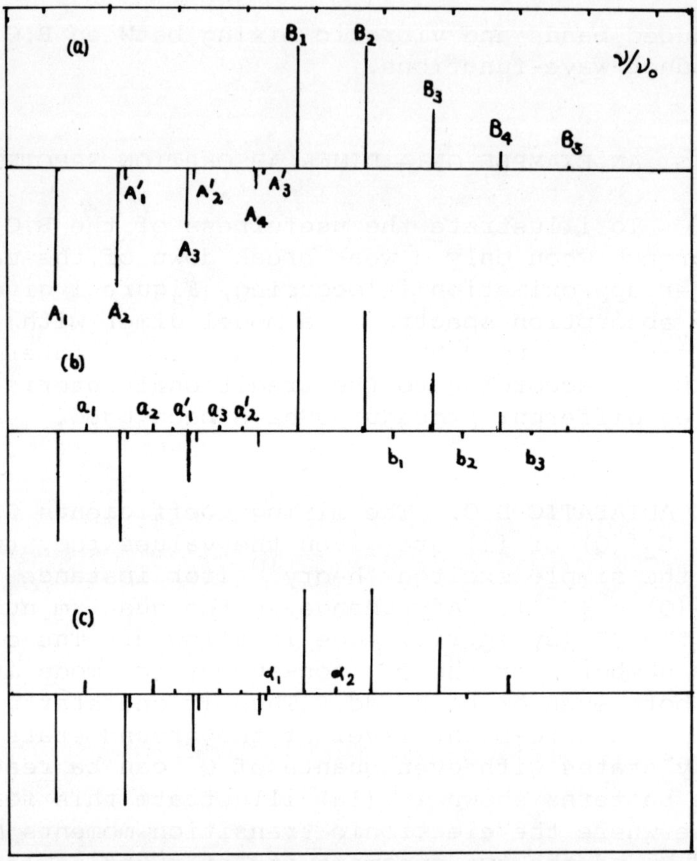

Figure 1 Absorption spectra of a dimer calculated with
(a) the B.O. non adiabatic
(b) B.O. adiabatic, and
(c) vibronic procedures. The transition moments of the monomers are at right angles. Parameters as given in the text.

from the 0-0 and 0-2 transitions of the Q^- mode respectively.

Plus system. The series B_1, B_2, B_3, B_4,.... is a Franck-Condon progression of Q^+ originating from 0-0 of Q^-.

ADIABATIC B.O. The dependence of $C_1^{\pm}(Q)$ and $C_2^{\pm}(Q)$ with respect to Q is now taken into account. States with an odd number of quanta in Q^- can now be reached. New bands appear in the spectra, which are the vibrationally induced bands of the Herzberg-Teller theory.[11] Thus in the minus system, a_1, a_2, a_3.... and a_1', a_2',.... represent Franck-Condon progressions of Q^{+2} originating from 0-1 and 0-3 of Q^-, while in the plus system b_1, b_2, b_3,.... is a Q^+ progression originating from 0-1 of Q^-.

VIBRONIC. There are some changes in the intensities of the weaker bands, and two new bands, α_1 and α_2 are present in the plus system. These are due in fact to a weak breakdown of the B.O. approximation. The vibronic levels belonging to the upper state with zero quanta in Q^- and either zero or one quanta in Q^+ give rise to the strong bands B_1 and B_2 in (1b). On the other hand the vibronic levels belonging to the lower state with five quanta in Q^- and either zero or one quanta in Q^+ are not accessible in the B.O. approximation because of the unfavorable positions of the turning points in the Q^- mode. They are mixed by T_N with the functions producing B_1 and B_2 and borrow intensity from them.

Two remarks concerning the spectra (b) and (c) may be of general interest for the interpretation of the spectra of dimers.

(1) Plus bands associated with the lower electronic state are present in (b). This shows that even for a sandwich dimer, there are allowed transitions toward this state. In the same way, minus bands are associated with the upper electronic state, so that allowed transitions toward this state are present in the head to tail dimer. It is thus not necessary to invoke a departure from a parallel or colinear arrangement of the monomers to make these transitions allowed.

(2) The changes in the intensities of the Herzberg-Teller bands of (b) when going to (c) indicates that the "vibronic" effects (that is to say departure from the B.O. approximation) may be as important as the adiabaticity in determining these intensities.

IV. CONCLUSIONS

Whenever applicable, the zeroth order B.O. approximation, and the changes due to the weak breakdown of this approximation provide a useful characterization of the bands in the absorption spectra of dimers. Similar arguments apply to the fluorescence spectra.

REFERENCES

1. M. Born and J. R. Oppenheimer, Ann. Physik. 84, 457 (1927); M. Born, Fetschrift. Gött. Math. Phys. Kl. 1, (1951).
2. A. Witkowski and W. Moffitt, J. Chem. Phys. 33, 872 (1960).
3. R. E. Merrifield, Rad. Res. 20, 154 (1963).
4. R. L. Fulton and M. Gouterman, J. Chem. Phys. 41, 2280 (1964).
5. R. Lefebvre and M. Garcia-Sucre, Int. J. Quant, Chem. 15, 339 (1967).
6. M. Garcia-Sucre, F. Geny and R. Lefebvre, J. Chem. Phys. (in the press).
7. E. F. McCoy and I. G. Ross, Austr. J. Chem. 15, 573 (1962).
8. A. Witkowski, Roczchi. Chem. 35, 1399 (1961).
9. W. T. Simpson and D. L. Peterson, J. Chem. Phys. 26, 588 (1957).
10. M. Kasha, Rad. Res. 20, 55 (1963).
11. G. Herzberg and E. Teller, Z. Phys. Chem. B21, 410 (1933).

LUMINESCENCE AND INTRAMOLECULAR ENERGY TRANSFER IN RIGID MODEL COMPOUNDS*

J. A. Hudson and R. M. Hedges

Department of Chemistry
Texas A & M University
College Station, Texas 77843

INTRODUCTION

The intramolecular electronic energy transfer between nonconjugated chromophores having an essentially fixed donor-acceptor separation and orientation has been studied for the spirans pictured in Figure 1. Keller[1] has recently studied intramolecular electronic energy transfer in these spirans obtaining significantly different phosphorescence results than reported here.

*Supported in part by the Robert A. Welch Foundation.

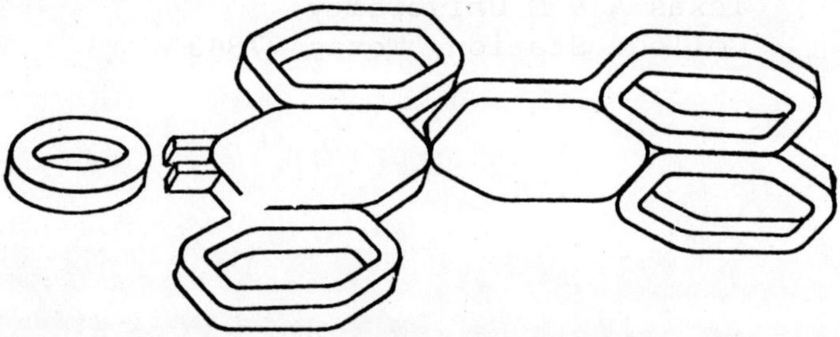

Spiran I

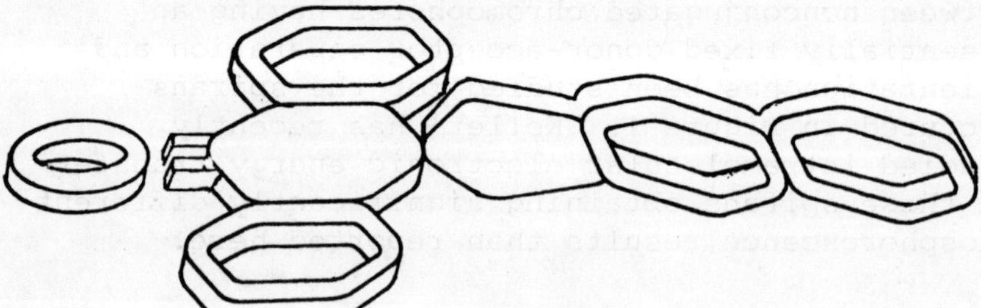

Spiran II

Figure 1 The structures of the spirans studied in this work.

EXPERIMENTAL

The spirans were synthesized in a manner similar to that reported by Keller. Spiran 1, spiro[anthracene-9(10H),2'(3'H)-phenalene]-10-one, was prepared by treating anthrone in t-BuOH with t-BuOK in t-BuOH, toluene mixed solvent, refluxing and adding 1,8-bis(bromomethylene)-naphthalene and refluxing further. Addition of dilute HCl, extraction with hot toluene, filtration and finally extraction with hot ethanolic potassium hydroxide gave 1. Spiran 2, sprio[anthracene-9(10H), 2'(3'H)-benz[f]indene]-10-one, was prepared in similar fashion as 1 above using 2,3-bis(bromomethylene)naphthalene. (10,10-dimethylanthrone, one of our reference compounds, was also prepared in the manner of spirans 1 and 2.) These spirans are very nearly insoluble in all organic solvents.

Spirans 1 and 2 and 10,10-dimethylanthrone were chromatographed repeatedly using Alcoa F-20 activated alumina until only a light yellow band emerged from the column; 2 and 10,10-dimethylanthrone were chromatographed further using Woelm basic alumina. Toluene eluent was used for 1 and 2 and petroleum ether, bp 60-80°, was used for 10,10-dimethylanthrone. These compounds were recrystallized from dilute, distilled (middle fraction) reagent grade pyridine. The spirans were recrystallized a second time from dilute, pure pyridine and the 10,10-dimethylanthrone a second time from dilute spectral grade acetonitrile. After 24 hour drying at 100° (1mm), the spirans melted sharply and were used for spectral work. 1,8-dimethylnaphthalene was purified by gas chromatographing it twice on a 16% methylsilicone gum rubber column. Purified 2,3-dimethylnaphthalene was purchased from the Henton Co. was used without further purification.

Absorption spectra were taken on a Cary 14R. Emission and excitation spectra were taken with a Baird-Atomics Fluorispec fluorescence spectrometer, model SF-1, equipped with a phosphoroscope accessory. Room temperature fluorescence spectra were taken in a 1 cm cuvette using cyclohexane solvent. Liquid nitrogen temperature spectra were taken in quartz sample tubes using methylcyclohexane-isopentane, 10:1 by volume as solvent; the samples were degassed by repetition of about 7 freeze-pump-thaw cycles. All spectra are uncorrected for instrument sensitivity and concentrations given refer to room temperature concentrations prior to degassing.

RESULTS

The compounds 10,10-dimethylanthrone, 1,8-dimethylnaphthalene, and 2,3-dimethylnaphthalene were used as spectral reference compounds since these structural units are found in the spirans. Figure 2 gives the relation between energy levels of anthrone and naphthalene showing the suitability of these moieties for energy transfer studies. The absorption spectrum of each of the spirans was quite similar to that of an equimolar mixture of the appropriate reference compounds as already noted by Keller.[1] The phosphorescence spectra of 10,10-dimethylanthrone and 1,8-dimethylnaphthalene are shown in Figure 3. Inspection of these spectra (as well as those of 10,10-dimethylanthrone compared to 2,3-dimethylnaphthalene, similar to Figure 2) reveal that the anthrone moiety phosphoresces over a wide wavelength region where the naphthalene unit does not. This fact allows a monitoring of possible triplet-triplet energy transfer from the anthrone unit to the naphthalene unit in both spirans 1 and 2. If such transfer is 100% efficient, no anthrone phosphorescence should be observable.

Absorption spectra of the separate chromophores in 1 and 2 indicate that irradiation at wavelengths between about 330 nm to 390 nm will

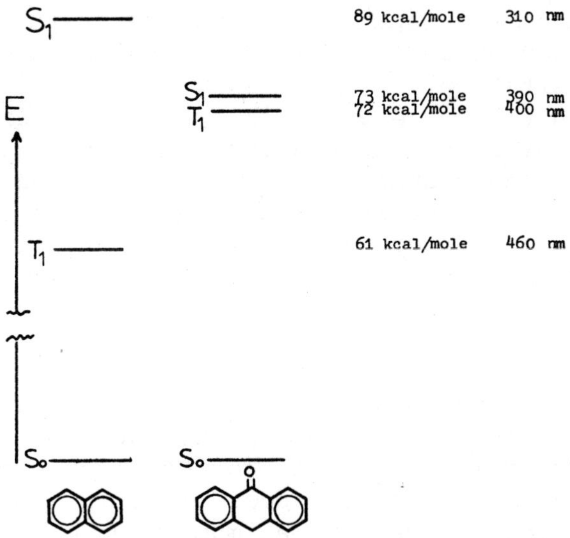

Figure 2 Energy level diagram for anthrone and naphthalene chromophores.

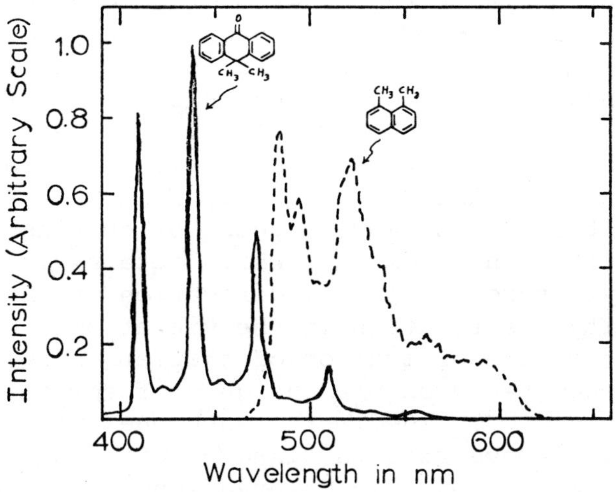

Figure 3 Phosphorescence spectra of 1,8-dimethylnaphthalene (1.0×10^{-5} M, dotted line), and 10,10-dimethylanthrone (1.0×10^{-5} M, solid line) with excitation at 305 nm. The two spectra refer to different intensity scales.

excite only the anthrone group (n-π* excitation). Excitation at 305 nm will excite both chromophores (π-π* excitation).

In Figures 4 and 5 the phosphorescence spectra of 1 and 2 are shown upon excitation at 369 nm. These spectra show that emission from <u>both</u> chromophores is taking place, not just from the naphthalene group, since peaks are present at wavelengths where 10,10-dimethylanthrone phosphoresces. When the rotating can shutter was removed and the total emission spectra recorded, the anthrone moiety phosphorescence intensity relative to that of the naphthalene unit was greatly increased. This is to be expected due to the millisecond lifetime[1] of phosphorescence of anthrone as compared to the 2.3 second lifetime for naphthalene, since the maximum speed of the rotating shutter is about 200-300 revolutions per second (i.e., the lapse time between excitation and observation is of the order of from one to several decay half-lives of the anthrone group phosphorescence). Phosphorescence from both chromophores in 1 and 2 is also observable upon excitation at 305 nm where both absorb. It is noticed that the distribution of intensity in the vibrational components of the anthrone moiety phosphorescence (i.e., the 410 and 439 nm peaks of spirans 1 and 2) is different from that which obtains in 10,10-dimethylanthrone. This modification of the intensity distribution in the vibrational components makes accurate estimation of triplet energy transfer efficiency based on peak heights of spirans 1 and 2 relative to 10,10-dimethylanthrone difficult.

The above results disagree with the previous study,[1] which reported observation of only naphthalene moiety phosphorescence from 1 and 2 in a 30% butyl alcohol-70% isopentane glassy matrix at 77°K. We were readily able to reproduce these observations under conditions that are likely to produce aggregation of molecules and therefore <u>intermolecular</u> transfer of the remaining anthrone

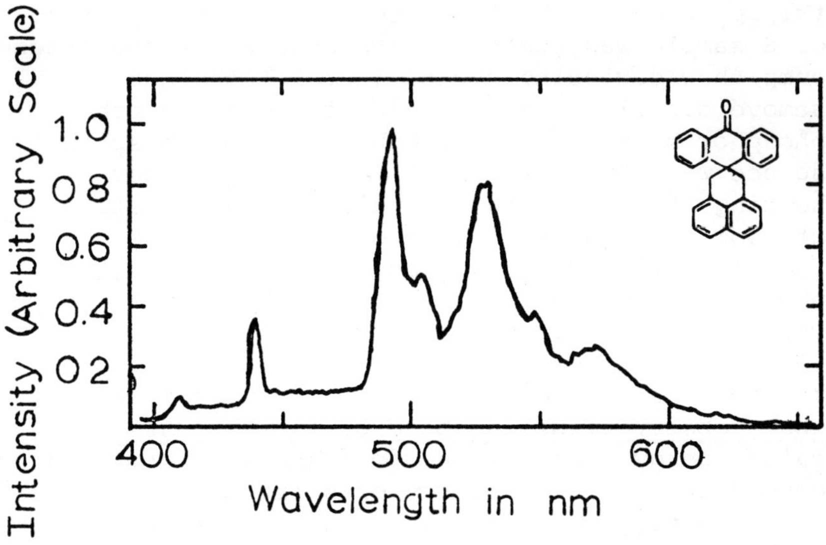

Figure 4 Phosphorescence spectrum of 1.00 x 10^{-5} M 1 with excitation at 369 nm.

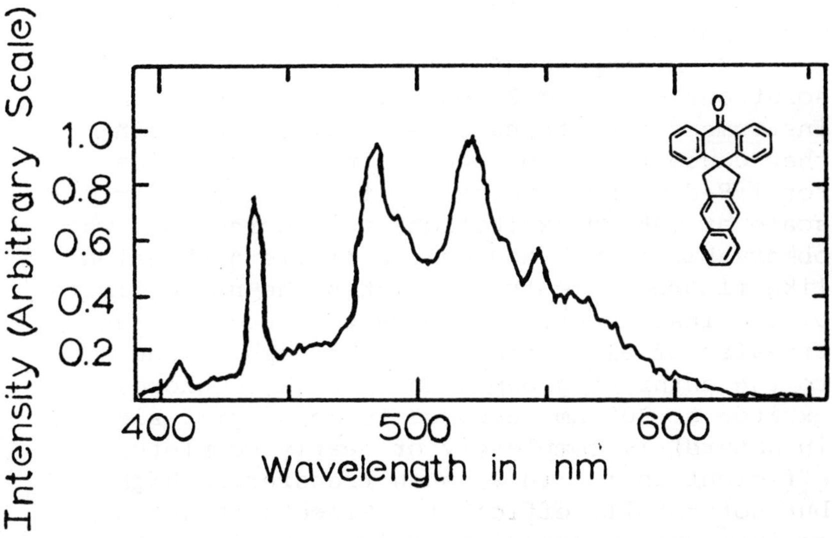

Figure 5 Phosphorescence spectrum of 1.00 x 10^{-5} M 2 with excitation at 369 nm.

triplet energy. When the total emission spectrum of a sample was taken at 77°K soon after the freeze-pump-thaw degassing cycle, (usual technique to remove dissolved oxygen which tends to quench phosphorescence) only naphthalene type phosphorescence was observed from 1 and 2. By either heating the sample tube or allowing it to stand at room temperature for several days and then freezing it to 77°K, it would show anthrone-type phosphorescence as well as the naphthalene-type. These two types of spectral observations were repeatable on sealed samples after appropriate treatment as above. It seems likely that the above observations can be explained by intermolecular energy transfer due to aggregate formation caused by the insolubility of spirans 1 and 2 relative to compounds like naphthalene. It is probable that the failure to observe anthrone emission in the previous work[1] is due to this effect; the spiran concentrations used in this work were an order of magnitude smaller than those used in the previous study but we had to be very careful in avoiding suppression of the anthrone group phosphorescence.

Room temperature fluorescence of 1.00×10^{-5} M solutions of 1 and 2 were also studied. Under instrument conditions of slit width and gain that cause the fluorescence intensity indication for 1,8-dimethylnaphthalene to go completely off-scale at 305 nm excitation, no fluorescence was observable from 1 and only a feeble naphthalene-like fluorescence from 2 within the noise limits of the instrument. These results suggest that transfer of excitation from the naphthalene group to the anthrone group when both chromophores are excited at 305 nm (assumed to be singlet-singlet in nature) is completely or nearly completely efficient in 1. In 2, such transfer is highly but not totally efficient. Since anthrone has an intersystem crossing efficiency close to unity, anthrone doesn't fluoresce and in a room temperature solution its phosphorescence is quenched.

The observation of the anthrone group phosphorescence as well as the naphthalene group phosphorescence in these spirans indicates that the rate of triplet energy transfer is within an order of magnitude of the anthrone phosphorescence decay rate (10^{-4} to 10^{-3} second). The unusual aspects of the triplet energy transfer in these spirans is probably due to the fact that the transition moments in the two chromophores are nearly but not exactly orthogonal.

REFERENCE

1. R. A. Keller, J. Am. Chem. Soc. 90, 1940 (1968).

THE ULTRAVIOLET ABSORPTION AND FLUORESCENCE PROPERTIES OF N-ARYLAMINONAPHTHALENESULFONATES AND RELATED MOLECULES*

Carl J. Seliskar, David C. Turner, James R. Gohlke, and Ludwig Brand

McCollum Pratt Institute
Johns Hopkins University
Baltimore, Maryland 21218

N-arylaminonaphthalenesulfonate dyes adsorb to specific, functionally important sites on several proteins.[1] The fluorescence quantum yields of these compounds are low in polar solvents. When they are dissolved in non-polar solvents or adsorbed to proteins their quantum yields and average energies of fluorescence emission increase and the half-maximum bandwidths of emission decrease. Since the spectroscopic properties of these dyes adsorbed to proteins closely reflect those in non-polar solvents, they have been widely used as "probes" for hydrophobic regions in protein molecules. Attempts have been made to evaluate

*Contribution 531 of the McCollum Pratt Institute. Supported by National Institutes of Health Grants GM 11632 and 5-71-GM 34, 951-02.

the effects of other environmental factors, such as pH, quenching of fluorescence by specific chemical complexing, viscosity, and solvent deuteration, on spectroscopic parameters. Based on such studies several mechanisms have been proposed to explain the variations observed.[2,3,4]

The aim of this research was to establish the electronic transitions of five aminonaphthalene derivatives in order to evaluate the solvent effects on the fluorescence of these molecules thereby making them more useful as "probes" in protein chemistry. The effects of solvent polarity on the fluorescence emission maxima of N-phenyl-2-aminonaphthalene-6-sulfonate and N-phenyl-N-methyl-2-aminonaphthalene-6-sulfonate are shown in Figure 1. The abscissa is the empirical solvent scale ("Z") proposed by Kosower.[5] The data show that the wavenumber of the fluorescence maximum is a smooth function of "Z", and that a decrease in the $S_o \leftarrow S_1$ transition energy occurs when these compounds are dissolved in polar solvents (higher "Z" values). Similar correlations for the wavenumber of the fluorescence maximum as a function of "Z" have been found for position isomers of N-phenyl-1-aminonaphthalenesulfonates.[4]

The absorption and fluorescence properties of five 2-aminonaphthalene derivatives are given in Table 1. In any one solvent the wavenumbers of the lowest energy absorption maxima and the fluorescence maxima decrease on substitution of the amine group. In general, for a given solvent the molar extinction coefficient of the lowest energy absorption maximum increases on substitution of the amine. N-phenyl-N-methyl-2-aminonaphthalene-6-sulfonate is an exception. The Stokes' shift, $\overline{\nu}_a(\text{max}) - \overline{\nu}_f(\text{max})$, remains roughly constant in ethanol, but increases in water on substitution of the amine. The absorption and fluorescence spectra in ethanol for the compounds in Table 1 are shown in Figs. 2-6. The relative intensities of the two lowest energy absorption bands are nearly the same.

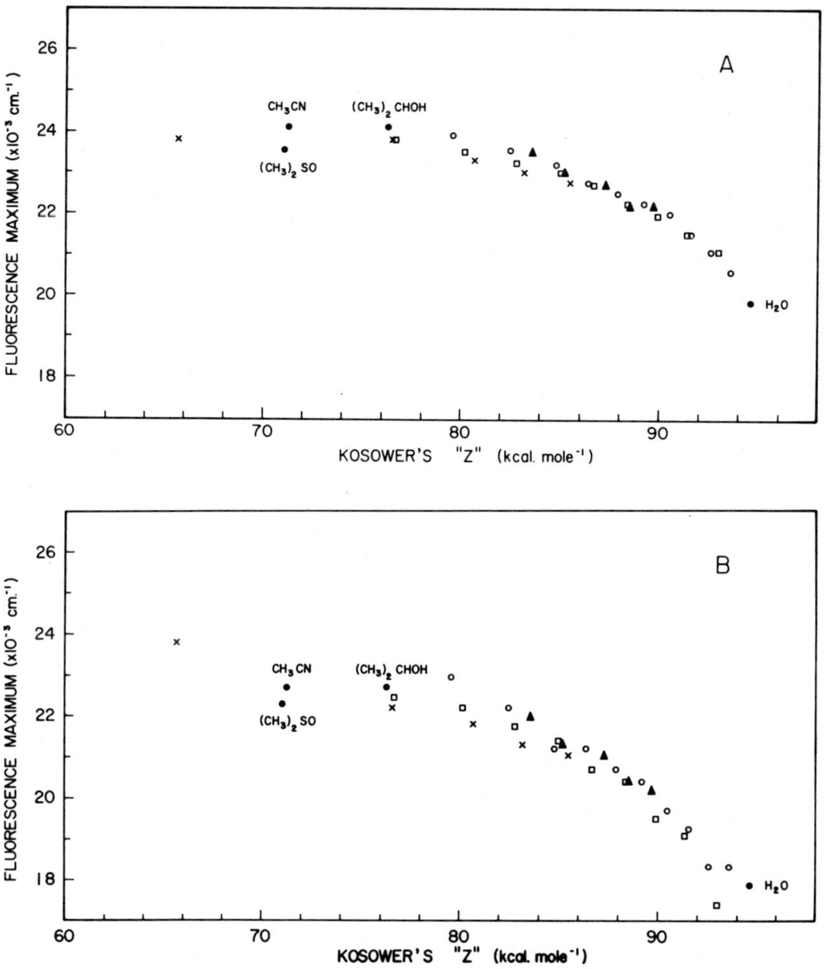

Figure 1 Fluorescence emission maximum as a function of Kosower's "Z". The solvents are indicated as follows: X, acetone-water mixtures; □ dioxane-water mixtures; ○, ethanol-water mixtures; ▲, methanol-water mixtures. A: N-phenyl-2-aminonaphthalene-6-sulfonate; B: N-phenyl-N-methyl-2-aminonaphthalene-6-sulfonate.

TABLE 1

Compound	Solvent	$\bar{\nu}_a$ (max) (10^{-3} cm^{-1})	$\varepsilon_m(\bar{\nu}_a)$ liter $mole^{-1}$ cm^{-1} (10^{-3})	$\bar{\nu}_f$ (max) (10^{-3} cm^{-1})	$\Delta\bar{\nu}$ (½ max) (10^{-3} cm^{-1})	$\bar{\nu}_a$ (max) − $\bar{\nu}_f$ (max) (10^{-3} cm^{-1})	Absolute Quantum Yield*
2-amino naphthalene	ethanol	29.3	2.00	$24.7\underline{1}$	$3.2\underline{4}$	4.6	0.59
	water	29.8	2.00	$24.1\underline{6}$	$3.4\underline{2}$	5.6	0.53
2-amino naphthalene-6-sulfonate	ethanol	29.1	2.22	$24.5\underline{5}$	$3.1\underline{1}$	4.5	0.53
	water	29.4	1.90	$23.7\underline{0}$	$3.5\underline{7}$	5.7	0.55
N-phenyl-2-aminonaphthalene	ethanol	28.7	4.26	$24.3\underline{5}$	$3.4\underline{2}$	4.3	0.44
N-phenyl-2-aminonaphthalene-6-sulfonate	ethanol	28.3	5.48	$24.0\underline{1}$	$3.4\underline{8}$	4.3	0.64
	water	28.2	5.01	$19.8\underline{4}$	$6.2\underline{2}$	8.4	0.010
N-phenyl-N-methyl-2-2 aminonaphthalene-6-sulfonate	ethanol	27.8	4.76	$23.0\underline{8}$	$4.1\underline{5}$	4.7	0.50
	water	27.5	4.65	$17.8\underline{7}$	$4.9\underline{6}$	9.6	0.006

* The quantum yields were determined using quinine sulfate as a standard assuming a quantum yield of 0.55. W. H. Meluish, J. Phys. Chem. 65, 229 (1961).

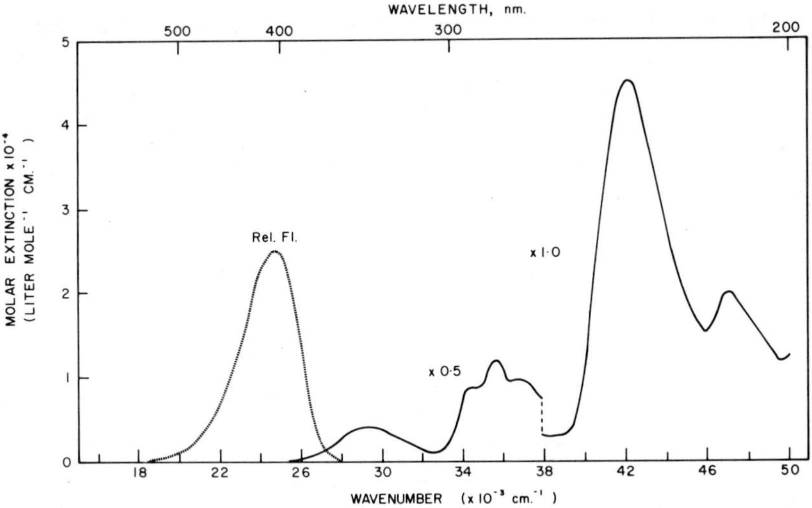

Figure 2 Absorption and fluorescence of 2-aminonaphthalene in ethanol; solid line: molar extinction; dotted line:relative fluorescence in arbitrary units.

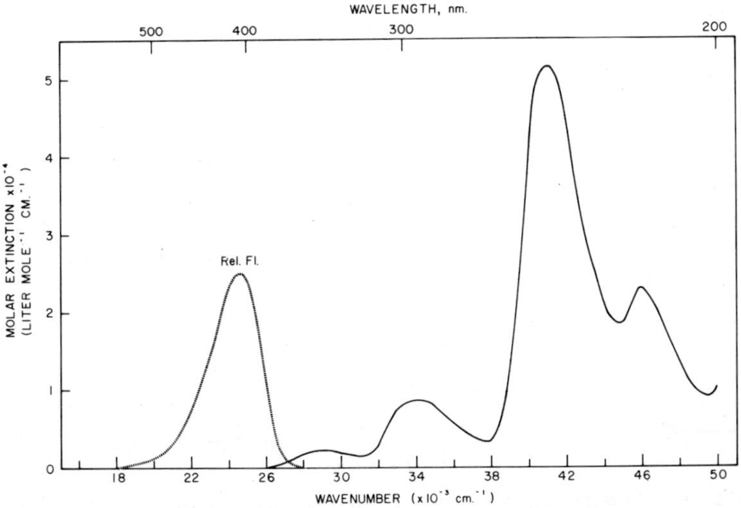

Figure 3 Absorption and fluorescence of 2-aminonaphthalene-6-sulfonate in ethanol; solid line:molar extinction; dotted line:relative fluorescence in arbitrary units.

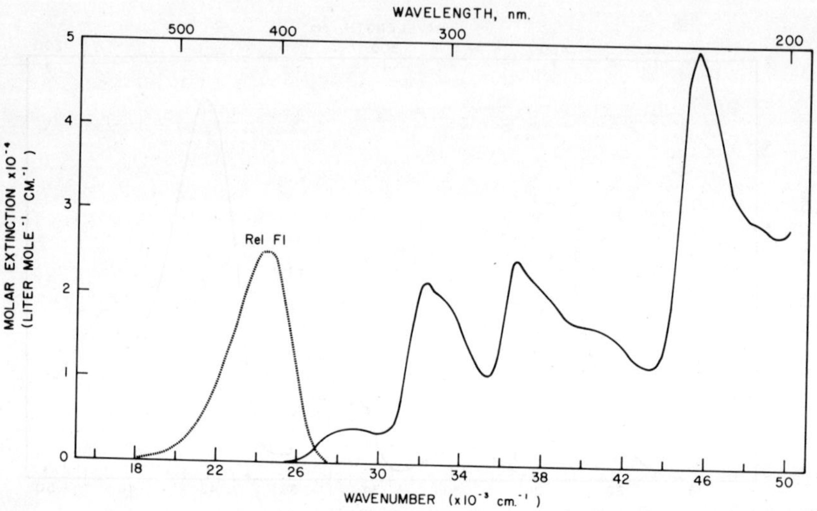

Figure 4 Absorption and fluorescence of N-phenyl-2-aminonaphthalene in ethanol; solid line: molar extinction; dotted line: relative fluorescence in arbitrary units.

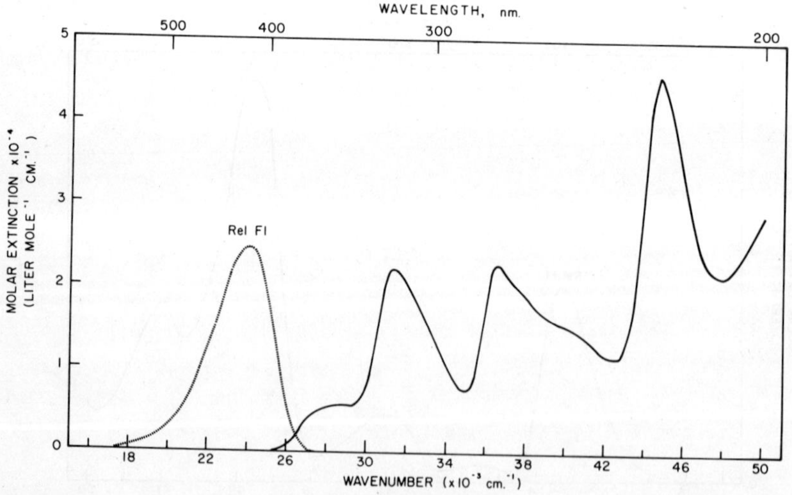

Figure 5 Absorption and fluorescence of N-phenyl-2-aminonaphthalene-6-sulfonate in ethanol; solid line: molar extinction; dotted line: relative fluorescence in arbitrary units.

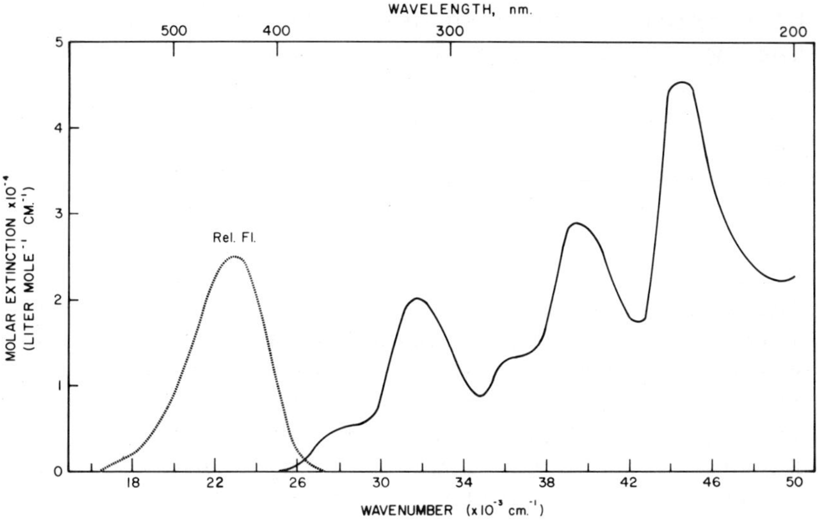

Figure 6 Absorption and fluorescence of N-phenyl-N-methyl-2-aminonaphthalene-6-sulfonate in ethanol; solid line: molar extinction; dotted line: relative fluorescence in arbitrary units.

The intramolecular charge-transfer transitions of aromatic amines, in which a nitrogen lone-pair electron is promoted to an antibonding orbital of π origin, have been designated $a_\pi \leftarrow \ell$ by Kasha.[6] The two lowest energy absorptions bands of aniline are thought to be $a_\pi \leftarrow \ell$ transitions,[7] and have been treated as perturbations of $\pi^* \leftarrow \pi$ bands of benzene.[8] We will now present evidence that the two lowest energy bands of these five aminonaphthalene derivatives are $a_\pi \leftarrow \ell$ transitions.

The decrease in the average energy of fluorescence in polar solvents for the compounds in Table 1 indicates that the dipole moment of the first excited singlet exceeds that of the ground state,[9] and is consistent with the assignment of the lowest energy electronic absorption band to a transition having charge transfer characteristics. Furthermore, if the lowest energy absorption band is an $a_\pi \leftarrow \ell$ intramolecular charge transfer transition the average energy of this band should decrease and its molar extinction should increase as the ionization potential of the amine group is decreased. The same effects are expected if a group is added to the naphthalene ring system which increases its electron affinity as is the case with the $-SO_3^-$ group.[10] For a series of aniline derivatives Kimura[11] has shown that the average energies of the intramolecular charge transfer bands decrease as the ionization potential of the amine group decreases in the order:

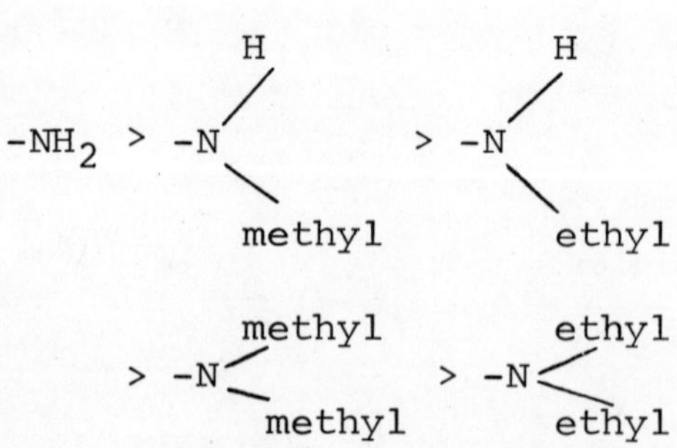

We therefore assume for the aminonaphthalene derivatives studied here that the ionization potentials of the amine groups are in the order:[12]

```
                 H              methyl
                /              /
-NH2  >  -N            >  -N
                \              \
                 phenyl         phenyl
```

The observed variations in the absorption maxima and molar extinctions (Table 1) are generally consistent with the pattern predicted from the effects of changing the ionization potential of the amine and the electron affinity of the ring system on intramolecular charge transfer transitions. The molar extinction coefficients are in the range designated for the $a_\pi \leftarrow \ell$ transition on the Molecular Electronic Transition f-Number Scale of Kasha.[13] The extinction of N-phenyl-N-methyl-2-aminonaphthalene-6-sulfonate may be lower than that of N-phenyl-2-aminonaphthalene-6-sulfonate due to hindrance to rotation about the $>N-C_2<$ bond, resulting in a lower transition moment because of an increased angle of twist between the lone pair orbital and the $2p\pi$ orbital of naphthalene.[12,14,15]

The $a_\pi \leftarrow \ell$ absorption band is known to disappear on protonation of the amine.[16] Absorption spectra of these aminonaphthalene derivatives, under conditions where the amine is protonated in the ground state, are nearly identical to that of naphthalene-2-sulfonate (Fig. 7). The absorption spectrum for protonated 2-aminonaphthalene is like that of protonated 2-aminonaphthalene-6-sulfonate. Protonated N-phenyl-2-aminonaphthalene-6-sulfonate has a spectrum identical to that of protonated N-phenyl-N-methyl-2-aminonaphthalene-6-sulfonate. The <u>three</u> lowest energy absorption bands of N-aryl-2-aminonaphthalene-6-sulfonates disappear upon protonation of the amine suggesting that the band observed at 37-39 x 10^3 cm^{-1} for these

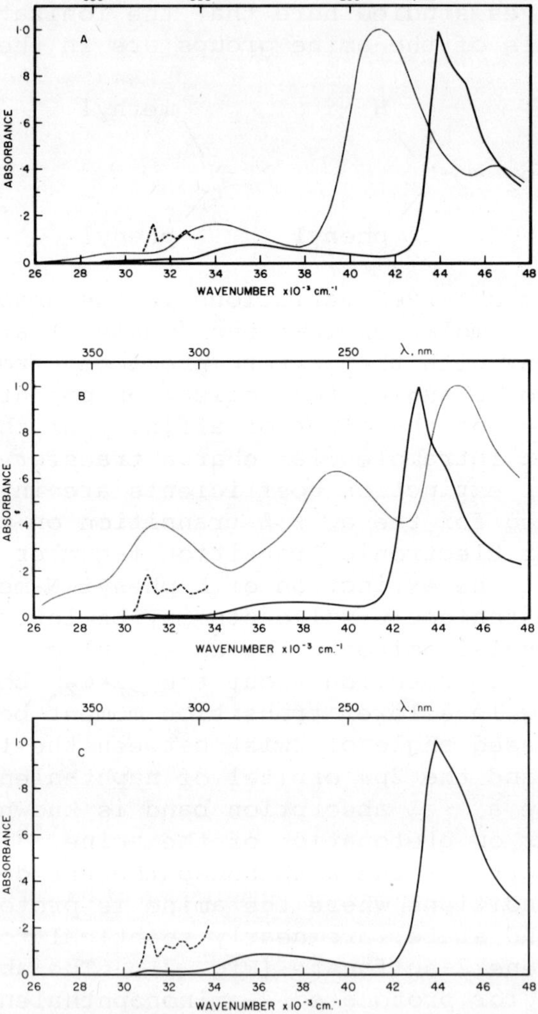

Figure 7 Absorption spectra of: A, 2-aminonaphthalene-6-sulfonate in H_2O, pH 7 (dotted line), and in 3N HCl (solid line); B, N-phenyl-N-methyl-2-aminonaphthalene-6-sulfonate in H_2O, pH 7 (dotted line), and in 6N HCl (solid line); and C, naphthalene-2-sulfonate in 3N HCl (solid line). The dashed lines are expansions of the solid lines.

molecules may correspond to the promotion of an "ℓ" electron to an antibonding π orbital of the phenyl substituent.

In view of the higher fluorescence quantum yield of N-phenyl-1-aminonaphthalene-8-sulfonate in D_2O than in H_2O, Stryer[3] has proposed that excited state ionization of the amine proton of N-arylaminonaphthalenesulfonates could explain the quenching of fluorescence in polar solvents. Measurements of the fluorescence quantum yields of N-phenyl-2-aminonaphthalene-6-sulfonate and N-phenyl-N-methyl-2-aminonaphthalene-6-sulfonate in aqueous solutions were made as a function of the mole fraction of D_2O added (Fig. 8) and both compounds exhibit an enhancement of nearly three in D_2O. A similar enhancement was recently reported for N,N-dimethyl-1-aminonaphthalene-5-sulfonate.[17] The mechanism of the fluorescence enhancement cannot be explained by an isotope rate effect on the deprotonation of the amine group during the lifetime of the first excited singlet state.

If excited state protonation or deprotonation did occur in primary amines it should be markedly pH dependent. The absorption spectrum of 2-aminonaphthalene-6-sulfonate in water at pH 7 and that in 1N KOH are identical; the same holds true for 2-aminonaphthalene, naphthalene-2-sulfonate, N-phenyl-2-aminonaphthalene-6-sulfonate, and N-phenyl-N-methyl-2-aminonaphthalene-6-sulfonate.[12] Therefore, no ground state ionization of the amine proton occurs under these conditions. The fluorescence emission spectra of 2-aminonaphthalene-6-sulfonate during an alkaline titration are shown in Figure 9. A new fluorescent species appears in the excited state (pK:11.8$\underline{6}$; isoemissive point: 19.5$\underline{7}$ x 10^3 cm^{-1}). Similar results were obtained for 2-aminonaphthalene (pK: 11.8$\underline{6}$; isoemissive point 19.8$\underline{4}$ x 10^3 cm^{-1}). This new emission may be attributed to the naphthylamide (sulfonate) ion. Aminopyrenesulfonates have been shown to exhibit similar behavior.[18] During the acid

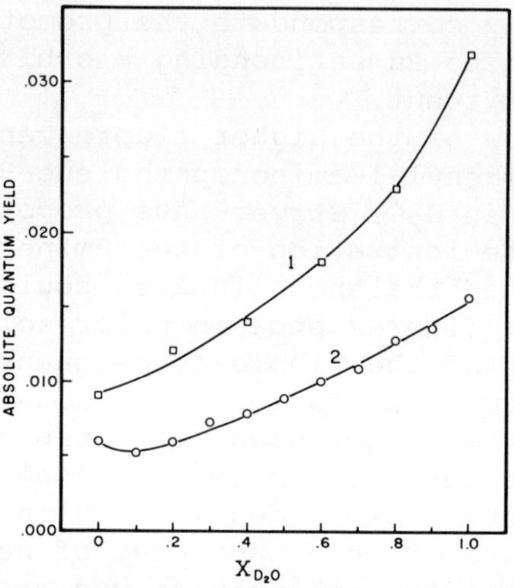

Figure 8 Absolute fluorescence quantum yield as a function of mole fraction of D_2O in H_2O. 1: N-phenyl-2-aminonaphthalene-6-sulfonate; 2: N-phenyl-N-methyl-2-aminonaphthalene-6-sulfonate.

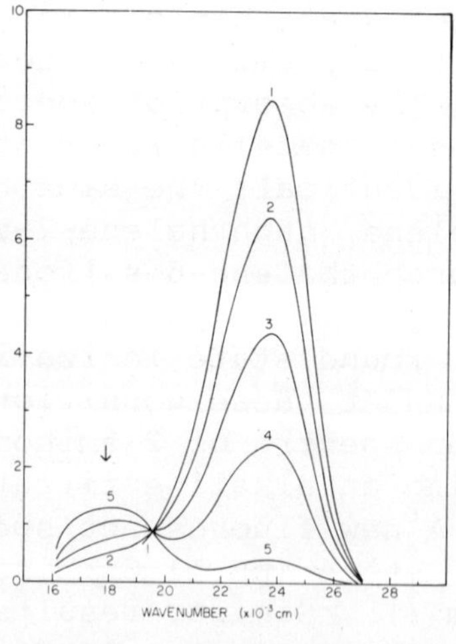

Figure 9 Fluorescence spectra of 2-aminonaphthalene-6-sulfonate during an alkaline titration; 1: pH 6.9; 2: pH 11.4; 3: pH 11.8; 4: pH 12.15; 5: pH ∿ 12.4. The arrow denotes the emission maximum of the lower energy fluorescence.

titration, the absorption spectra of 2-aminonaphthalene-6-sulfonate show the loss of the two lowest energy absorption bands (Figure 10). Isobestic points were found at $43.2\underline{9} \times 10^3$ cm^{-1}, $38.3\underline{1} \times 10^3$ cm^{-1}, and $36.3\underline{6} \times 10^3$ cm^{-1}. Titration of 2-aminonaphthalene showed isobestic points at $38.3\underline{1} \times 10^3$ cm^{-1}, $38.1\underline{7} \times 10^3$ cm^{-1}, and $36.5\underline{0} \times 10^3$ cm^{-1}. Measurements of the quantum yields of fluorescence of both compounds during the amine titration in the ground state showed that no new emission appeared and that the quantum yield remained a constant. A further increase in the acid concentration beyond that necessary to titrate the amine in the ground state of both compounds resulted in a decrease in the quantum yield and the appearance of a new, higher energy emission nearly identical in fine structure and energy to that of naphthalene-2-sulfonate. No changes occurred during either alkaline or acid titrations of naphthalene-2-sulfonate.

The titration curves for these two compounds are presented in Fig. 11. The curves were generated from the pK value which gave a minimum least-squares deviation from the experimental points. The following diagram describes the ground state and singlet excited state processes for these two molecules.[12]

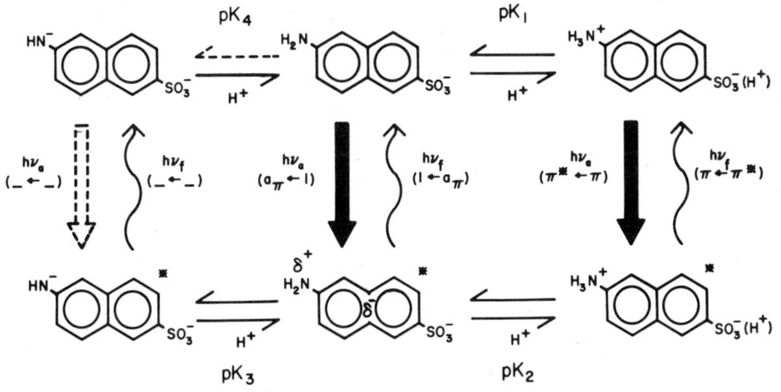

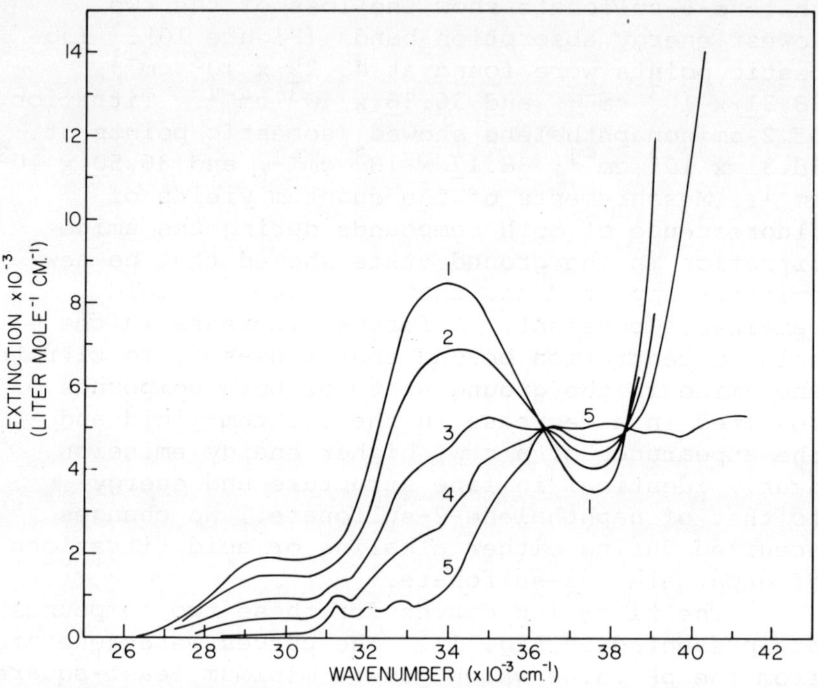

Figure 10 Absorption spectra of 2-aminonaphthalene-6-sulfonate during an acid titration; 1: pH 7.2; 2: pH 4.2; 3: pH 3.6; 4: pH 3.2; 5: pH 2.1.

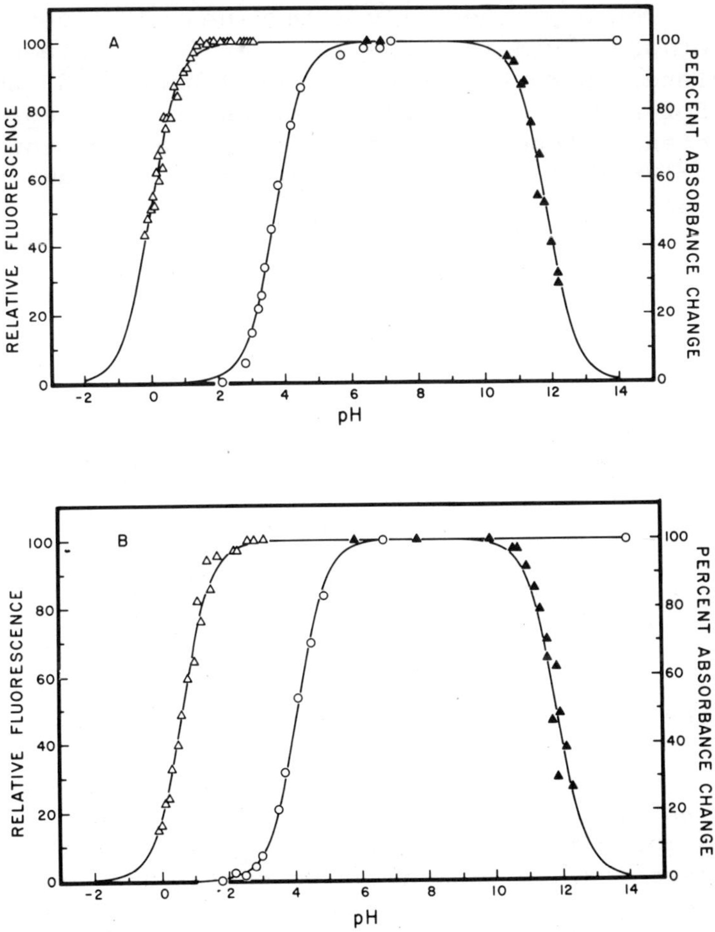

Figure 11 Titrations of 2-aminonaphthalene-6-sulfonate (A) and 2-aminonaphthalene (B). The percent absorbance change of the lowest energy band as a function of pH is denoted by circles. The open triangles denote fluorescence titrations in the acid region, obtained in each case by exciting the fluorescence at the isosbestic point in the absorption spectrum. The solid triangles represent fluorescence titrations in the alkaline region. The lines are calculated titration curves.

The experimentally determined pK values in water are given in Table 2. Even for 2-aminonaphthalene, where the amine is not substituted, the pK for excited state proton transfer is 11.8$\underline{6}$, and thus an isotope effect on excited state proton transfer would not be expected at neutral pH regions for this molecule.

The acidities of the first excited singlet states are greater than those of the ground states. From theoretical calculations on aniline,[8,15] it is expected that for intramolecular charge-transfer transitions of the type $a_\pi \leftarrow \ell$ the dipole moments, and hence the acidities will be in the order:

first excited singlet > first excited triplet > ground state singlet

Jackson and Porter[20] have presented data for 2-aminonaphthalene confirming these predictions.

From the above evidence, it is possible to offer a reasonable explanation for those changes in the spectroscopic properties of 2-aminonaphthalene and its derivatives which result from chemical modification and from interaction with different solvents. First, it is reasonable to expect that the dipole moments of the S_1, T_1 and S_o states will increase as the ionization potential of the amine is decreased. In all compounds the dipole moment of the triplet state (T_1) should remain intermediate in magnitude to those of the two singlet states (S_1, S_o). Second, because of the relative dipole moments of these states, the decrease of the energies of the states, due to dipole-dipole interactions between the solute and neighboring molecules of a given solvent, should be in the order:

$$\Delta E(S_1) > \Delta E(T_1) > \Delta E(S_o)$$

TABLE 2

Compound	pK	Experimental	Literature
2-amino-	pK_1	3.72	3.74[a]
naphtha-	pK_2	-0.02	-
lene-6-	pK_3	11.86	-
sulfonate	pK_4	>14	-
2-amino-	pK_1	4.08	4.11[a]
naphtha-	pK_2	0.64	∿-2[b]
lene	pK_3	11.86	-
	pK_4	>14	-

[a] Ref. 19.
[b] Ref. 20.

Third, for a given compound, the decrease in the energy due to the solvation of a given state should be increased in solvents of higher polarity. In addition, experimental evidence was recently presented indicating that a decrease in the ionization potential of the amine group of aniline increased spin-orbit coupling between the singlet states and the first excited triplet state.[7] The same effects would be expected for 2-aminonaphthalene and its derivatives, further increasing the probability of intersystem crossing.

There are two important consequences of these statements.

(1) If during the lifetimes of the excited states the solvent molecules can reach equilibrium orientations with respect to the solute molecule, the Stokes' shift, reflecting the greater solvation of the excited state relative to the ground state, should be increased in polar solvents. The magnitude of the effect of polar solvents on the Stokes' shift should be greatest for the compounds with the lowest amine ionization potentials, and hence, the largest dipole moments. Table 1 shows that these predictions are borne out.

(2) Similarly, in a series of solvents, increasing solvation should decrease the singlet-triplet energy difference. Since the probability of the $T_1 \leftarrow S_1$ transition varies as the square of the inverse of the singlet-triplet energy difference, solvation of molecules with $a_\pi \leftarrow \ell$ charge transfer bands in polar solvents would facilitate radiationless decay of the first excited singlet energy via the triplet state. This correspondence between a decrease in the singlet-triplet energy split and in the fluorescence quantum yield would be expected to be greater in those compounds which have larger dipole moments, and hence smaller singlet-triplet energy differences to begin with. The fluorescence quantum yields in the relatively non-polar solvent, ethanol, remain

high while those in water decrease as the dipole moments increase (Table 1).

In summary, there are a number of factors which contribute to the solvent dependence of the $a_{\pi} \leftarrow \ell$ intramolecular charge transfer transition, and hence to the spectroscopic properties of these molecules. In any one solvent, a decrease in the ionization potential of the amine or an increase in the electron affinity of the naphthalene ring system decreases the singlet-triplet energy difference and increases the spin-orbit coupling between the singlet and triplet states, facilitating fluorescence quenching via intersystem crossing. For any one molecule, more polar solvents increase the solvent-solute interaction energies of the lower lying electronic states, and again produce a decrease in the singlet-triplet energy difference. From those factors it follows that N-arylaminonaphthalenesulfonates would be expected to have the lowest quantum yields in water of all these compounds.

ACKNOWLEDGEMENT

The authors thank Prof. M. Kasha for a preprint of his paper and Mrs. L. McKelvy for her excellent technical assistance.

REFERENCES

1. G. M. Edelman and W. O. McClure, Acct. Chem. Res. 1, 65 (1968).
2. W. O. McClure, and G. M. Edelman, Biochemistry 5, 1908 (1966).
3. L. Stryer, J. Am. Chem. Soc. 88, 5708 (1967).
4. D. C. Turner and L. Brand (manuscript in preparation).
5. E. M. Kosower, J. Am. Chem. Soc. 80, 3253 (1958).
6. M. Kasha, in Light and Life, W. D. McElroy and B. Glass, Eds. (Johns Hopkins Press, 1961), p. 35.
7. E. C. Lim and S. K. Chakrabarti, J. Chem. Phys. 47, 4726 (1967).
8. K. Kimura and H. Tsubomura, Molec. Phys. 11, 349 (1966).
9. E. Lippert, in Optische Anregung Organischer Systeme Verlag Chemie (Weinheim, Germany, 1966), p. 342.
10. A. Bryson, Trans. Faraday Soc. 47, 528 (1951).
11. K. Kimura, H. Tsubomura and S. Nagakura, Bull. Chem. Soc. (Japan) 37, 1336 (1964).
12. C. J. Seliskar and L. Brand (manuscript in preparation).
13. M. Kasha and H. R. Rawls, Photochem. Photobiol. (in press).
14. E. G. McRae and L. Goodman, J. Molec. Spectry. 2, 464 (1958).
15. M. Godfrey and J. N. Murrell, Proc. Royal Soc. A278, 71 (1964).
16. M. Kasha, in Fluorescence, Theory, Instrumentation, and Practice, G. Guilbault, Ed. (Dekker, Inc., 1967), p. 208.
17. T. Förster and K. Rokos, Chem. Phys. Letters, 1, 279 (1967).
18. T. Förster, Z. Elektrochemie 54, 42 (1950).
19. A. Bryson, Trans. Farad. Soc. 47, 522 (1951).
20. G. Jackson and G. Porter, Proc. Royal Soc. A260, 13 (1961).

INTRAMOLECULAR ENERGY TRANSFER BETWEEN NONCONJUGATED CHROMOPHORES

Nicolae Filipescu

Department of Chemistry
George Washington University
Washington, D. C.

INTRODUCTION

Intermolecular energy transfer of both singlet and triplet excitation energy has been of great interest both theoretically and experimentally because of its importance in a number of fields such as molecular spectroscopy, photochemistry, biology, and radiochemistry. Numerous systems in which the donor and acceptor molecules are present as non-associated cosolutes have been investigated in detail.[1] In constrast, intramolecular migration of electronic energy between nonconjugated chromophores, a much better defined donor-acceptor system, has received attention only during the past ten years in an attempt to establish a detailed understanding of the transfer mechanism. Change from randomly distributed chromophores in mixed solutions to model compounds in which the spacial disposition of the two electronic systems is accurately known may either verify or alter the simple theoretical concepts presently used to explain energy transfer processes. The purpose of the present paper is to outline briefly the theoretical foundations developed for singlet and triplet transfer and to review the attempts to test theoretical predictions on model compounds suitable for intramolecular energy transfer.

SINGLET-SINGLET TRANSFER

Although there is evidence for collisional singlet-singlet energy transfer between organic chromophores,[2-5] the long range transfer taking place at distances much greater than molecular diameters is considered more important. The classical resonance concept originally used by J. Perrin[6] to explain concentration depolarization was treated quantum mechanically later by F. Perrin,[7] and was refined by Förster.[8-11] In general, the nonradiative coupling includes both Coulomb and exchange interaction terms but the latter become insignificant at separation distance in excess of a few angströms. The Coulomb interaction can be expanded in a multipole series in which the dipole-dipole coupling predominates.

The probability of inductive-resonance transfer is given by $P_{D^* \rightarrow A^*} = \rho \left| \int \Psi_i H' \Psi_f d\tau \right|^2$ where the wave functions for the initial and final states are respectively $\Psi_i = \Psi_{D^*}\Psi_A$ and $\Psi_f = \Psi_D \Psi_{A^*}$ with Ψ_{D^*}, Ψ_{A^*} and Ψ_D, Ψ_A the excited and ground state wave functions for donor D and acceptor A. H' represents the interaction Hamiltonian and ρ the density of states available for interaction. When the donor and acceptor are different species, degeneracy of initial and final states required by resonance is made possible by closely spaced vibrational levels in the excited electronic state of the acceptor and in the ground state of donor. Assuming that resonance transfer at distances larger than collisional diameters is due only to coupling between respective transition dipoles in a given donor and acceptor pair the predicted rate constant for transfer $k_{D^* \rightarrow A^*}$ should be inversely proportional to the sixth power of the D-A separation distance R and dependent on the mutual orientation of the two dipole transition vectors:

$$k_{D^* \rightarrow A^*} = C\frac{K^2}{R^2} \qquad (1)$$

The experimental constant C is given by:

$$C = \frac{9000\eta_D \ln 10}{128\pi^6 n^4 N\tau_D}\int_0^\infty f_D(\omega)\,\varepsilon_A(\omega)\frac{d\omega}{\omega^4} \qquad (2)$$

where η_D is the fluorescence quantum yield of the donor, n the refractive index of the solvent, N Avogadro's number, τ_D the mean lifetime of excited state of donor, $f_D(\omega)$ the spectral distribution of donor fluorescence (in quanta on a wavenumber scale and normalized to unity), and $\varepsilon_A(\omega)$ the molar decadic extinction coefficient of the acceptor at wavenumber ω. The expression for the orientation factor K is given by

$$K = \cos\Phi_{DA} - 3\cos\Phi_D\cos\Phi_A \qquad (3)$$

where Φ_{DA} is the angle between the transition vectors of D and A, and Φ_D, Φ_A the angles between these vectors and the line joining the centers of D and A, respectively.

Equation (1) suggests that the probability of electronic energy transfer by inductive resonance is a function only of the mutual orientation and separation distance for any given donor and acceptor pair. It also predicts that if the transition dipoles of D and A lie perpendicular to one another and perpendicular to the separation line, the transfer probability by dipole-dipole resonance interaction should vanish. When the respective transitions in randomly oriented donor and acceptor molecules are fully allowed and there is good donor-emission-acceptor-absorption spectral overlap, the dipole-induced dipole transfer predicted by Eq. (1) is significant even for separation distances of 50-100 Å. Förster[12,13] reported for the first time quantitative results for trypaflavin fluorescence quenching by rhodamine and demonstrated that transfer was effective over a distance of at least 70 Å. Since then many investigators have employed numerous donor-acceptor pairs to verify the dependence of singlet-singlet transfer efficiency on the average separation distance.[14-19] Of particular importance was the work of Bowen et al.[14-15] who found efficient energy transfer from 1-chloroanthracene to perylene in spite of the low fluorescence quantum efficiency of the donor ($\Phi_f = 0.05$). This indeed excluded trivial reabsorption as a possible mechanism in the sensitization process. The transfer rate constants for the 1-chloroanthracene-perylene pair in a variety of solvents at room temperature and in rigid matrix at 77°K were found to be viscosity-independent and significantly greater than those expected for diffusion-controlled processes. In all experiments with mixed concentrated solutions of donor and acceptor, an arbitrary estimate was made for the average separation distance between the two kinds of chromophores. Also, a value of 2/3 was used for K^2, corresponding to an assumed random relative orientation. Within these limitations, experimental results obtained for long range singlet-singlet sensitization,[12-18] fluorescence depolarization,[19] and distant triplet-singlet transfer[20-23] can be satisfactorily interpreted in terms of the inductive-resonance concept. Spectrophotofluorometry[24] has been used almost exclusively in singlet energy transfer experiments. In addition to usual emission and excitation spectroscopic measurements, this method specifically includes determinations of donor and acceptor fluorescence intensity as a function of acceptor concentration and measurements of radiative lifetime of donor or rise in acceptor emission.

TRIPLET-TRIPLET TRANSFER

Triplet-triplet sensitization was first observed in rigid solutions of mixed donor and acceptor at $77^{o}K$, when selective excitation of the donor led to phosphorescence from the acceptor.[25,26] Later, flash spectroscopy allowed observation of the phenomenon in fluid solution at room temperature by determination of T-T absorption in the acceptor.[27,28] Other efficient ways to investigate the migration of triplet energy in solution were provided by the use of α-diketones[29,30] or lanthanide ion acceptors[31,32] which exhibit quantitatively measureable luminescence in fluid solution corresponding to transitions involving a change of multiplicity of two. Useful information on triplet transfer has also been obtained from measurements on photosensitized reactions[33] e.p.r. determinations[34-36] and excitation with polarized light.[36,37]

Since it involves forbidden transitions in both donor and acceptor, triplet-triplet energy transfer is unlikely to occur over large distances. However, it becomes allowed by an exchange mechanism when there is spacial overlap of donor and acceptor orbitals.[38] Therefore, the probability of triplet energy transfer which is proportional to $|\int \Psi_{D_T} \Psi_{A_{S_O}} H' \Psi_{D_{S_O}} \Psi_{A_T} d\tau|^2$ should depend on relative orientation of the two chromophores. Contrary to theoretical predictions, triplet-triplet energy transfer at average distances of 15 Å has been reported.[25,26] At this separation the maximum value of the overlap integral of 2p orbitals on two carbon atoms is of the order of 10^{-17}. It is doubtful that this insignificant overlap could be responsible for triplet energy migration by exchange interaction. A vaguely defined "sphere of influence" or "active volume" has been postulated to reconcile theory with apparent experimental transfer distances.[25,39] Since all molecules have a nonspherical electron-cloud distribution one would expect the exchange transfer probability to depend not only on distance but on relative orientation as well.

INTRAMOLECULAR ENERGY TRANSFER

Intermolecular energy transfer studies outlined above have an essential limitation: One must use an arbitrary average value for the donor-acceptor separation distance and a random mutual orientation. The two parameters should be accurately defined, for they are critical in the detailed understanding of the transfer process. This inadequacy has led to experiments with model compounds in which the donor and acceptor chromophores are held within the same molecular framework in an attempt to fix the D-A separation distance and their relative orientation.

In some initial intramolecular energy transfer experiments using complex organic molecules, the spacial disposition of donor and acceptor chromophores and their average separation distance were as poorly defined as in the cosolute systems.[40-45]. Meaningful results were obtained only when the selected model compounds were specifically synthesized for energy transfer studies.

Schnepp and Levy[46] reported intramolecular energy transfer for three homologs of 9-anthryl-1'-naphthyl-alkanes (Structures 1-3) in which the anthracene and naphthalene chromophores are joined by saturated hydrocarbon chains of one, two, and three methylene units. On selective excitation of the naphthalene group only the anthracene chromophore fluorescence was detected. Calculated values for naphthalene to anthracene singlet-singlet energy transfer efficiencies were found to be identical for all three model compounds. Consequently, no conclusive information concerning the variation of energy transfer probability with donor-acceptor distance or orientation was obtained.

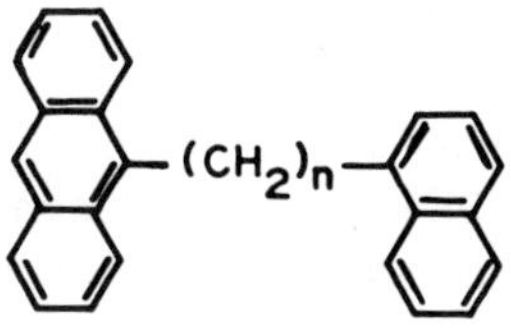

n= 1,2,3

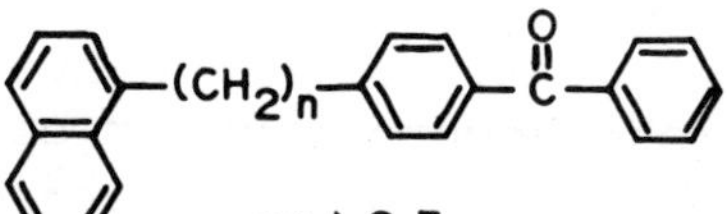

n= 1,2,3

1: n = 1
2: n = 2
3: n = 3

4: n = 1
5: n = 2
6: n = 3

Lamola et al.[47] replaced the anthracene moiety in models 1-3 with benzophenone (4-6). In mixed solutions of 4-methylbenzophenone and 1-methylnaphthalene in rigid matrix only characteristic benzophenone phosphorescence was observed regardless of the excitation wavelength. On the contrary for compounds 4, 5, and 6 only naphthalene phosphorescence was detected. It was concluded that energy migration from naphthalene to benzophenone chromophore was taking place in both mixture and model compounds via singlet-singlet resonance transfer. However, because of proximity of the two chromophores in model compounds 4-6, transfer of triplet energy from previously sensitized benzophenone back to naphthalene takes place by an exchange interaction. A similar methylene-separation study was reported recently by Breen and Keller (33) in which the acceptor naphthalene chromophore was separated from the donor phthalimide or carbazole by one, two, or three CH_2 groups. Again, complete transfer of excitation energy was observed.

In all above compounds interposing methylene groups did not lead to accurately known separation distances or mutual orientation because of free rotation in the CH_2 links. In addition, anomalous bands present in the absorption spectrum of model compounds but not in the equivalent separated-chromophores mixture must be attributed to charge-transfer complexation or some other mutual perturbation which removes the original premise of two independent chromophores.

Although the average distance was known more accurately for compounds in which the chromophores R_1 and R_2 were connected to the saturated bisteroidal frame in compounds 7 and 8, their mutual orientation was essentially random because of rotation about the connecting bond.[48] However, by assuming a totally random mutual orientation between R_1 and R_2 in compounds 7 and 8, Latt et al. obtained good agreement between the calculated critical transfer distance R_0 and those obtained from experiment.[48]

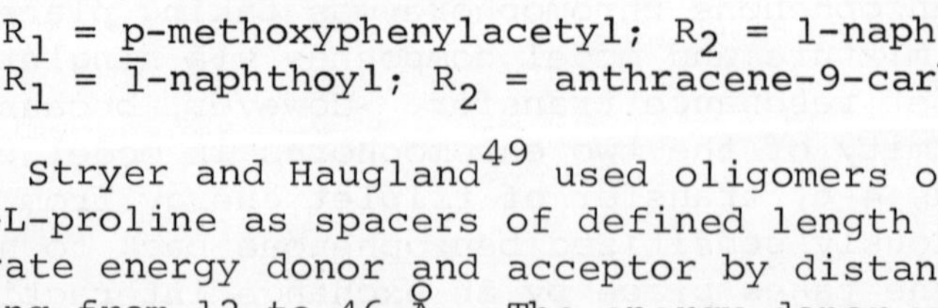

7: R_1 = p-methoxyphenylacetyl; R_2 = 1-naphthoyl
8: R_1 = 1-naphthoyl; R_2 = anthracene-9-carbonyl

Stryer and Haugland[49] used oligomers of poly-L-proline as spacers of defined length to separate energy donor and acceptor by distances ranging from 12 to 46 Å. The energy donor was an α-naphthyl group at the carboxyl end of the polypeptide, while the energy acceptor was a dansyl group at the imino end (9).

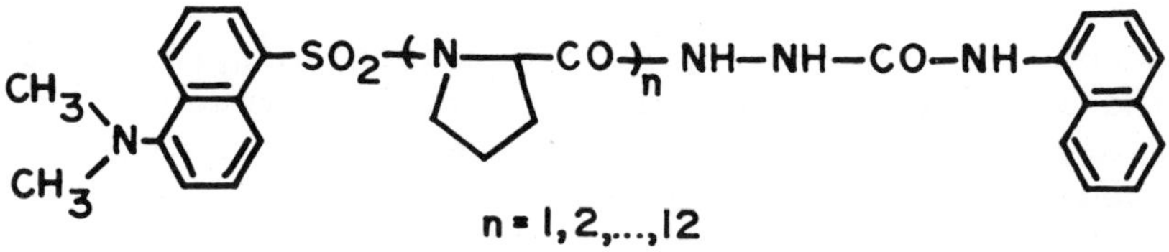

9

It seems that the polypeptide backbone assumes a helical conformation sufficiently defined to estimate separation distances between the two end groups. However, the angular relationship between the dansyl and α-naphthyl transition moments is substantially randomized by free rotation along the connecting σ-bonds.

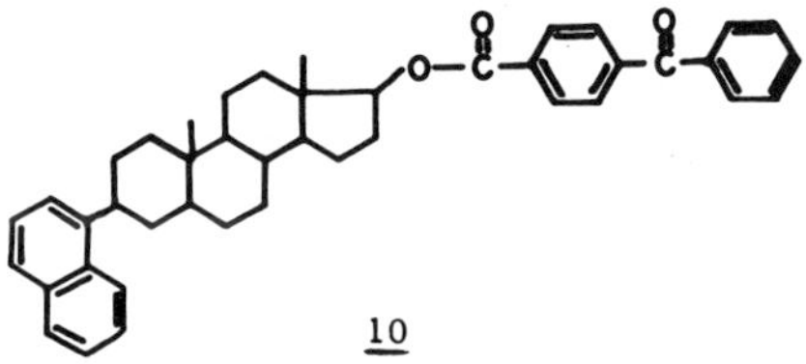

10

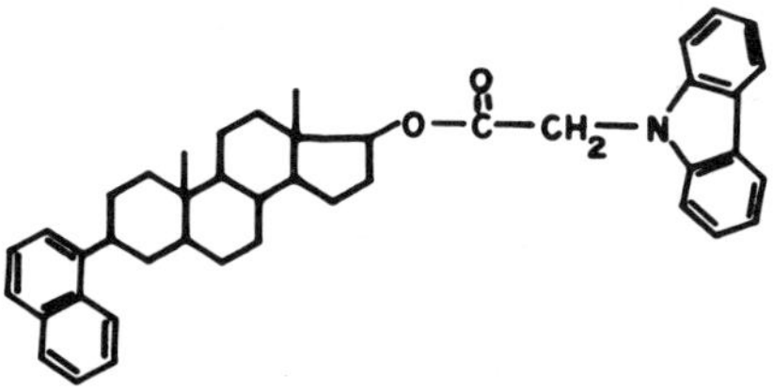

11

Keller and Dolby[50] have used benzophenone-4-carboxylic acid or carbazole triplet donors coupled with naphthalene acceptor in compounds 10 and 11, respectively. The chromophores were again connected to a steroidal frame by single bonds, rotating freely at about 10-16 Å in random orientation. To explain the 1000 times more efficient transfer in 10 compared to 11 the authors suggested spin-orbital coupling to the singlet in the donor combined with dipole-dipole transfer to the acceptor at the singlet level and intersystem crossing back to the triplet in the acceptor. Apparently such a mechanism agrees with the difference in triplet lifetimes between the two donors and with the absence of orbital overlap needed for exchange interaction.

Kuhn and coworkers have employed monomolecular layers of successive hydrophilic and hydrophobic carriers on which fluorescent dyes like 12-14 were absorbed.[51-53] The chromophores, having both hydrophobic and hydrophilic groups, can be combined in double layers where the separation of the chromosphore planes is between 0 and 60 Å.

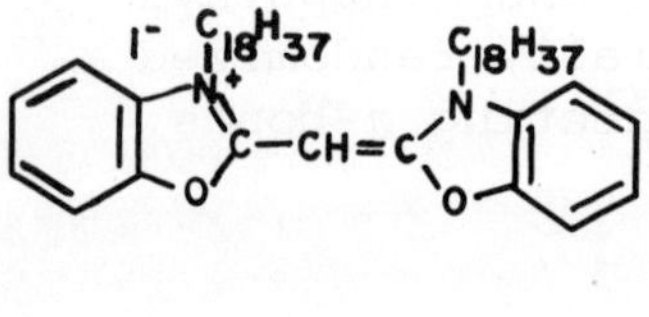

12

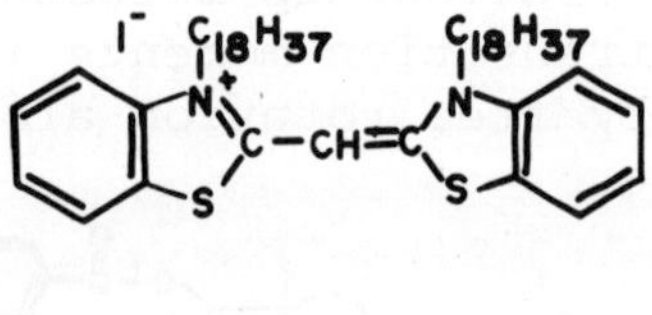

13

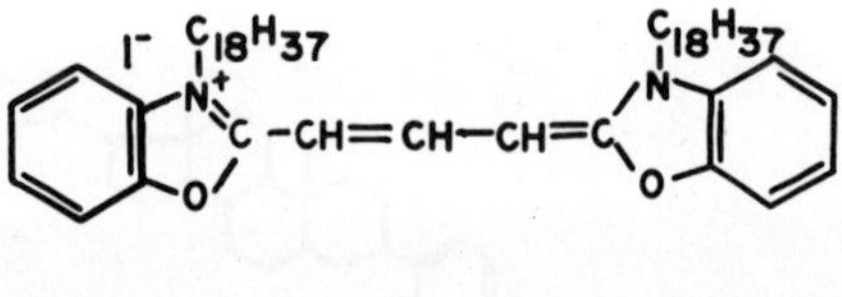

14

The dependence of singlet transfer efficiency on this distance was found to be consistent with the behavior predicted by the resonance theory.

In all molecular systems reviewed so far the mutual orientation of donor and acceptor molecules was essentially random. Only recently Keller has prepared model compounds having a distinct donor-acceptor relative orientation.[54] He presented evidence of total energy transfer between presumably perpendicular anthrone and naphthalene chromophores in <u>spiro</u>-compounds 15 and 16.

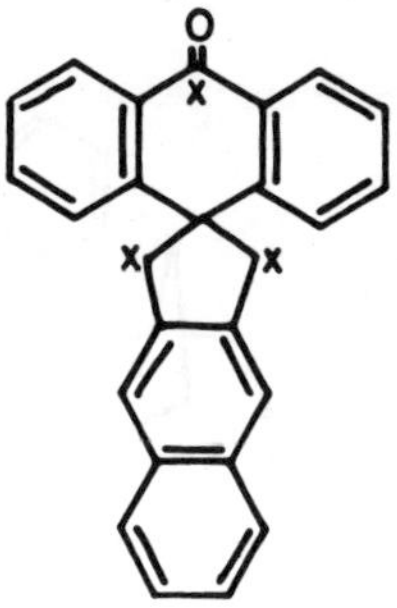

15

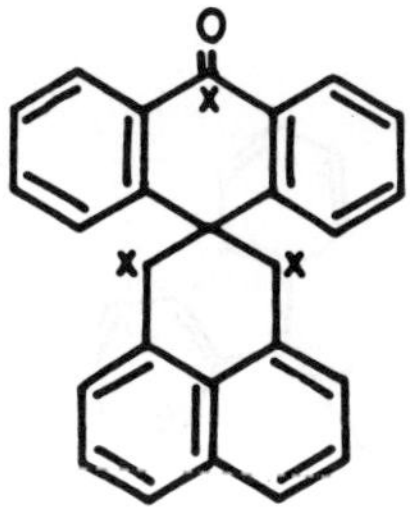

16

The author considered both dipole-dipole coupling and exchange interaction as very improbable mechanisms for either singlet-singlet or triplet-triplet transfer because of mutual orientation of respective transition dipoles and lack of orbital overlap. This conclusion seemed to contradict previously established transfer concepts. However, the explanation for occurrence of transfer in compounds 15 and 16 is probably found in the inaccurate evaluation of relative orientation. First, the anthrone chromophore is not planar, the center ring being tub-shaped. Second, rotation along the bonds marked by asterisks allows at least two conformers for each 15 and 16 with practically no activation energy for interconversion between the steroisomers. In addition, the assumption that n,π* lowest triplet energy in anthrone is localized exclusively in the carbonyl group is only a simplifying approximation for conjugated C=O chromophores. The subject of spiro-connected anthrone and naphthalene is again discussed at the present conference.[55]

Filipescu and DeMember have synthesized a model compound in which p-dimethoxybenzene and fluorene chromophores are rigidly connected to an inflexible norbornane-spirocyclopropane frame.[56,57]

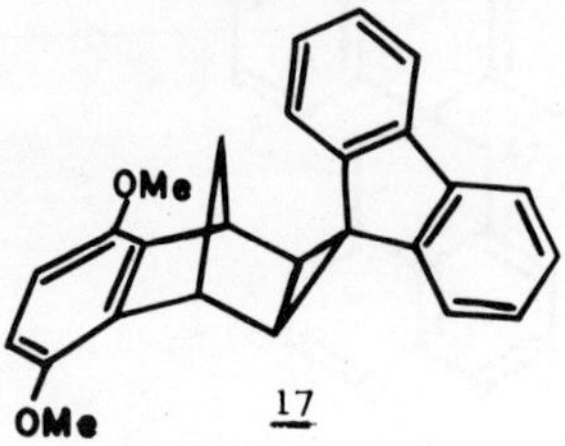

17

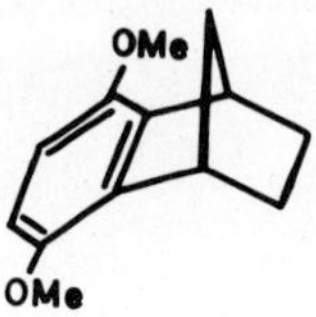

18

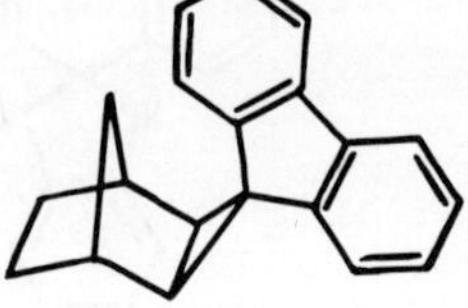

19

The exact positions of the two chromophores in 17 was unambiguously known and their lowest excited singlet and triplet states had appropriate energetic location for both S-S and T-T transfer. In random orientation in mixed solution (one-to-one, 10^{-3} M) of separated chromophores 18 and 19 efficient singlet-singlet transfer from fluorene to p-dimethoxybenzene was detected. At very large separation distances corresponding to 10^{-5} M concentration no interaction between 18 and 19 was observed.

When the same two chromophores were held at distances of less than 10 Å by an inflexible saturated frame in 17 in a mutually perpendicular orientation, no S-S or T-T transfer of energy could be detected. The absence of singlet transfer is consistent with theoretical predictions since the transition dipoles in the two chromophores are perpendicular to each other and to the line connecting the centers of the two chromophores.[57]

The fact that p-dimethoxybenzene triplet energy was not transferred to the lower fluorene triplet strongly suggested an orientation dependence for T-T transfer as well, since the two π-systems are only 7 Å apart in 17, well within the 12-16 Å distances reported for intermolecular exchange interaction.[25,26,34,58]

The concept of average separation distance between two cosolutes is well defined for dilute solutions in which no complexation or other kind of association occurs but it is rather misleading at very high concentrations at 77°K. Polar interactions and microcoprecipitation cannot be ruled out at such close proximity and low temperatures. In addition, the heat liberated by radiationless transitions from excited solute molecules may cause local melting of the glass matrix and thus decrease the actual distances of approach with respect to the values calculated assuming random distribution. The "active volume" concept[25] is obviously inadequate for the much better defined molecular system 17.

A preferential donor-acceptor orientation in T-T transfer has been reported by Roy and El-Sayed[59] for benzophenone-phenanthrene-d_{10} pair at 77°K. The two separated chromophores had random geometrical distribution and photoselection[60] had to be used to evaluate orientation. Considerable concentration depolarization in both donor and acceptor molecules and admitted possibility of association might have rendered the results inconclusive.

Siegel and Goldstein used magnetophotoselection to monitor T-T transfer in benzophenone-naphthalene-d_8 and phenanthrene-d_{10}-naphthalene-d_8 pairs dissolved in ethanol at 77°K.[36] They interpreted their data as proof that the probability of T-T transfer has practically no dependence on mutual donor-acceptor orientation. In their opinion, this result strongly discounted the need for chemical complex formation as operative mechanism in concentrated cosolute experiments. These conclusions are certainly contradicted by the absence of T-T transfer in compound 17.

Efficient but not total intramolecular triplet-triplet energy transfer between tetralin-1,4-dione and fluorene chromophores was reported recently by Filipescu and DeMember in rigid model compound 20.[56,62]

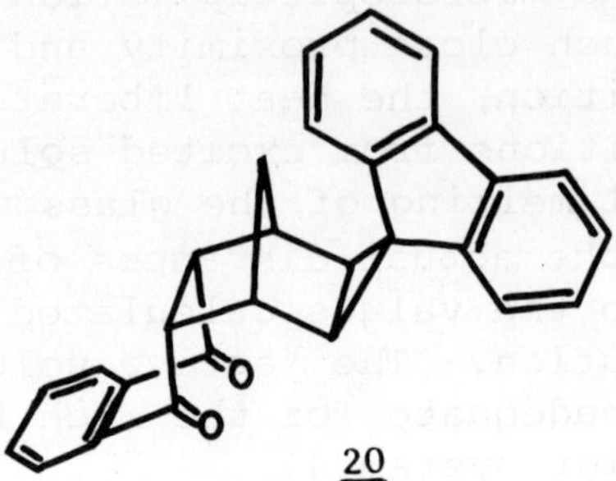

20

The stereographic representation of 20 is shown in Figure 1.

The edges of the two chromophores nearest to each other are the n-orbital on oxygen and the 2p orbital on C_1 of fluorene which are 5.2 Å apart. The overlap integral calculated with Slater 2p orbitals was of the order of 10^{-6}. Combined vibrational distortions in the connecting frame cannot change this insignificant overlap value since the C-C sigma bond is a rather stiff spring with a maximum amplitude in the fundamental stretching mode of 0.1 Å. The contour around the nonbonding n orbital on oxygen and the 2p atomic orbital on the C_1 atom in fluorene encloses more than 0.99999 of the probability density.

Direct frame participation to an exchange transfer seems to be ruled out by the absence of T-T transfer in model compound 17. An apparently possible mechanism for distant triplet-triplet energy migration in 20 is by dipole-dipole and quandrupole-dipole coupling of the singlet character admixed in the lowest triplet of the donor and acceptor chromophores.[62]

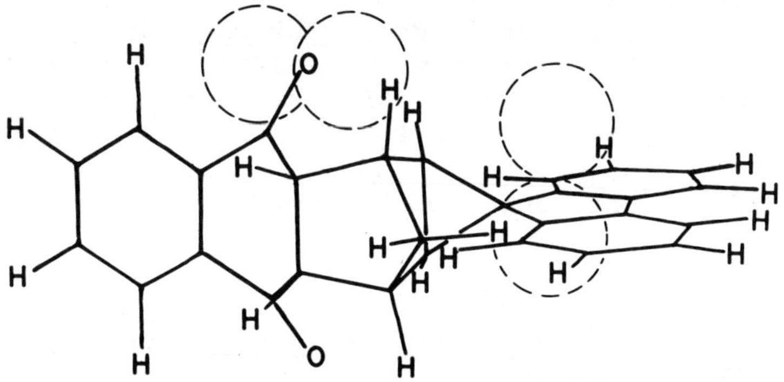

Figure 1 Stereographic view of model compound 20. The contour around the nonbonding n orbital on oxygen and the 2p atomic orbital on the C_1 atom in fluorene encloses more than 0.99999 of the probability density.

REFERENCES

1. For recent reviews see
   (a) N. J. Turro, Molecular Photochemistry, (Benjamin, New York, 1967), Chapter 5;
   (b) M. W. Windsor, "Luminescence and Energy Transfer," in Physics and Chemistry of the Organic Solid State, D. Fox, Ed. (Interscience, New York, 1965), Chapter 4, Vol. II.
   (c) F. Wilkinson, Quart. Revs. 20, 403 (1966).
2. J. T. Dubois and B. Stevens, Luminescence of Organic and Inorganic Molecules, (J. Wiley, New York, 1962).
3. J. T. Dubois and M. Cox, J. Chem. Phys. 38, 2536 (1963).
4. J. T. Dubois and R. L. Van Hemert, J. Chem. Phys. 40, 923 (1964).
5. A. D. Osborne and G. Porter, Proc. Roy. Soc. A284, 9 (1965).
6. J. Perrin, Compt. Rend. 184, 1097 (1927).
7. F. Perrin, Ann. Chim. Phys. 17, 283 (1932).
8. T. Förster, Naturwiss. 33, 166 (1946).
9. T. Förster, Ann. Physik. 2, 55 (1948).
10. T. Förster, Disc. Faraday Soc. 27, 7 (1959).
11. T. Förster, Fluoreszenz Organischer Verindungen (Vandenhoeck & Ruprecht, Göttingen, 1951).
12. T. Förster, Z. Naturforsch, 4a, 321 (1949).
13. T. Förster, Z. Elektrochem. 53, 93 (1949).
14. E. J. Bowen and R. Livingston, J. Am. Chem. Soc. 76, 6300 (1954).
15. E. J. Bowen and B. Brockelhurst, Trans. Faraday Soc. 49, 131 (1953); ibid. 51, 774 (1955).
16. R. G. Bennett, J. Chem. Phys. 41, 3037 (1964).
17. G. Weber, Biochem. J. 75, 335 (1960).
18. A. G. Tweet, W. D. Bellamy, and G. L. Gaines, J. Chem. Phys. 41, 2068 (1964).
19. G. Weber, Trans. Faraday Soc. 50, 552 (1954).

20. V. L. Ermolaev and E. B. Sveshnikova, Soviet Physics 8, 373 (1963).
21. V. L. Ermolaev, Opt. and Spectry. 17, 321 (1964).
22. R. E. Kellogg and R. G. Bennett, J. Chem. Phys. 41, 3042 (1964).
23. R. G. Bennett, R. P. Schwenker and R. E. Kellogg, J. Chem. Phys. 41, 3040 (1964).
24. F. Wilkinson and J. T. Dubois, J. Chem. Phys. 39, 377 (1963).
25. A. N. Terenin and V. L. Ermolaev, Trans. Faraday Soc. 52, 1042 (1956).
26. V. L. Ermolaev, Soviet Phys. Usp. 80, 333 (1963), English translation.
27. G. Porter and M. R. Wright, J. Chem. Phys. 55, 705 (1958).
28. G. Porter and F. Wilkinson, Proc. Roy. Soc. A264, 1 (1961).
29. H. L. J. Bäckström and K. Sandros, Acta Chem. Scand. 12, 823 (1958); ibid., 14, 48 (1960).
30. K. Sandros and H. L. J. Bäckström, Acta Chem. Scand. 16, 958 (1962).
31. A. Heller and E. Wasserman, J. Chem. Phys. 42, 949 (1965).
32. N. Filipescu and G. W. Mushrush, J. Phys. Chem. (in press, 1968).
33. G. S. Hammond et al., J. Am. Chem. Soc. 86, 3197 (1964); ibid. 86, 3203 (1964).
34. J. B. Farmer, C. L. Gardner and C. A. McDowell, J. Chem. Phys. 34, 1058 (1961).
35. B. Smaller, E. C. Avery, and J. R. Remko, J. Chem. Phys. 43, 922 (1965).
36. S. Siegel and L. Goldstein, J. Chem. Phys. 43, 4185 (1965).
37. J. K. Roy and M. A. El-Sayed, J. Chem. Phys. 40, 3442 (1964).
38. D. L. Dexter, J. Chem. Phys. 21, 836 (1953).
39. F. Perrin, Compt. Rend. 178, 1978 (1924).
40. G. Weber, Trans. Faraday Soc. 50, 552 (1954).
41. G. Weber, and F. W. J. Teale, Disc. Far. Soc. 27, 134 (1959).

42. V. Shore and A. Pardee, Arch. Biochem. Biophys. 62, 355 (1956).
43. G. Weber, Nature, 180, 1409 (1957).
44. T. T. Bannister, Arch. Biochem. Biophys. 49, 222 (1954).
45. R. Bersohn and I. Isenburg, J. Chem. Phys. 40, 3175 (1964).
46. O. Schnepp and M. Levy, J. Am. Chem. Soc. 84, 172 (1962).
47. A. A. Lamola, P. A. Leermakers, G. W. Byers and G. S. Hammond, J. Am. Chem. Soc. 85,2670 (1963); ibid. 87, 2322 (1965).
48. S. A. Latt, H. T. Cheung and E. R. Blout, J. Am. Chem. Soc. 87, 995 (1965).
49. L. Stryer and R. P. Haugland, Proc. Nat. Acad. Sci. 58, 719 (1967).
50. R. A. Keller and L. Dolby, J. Am. Chem. Soc. 89, 2768 (1967).
51. H. Kuhn, Pure Appl. Chem. 11, 345 (1966).
52. H. Kuhn, et al., Mol. Cryst. 2, 199 (1967).
53. H. Kuhn, Naturwiss. 54, 429 (1967).
54. R. A. Keller, J. Am. Chem. Soc. 90, 1940 (1968).
55. J. A. Hudson and R. M. Hedges, International Conference on Molecular Luminescence, Chicago, August 20-23, 1968.
56. N. Filipescu and J. R. DeMember, International Conference on Molecular Luminescence, Chicago, August 20-23, 1968.
August 20-23, 1968.
57. J. R. DeMember and N. Filipescu, J. Am. Chem. Soc. (scheduled for the November 1968 issue).
58. M. Inokuti and F. Hirayama, J. Chem. Phys. 43, 1978 (1965).
59. J. K. Roy and M. A. El-Sayed, J. Chem. Phys. 40, 3442 (1964).
60. A. C. Albrecht, J. Molec. Spectry. 6, 84 (1961).
61. S. Siegel and L. Goldstein, J. Chem. Phys. 43, 4185 (1965).
62. N. Filipescu and J. R. DeMember (to be published).

THE INTERSYSTEM CROSSING TO AND THE PHOSPHORESCENCE FROM THE INDIVIDUAL SUBLEVELS OF THE LOWEST TRIPLET STATE IN PYRAZINE AT 1.6°K

M. A. El-Sayed*

Department of Chemistry
University of California
Los Angeles, California 90024

I. INTRODUCTION

In the field of triplet state spectroscopy, two of the most active research areas are those involved in determining: (1) the exact mechanism(s) by which the absorbed singlet-singlet excitation is transferred to the lowest triplet state and (s) the exact mechanism(s) by which the lowest triplet state loses its energy by the emission of radiation (phosphorescence).

*Alfred P. Sloan and John Simon Guggenheim Fellow. Contribution No. 2285 from UCLA.

Studies in the first field consist of examining the fluorescence:phosphorescence intensity ratio as a function of the order of, and energy separation between, the low energy triplet states and the lowest singlet state. Nitrogen heterocyclics present an interesting series of compounds for such studies. Using the Born-Oppenheimer approximation, the one-electron spin-orbit operators, and the first-order perturbation theory, the following simple selection rules are concluded:[1] $S_{n,\pi^*} \leftrightsquigarrow T_{\pi,\pi^*}$; $S_{n,\pi^*} \not\leftrightsquigarrow T_{n,\pi^*}$; and $S_{\pi,\pi^*} \not\leftrightsquigarrow T_{\pi,\pi^*}$. The luminescence properties of a great number of heterocyclic compounds are found to be explained using these simple selection rules. Exceptions can also be found. However, this qualitative technique is subjected to complications resulting from photochemical changes and radiationless transitions from the lowest singlet state to the ground state. Recently, the decay results of quinoxaline (1,4-diazanaphthalene) phosphorescence in durene and its dependence on magnetic field have been found to be at least qualitatively explained[2] by an intersystem crossing process which follows the above selection rules. Instead of using flash techniques,[2] we have used steady state experiments which have enabled us to extract more constants characterizing the decay and the intersystem crossing processes in pyrazine (1,4-diazabenzene) in host lattices.

Studies concerning the phosphorescence mechanisms are done by determining the emission polarization of the molecule of interest dissolved in a suitable host at low temperatures.[3] All the polarization measurements have been done so far at temperatures for which the spin-lattice relaxation between the three sublevels is faster than the radiative lifetime. Under these conditions, the observed emission is a superposition of the emission from the different sublevels of the triplet state. If the zero field splitting in the emitting triplet state is large enough to be resolved on a high-resolution spectrograph, one can measure the polarization of the individual emission lines from each sublevel of the triplet state. So far, this method has not yet been employed (perhaps due to the large line width as compared to the zero field splitting). However, one might be able to observe individual sublevel emissions by resolving them in time rather than in energy. This is possible at very low temperatures and in cases for which the spin-lattice relaxation process between the different spin sublevels is slower than the radiative lifetimes from these states. When this is possible, the phosphorescence mechanisms from the individual sublevels of the lowest triplet state can be revealed. The preliminary results obtained for the pyrazine emission are here summarized, discussed and compared with theoretical predictions.

II. THEORETICAL CONSIDERATIONS CONCERNING THE INTERSYSTEM CROSSING PROCESS IN PYRAZINE

A. DIRECT SPIN-ORBIT PERTURBATION. Pyrazine molecule belongs to the D_{2h} point group. Its lowest singlet state is of the $^1B_{3u}(n,\pi^*)$ type (the x and z axes correspond to the out-of-plane and the N...N axes, respectively, in the pyrazine molecule). The three spin functions, τ_x, τ_y and τ_z, belong* to the b_{3g}, b_{2g} and b_{1g} irreducible representation respectively, whereas the singlet state spin function is of an a_g symmetry. For an allowed intersystem crossing process between two states, selection rules require that the electronic integral of the radiationless transition

*It is shown[2] that these three functions describe the two spins in the yz, xz and xy planes respectively for molecules of C_{2v} or containing C_{2v} symmetry.

probability between the two states not vanish. Independent of which theory, Robinson's and Frosch's or Gouterman's, the electronic integral involves the mixing of the singlet and triplet states with the spin-orbit type of interaction. In both theories, the Born-Oppenheimer approximation is assumed. If the perturbation results from the direct spin-orbit interaction ($H_{s.o.}$), the electronic integral can be shown to have the following form:

$$\langle {}^1\Psi_{n,\pi^*} | H_{s.o.} | {}^3\Psi_x \rangle \quad (1)$$

There are at least two triplet states, $^3B_{1u}(\pi,\pi^*)$ and $^3B_{3u}(n,\pi^*)$, below the lowest singlet state, with the latter state being lowest in energy. The $^3B_{2g}(n,\pi^*)$ might be above the lowest triplet state. The corresponding spin-orbit functions of these triplet states are given in Table 1.

The spin-orbit function of the lowest singlet state is $B_{3u} \times a_g = B_{3u}$. Since $H_{s.o.}$ is an interaction energy, it should be totally symmetric (even though the individual orbital part or the spin part of the operator is non-totally symmetric in the electron space and spin domain respectively). Thus the only nonradiative transitions involved in the intersystem crossing process from the $^1B_{3u}(n,\pi^*)$ state are those crossing to a triplet state of total spin-orbit function of symmetry B_{3u}. Only the $^3B_{1u}(\pi,\pi^*)$ state having a spin function τ_y satisfies this selection rule. This is in agreement with previous theoretical predictions[1] that $S_{n,\pi^*} \leftrightsquigarrow T_{\pi,\pi^*}$ is allowed but $S_{n,\pi^*} \leftrightsquigarrow T_{n,\pi^*}$ is forbidden.

It is clear that, as a result of the selection rules imposed on the intersystem crossing process in pyrazine, the triplet state is initially formed from the lowest singlet state with its unpaired electrons in the xz molecular plane. It is thus obvious that as a result of excitation in the singlet manifold and because of the selection

TABLE 1: The Spin-orbit Functions of the Different Triplet States that are Located Below the Lowest Singlet State ($^1B_{3u}$ n, π*) in Pyrazine

Triplet state	Spin function	Spin orbit functions[a]
$^3B_{1u}(\pi,\pi^*)$	τ_x	B_{2u}
	τ_y	$\underline{B_{3u}}$
	τ_z	A_u
$^3B_{2g}(n,\pi^*)$	τ_x	B_{1g}
	τ_y	A_g
	τ_z	B_{3g}
$^3B_{3u}(n,\pi^*)$	τ_x	A_u
	τ_y	B_{1u}
	τ_z	B_{2u}

[a] The underlined state has nonvanishing electronic integral in the radiationless transition probability expression for the intersystem crossing process from the $B_{3u}(n,\pi^*)$ singlet level.

rules of the intersystem crossing process, the triplet state is first formed in a spin-polarized state. At temperatures for which the spin-lattice relaxation time is slower than 10^{-11} sec (the time for the internal conversion process in the triplet manifold), the molecule loses vibration and electronic energy, but not spin direction, until it finally reaches the lowest triplet state. Since the lowest triplet state is of $^3B_{3u}(n,\pi^*)$ spatial symmetry and the spin of the molecule is polarized in the xz plane ($\Gamma_{\tau_y} = b_{2g}$), the triplet total function is of B_{1u} symmetry. At temperatures for which the spin-lattice relaxation is slower than the emission lifetime from the B_{1u} sublevel, the emission characteristics of the molecule are completely determined by the radiative properties of this sublevel.

B. SPIN-VIBRONIC AND SECOND-ORDER PERTURBATIONS. One might wonder whether or not spin-vibronic or second-order (spin-orbit-vibronic) perturbations could introduce new intersystem crossing routes which could result in forming the lowest triplet state with its spin polarized in the other two planes (the xy and yz planes). The spin-vibronic perturbation is written in the following form:

$$H_{s.v.} = \sum_a \left(\frac{\partial H_{s.o.}}{\partial Q_a}\right)_0 Q_a \tag{2}$$

where the Q_a's are the normal coordinates of the different normal modes of the pyrazine molecule. Since $H_{s.v.}$ is totally symmetric, $\Gamma\left(\frac{\partial H_{s.o.}}{\partial Q_a}\right)_0$ would have the same symmetry property in the electron-spin-space domain as does Q_a in the nuclear domain. The spin vibronic integral can then be written as:

$$<^1\psi^1\theta^1X|H_{s.v.}|^3\psi^3\theta^3X> =$$

$$\sum_a <^1\psi^1X|\left(\frac{\partial H_{s.o.}}{\partial Q_a}\right)_0|^3\psi^3X><^1\theta|Q_a|^3\theta> \qquad (3)$$

where Ψ, θ and X are the electronic, vibration and spin functions respectively. Since $^1\theta$ is of a_g symmetry at low temperatures (the zero point function of the lowest singlet state), the perturbation in electronic space $\left(\frac{\partial H_{s.o.}}{\partial Q_a}\right)_0$ must have the the same symmetry as Q_a. The latter should have the same symmetry as $^3\theta$, the perturbing vibration in the triplet state, i.e., $\Gamma\left(\frac{\partial H_{s.o.}}{\partial Q_a}\right) = \Gamma_{^3\theta}$. From equation (3), and the last conclusion, $\Gamma_{^1\psi^1X} \times \Gamma_{^3\psi^3X} = \Gamma_{^3\theta}$. Using this equality, the symmetry type of perturbing vibrations in the triplet manifold ($\Gamma_{^3\theta}$) that might be responsible for the different intersystem crossing processes between the $B_{3u}(n,\pi^*)$ state and the three triplet states below it is concluded and given in Table 2. The spin polarization that results from the spin-vibronic interaction with the different vibrations in different triplet states is also given in the same table. Since the molecular vibrations in pyrazine are distributed over all the symmetry species in the D_{2h} point group, it is concluded that group theory does not impose restrictions on the route to be followed by the pyrazine molecule undergoing an intersystem crossing process under spin-vibronic-type perturbation. But how important is the spin-vibronic interaction as compared to the direct spin-orbit interaction? In order to answer this question, let us use Albrecht's[6] approximate equation:

$$<\Psi_T|\left(\frac{\partial H_{s.o.}}{\partial Q_a}\right)_0 Q_a|\Psi_S> = \xi<\Psi_T|H_{s.o.}|\Psi_S> \qquad (4)$$

TABLE 2: The Types of Vibrations Involved in the Spin Vibronic Perturbations that might be Involved in the Intersystem Crossing Process in Pyrazine

Triplet state	Spin function	Vibration of the triplet state
$^3B_{1u}(\pi,\pi^*)$	τ_x	b_{1g}
	τ_y	a_g
	τ_z	b_{3g}
$^3B_{2g}(n,\pi^*)$	τ_x	b_{2u}
	τ_y	b_{3u}
	τ_z	a_u
$^3B_{3u}(n,\pi^*)$	τ_x	b_{3g}
	τ_y	b_{2g}
	τ_z	b_{1g}

where ξ is a constant ≈ a typical nuclear displacement/a typical molecular dimension $\leq 10^{-1}$. It thus follows that:

$$|\langle\Psi_T|\left(\frac{\partial H_{s.o.}}{\partial Q_a}\right)_0 Q_a|\Psi_S\rangle| \leq 10^{-1}|\langle\Psi_T|H_{s.o.}|\Psi_S\rangle| \quad (5)$$

This equation is found to explain the fact that more than 99% of the total intensity of the pyrazine emission is explained by direct spin-orbit orbit perturbation. It is thus concluded that, according to group theory, spin-vibronic perturbation can give rise to spin polarization in any direction, but the perturbation is probably weaker than the direct spin-orbit perturbation in the framework of the Born-Oppenheimer approximation.

Let us turn our attention to the second-order spin-orbit-vibronic perturbation, but neglect the second-order spin-vibronic-vibronic perturbation. In this type of perturbation, vibronic coupling mixes states in the triplet manifold. This is then followed by spin-orbit interaction with the $^1B_{3u}(n,\pi^*)$ state. The latter state interacts only with states of $^3B_{1u}$ and $^3B_{2u}$ symmetry via spin-orbit perturbation. The interaction with the first state results in a spin polarization in the xz plane and that with the latter state gives rise to spin polarization in the xy plane. The $^3B_{1u}$, $^3B_{2g}$ and $^3B_{3u}$ states that are located below the lowest singlet state can vibronically couple to the $^3B_{2u}$ state by vibration of b_{3g}, a_u and b_{1g} symmetry respectively. This is the only vibronic coupling that can give rise to spin polarization different from that produced by the direct spin-orbit interaction.

In conclusion, if the crystal field is very weak and pyrazine is assumed to have D_{2h} symmetry, group theory predicts that the intersystem crossing process gives rise to spin polarization only in the xz plane if direct spin-orbit perturbation is important, in the xz and xy planes if second-order spin-orbit-vibronic perturbation is important, and in all three planes if spin-vibronic perturbation is important. If spin-lattice relaxation is very slow, spin polarization can be obtained under steady state excitation in the latter case if the three different spin-vibronic routes have different transition probabilities or if the rate of deactivation of the three sublevels is different. It should be mentioned that the above selection rules can be relaxed if the crystal field is strong and the site symmetry strongly changes the internal D_{2h} symmetry of the molecule.

III. INTRAMULTIPLET NONRADIATIVE PROCESSES IN THE LOWEST TRIPLET STATE

SPIN-LATTICE RELAXATION. As a result of the intersystem crossing process in pyrazine, the phosphorescence can originate from a spin-polarized state under the following conditions:

(1) The spin-lattice relaxation time is slower than both the triplet-triplet internal conversion process and the phosphorescence process.

(2) The perturbation(s) responsible for the intersystem crossing process ($S_1 \rightsquigarrow T_1$ and $T_1 \rightsquigarrow S_0$) are such that they result in different population for the three different multiplets of the triplet manifold.

It was concluded in the previous section that (a) first-order (direct) spin-orbit perturbation can populate only one sublevel (τ_y), (b) the second-order spin-orbit-vibronic perturbation can populate both τ_y and τ_z, and (c) the spin-vibronic perturbation can populate the three sublevels. The relative probability of populating the different sublevels by the last two perturbations is unknown theoretically. However, it is expected that the direct spin-orbit perturbation is the most probable. Therefore if condition (1) is satisfied, it is expected that the phosphorescence is emitted from a spin-polarized state. For this reason, we will summarize below the factors that determine spin-lattice relaxation time.

The mechanisms involved in the spin-lattice relaxation process of a paramagnetic impurity in an ionic solid have been carefully examined both experimentally and theoretically.[7] Waller[8] proposed a mechanism in 1932 in which the modulation of the magnetic dipolar interaction by the phonon field of lattice vibrations causes spin-lattice relaxation. This mechanism does not explain the observed temperature and magnetic field effects on the relaxation process. Heitler and Teller[9] pointed out that the modulation of the electric field by the lattice vibrations could modulate the orbital motion of the electron, which is coupled to the spin motion via spin-orbit coupling. The modulation of the orbital motion is then felt by the spin system and as a result undergoes spin relaxation. The theory for this mechanism was later developed quantitatively.[10] A number of processes are now known to be responsible for the spin-lattice relaxation and they differ in their temperature dependence. The direct process prevails at low temperatures and involves the exchange of the spin quantum with one phonon. This process is found to have a spin relaxation time T_1 which is inversely proportional to the absolute temperature (T). The Raman process in which the spin system absorbs a quantum of one frequency and scatters that of another is important at higher temperatures. This process is found to give a relaxation time T_1, which is proportional to T^{-7} (or T^{-9}). In some systems in which the crystal field splitting Δ is smaller than the maximum phonon energy, a third mechanism is found which accounts for their relaxation process. This mechanism involves the simultaneous absorption of a phonon of energy δ', and the emission of another of energy $\delta' + \delta$ along with spin flip from one spin level to a lower one having a separation of δ. This process[11] has a relaxation time $T_1 \alpha e^{-\Delta/kT}$.

Spin-lattice relaxation processes of a spin impurity in molecular crystals have not as yet been carefully investigated. The presence of spin system in the ground state of molecular crystals (free radicals) is not too common. The triplet state, however, can offer a method of introducing unpaired spins in molecular crystals. It would be interesting to determine T_1 in molecular crystals, compare it with that observed in ionic crystals, and examine the importance of the above mechanisms in the process of spin-lattice relaxation in molecular crystals. In all the above mechanisms, the relaxation time is found to be inversely proportional to the square of both the orbital-lattice interaction (H_{OL}) and the spin-orbit interaction (H_{SO}). In addition to H_{OL} and H_{SO}, quantities like the velocity of sound, phonon density and occupation number enter into the expression for the spin-lattice relaxation time.

IV. SUMMARY AND DISCUSSION OF THE DECAY RESULTS

It is well-known[3] that the pyrazine phosphorescence in rigid glasses has a lifetime of $\sim$ 20 millisec at 77°K. The fact that the quantum yield is 0.5 indicates that the observed lifetime is very close to the radiative one. The calculated lifetime, using the S.O. coupling between the ${}^3B_{3u} \leftrightsquigarrow {}^1A_g$ transition and both the ${}^3B_{3u} \leftrightsquigarrow {}^3B_{2g}$ and the ${}^1B_{1u} \rightarrow {}^1A_g$ transitions, is found[12] to be in good agreement with the observed one.

In cyclohexane or benzene matrix, the pyrazine phosphorescence is found to be exponential with only one lifetime of 18 millisec at 77°K. At 1.6°K, a nonexponential decay is observed which can be resolved[13] into three exponential decays of lifetimes: 6, 130 and 400 millisec. These lifetimes remain constant in the temperature range 1.6-3°K. At 4.2°K, the three lifetimes resolved are: 6, 60 and 320 millisec. Between 4.2-10°K, the decay is rather nonexponential and complex and above 10°K, the decay becomes exponential with only one lifetime, 18 millisec (the same as that observed at 77°K). The decay characteristics change by the application of a magnetic field at 1.6°K (see Figure 1) and 4.2°K but not at 77°K.

The fact that the long- and medium-lived components disappear above 10°K eliminates the possibility that the emission is due to impurities. The great change in the decay curve between 1.6°K and 10°K is not accompanied by any change in the relative intensity of the emission of the different sites. This eliminates the possibility that the three decays belong to emission from three different sites. In addition, the same decay constants are obtained in two different hosts, cyclohexane and benzene, in which the distribution and the energy of the different sites are different. The fact that the three different decays are observed for the 0,0 as well as for other vibronic bands might eliminate the possibility that the emission results from states of different electronic origin (e.g., $^3B_{3u}$ as well as $^3B_{2g}$ or $^3B_{1u}$). It is thus very probable that we are observing emission from molecules in different sublevels of the triplet state. In support of this is the great sensitivity of the three decay constants to the magnetic field strength. In the following section, we will propose mechanisms that might successfully explain the observed results.

Following the absorption process (see Figure 2), the excited pyrazine molecules are deactivated to the zero point level of the lowest $^1B_{3u}(n,\pi^*)$ state in $\sim 10^{-11}$ sec. This is followed by the intersystem crossing processes discussed in

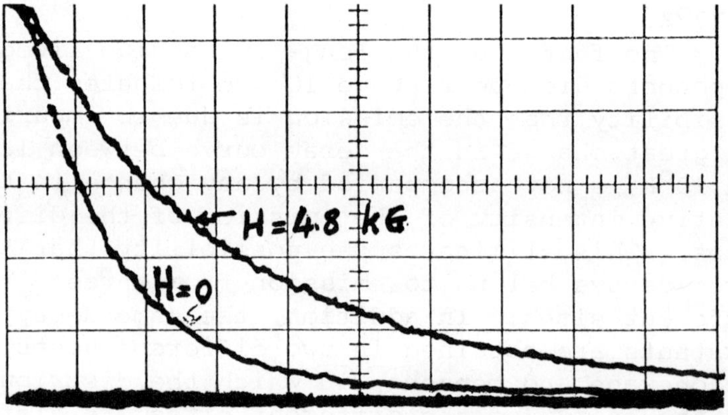

Figure 1 The effect of 4.8 k Gauss magnetic field on the decay of pyrazine phosphorescence in benzene matrix at 1.6°K. The horizontal axis represents time (5 msec/div.) and the vertical axis is a linear relative intensity scale. The decay curve at bottom is recorded in the absence of the magnetic field, whereas that on top is that in the presence of the field. The apparent increase in lifetime on the application of the field is actually a result of an increase in the lifetime of the short-lived component and a decrease in the lifetimes of the other two long-lived components of the decay.

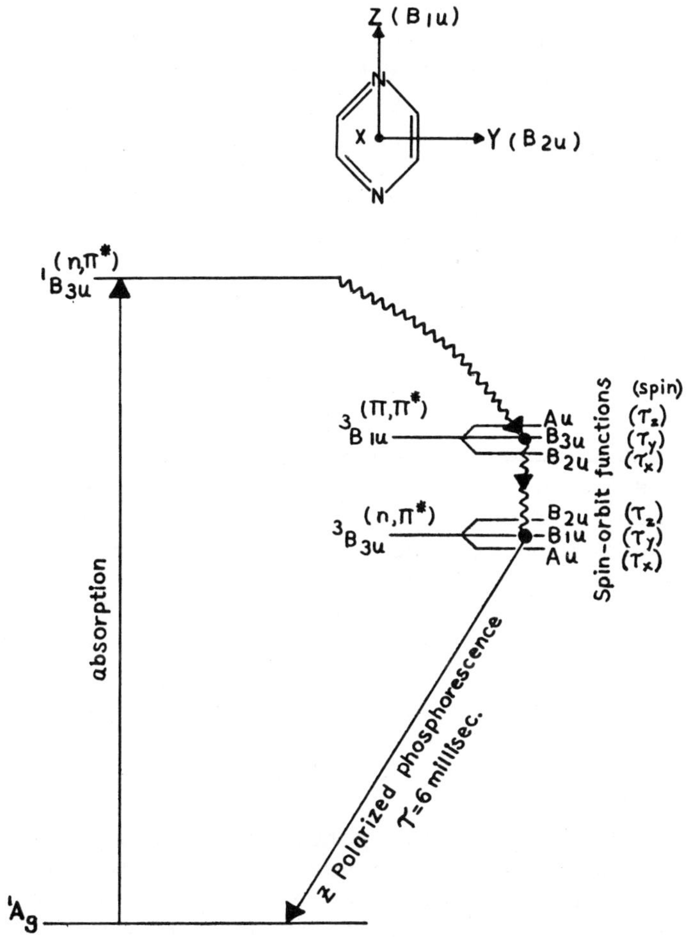

Figure 2 Spin polarization and phosphorescence resulting from the most probable intersystem crossing route and following the direct absorption in pyrazine at temperatures for which the spin-lattice relaxation is slower than the phosphorescence as well as the internal conversion processes. The different spin sublevels of the $^3B_{1u}(\pi, \pi^*)$ and $^3B_{3u}(n, \pi^*)$ triplet states are drawn arbitrarily in the order of increasing energy, $\tau_x(B_{3g})$, $\tau_y(B_{2g})$ and $\tau_z(B_{1g})$.

Section II. The $^1B_{3u}(n,\pi^*) \rightsquigarrow {}^3B_{1u}(\pi,\pi^*)$ process (which corresponds to a transition between states of total functions of B_{3u} symmetry) is shown in Section II to be the most probable intersystem crossing process in pyrazine. We will first follow the fate of those molecules that cross to the triplet manifold via the latter process. The intersystem crossing process is followed by the internal conversion process $^3B_{1u}(\pi,\pi^*)$ $(\tau_y) \leftrightsquigarrow {}^3B_{3u}(n,\pi^*)$ (τ_y), which takes place in $\sim 10^{-11}$ sec. At 1.6°K, this time is short compared to the spin-lattice time, T_1. Thus the molecules are found in the $^3B_{3u}(n,\pi^*)$ state with the spinning electrons in the xz plane. Whether the emission will result only from the τ_y sublevel of the triplet state or from the others depends mainly on the magnitude of the spin-lattice relaxation time (T_1) between the different spin levels as compared to the radiative lifetime of the transition from the τ_y sublevel to the ground state. In pyrazine, the triplet sublevel τ_y of the $^3B_{3u}(n,\pi^*)$ state strongly couples to the $^1B_{1u}(\pi,\pi^*)$ by first-order spin-orbit perturbation to give rise to the observed N...N-polarized* phosphorescence. Thus the sublevel which is populated as a result of the most probable intersystem crossing process is the one that has the strongest radiative transition probability. The observed radiative lifetime of the $B_{3u}(n,\pi^*)$ $(\tau_y) \rightarrow {}^1A_g$ is thus 6 millisec (not 18 millisec as has been previously assumed).

There are at least two possible mechanisms that might explain the medium- and long-lived emission. In both mechanisms, we will assume that either vibronic and second-order spin-orbit-

*The mixing between the ground state and τ_y function of the $^3B_{2g}(n,\pi^*)$ state gives rise to N...N polarized emission[12] due to the radiative charge transfer transition $^3B_{3u}(n,\pi^*)$ $(\tau_y) \leftrightarrow {}^3B_{2g}(n,\pi^*)$.

vibronic or crystal field perturbations succeed in populating the other two sublevels of the lowest triplet state (τ_x and τ_z). The observed medium- or long-lived emission can result from one (or both) of the following mechanisms:

$$\tau_z \text{ or } \tau_x \xrightarrow{\text{S.L.R.}} \tau_y \rightarrow (\text{phosphorescence})_a \qquad \text{(a)}$$

$$\tau_z \text{ or } \tau_x \rightarrow (\text{phosphorescence})_b \qquad \text{(b)}$$

Mechanism (a) is effective when spin-lattice relaxation (S.L.R.) time is shorter than the radiative lifetime from sublevels τ_x or τ_z. Mechanism (b) is operative if the spin-lattice relaxation process is slower than the radiative process from the three sublevels. If mechanism (a) is the correct one, then the lifetimes of 130 and 400 millisec observed at 1.6°K represent spin-lattice relaxation times from τ_x or τ_z to τ_y.

It is obvious that the polarization of phosphorescence (a) and that of (b) should be different. The polarization of phosphorescence (a) should be similar to that for the short-lived emission (along the N...N axis), whereas that of phosphorescence (b) should be differently polarized. The polarization of the decay curve has recently been measured,[16] and the results show that at least the medium- and short-lived emissions appear to have slightly different polarizations. This indicates that at least part of the medium-lived emission originates according to mechanism (b).

V. COMPARISON OF THEORY AND EXPERIMENTS

A. THE RADIATIVE PROCESS. Goodman and Krishna calculated[12] for the radiative lifetime of the $^3B_{3u} \rightarrow {}^1A_g$ transition a value of one millisec. They used the $^1B_{1u} \leftrightarrow {}^1A_g$ and the $^3B_{2g} \leftrightarrow {}^3B_{3u}$ to perturb the $^3B_{3u}$ and ^1A_g states respectively. In both cases one can show that the τ_y sublevel of the triplet state is involved. They compared their calculated result with the lifetime observed at 77°K instead of the radiative lifetime of the τ_y sublevel. The relation between the observed value of the lifetime and those observed for the individual components is given below.

At temperatures for which the S.L.R. is very fast as compared to the radiative lifetimes, the observed rate constant for the emission is given[2] by:

$$k = \sum_{i}^{3} n_i k_i$$

where n_i and k_i are the fraction population and the radiative rate constant of sublevel i of the lowest triplet state. At this temperature $n_i = 1/3$ and the above formula is written as: $k = 1/3$ $(k_{\tau_x} + k_{\tau_y} + k_{\tau_z})$. For pyrazine, one can neglect k_{τ_x} and k_{τ_z} as compared to k_{τ_y}. This leads to a value of $k = 1/3 \times 1/6 = 1/18$ millisec^{-1}, corresponding to a lifetime of 18 millisec in excellent agreement with the observed value at 77°K. It is interesting to point out that only if $k_{\tau_x} = k_{\tau_y} = k_{\tau_z}$ would the observed lifetime equal that observed from any of the individual lifetimes at very low temperatures.

Let us discuss the radiative mechanism of the medium-lived emission. If one assumes that the short-lived emission is polarized along the N...N axis (z axis), then the medium-lived emission might be polarized along the y or the x molecular axes. Work is now in progress to determine the exact polarization direction. Theoretically, in addition to the z-polarized emission, only y-polarized emission is predicted to originate as a result of direct spin-orbit interaction in the D_{2h} point group. Since most of the emission is a result of direct spin-orbit perturbation, x-polarized emission should not be emitted if the molecule has a D_{2h} site symmetry. The medium-lived emission might thus be y-polarized and thus originate from perturbing the emitting triplet state $B_{3u}(n,\pi^*)$ (τ_z) with the $B_{2u}(\pi,\pi^*) \leftrightarrow {}^1A_g$. Certainly, the latter transition is electric dipole-allowed. Its inferior perturbation (as compared to that giving rise to the short-lived emission) is blamed on the fact that the spin-orbit interaction involved has no one-center terms on the nitrogen, as shown below:

$$\langle {}^3B_{3u}(n,\pi^*)\ (\tau_z)|H_{s.o.}|{}^1B_{2u}(\pi,\pi^*)\rangle =$$

$$\langle (n,\pi_4)|H_{s.o.}|\pi_3,\ \pi_4\rangle = \langle n|H_{s.o.}|\pi_3\rangle \qquad (6)$$

Since π_3 has a node plane perpendicular to the molecular plane and passing through the nitrogen atoms, integral (6) has no one-center terms on the nitrogen. The only one-center terms that can result from integral (6) are those on the carbon atoms arising because of the delocalization of the lone pair of electrons on the C-C and C-H bonds. It might be interesting to estimate the ratio of the spin-orbit interaction resulting from this mechanism as compared to that resulting from the radiative perturbation of the τ_y sublevel. The latter is perturbed by the ${}^1B_{1u}(\pi,\pi^*)$ state, which gives rise to the following integral:

$$\langle B_{3u}(n,\pi^*)\ (\tau_y)|H_{s.o.}|{}^1B_{1u}(\pi,\pi^*)\rangle = (n,\pi_4|$$

$$H_{s.o.}|\pi_2,\pi_4) = \langle n|H_{s.o.}|\pi_2) \qquad (6)$$

Since π_2 has no nodes through the nitrogen atoms, one-center terms on the nitrogen and the carbon atoms (because of the delocalization of the lone pairs) are nonvanishing.

If one makes the following assumptions: (a) the observed 6-millisec and 120 millisec lifetimes for the short- and medium-lived emission correspond to radiative lifetimes, and (b) the intensity and energy of the $^1B_{1u} \leftrightarrow {}^1A_g$ and $^1B_{2u} \leftarrow$ $\rightarrow A_g$ transitions are comparable, then

$$\left| \frac{\langle B_{3u}(n,\pi^*)|H_{s.o.}|B_{1u}(\pi,\pi^*)\rangle}{\langle B_{3u}(n,\pi^*)|H_{s.o.}|B_{2u}(\pi,\pi^*)\rangle} \right|^2 \geq \frac{1/6}{1/120}$$

$$\geq \frac{120}{6} \geq 20$$

i.e., the spin-orbit interaction having one-center terms on the nitrogen and carbon is $\geq$ 4.5 times larger than that with only one-center terms on carbon. This fact might support the recent calculations[17] showing large delocalization of the lone pairs in pyrazine.

B. NONRADIATIVE INTERSYSTEM CROSSING PROCESSES. The decay measurements are performed in the following manner. The steady state illumination of pyrazine is cut off in 1 millisec with a shutter which simultaneously triggers the scope. The reproducibility of the decay curve is excellent. Decay curves are followed up to 2 sec, i.e., over 300 short lifetimes, seventeen medium lifetimes and five long lifetimes. From log I vs time plots, the different decay components can be resolved successfully at 1.6°K. By extrapolating log I vs time to t = 0, the initial steady state intensity I_s^0, I_m^0 and I_l^0 of the emission from molecules in the τ_y, τ_z and τ_x sublevels is determined.

Let us consider the short- (s) and medium- (m) lived emission. The short-lived emission originates from the τ_y sublevel. The population of this sublevel is accomplished by an intersystem crossing process for which the direct spin-orbit interaction is responsible. This process is represented by:

$$^1B_{3u}(n,\pi^*) \xrightarrow{k_{IS_1}} {}^3B_{1u}(\pi,\pi^*)\ (\tau_y)$$

$$\xrightarrow{k_{IC}} {}^3B_{3u}(n,\pi^*)\ (\tau_y) \tag{7}$$

The medium-lived emission is probably from the τ_z sublevel; but more important, a vibronic-type interaction (in the form of spin-vibronic or second-order spin-orbit-vibronic) or strong crystal field that relaxes the D_{2h} selection rules is involved in the intersystem crossing process

$$^1B_{3u}(n,\pi^*) \xrightarrow{k_{IS_2}} {}^3B_{3u}(n,\pi^*)\ (\tau_z)$$

(see Section II). It would be of theoretical interest to calculate the ratio k_{IS_1}/k_{IS_2}. It can be shown that in the steady state approximation at 1.6°K:

$$k_{IS_1}[^1B_{3u}] = k_{IC}[^3B_{1u}] = k_{\tau_y}[\tau_y] = CI_s^o$$

where [ ], k_τ and C represent concentration sign, radiative rate constant and a constant, respectively. This equation assumes that:

(a) the intersystem crossing takes place only from the lowest singlet level ($^1B_{3u}$)

(b) the only deactivating mechanism for molecules in the τ_y sublevel is via radiation to the ground state. The latter assumption is based on the fact that the quantum yield is reasonably high and at 1.6-3°K, the spin-lattice relaxation is slow, as shown by the insensitivity of the decay constants to temperature in this region. Using similar assumptions, one can write for the intersystem crossing process populating τ_z for the following equations, depending on the mechanism involved:

$$k_{IS_2}[^1B_{3u}] = k_{IC}[\tau_z] = k_{\tau_z}[\tau_z] = CI_m^o \tag{9a}$$

$$k_{IS_2}\left[{}^1B_{3u}\right] = k_{\tau_z}\left[\tau_z\right] = CI_m^o \qquad (9b)$$

From equations 8 and 9:

$$\frac{k_{IS_1}}{k_{IS_2}} = \frac{I_s^0}{I_m^0} \approx 30^*; \text{ i.e., } k_{IS_1} = 30 \times k_{IS_2}.$$

Thus the transition probability for the intersystem crossing process is ∿ 30 times greater if the process is a result of the direct first-order spin-orbit perturbation than when it involves spin-vibronic, second-order spin-orbit-vibronic, or crystal field perturbations.

A few comments need to be made concerning the rate of the S.L.R. process and the nonradiative transitions between the lowest triplet state and the ground state. If the polarization results are interpreted correctly, then a lower limit for the S.L.R. time and the lifetime of the nonradiative processes between the lowest triplet state and the ground state can be set at 130-400 millisec at 1.6°K.

ACKNOWLEDGEMENTS

The author would like to thank Dr. W. R. Moomaw, Dr. D. S. Tinti and Mr. L. Hall for their collaboration and stimulating discussions. The support of the U. S. Atomic Energy Commission of this work is greatly appreciated, and the partial support of the John Simon Guggenheim Foundation and the Alfred P. Sloan Foundation is gratefully acknowledged.

---

*Experimentally determined value in cyclohexane matrix at 1.6°K: L. Hall and M. A. El-Sayed, J. Chem. Phys. (in press).

REFERENCES

1. M. A. El-Sayed, J. Chem. Phys. 36, 573 (1962); 38, 2834 (1963).
2. J. H. van der Waals and M. S. de Groot, The Triplet State, A. B. Zahlan, Ed. (Cambridge University Press, 1967), p. 124.
3. S. K. Lower and M. A. El-Sayed, Chem. Rev. 66, 199 (1966).
4. G. W. Robinson and P. Frosch, J. Chem. Phys. 37, 1962 (1962); ibid 38, 1189 (1963).
5. M. Gouterman, ibid 36, 2846 (1962).
6. A. Albrecht, ibid 38, 354 (1963).
7. For a complete collection of all the important papers in the field of ionic crystals see: Spin Lattice Relaxation in Ionic Solids, A. A. Manenkov and R. Orbach, Eds. (Harper and Row Publishers, 1966).
8. I. Waller, Z. Physik. 79, 370 (1932).
9. W. Heitler and E. Teller, Proc. Roy. Soc. (London) A155, 629 (1936).
10. J. H. van Vleck, Phys. Rev. 57, 426 (1940).
11. R. Orbach, Proc. Roy. Soc. (London) A264, 458 (1961).
12. L. Goodman and V. K. Krishna, Rev. Mod. Phys. 35, 541 and 735 (1963).
13. L. Hall, A. Armstrong, W. Moomaw, and M. A. El-Sayed, J. Chem. Phys. 48, 1395 (1968).
14. V. Krishna and L. Goodman, ibid 37, 912 (1962).
15. M. A. El-Sayed and R. G. Brewer, ibid 39, 1623 (1963).
16. W. R. Moomaw, D. S. Tinti, and M. A. El-Sayed, ibid (in press).
17. M. D. Newton, F. P. Boer and W. N. Lipscomb, J. Am. Chem. Soc. 88, 2379 (1966).

AN UNUSUAL SITE INTERACTION IN THE TRIPLET EMISSION SPECTRUM OF PYRAZINE

Edward F. Zalewski* and Donald S. McClure**

Department of Chemistry and
James Franck Institute
University of Chicago
Chicago, Illinois

INTRODUCTION

Site effects altering the spectrum of an impurity molecule at a low concentration in a host crystal are usually related to the existence of several minima in the potential function governing the position of the impurity in the host lattice. If these minima are at sufficiently different energies, one may then observe a site splitting in all the vibronic lines of the spectrum of the impurity molecules. At higher concentrations, the probability of two impurity molecules existing as nearest neighbors increases and the

*Present Address: National Bureau of Standards, Washington, D. C.
**Present Address: Department of Chemistry, Princeton University

interaction between them becomes an important perturbation of the spectrum. For an impurity differing from the host only in degree of isotopic substitution, only the latter effect would normally be expected to occur.

EXPERIMENTAL

The pyrazine (1,4-diazabenzene) used was obtained from the Aldrich Chemical Company and the tetradeuteropyrazine from Merck Sharp and Dohme of Canada. The cis-dideuteropyrazine was prepared from 2,3-pyrazinedicarboxylic acid according to the method described by Califano et al.[1] The samples were purified by sublimation through a column of P_2O_5. Crystals were grown from the melt.

All spectra were recorded photographically with a 3.4 meter Ebert mount Jarrell-Ash spectrograph. A 30,000 lpi grating was used in the first order. The emission spectrum was excited by a General Electric AH-6 high pressure mercury arc filtered by a small Bausch and Lomb grating monochromator to isolate the Hg lines near 3130A. The source used to observe the absorption spectrum was a 150 watt Hanovia xenon arc.

The samples were immersed in liquid helium. The temperature was lowered by pumping on the helium chamber and the temperature determined from the helium vapor pressure.

RESULTS AND DISCUSSION

The phosphorescence spectrum of pyrazine ($C_4N_2H_4$) was studied at a concentration of a few per cent in host crystals of tetradeuteropyrazine and cis-dideuteropyrazine. The origin and all the vibronic lines of the spectrum at liquid helium temperature are three and five part multiplets in host crystals of $C_4N_2D_4$ and $C_4N_2D_2H_2$, respectively. This is displayed in Figs. (1) and (2). The individual lines in each multiplet are quite sharp, having a width of about 2 cm^{-1}. The separation between each line is 4.0 $\pm$ 0.2 cm^{-1}. Fig. (2) shows the effect of a temperature change on the relative emission intensity of the multiplets of one of the vibronic lines of pyrazine at a concentration of five per cent in a totally deuterated host crystal.

Two separate conclusions can be drawn from this experiment illustrated in Fig. 2. First, if it is assumed that pairs of $C_4N_2H_4$ are interacting, then because the same splitting is observed in all vibrational levels and the relative population of each member of the multiplet is a function of the temperature, the splitting must occur in the zeroth vibrational level of the excited state. On the other hand if the effect is due to the nature of the site occupied by the emitting molecule, then the excitation must be migrating to the sites of differing energy. In the former case this means that the observed splitting would be a direct observation of an exchange interaction[2] other than the one that leads to the Davydov splitting observed in the S $\rightarrow$ T absorption spectrum of the pure crystal.[3] This would indeed be an interesting result. Before further speculation, however, additional experimental information must be considered.

Fig. (3) shows the S $\rightarrow$ T absorption spectrum of cis-dideuteropyrazine. The origin band is broad and structureless. Some of the sharper vibronic bands, however, exhibit a five part multiplet splitting with a 4 cm^{-1} separation. (This splitting is shown in greater detail in Fig. (6).) The number of lines and the energy separation are the same as that observed in the emission spectrum of pyrazine in a host crystal of this material and could very probably be due to the same effect. Any other explanation would have to be attributable to an idiosyncrasy of the dideuteropyrazine isotope

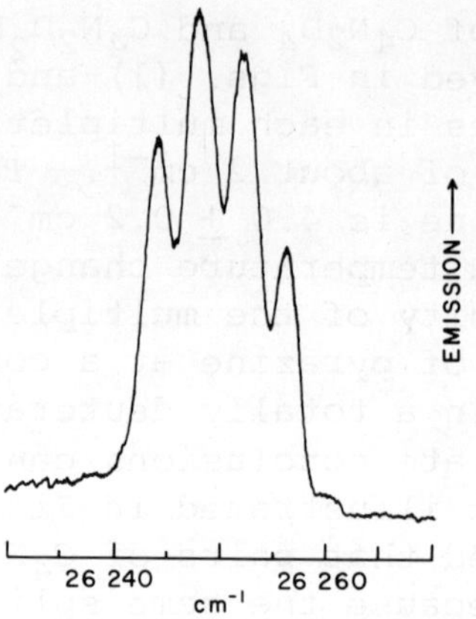

Figure 1 Origin band in the emission spectrum of pyrazine in a host crystal of cis-dideuteropyrazine. Isotopic composition of the sample (determined mass spectroscopically, error for each component: ± 0.3%) $C_4N_2H_4$, ± 3.3%; $C_4N_2DH_3$, 2.6%; $C_4N_2D_2H_2$, 93.9%; $C_4N_2D_4$, 0.7%.

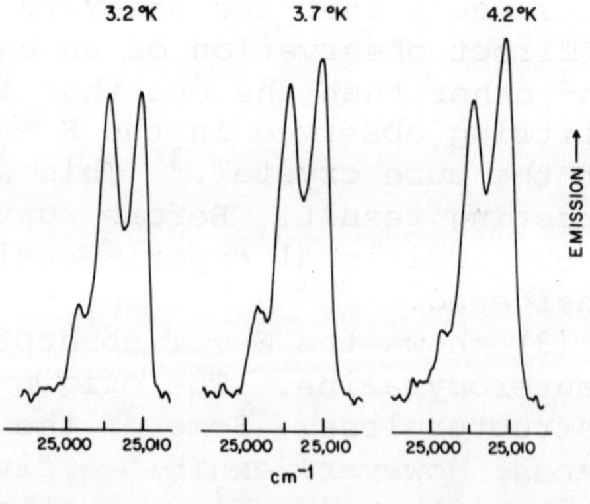

Figure 2 Effect of a temperature change on the relative intensity of the components of the vibronic lines in the emission spectrum of pyrazine in a tetradeuteropyrazine host. The line pictured is the ν_{9a} addition. Isotopic composition of the sample: $C_4N_2H_4$, 4.8%; $C_4N_2D_2H_2$, 0.4%; $C_4N_2D_3H$, 3.1%; $C_4N_2D_4$, 92.5%; error for each component, ± 0.3%.

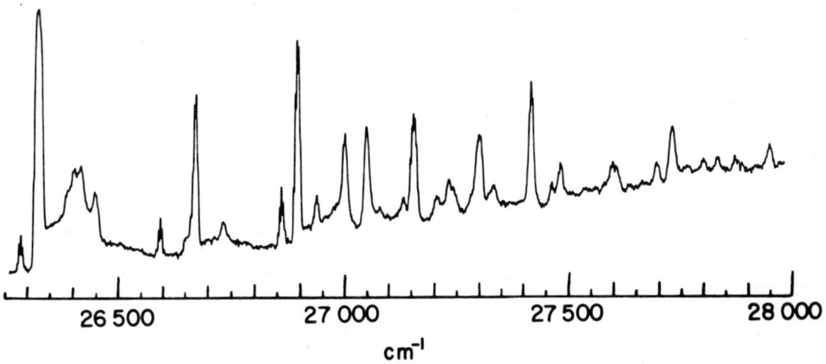

Figure 3 Cis-dideuteropyrazine S → T absorption spectrum 4.2°K. Sample composition same as that of Fig. 1.

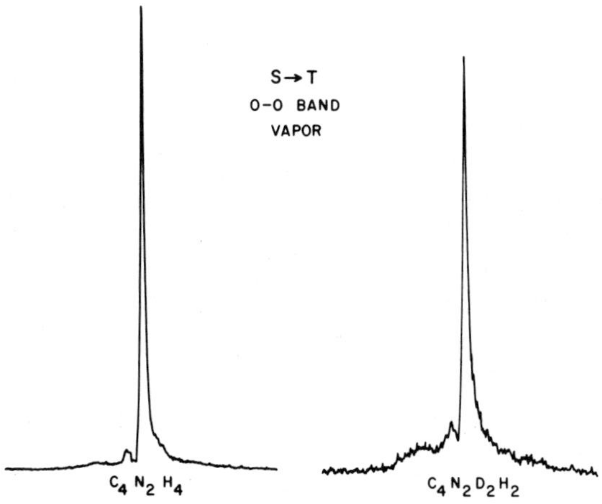

Figure 4 Comparison of pyrazine and cis-dideuteropyrazine vapor S → T absorption. The width of the Q-branch at half height is 2 to 3 cm^{-1} in these microdensitometer tracings. (After John E. Wessel, unpublished results.)

since the absorption spectra of pure crystals of pyrazine and tetradeuteropyrazine have sharp vibronic lines which are not split.[3] Further, since the splitting occurs with the same magnitude in several vibronic lines, independent of the total intensity, it is not due to an exchange interaction.[4] The only possible cause of the splitting in the absorption spectrum which would be unrelated to that of the emission spectrum is if all three isomers of $C_4N_2D_2H_2$ were present in the sample. There could conceivably be a 4 cm^{-1} difference in the zero-point energy of each of the isomers. Since the width of the Q-branch head is only 2 or 3 cm^{-1},[5] the 4 cm^{-1} difference should then be clearly observable in the S → T vapor absorption spectrum of this material. That it is not observed is shown in Fig. (4). It may be reasonably assumed now that the cause of the splitting in both the emission spectrum of pyrazine in a deuterated host crystal and the absorption spectrum of cis-dideuteropyrazine is the same and, therefore, it is a site effect not related to excitation exchange.

Following this assumption it remains then to consider the probable nature of the interaction giving rise to this peculiar site effect. Since all the molecules under consideration differ only in degree of deuteration and since the effect is only observed in crystals, the splitting may somehow be due to the energy difference between intermolecular hydrogen and deuterium bonds.

In the pyrazine crystal,[6] each nitrogen atom participates in two hydrogen bonds: there are, therefore, four C-H···N bonds for each pyrazine molecule.[7] These bonds are to four of the eight nearest molecules which are translationally inequivalent. If all four of these hydrogen bonds are identical, then deuterium substitution leads to five possible sites for each molecule in the crystal. This model accounts for the different intensity patterns in the two host crystals. In a totally deuterated host crystal the most probable site is one with four C-D···N bonds (single impurity molecule), the next most probable has three C-D···N bonds and one C-H···N (impurity pair), etc., leading to an intensity pattern where a strong line is followed on one side by several lines of decreasing intensity. In a dideuteropyrazine host, however, the most probable site is one with two C-D···N and two C-H···N bonds. The central line should, therefore, be most intense. This is found in absorption and is also true in emission when the thermal population of each site is considered. From this model the relative energy of each site is now known, the fully deuterated site being at highest energy.

There are two possible causes of this site effect. First, it could be assumed to originate in the change of intermolecular potential due to the difference in C-H···N and C-D···N bond strength. Since the transition involves the electrons localized on the nitrogen atoms, substitution of hydrogen for deuterium may be expected to increase the stabilization energy of the ground state and have little effect on the excited state. This leads to a blue-shift upon hydrogen substitution analogous to the hydrogen-bonding solvent shift for $n \rightarrow \pi^*$ transitions.[8] This is, of course, incorrect since a red-shift is observed upon hydrogen substitution.

The effect may also be assumed to originate from the zero-point energy shift due to a change in the lattice modes. Since the hydrogen-bond force constant is expected to be greater than that of a corresponding deuterium bond, the sum of the ground state frequencies will be higher for the former. The difference between the two frequency sums is expected to be smaller in the excited state. This leads, therefore, to a red-shift on hydrogen substitution and qualitatively agrees with the experiment.

In order to test this model, one may expect to see upon addition of isotopic impurities a manifestation of this site effect in the absorption spectra of the pure crystal. This is shown for tetradeuteropyrazine in Fig. 5 where satellite lines appear 4 and 8 cm^{-1} to the red when a protonated impurity is added. This is also illustrated for cis-dideuteropyrazine in Fig. 6. Here the relative intensity is seen to shift to the blue when a deuterated impurity is added.

The experiment pictured in Fig. 2 can now be reexamined in the light of the model we have just developed. Each impurity molecule has four interacting (translationally inequivalent) and ten noninteracting (six equivalent and four nonequivalent) nearest neighbors. In a five per cent solution of pyrazine in perdeuteropyrazine, the statistically* expected concentration of single (nonhydrogen-bonded) impurity molecules is 3.96%, of hydrogen-bonded pairs 0.96%, and of hydrogen-bonded triples 0.09%. If the thermal equilibration time is short compared to the emission lifetime then the ratio of single to paired molecule emission intensity is calculated to be: 0.7 (3.2°K), 0.85 (3.7°K), and 1.0 (4.2°K).

At 3.2°K the observed intensity ratio of the single to paired molecule emission is approximately 1.0 and is, therefore, the most accurate measurement since all inherent errors cancel. This ratio indicates that about 76% of the single impurity molecules transferred their energy to impurity pairs as compared to an 83% predicted transfer at thermal equilibrium. Since the probability is only 0.40 that one of the ten nonhydrogen-bonded nearest neighbors would be another impurity molecule, next nearest neighbor (probability = 0.88) energy transfer must occur. From unit cell dimensions[6] the average triplet-triplet energy transfer distance of 12A obtained from this experiment is of the same order as that

---

*These calculations include the effect due to a 3% concentration of $C_4N_2D_3H$.

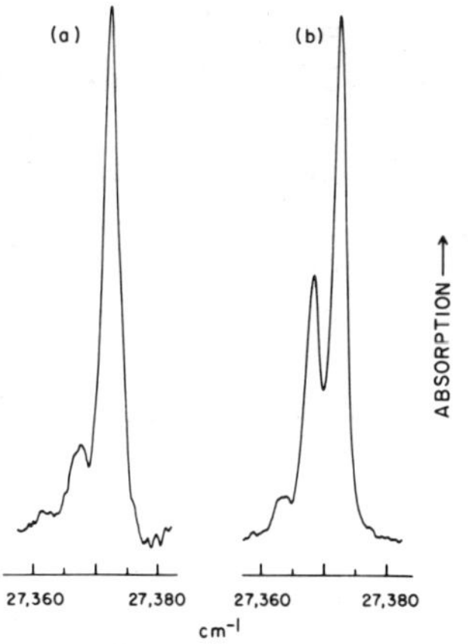

Figure 5 Effect of isotopic impurities on the tetradeuteropyrazine S → T absorption spectrum 4.2°K. (a) $C_4N_2H_4$, 2.1%; $C_4N_2D_2H_2$, 1.1%; $C_4N_2D_3H$, 2.2%; $C_4N_2D_4$, 95.5%. (b) $C_4N_2H_4$, 6.7%; $C_4N_2DH_3$, 0.3%; $C_4N_2D_2H_2$, 13.2%; $C_4N_2D_3H$, 1.4%; $C_4N_2D_4$, 78.4%. Error for each component, ± 0.3%.

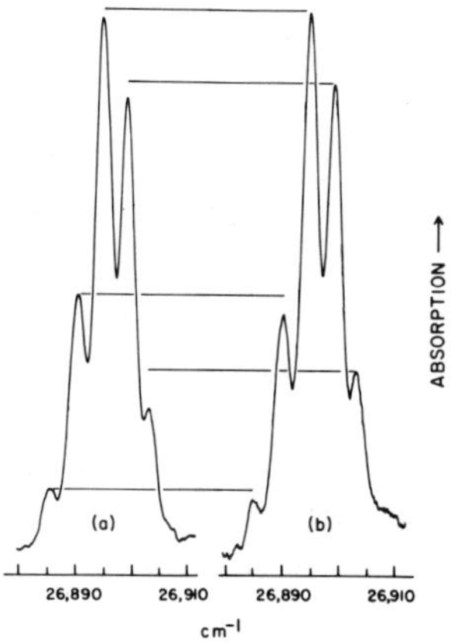

Figure 6 Effect of isotopic impurities on the cis-dideuteropyrazine S → T absorption spectrum 4.2°K. (a) $C_4N_2H_4$, 3.3%; $C_4N_2DH_3$, 2.6%; $C_4N_2D_2H_2$, 93.9%; $C_4N_2D_4$, 0.7%. (b) $C_4N_2H_4$, 4.1%; $C_4N_2DH_3$, 2.3%; $C_4N_2D_2H_2$, 79.5%; $C_4N_2D_4$, 14.5%. Error for each component. ± 0.3%.

measured by previous experimenters.[9]

Although the major interaction between two impurity pyrazine molecules in an isotopically substituted host has been shown to be due to a deuteration shift originating in the lattice modes, there is strong evidence supporting the existence of excitation exchange. The magnitude of some of the resonance interaction integrals can be estimated from the observed Davydov splitting in the S → T absorption spectra of pyrazine and perdeuteropyrazine. The total Davydov splitting is between 12 and 16 cm^{-1}.[3] This leads to a value of less than 1 cm^{-1} for the interaction between two translationally inequivalent nearest neighbors and may be a major contribution to the line width.

The translationally equivalent molecule interaction is, however, experimentally unknown and may be quite large. If it coincides with the deuteration shift, then the relative concentration of the singles to pairs would be slightly altered. In this event we may assume that only two of the six molecules of this type will have interactions of the correct magnitude. The concentration of singles and pairs is now 3.57 and 1.24% respectively, and the predicted intensity ratios are: 0.5 (3.2°K), 0.6 (3.7°K), and 0.7 (4.2°K). This means that at 3.2°K 65% of the single impurity molecules actually transfer energy to pairs compared with a predicted transfer of 84%. The probability of another impurity being a noninteracting nearest neighbor is now only 0.33. It is, therefore, still necessary to invoke long range triplet-triplet energy transfer to explain the near achievement of thermal equilibrium.

REFERENCES

1. S. Califano, G. Adembri, and B. Sbrana, Spectrochim. Acta 20, 385 (1964).
2. J. Jortner, S. Rice, J. Katz, and S. Choi, J. Chem. Phys. 42, 309 (1965).
3. E. Zalewski, Ph.D. thesis, University of Chicago (1968).
4. D. McClure, Electronic Spectra of Molecules and Ions in Crystals (Academic Press, New York, 1959).
5. K. Innes and L. Giddings, Disc. Faraday Soc. 35, 192 (1963).
6. P. Wheatley, Acta Cryst. 10, 182 (1957).
7. M. Ito and T. Shigeoka, J. Chem. Phys. 44, 1001 (1966).
8. M. Kasha, Disc. Faraday Soc. 9, 14 (1950); J. Sidman, Chem. Revs. 58, 689 (1958).
9. D. Breen and R. Keller, J. Am. Chem. Soc. 90, 1935 (1968), and references therein.

REFERENCES

1. S. Califano, G. Adembri, and G. Sbrana, Spectrochim. Acta 20, 385 (1964).
2. J. Jortner, S. Rice, J. Katz, and S. Choi, J. Chem. Phys. 42, 309 (1965).
3. R. Zalewski, Ph.D. thesis, University of Chicago (1968).
4. D. McClure, Electronic Spectra of Molecules and Ions in Crystals (Academic Press, New York, 1959).
5. K. Innes and L. Giddings, Disc. Faraday Soc. 35, 192 (1963).
6. P. Wheatley, Acta Cryst. 10, 182 (1957).
7. M. Ito and T. Shigeoka, J. Chem. Phys. 44, 1001 (1966).
8. M. Kasha, Disc. Faraday Soc. 9, 14 (1950); Sidman, Chem. Revs. 58, 689 (1958).
9. R. Breen and R. Keller, J. Am. Chem. Soc. 90, 1935 (1968) and references therein.

EFFECT OF TRIPLET EXCITON TRAP SATURATION AND BIMOLECULAR DECAY ON THE DELAYED FLUORESCENCE OF ANTHRACENE

D. H. Goode

National Research Council of Canada
Radio and Electrical Engineering Division
Ottawa 7, Canada

INTRODUCTION

When anthracene crystals are excited with red light in the triplet region they emit delayed blue fluorescence.[1] The delayed fluorescence is caused by the bimolecular annihilation of pairs of triplet excitons and so has a decay rate which is controlled by the triplet lifetime. Under conditions of weak illumination the delayed fluorescence intensity depends upon the square of the excitation intensity because the triplet concentration is low and nearly all the triplets decay by the usual monomolecular process to the ground state.[2] When the illumination is intense the delayed fluorescence becomes proportional to the exciting light intensity because the high triplet population causes bimolecular annihilation to be the predominant decay process.

At low temperatures the situation becomes more complicated. The triplet excitons can be trapped and much of the fluorescence is due to free excitons annihilating with trapped excitons. The temperature dependence of delayed fluorescence excited with weak illumination has been satisfactorily explained by Siebrand[3] using kinetic equations which included triplet traps. The temperature dependence gives information about some of the trap properties but the experimental measurement is difficult because the triplets are uniformly distributed throughout the crystal and re-absorption of the blue fluorescence is serious. This re-absorption is also temperature dependent.

In some recent experiments[4] in which anthracene crystals were excited with a broad band of red light (5400-7200 A) it was found that the "weak illumination" kinetics started to break down when the excitation exceeded 10^{14} photons/cm^2. The delayed fluorescence was no longer proportional to the square of the excitation intensity and this departure from the square law was most marked at low temperatures where the traps were operative. For small departures from the square law the experimental results could be expressed by the relation

$$I_F = \text{const.}I^2(1 + \Delta I)$$

where I_F is the intensity of blue delayed fluorescence, I the intensity of red exciting light and Δ a temperature dependent parameter.

To explain these experimental results the theory was extended to include both the saturation of traps and the bimolecular decay of triplets. The new equations give the dependence of delayed fluorescence on both temperature and excitation intensity and can be used to determine additional trap properties such as the number of free-trap collisions required to produce a single annihilation.

KINETIC EQUATIONS

Consider an anthracene crystal which contains several types of triplet trap. The properties of each type of trap are labelled by the subscript i. As shown in Fig. (1), the probability of trapping b_i and of thermal release q_i are given by

$$b_i = Z_i(N_i - y_i)$$

$$q_i = Z_i N \exp(E_i/kT)$$

where N_i is the trap concentration, y_i is the concentration of trapped triplet excitons, N is the number of anthracene molecules/cm^3 and E_i is the depth of the traps. Z_i is the collision rate between free excitons and the traps.

It can be seen from Fig. (2) that the rate equations for steady excitation are

$$dy/dt = \alpha I + \sum_i q_i y_i - (\beta + \sum_i Z_i N_i - \sum_i Z_i y_i + \gamma \sum_i c_i y_i) y - \gamma y^2 = 0$$

$$dy_i/dt = Z_i N_i y - (q_i + \rho_i \beta + Z_i y + \gamma c_i y) y_i = 0$$

$$I_F = \tfrac{1}{2}\gamma' y (y + \sum_i c_i y_i)$$

where α is the triplet absorption coefficient, I is the excitation intensity (photons/cm^2), y is the concentration of free triplets and β and $\rho_i\beta$ are the monomolecular decay rates for free and trapped triplet excitons. γ' is the annihilation rate constant for free triplets which produce excited singlets, γ is the "total" annihilation rate for free triplets leading to depopulation of the

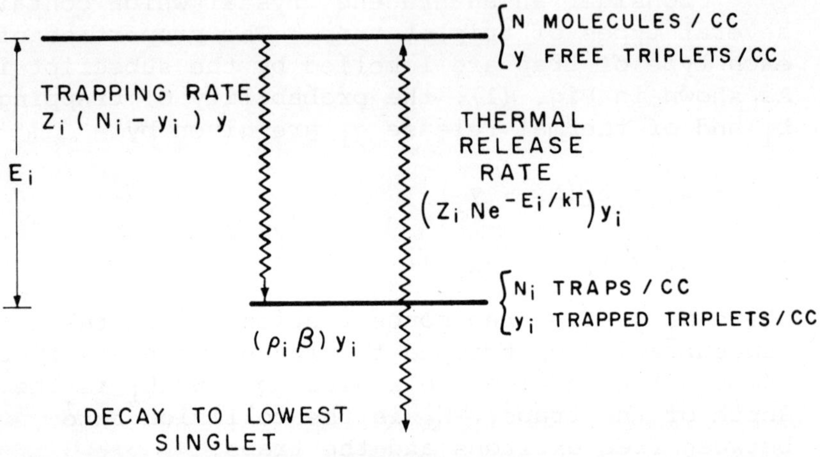

Figure 1 Kinetics of a trap to the lowest triplet state T_1.

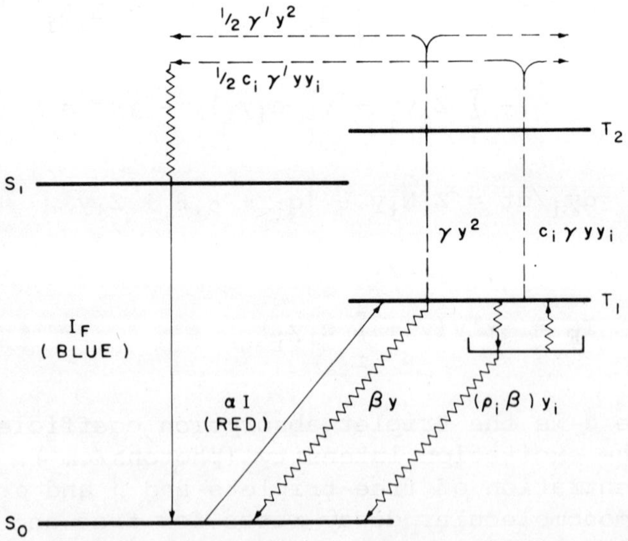

Figure 2 Kinetics relating the absorption of red light by anthracene and the emission of blue delayed fluorescence. Only the most important rate processes are considered.

triplets and $c_i\gamma'$ and $c_i\gamma$ are the "singlet" and "total" annihilation rates for free and trapped triplets.

γ' and γ are related. The spins of a pair of triplets can be arranged in nine ways and statistically one will produce an excited singlet and three a higher excited triplet. The remainder would produce quintets but anthracene does not have quintets in the correct energy region so no annihilation is possible for these. The higher excited triplets produced will rapidly decay to the lowest triplet again so only half of the excitons used in forming higher triplets would be lost. These statistics imply $\gamma = 2.5\gamma'$ and this has been verified in recent measurements of recombination fluorescence.[5] The annihilation rate also sets a lower limit to the collision rate and for the case of free-trap annihilation this would be $Z_i \geq 3.6c_i\gamma$ or $Z_i \geq 9c_i\gamma'$.

SOLUTION TO KINETIC EQUATIONS FOR WEAK ILLUMINATION

Siebrand[3] has solved the kinetic equations for weak illumination by neglecting all the bimolecular terms y^2 and yy_i in the rate equations for dy/dt and dy_i/dt. This gives

$$I_F = \tfrac{1}{2}\gamma'(\alpha I/\beta)^2(1 + \sum_i c_i A_i)/(1 + \sum_i \rho_i A_i)^2$$

where

$$A_i = Z_i N_i/[Z_i N\exp(-E_i/kT) + \rho_i\beta]$$

Typical curves of I_F/I^2 against $\rho_i A_i$ for a single trap are shown in Fig. (3). This is essentially a plot against temperature because $\rho_i A_i$ is a monotonic function of temperature being virtually zero at high temperatures and increasing to $Z_i N_i/\beta$ at low temperatures. If all the traps present in the

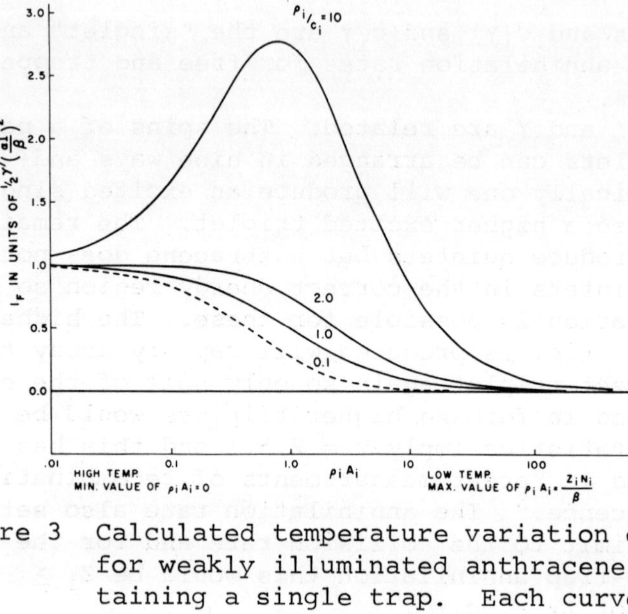

Figure 3 Calculated temperature variation of I_F/I^2 for weakly illuminated anthracene containing a single trap. Each curve represents a different type of trap.

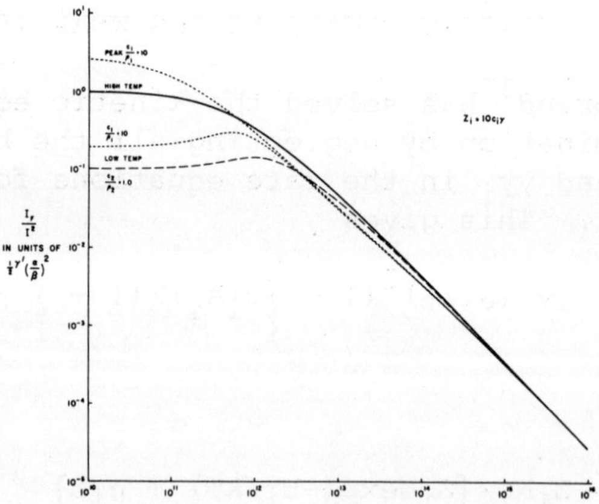

Figure 4 Calculated variation of I_F/I^2 with I for an anthracene crystal containing a single trap at various temperatures. $\gamma = 2 \times 10^{-11}$, $\beta = 40$. Two types of trap are shown: $c_1/\rho_1 = 10$; $Z_1N_1 = 2,000$; $Z_1 = 10c_1\gamma$: $c_2/\rho_2 = 1.0$; $Z_2N_2 = 360$; $Z_2 = 10c_2\gamma$.

crystal produce well separated peaks in the I_FvT curve then c_i/ρ_i and Z_iN_i/β can be determined for each trap. If one of the traps does not produce a peak then Z_iN_i/β can only be determined as a function of c_i/ρ_i.

SOLUTION OF THE KINETIC EQUATIONS FOR ALL EXCITATION INTENSITIES

The kinetic equations can be solved with all the bimolecular terms included but both I_F and I have to be expressed in terms of the free exciton concentration y.

$$I_F = \tfrac{1}{2}\gamma' y^2 \left[1 + \sum_i \frac{c_i A_i}{1 + y(A_i/n_i)}\right]$$

$$\frac{\alpha I}{\beta} = y\left[1 + \sum_i \frac{\rho_i A_i + 2yc_i A_i(\gamma/\beta)}{1 + y(A_i/n_i)} + y(\gamma/\beta)\right]$$

where $n_i = N_i/(1 + c_i\gamma/Z_i)$. The restriction on Z_i limits n_i to $N_i \geq n_i \geq 0.783\ N_i$.

Calculated curves showing the relationship between I_F/I^2 and I for an anthracene crystal containing a single trap are shown in Fig. (4). The "high temperature" curve is determined by the properties of the free triplets because all the traps are thermally depopulated. It can be seen that I_F is proportional to I^2 at low intensities and proportional to I at high intensities. However additional information is contained in departure of the curve from these two limiting cases and this is explained in the next two sections.

APPROXIMATE SOLUTION APPLICABLE WHEN DEPARTURE FROM THE SQUARE LAW IS SMALL

If I is comparatively small an approximate

solution can be obtained by expanding the correction term $(1 + yA_i/n_i)$ as a power series in y, neglecting y^2 and higher powers and substituting in the expression for y valid at low intensities.

$$I_F = \tfrac{1}{2}\gamma'\left(\frac{\alpha I}{\beta}\right)^2 \frac{(1 + \sum_i c_i A_i)}{(1 + \sum_i \rho_i A_i)^2}\left[1 + \delta\left(\frac{\alpha I}{\beta}\right)\right]$$

$$\delta = \frac{2\sum_i \rho_i A_i (A_i/n_i) - (4\sum_i c_i A_i + 2)(\gamma/\beta)}{(1 + \sum_i \rho_i A_i)^2}$$

$$- \frac{\sum_i c_i A_i (A_i/n_i)}{(1 + \sum_i \rho_i A_i)(1 + \sum_i c_i A_i)}$$

This expression had the form expected from the experimental measurements. δ measures the departure from the square law and can be evaluated by plotting I_F/I^2 against I.

The two terms in δ involving (A_i/n_i) are caused almost entirely by saturation of the traps while the other two terms containing (γ/β) arise from bimolecular decay of the triplets. The temperature dependence of these two components for a single trap is shown in Fig. (5). The contribution from bimolecular decay δ_{TT} gives rise to a minimum if $c_i/\rho_i > 1$ and the size of this trough depends on (c_i/ρ_i) and (γ/β). On the other hand the saturation term δ_{SAT} is normally positive and has its greatest effect at "low temperatures," i.e. temperatures low enough to ensure no thermal release from the trap. Under these conditions δ_{SAT} and δ_{TT} are related because

$$(A_i/n_i) = (1 + Z_i/c_i\gamma)(c_i/\rho_i)(\gamma/\beta)$$

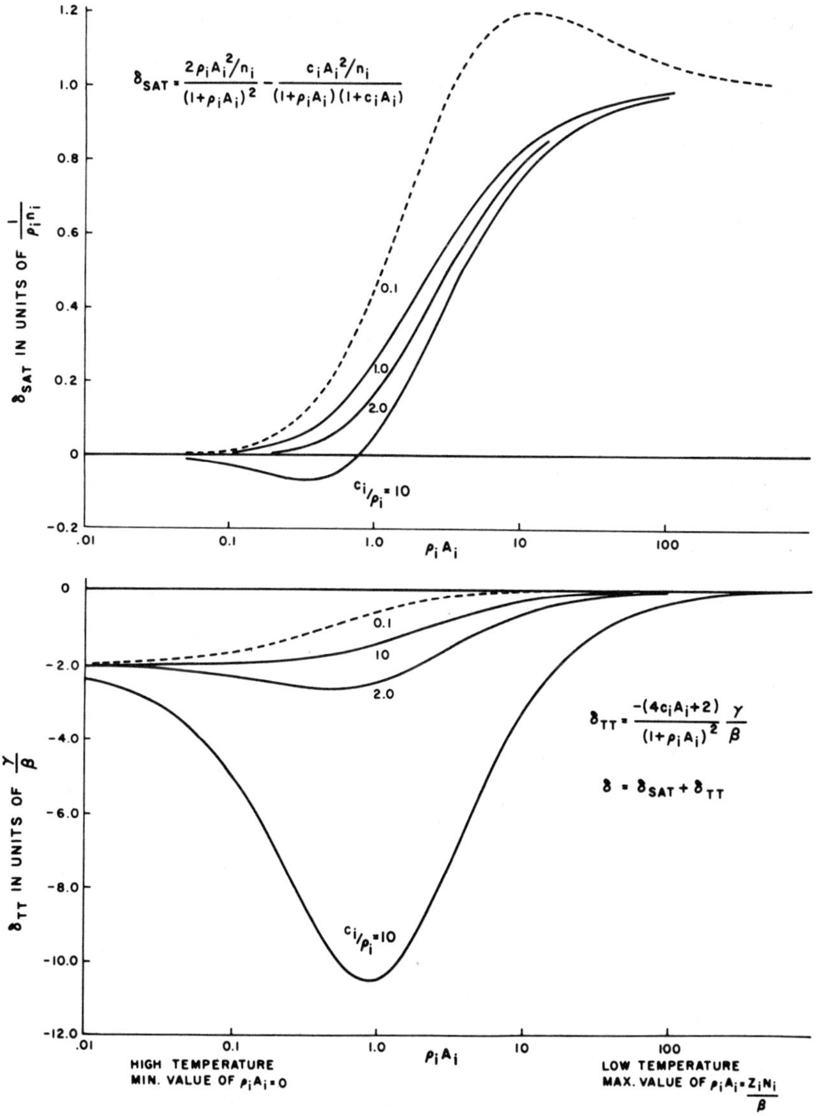

Figure 5 Variation of the two components of δ with temperature for a single trap. δ_{SAT} is the contribution from saturation of traps and δ_{TT} is the contribution from bimolecular decay of the triplets.

The "low temperature" value of δ depends on $(Z_i/c_i\gamma)$, (γ/β), (c_i/ρ_i) and (Z_iN_i/β) and typical curves showing its variation with trap concentration are shown in Fig. (6). The value of γ/β can easily be determined by comparison with the value of δ at "high temperatures," i.e., temperatures high enough to thermally depopulate the trap.

APPROXIMATE SOLUTION FOR SMALL DEPARTURES FROM LINEAR EXCITATION DEPENDENCE

When I_o is comparatively large ($\sim 10^{22}$ photons/cm^2 at 6200 Å) so that $y \gg n_i/A_i$ another approximate solution can be obtained.

$$I_F = \tfrac{1}{2}\gamma'(\alpha I/\gamma)\left[1 - (\beta/\gamma + \sum_{i=1}^{j} c_i n_i)(\gamma/\alpha I)^{\frac{1}{2}}\right]$$

The restriction on the size of y implies that the temperature is low enough to ensure no thermal release from any of the j traps considered in the summation. The term

$$(\beta/\gamma + \sum_{i=1}^{j} c_i n_i)(\gamma/\alpha)^{\frac{1}{2}}$$

can be evaluated by plotting I_F/I against $I^{-\frac{1}{2}}$. As with the other approximation the "high temperature" value gives $(\alpha\gamma/\beta^2)$ and the "low temperature" value measures $(Z_i/c_i\gamma)$.

APPLICATION OF THE EQUATIONS

These equations are useful in determining trap properties if it can be assumed that α, β and γ are constant between the temperature at which the traps are thermally depopulated and the temperature at which there is no thermal release from the

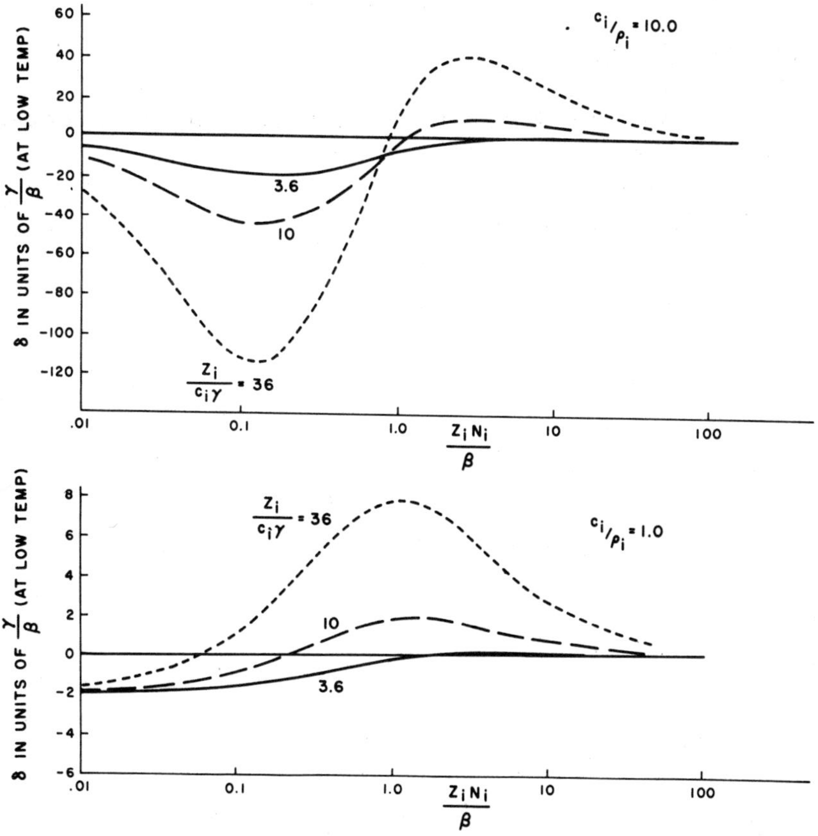

Figure 6 Variation of the "low temperature" value of δ with Z_iN_i. Curves apply to a single trap.

traps. Once β, c_i/ρ_i and Z_iN_i have been determined from the decay and temperature dependence of the delayed fluorescence either of the two new equations can be used to determine $\alpha\gamma$ and $Z_i/c_i\gamma$. Once (the triplet absorption coefficient) has been accurately determined this appears to be an excellent way of measuring γ. The ratio $Z_i/c_i\gamma$ is also of interest because it shows the average number of collisions required before annihilation takes place and so shows if the process is diffusion limited.

ACKNOWLEDGEMENTS

I wish to thank F. R. Lipsett and W. Siebrand for some helpful discussions.

REFERENCES

1. S. Singh, W. J. Jones, W. Siebrand, B. P. Stoicheff and W. G. Schneider, J. Chem. Phys. 42, 330 (1965).
2. D. H. McMahon and M. Kestigian, J. Chem. Phys. 46, 137 (1967).
3. W. Siebrand, J. Chem. Phys. 42, 3951 (1965).
4. D. H. Goode and F. R. Lipsett (to be published).
5. W. Helfrich and W. G. Schneider, J. Chem. Phys. 44, 2902 (1966).

EXCITON MIGRATION IN TRIPLET STATES OF PYRAZINE AND DEUTERATED PYRAZINES IN THE CRYSTAL

Motohiko Koyanagi, Tadayoshi Shigeoka*
and Yoshiya Kanda

Department of Chemistry
Faculty of Science
Kyushu University
Fukuoka, Japan

INTRODUCTION

In general, it is very difficult to study the crystal phosphorescence because of rapid rates of triplet-triplet annihilation and triplet energy migration in the crystal.[1] Recently, several phosphorescence spectra have been reported in the crystalline state, such as p-dibromobenzene,[2] anthracene,[3] benzophenone,[4] etc. Moomaw and El-Sayed have also studied the phosphorescence spectrum of the pyrazine crystal at 77°K and pointed out the important role of exciton-phonon interaction in the crystal phosphorescence on the basis of the analysis of the phononic and phonon-vibronic

*Present Address: Central Research Institute of Mitsubishi Kasei Co. Ltd., Kawasaki, Japan.

bands obtained.[5] The 0-0 band which they observed in emission is found to be lower by 102 cm^{-1} in energy than the 0-0 band in absorption. They attributed this energy gap tentatively to luminescence from self-trapped excitons which might lead to a large Stokes' shift.

Prior to this, Kanda, Gondo and Watabe observed the phosphorescence spectrum of the pyrazine crystal at 4.2°K with a medium quartz spectrograph and found the first band group at 26149 m, 26131 m, 26103 vs, 26067 cm^{-1} vs, and so on.[6] On the other hand, Azumi, Udagawa, Ito and Nagakura reported also the phosphorescence spectrum of the pyrazine crystal with and without the magnetic field.[7] Although each result is somewhat different both in band spacings and intensity distributions, the band at the shortest wavelength in emission is, in all the cases, located lower in energy by more than 100 cm^{-1} than the 0-0 band in absorption.

It is very important to decide whether the observed emissions come truly from the "intrinsic" triplet state of the crystal or not, i.e., whether they are based on self-trapped excitons or impurity traps and/or crystal imperfections, and to investigate a possibility of emission from the Frenkel type exciton in the pyrazine crystal as well as in the benzene and benzophenone crystals. From a point of view of excitation transfer, pyrazine belongs neither to one of the molecules having long range interactions such as benzene, whose triplet radiative lifetime is very long and whose excitation energy is delocalized over all the molecules in the crystal, nor to one of those of short range interactions such as benzophenone, whose triplet lifetime is very short and whose excitation energy is mainly localized in the carbonyl group. Which of the two categories is the pyrazine crystal closest to?

The method of variation of energy denominators by Nieman and Robinson gives much valuable information for a study of triplet states of the crystal[8] and, therefore, this method has been employed in this work. Deuterated pyrazines were synthesized and the phosphorescence spectra have been studied in detail at various temperatures.

EXPERIMENTAL

Deuterated pyrazines were synthesized according to Perkampus and Baumgarten.[9] Pyrazine, the starting material, was obtained from Tokyo Kasei Co., Ltd. and sublimed in vacuum. The material was introduced and degassed in a glass tube of 50 cm in length and 8 mm in internal diameter and zone-refined 50 times. Finally it was sublimed in nitrogen atmosphere. The isotope concentration was examined by means of ultraviolet absorption spectra of the gasses and infrared absorption spectra of the crystals. Crystals of about 0.3 mm in thickness were grown in the polycrystalline state from the mixture in a sealed capillary tube. A carbon resistor was embedded in a similar capillary tube and set aside with the sample tube. Temperature was determined within an accuracy of $\pm$ 0.1° at 5°K, $\pm$ 0.2° at 10°K, and $\pm$ 0.6° at 15°K. A super high pressure 1 kw Hg lamp and a 500 w xenon arc lamp were used as a light source. Combination filters of a Corning 5970 and an $NiSO_4$-$CoSO_4$ aqueous solution were used in order to prevent the sample from photoisomerization[10] and local elevation in temperature. Spectral positions and intensities were determined photoelectrically with a Shimadzu double pass spectrophotometer GDT-750. It has a Bausch and Lomb grating of 102 x 102 mm^2 in ruled area, 1200 lines/mm and a blazing angle at 4000 Å, and an off-axis mirror of 750 mm in focal length. The dispersion was 5.35 Å/mm. The calibration of the wavelength was made with respect to Hg 3650 and 4048 Å lines. Mechanical errors in the spectral position lie within at most 0.5 Å or between 3.4 cm^{-1} and 2.6 cm^{-1} in the spectral region of the phosphorescence. Intensity was taken to be proportional to the band peak height with reproducibility of 3% in error. A Hilger E2 spectrograph was used for longer exposure for the phosphorescence of the crystal and some phosphorescence studies in matrices. The phosphorescope similar to that described previously[11] was used.

RESULTS AND DISCUSSION

The phosphorescence spectra of an isotopically mixed crystal at various temperatures are shown in Fig. 1. The crystal consisted of 95% $C_4D_4N_2$, 3% $C_4D_3HN_2$, 0.9% $C_4D_2H_2N_2$, 0.2% $C_4DH_3N_2$ and less than 0.2% of $C_4H_4N_2$. Because of zero-point vibration effects the $T \leftarrow S$ absorption 0-0 band of pyrazine-h_4 was found lower in energy by 140 cm^{-1} than that of pyrazine-d_4 in the crystal at 4.2°K. Further phosphorescence studies clarified that substitution of an H by a D in pyrazine raises an electronic transition energy by about 35 cm^{-1} each. Since trap concentration decreases with increasing trap energy, one may expect that the phosphorescence spectrum from the shallowest trap appears predominantly at 0°K and those from deeper traps begin to dominate gradually with an increase in temperature. Investigating such rise and fall of bands in intensity is very useful for vibrational analyses of the phosphorescence spectra.

The spectrum e in Fig. 1 was very similar to the phosphorescence spectrum of pyrazine-h_4 in pyrazine-d_4 at 4.2°K and consisted mainly of the pyrazine-h_4 bands and a phosphorescence spectrum from an unknown trap, most probably from a pyrazine-d_4 trap site (at 26031 cm^{-1}). The 0-0 band of the pyrazine-h_4 phosphorescence spectrum is located at 26260 ± 5 cm^{-1} and is in good agreement with the 0-0 band of the absorption

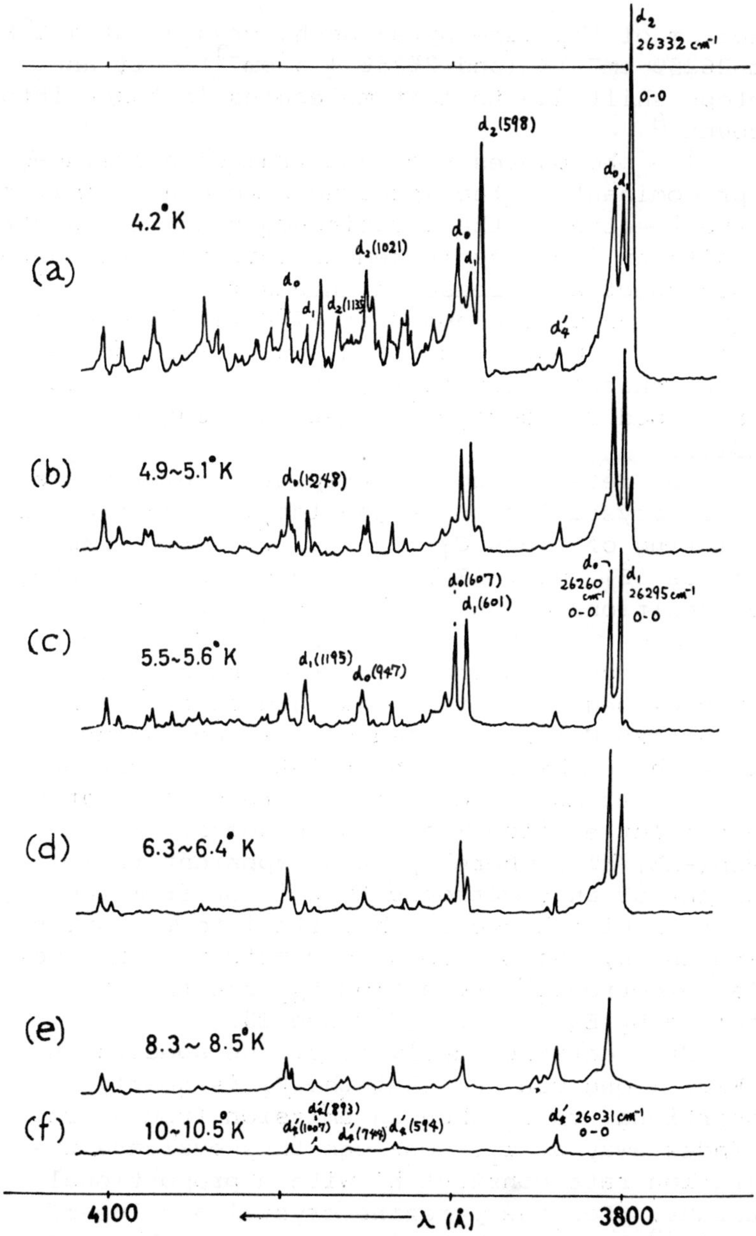

Figure 1 The phosphorescence spectra of pyrazine and deuterated pyrazines in the crystal at various temperatures.

spectrum of the pure pyrazine-h_4 crystal at 4.2°K (at 26259 cm^{-1})[5] (and 26256 ± 5 cm^{-1})[12] if an isotope shift due to host molecules is taken into account.[8]

The phosphorescence spectrum of pyrazine-d_1 is predominant in the spectrum b to c and similarly so the spectra of the pyrazine-d_2's are in spectrum a. With an increase in temperature the phosphorescence spectra decrease in intensity and no spectrum was photographed at 77°K with a distinct structure. These spectra in Fig. 1 were not only photographically but also photometrically recorded with a good reproducibility at any temperature studied.

For determining the triplet-triplet migration rate in crystalline pyrazine let us assume a system consisting of traps C_1, C_2, C_3,.... with trap energies ΔE_1, ΔE_2, ΔE_3,...., respectively, under the conditions of $\Delta E_1 < \Delta E_2 < \Delta E_3 <$.... and $C_1 \gg C_2 \gg C_3 \gg$ .... where C_i means a concentration of a trap C_i. When an emission from a trap C_i begins to fade away and an emission from a trap $C_{(i+1)}$ appears at a temperature T_i, one may have the following relation for estimating the order of magnitude of k', a rate constant of the triplet exciton migration process: $k_i' = k'\exp(-\Delta E_i/kT)$, where k_i' is an apparent rate constant of an electronic transition from the lowest triplet state of the site i to the ground state and k, the Boltzmann's constant. Intermolecular electronic interaction β_{el} can then be obtained by Eq. 11 of reference 13.

From detailed analyses of the spectra shown in Fig. 1 one can see that the E_i is nearly proportional to T_i when an emission from a trap C_i fades away at T_i. One can thus evaluate the migration rate constant k' with a proportional constant. For the pyrazine crystal a value of $k' = 10^{10}$ sec^{-1} was obtained since an observed phosphorescence lifetime τ_p was 4×10^{-2} sec at 4-10°K. This k' is considerably large. For the benzene crystal we have $k' = 10^{12}$ sec^{-1}. It is, therefore, concluded that the "intrinsic" phosphorescence of crystalline pyrazine is too weak to be observed.

REFERENCES

1. H. Sternlicht, G. C. Nieman and G. W. Robinson, J. Chem. Phys. 38, 1326 (1963).
2. G. Castro and R. M. Hochstrasser, J. Chem. Phys. 46, 3617 (1967).
3. D. F. Williams, J. Chem. Phys. 47, 344 (1967).
4. A. Nakahara, M. Koyanagi and Y. Kanda, J. Chem. Phys. (in press).
5. W. R. Moomaw and M. A. El-Sayed, J. Chem. Phys. 45, 3890 (1966); 47, 2193 (1967); 48, 2502 (1968).
6. Y. Kanda, Y. Gondo and H. Watabe, Preprint of the Symposium on the Electronic Processes in Molecules, Tokyo, Japan, 1964, p. 13.
7. T. Azumi, Y. Udagawa, M. Ito and S. Nagakura, J. Chem. Phys. 47, 4850 (1967).
8. G. C. Nieman and G. W. Robinson, J. Chem. Phys. 39, 1298 (1963).
9. H. H. Perkampus and E. Baumgarten, Spectrochim. Acta, 19, 1473 (1963).
10. F. Lahmani, N. Ivanoff and M. M. Magat, Compt. Rend. 263, 1005 (1966).
11. Y. Kanda and R. Shimada, Spectrochim. Acta, 15, 211 (1959).
12. M. Koyanagi, M. Inomoto, T. Shigeoka and Y. Kanda, Preprint of the Symposium on Electronic Processes in Molecules, Sapporo, Japan, 1967, p. 207.
13. G. W. Robinson and R. P. Frosch, J. Chem. Phys. 38, 1187 (1963).

LOW TEMPERATURE STUDIES OF FLUORESCENCE EMISSION FROM ANTHRACENE CRYSTALS

L. M. Logan, I. H. Munro, D. F. Williams and F. R. Lipsett

National Research Council of Canada
Ottawa, Canada

INTRODUCTION

For many years an understanding of the absorption and luminescence properties of crystalline anthracene was obscured by the presence of impurities in the samples. Only following the application of zone refining techniques for purification was a fluorescence spectrum obtained[1] which could be related to crystal levels as distinct from chemical traps. An assignment of the spectrum was then made on the basis of emission from the lower energy b-polarized Davydov component as seen in absorption. However, even in crystals of high chemical purity, surface and bulk physical defects are present, each with a concentration which varies according to the mode of crystal growth. These physical defects have been shown to act as singlet exciton traps and at low temperatures provide an essentially continuous background to the fluorescence spectrum.[2] Also, delayed fluorescence studies on these crystals show variations in delayed fluorescence intensity and decay rate with temperature which can be related to the trapping of triplet excitons, though the experimental situation is too complex to give much information concerning the physical properties of these trapping centers.[3] In the present work, singlet lifetime and fluorescence spectrum measurements have been made between $350^{\circ}K-2^{\circ}K$ on anthracene crystals and on solid solutions of anthracene in polymethylmethacrylate to gain further information concerning the pertinent energy decay processes.

EXPERIMENTAL

The anthracene samples were purified by a multi-stage process involving chromatography, sublimation and zone refining. (For details of the purification technique see Lupien and Williams.[4]) Crystals were grown from the pure anthracene by three different methods. These were: (a) sublimation in an inert atmosphere to give flakes approximately 10μ thick; (b) sublimation across a controlled temperature gradient to give large single crystals approximately 1 mm thick;[5] (c) growth from the melt (Bridgman method). All crystals have a high level of chemical purity, but could be expected to have varying concentrations of lattice defects according to method of growth. The triplet state decay time—a sensitive measure of crystal purity—was recorded for all crystals; it varied from 10 to 25 msec.

Spectral measurements were made with a spectrofluorimeter having a band-pass of 2 Å. The photomultiplier output was digitized and recorded on magnetic tape. The results were then processed by a computer; first, corrections to spectral intensities were made for the response of the detection system; second, total areas under the spectra were calculated to provide relative quantum efficiency measurements; and third, an output of accumulated area as a function of wavelength was made for ultimate use in corrections to the measured lifetimes for reabsorption.

The fluorescence lifetimes were measured using a pulse sampling technique.[6] The apparatus response was eliminated by computing decay curves arising from an assumed exponential decay and the measured apparatus response. These decay curves were then compared with those experimentally measured. Excitation over the wavelength region from 3300 Å to 3800 Å was used for both spectral and lifetime measurements, through the intensity distribution throughout the region differed slightly due to the spectral distributions of the xenon and hydrogen lamps used.

The specimen was mounted in a strain-free support such that either front surface or transmission viewing could be obtained using identical geometry for both lifetime and spectral measurements. The sample was cooled in a stream of helium gas and its temperature maintained constant to better than $\pm$ 0.5°K for measurements at all temperatures in the range 2°K to 350°K. Scattered light was negligible in all measurements and the anthracene samples were mounted so as to avoid emission being received from the edges of the crystals.

RESULTS: ANTHRACENE DISSOLVED IN POLYMETHYLMETHACRYLATE

The fluorescence spectra of anthracene (concentration 2.9×10^{-4} M) in polymethylmethacrylate at 295°K and 4.2°K are shown in Fig. 1. The spectrum only sharpens slightly over this temperature range and the degree of reabsorption is unaffected by the reduction in temperature. There

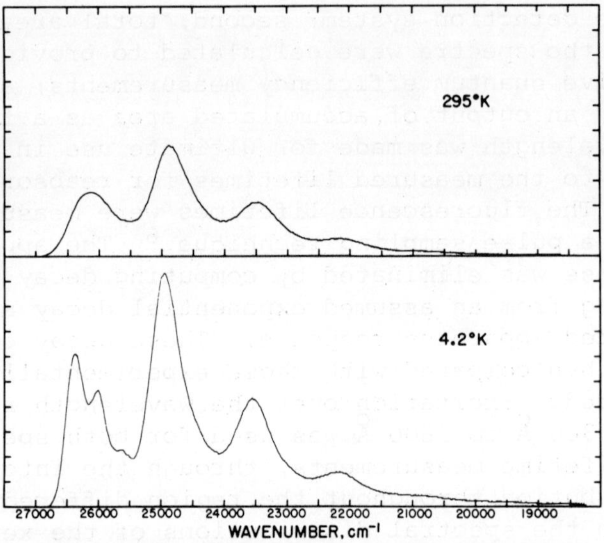

Figure 1 Fluorescence spectra of anthracene, 2.9 x 10^{-4} M, in polymethylmethacrylate at $295^{O}K$ and $4.2^{O}K$.

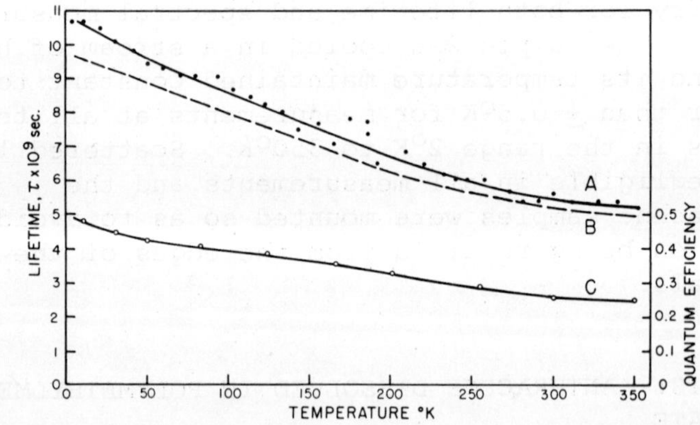

Figure 2 Variation of fluorescence lifetime of 2.9 x 10^{-4} M anthracene in polymethylmethacrylate with temperature. A: experimental results; B: results after correction for reabsorption of the fluorescence; C: change area under the fluorescence spectrum with temperature.

is no evidence of the presence of microcrystals— the spectrum is blue shifted and there is no anomalous emission at characteristic crystal frequencies.

The steady increase in singlet lifetime with decreasing temperature is shown in Fig. 2—(A) before and (B) after corrections for reabsorption. The reabsorption correction is small due to the low quantum yield of 0.25 for anthracene dissolved in polymethylmethacrylate.[7] Curve (C) in Fig. 2 shows the variation with temperature of the area under the fluorescence spectrum. Since the spectra show that the probability of reabsorption remains essentially constant over the temperature range, the quantum efficiency variation should be equivalent to the area variation.

DISCUSSION

The correlation between relative fluorescence efficiency and singlet lifetime (Fig. 2) indicates that the temperature behavior is a result of radiationless energy loss from the singlet becoming increasingly effective as the temperature is increased. The process competing with radiation is intersystem crossing to the triplet level[8] T_2 which lies approximately 400 cm^{-1} below the S_1 level (Fig. 3). The energy of the triplet level given is that reported by Kellogg;[8] the value of 26430 $\pm$ 20 cm^{-1} for S_1 was that measured in the present work for the peak of the 0-0 band in absorption in the plastic solution at room temperature. This is to be compared with a peak frequency of 26380 $\pm$ 20 cm^{-1} for the 0-0 band in fluorescence at $4.2^{o}K$. (The peak position in fluorescence could be expected to be slightly red shifted because of reabsorption.)

We ascribe the measured temperature dependence to a variation in the S_1—T_2 intersystem crossing rate as the vibrational energy content in state S_1

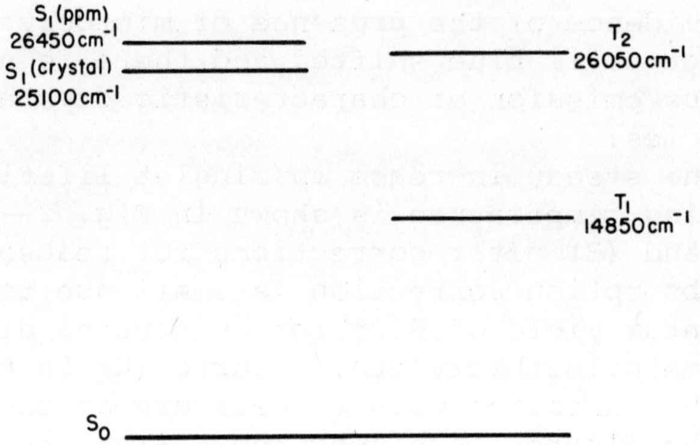

Figure 3 Energy level diagram for anthracene in crystal and polymethylmethacrylate.

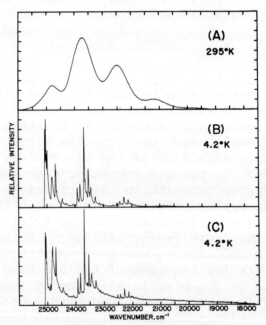

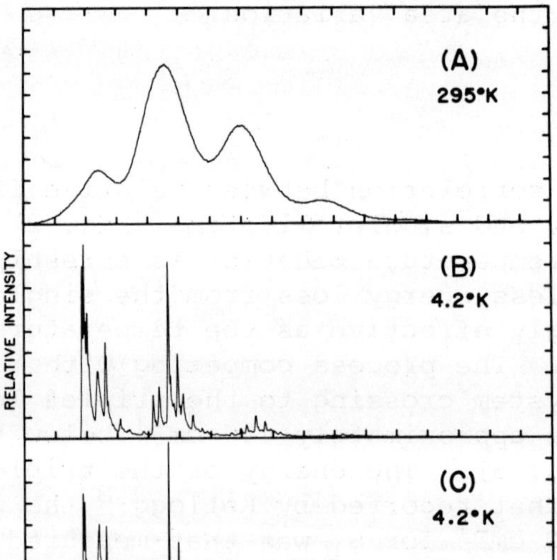

Figure 4 Front surface fluorescence spectra from anthracene crystals. A, B, are emission from a defect-free crystal at 295°K and 4.2°K respectively. C, emission at 4.2°K from a crystal with a high proportion of defects.

changes with temperature. The importance of the vibrational overlap integral between initial and final states involved in radiationless transitions is well recognized.[9-11] In fact, it is the variation in the vibrational overlap integral which accounts for the observed range of radiationless transition rates in aromatic molecules when agreement, commonly within an order of magnitude, has been established between experimental decay rates and those calculated on the basis of vibrational overlap alone.[11,12] However, these theories do not provide a quantitative description of the nature of the energy levels used to establish the precise energy matching required in the transition; the overlap from the zero-point level of the initial electronic state to particular vibrational levels of the final electronic state is calculated, the finer details of the energy matching being left to other vibrational levels in the molecule and to the environment. It is only for small energy gaps where the density of vibrational states is low, that the details of energy matching are likely to become significant. The importance of the density of final states has been emphasized recently by Robinson[12] in discussions of radiationless transitions in gaseous molecules. In anthracene, where the $S_1 - T_2$ energy gap is only $\sim 400\ cm^{-1}$, it appears that at 4^oK the intersystem crossing rate is affected by the low density of final states. At higher temperatures where many vibrational levels of S_1 become populated, new radiationless pathways from the singlet level are introduced which involve high energy, and hence more closely spaced, triplet levels. A faster intersystem crossing rate results. However, the temperature dependence shows no activation energy, which indicates that, within the range of experimentally accessible vibrational levels, no single level is especially efficient in the intersystem crossing process.

RESULTS: ANTHRACENE CRYSTALS

Measurements of the fluorescence spectrum and lifetime as a function of temperature were made on a number of crystals produced by different techniques. Figure 4 illustrates front surface fluorescence spectra obtained for a sublimation flake at 295°K (A) and 2°K (B), and for a melt-grown crystal at 2°K (C). The main difference is the broad background found for the melt-grown crystal, on which the sharp bands are superimposed. This background fluorescence is most prominent at low temperatures and is attributed to emission from physical defects on strain sites within the anthracene lattice and is not associated with chemical impurities.

While such differences were found between the spectra of different crystals particularly at low temperatures, at any given temperature the singlet lifetimes of all crystals were approximately the same. Figure 5A records the measured change in lifetime for front surface illumination of a defect free anthracene flake. Unfortunately, the overlap between the emission and absorption spectra of anthracene and the high extinction coefficient in the region of overlap, produce a considerable amount of fluorescence reabsorption which introduces large modifications to the singlet lifetime. Formulas have been derived[13] to correct for reabsorption and after the correction is applied, it is seen that the lifetime changes very slowly from approximately 5 μsec at 4°K to approximately 6.5 μsec at 295°K with indications of a slight decrease at even higher temperatures.

DISCUSSION

A quantitative assessment of any measurements made on anthracene crystals is complicated considerably by three unknown factors: The

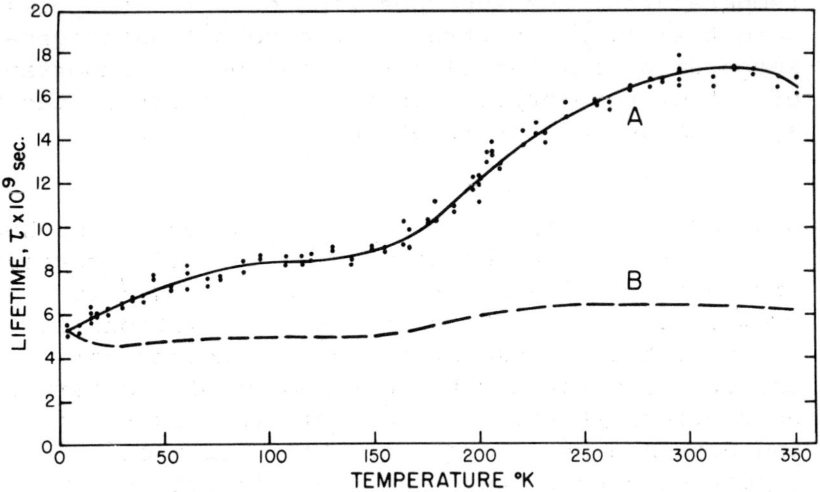

Figure 5 Variation of lifetime with temperature of a defect-free anthracene crystal.
A; experimental results
B; results after correction for the effect of reabsorption.

dependence of fluorescence quantum efficiency on temperatures; the superposition of a structureless defect emission spectrum on the normal anthracene spectrum at low temperatures; and by the important effect of reabsorption on the measurement of the spectrum and of the lifetime.

QUANTUM EFFICIENCY. It has been assumed throughout this work that the quantum efficiency of anthracene crystals is unity, as reported by Kellogg[8] for room temperature. Owing to large variations in the amount of reabsorption and to geometrical effects associated with measurement of the sample on cooling, it was only possible to show the independence of fluorescence efficiency on temperature to better than approximately $\pm$ 10%.

DEFECT EMISSION. The defect emission was found to be a broad structureless band which peaked at ∿4900 Å and extended far to the red of the anthracene exciton fluorescence (see Fig. 4C). It probably arises from excitons trapped at defect sites and was most apparent below 60°K in melt-grown crystals—at 4°K in these crystals, the typical spectrum was one in which emission from defects predominates. In this case it is difficult to assess the degree of fluorescence reabsorption accurately though it is certainly much less than in the defect free crystals. The lifetimes, however, are closely similar to those measured in the presence of considerable reabsorption. These measurements indicate that there is a longer lifetime associated with emission from defect sites.

FLUORESCENCE REABSORPTION. The correction formulas for reabsorption rely on the assumption that the probability of photon reabsorption at any point in the crystal is constant and that it is reflected in the measured emission spectrum. In our experimental situation neither of these assumptions is strictly valid. Since the exciting light is absorbed close to the surface, the probability of reabsorption will not be isotropic; spectra recorded with different viewing geometries (e.g. front and back surface) will show different amounts of reabsorption. The desired parameter for reabsorption corrections is the average probability of reabsorption—i.e., the probability of reabsorption integrated over all directions—for it is this which determines the probability that emitted photons will escape from the crystal.

In the present work, the use of front surface spectra in assessment of reabsorption would tend to give the lower limit rather than the average probability of reabsorption. Further work on this aspect of the problem is required before a final conclusion can be reached concerning the temperature dependence shown in Fig. 5B. At the present time it seems reasonable to conclude that the remaining temperature dependence is a consequence of slight undercorrection for reabsorption. It is also possible that at low temperatures a change in lifetime may be caused by the changing population of levels within the exciton band which have differing decay rates. If we consider only the $k = 0$ levels and the intensities and splitting found by Matsui,[14] a lifetime change is predicted which is similar to that shown in Fig. 5B. The quantum yield of crystalline anthracene is nearly unity at room temperature[8] and, on the basis of the present understanding of radiationless transitions, there is little reason to believe that the quantum yield, or radiationless transition rate, should show any appreciable variation with temperature. However, such confident assertions cannot be made concerning the possible variations with temperature of the radiative decay rate in molecular crystals where emission can originate from different levels in the exciton band. For naphthalene, a variation in lifetime with temperature[15] has been ascribed to changing populations of the Davydov components which have different decay rates. This result is to be contrasted with the latest theoretical description of exciton band-band transitions which suggests that if a weak interaction model applies, transitions from all $\underline{k}$ levels, i.e., <u>not</u> only the $\underline{k} = 0$ Davydov levels, should be considered.[16]

REFERENCES

1. A. R. Lacey and L. E. Lyons, J. Chem. Soc. 1964, 5393.
2. W. Helfrich and F. R. Lipsett, J. Chem. Phys. 43, 4368 (1965).
3. D. H. Goode and F. R. Lipsett
4. Y. Lupien and D. F. Williams, Molecular Crystals (in press).
5. G. J. Sloan, Molecular Crystals 2, 323 (1967).
6. J. B. Birks and I. H. Munro, Progress in Reaction Kinetics (Pengamon Press, Oxford and New York, 1967) Vol. 4.
7. A. Schmillen and R. Legler, Luminescence of Organic Substances, (Springer-Verlag, Berlin-Heidelberg-New York, 1967).
8. R. E. Kellogg, J. Chem. Phys. 44, 411 (1966).
9. G. W. Robinson and R. P Frosch, J. Chem. Phys. 38, 1187 (1963).
10. J. P. Byrne, E. F. McCoy and I. G. Ross, Australian J. Chem. 18, 1589 (1965).
11. W. Siebrand, J. Chem. Phys. 46, 440 (1967).
12. G. W. Robinson, J. Chem. Phys. 47, 1967 (1967).
13. J. B. Birks, Theory and Practice of Scintillation Counting (Pergamon Press, Oxford and New York, 1964); A. M. Samson, Optics and Spectroscopy 8, 43 (1960).
14. A. Matsui, J. Phys. Soc. Japan 21, 2212 (1966).
15. A. Hammer and H. C. Wolf, Organic Scintillation Symposium, Chicago, 1966.
16. S. D. Colson, D. M. Hanson, R. Kopelman and G. W. Robinson, J. Chem. Phys. 48, 2215 (1968).

THE LUMINESCENCE OF SALTS OF SIMPLE POLYATOMIC ACIDS*

H. J. Maria, B. N. Srinivasan and S. P. McGlynn
Coates Chemical Laboratories
Louisiana State University
Baton Rouge, Louisiana 70803

I. INTRODUCTION

This paper is concerned with the luminescence of polyatomic anions such as nitrate, nitrite, acetate, thiocyanate, etc. The manner in which this luminescence is affected by the presence of metal counter-ions is very pertinent in that it leads to an understanding of the colors associated with many non-transition heavy metal salts of the simple oxy-acids. Indeed, our paper might be subtitled: "The Colors of Post-Transition Metal Salts of the Oxy-Acids."

*This work was supported by a research contract between the United States Atomic Energy Commision-Biology Branch and the Louisiana State University.

The work reported will emphasize the phosphorescence of nitrite salts. The reason for this is that sufficient experimental evidence has been accumulated to locate the lowest energy triplet state of the nitrite ion and to establish that heavy-atom coordination to this ion produces very large spin-orbital coupling enhancement of the lowest energy spin-forbidden triplet ↔ singlet transition of the NO_2^- entity. The discussion will then be extended to the triplet electronic states of other polyatomic anions. Our purpose, it must be emphasized, is not so much the provision of experimental detail or definite conclusions as it is to pose a way of thinking about simple inorganic salts.

Literature examination reveals a dearth of knowledge about the electronic states of polyatomic anions, whereas the information available concerning transition metal ions and their complexes is quite extensive. Whenever a polyatomic anion enters into a complex with a transition metal ion, it is usually discussed only insofar as it affects the d-d (or f-f) transitions of the metal or induces charge-transfer transitions of ligand ↔ metal type. The internal electronic transitions of the anion are rarely mentioned. The principal reason for this is that the internal transitions of the majority of simple polyatomic anions occur in or near the vacuum ultraviolet. However, perturbation of anion by metal counter-ions may produce a number of effects:

(i) The allowed transitions of the anion may be shifted into a more accessible region of the spectrum;

(ii) Charge-transfer transitions of anion ↔ metal ion type may occur;

(iii) Orbitally forbidden transitions of the anion may acquire more allowedness in the anion-metal ion associate; and

(iv) Spin-forbidden transitions of the anion may become more allowed if the metal ion provides an efficient spin-orbital coupling center for the "anionic" electrons.

Effects of types (i)-(iv) are difficult to extract from the already crowded spectra of transition metal salts. Furthermore, since our primary interest is in item (iv), and since the phosphorescence technique provides an easy and systematic way of investigating spin-forbidden transitions, it is advisable to ensure that none of the excited electronic levels of the metal ion lie at lower energies than the lowest energy triplet state of the anion. Thus it is that our investigations are usually restricted to metal ions of the alkali, alkaline earth or post-transition metal type.

II. THE LOWEST ENERGY TRIPLET STATES OF SOME POLYATOMIC ANIONS

A. NITRITE SALTS. The absorption spectra of aqueous solutions of nitrite salts have a common weak absorption band at ∿425 mμ. The extinction coefficient of this band depends upon the positive counter-ion and increases from 3×10^{-3} cm^{-1} $(mole/liter)^{-1}$ in sodium nitrite to 12 cm^{-1} $(mole/liter)^{-1}$ in lead nitrite. Correspondingly, the color of these salts increases from almost colorless in Na(I) to pale yellow in Ag(I) to sulfur yellow in Hg(I) to bright yellow (almost orange) in Pb(II). We therefore attribute the color of these salts to this weak absorption band which we assign as the first triplet ← singlet transition of the nitrite ion. The increase in intensity is understood as a spin-orbit coupling effect made possible by the coordination of the nitrite ion to the heavy metal ion.[1]

The nitrite salts also phosphoresce.[2] It has been shown that the position of this phosphorescence and the dependence of its lifetime on the metal counter-ion are consistent with its assignment as the inverse of the process responsible for the color of these salts; in other words, the phosphorescence of the nitrite ion is of $T_1 \rightarrow S_0$ nature. Data on the absorption and emission characteristics of nitrite salts are summarized in Table 1.

B. ACETATE AND BENZOATE SALTS. Acetate and benzoate salts differ in one important respect: The lowest energy triplet state of the benzoate ion is of π,π^* nature whereas that of the acetate ion is of n,π^* nature. The π-electron system associated with the benzene ring of benzoate ion does not possess significant amplitude on the carboxyl group. Consequently, the lowest triplet state of the benzoate ion should not be significantly affected by heavy-metal association at the carboxyl group. On the other hand, the lowest triplet state of the acetate ion, involves electron promotion on the carbonyl residue; consequently, provided the heavy-metal acetate salts have appreciable covalent character, it would be expected that spin-orbital perturbation of the triplet state should occur. Thus, it is of some significance to compare the phosphorescence characteristics of these two groups of salts.

Levshin and Rebane[3] studied the absorption and phosphorescence spectra of benzoic acid and its Na, K, Cu and Pb salts in various solvents. They showed that:

(i) Undissociated species exist in solution;

(ii) The low energy absorption bands have the charactersitics of $\pi^* \leftarrow \pi$ transitions; and

(iii) The phosphorescence spectrum and lifetime of the benzoates are independent of the metal ion and are essentially identical to those of benzoic acid. (The lifetime in all cases was 2.55-2.60 seconds).

The phosphorescence of acetic acid and its salts has not been discussed in the literature.

TABLE 1: Nitrate Salts

Counter-ion	Color	$T_1 \leftarrow S_o$ Absorption $[\bar{\nu}_{max}(kK)]$	$[cm^{-1}(mole/l)^{-1}]$	$T_1 \rightarrow S_o$ Emission $[\bar{\nu}_{max}(kK)]$	Mean Phosphorescence Lifetime (seconds): Measured at 77°K	Mean Phosphorescence Lifetime (seconds): Calculated from extinction coefficient
Na(I)	Colorless-yellow	22.2	3×10^{-3}	-	-	1×10^{-1}
Cd(II)	Yellowish	23.4	2.3×10^{-2}	18.5	3.3×10^{-1}	5×10^{-2}
Ag(I)	Pale Yellow	22.2	-	18.5	3.2×10^{-4}	-
Hg(I)[a]	Sulfur Yellow	-	-	18.2	-	-
Pb(II)	Bright Yellow	22.8	11.7	18.2	7.0×10^{-5}	5×10^{-5}
Tl(I)	Orange	21.9	0.64	17.4	9×10^{-5}	6×10^{-4}

[a] We wish to point out that the emission spectrum attributed to $Hg(NO_2)_2$ in our first paper[2] must be attributed to some other species. This is because the procedure described in the experimental section for the preparation of $Hg(NO_2)_2$ does not in fact yield this compound. We have since prepared $Hg_2(NO_2)_2$ by the action of nitric acid on mercury (P. C. Ray, Trans. Chem. Soc. 71, 337 (1897)) and we wish now to report that this compound is sulfur yellow and that it has an emission with a maximum at 550 mμ (in the solid state and at 77°K) and with a short lifetime. This emission of $Hg_2(NO_2)_2$ is in accord with the luminescence of other nitrites.

Osada[4,5] has observed an emission of long duration from acetic acid and its sodium salt. However, he concluded that the emission, in both instances, was due to sodium ions which are also present as impurity in the acetic acid. He reports the following concerning the emission of sodium acetate:

(i) The phosphorescence spectrum is independent of temperature in the range 330-120°K;

(ii) The emission intensity is quenched by adsorbed molecular oxygen, but is sensitized by increasing the water content of the specimen; and

(iii) The lifetime of the emission remains essentially constant ($\sim$ 2 seconds) at all temperatures below 210°K.

The above features are reminiscent of the characteristics of the phosphorescence of organic substances and it is, therefore, of interest to inquire whether this emission is from a triplet state of the acetate ion.

Preliminary experiments in this laboratory on the luminescence of acetate salts indicate that a number of these salts possess an emission of long duration with a maximum at about 425 mμ. Table 2 summarizes the data on the lifetime of this phosphorescence. These preliminary results indicate that the luminescence of the acetates is characteristic of the acetate ion and that it may be attributed to a $T_1 \rightarrow S_o$ phosphorescence process. The heavy-atom effect on the lifetime is in accord with this interpretation.

Post-transition metal salts of the benzoate or acetate ions are not colored; the 0,0 band of the triplet state, in both instances, lies at energies considerably higher than 25kK ($\lambda <$ 400 mμ). On the other hand, it is clear that the phenomenology exhibited by the salts of a purely organic anion (i.e., acetate) is completely equivalent to that found in the salts of a purely inorganic anion (i.e., nitrite).

TABLE 2: Lifetime of the Phosphorescence of Acetate Salts

Counter-ion	Mean Lifetime (sec) at $77^{o}K$ Solid	Solution[a]
Na(I)	1.1	1.5
Ba(II)	0.9	-
Cd(II)	0.90	1.23
Pb(II)	2.2×10^{-2}	-
Hg(II)	7×10^{-3}	7×10^{-2}

[a] The solvent used is a mixture of methyl, isopropyl and ethyl alcohols.

C. NITRATE SALTS. As far as we are aware, no phosphorescence emission of any nitrate salt has been reported. This is not surprising: The heavy metal nitrate salts are thermally unstable and they tend to photodissociate in ultraviolet light. As a result, the possibility of impurity luminescence poses certain questions. Nonetheless, we have been able to measure phosphorescence emission and $T_1 \leftarrow S_o$ absorption spectra of a large number of nitrate salts. The triplet state of the NO_3^- ion has a 0,0 energy of $\sim$ 26.3kK (λ = 380 mμ). The luminescence characteristics of some nitrate salts are given in Table 3; this tabulation of data is presented without comment, because we are as yet uncertain about the physical meaning of a number of the experimental observations. These observations are:

(i) The presence of two lifetime components in the phosphorescence decay process;

(ii) The red-shifts of the luminescence which usually occur in the crystalline specimens (relative to solution);

(iii) The non-dependence of solution lifetimes on the counter-ion;

(iv) The apparent dependence of solution intensities on the counter-ion;

(v) The non-phosphorescence of crystalline $Cr(NO_3)_3$, $Tl(NO_3)$, $Co(NO_3)_2$, $Ni(NO_3)_2$ and $Cu(NO_3)_2$, whereas glassy solutions of the same salts are luminescent; and

(vi) The apparent non-luminescence of either crystals or solutions of the alkali-metal salts.

In any case, it is expected that the majority of nitrate salts of the post-transition metal ions will be colorless. However, by virtue of the close proximity T_1 to 400 mμ, it is conceivable that thermal broadening of this band into the visible

TABLE 3: Phosphorescence of Nitrate Salts (77°K)

Counter-ion	State or Medium	Excitation (λ, mμ)	Emission (λ_{max}, mμ)	Lifetime ($\tau_{1/2}$, sec)
Alkali Metal	Crystal	-	None	-
	Glassy Solution	-	None	-
Al(III)	Powdered Crystal	365	450	0.6
	EPA glass	265	480	<0.1
Cr(III)	Crystal	-	None	-
	EPA glass	270	430	2.0;0.2
Fe(III)	Crystal	-	None	-
	EPA glass	-	None	-
Cu(II)	Crystal	-	None	-
	EPA glass	325	470	0.5;0.25
Co(II)	Crystal	-	None	-
	EPA glass	265;315	440	2.0;0.4
Ni(II)	Crystal	-	None	-
	EPA glass	255;290	450	1.5;0.3
Zn(II)	Crystal	315	495	---;0.26
	Alcoholic glass	255;325	485	0.85;0.16
Sr(II)	Powdered crystal	300	480	0.46;0.09
	Alcoholic glass	270	430	0.80;0.28
		300	480	----;0.26
Pd(II)	Crystal	-	None	-
	EPA glass	-	None	-
Ag(I)	Crystal	-	None	-
	EPA glass	-	None	-
Cd(II)	Crystal	330	500	----;0.28
	Alcoholic glass	355	470	1.51;----
Ba(II)	Crystal	310	465	0.4;0.1
	EPA glass	270	435	2.2;0.2
		300	470	2.0;0.2
Ce(II)	Crystal	-	None	-
	EPA glass	-	None	-
Hg(I)	Crystal	335	550	<0.1
	EPA glass	280	465	1.5;0.2
Hg(II)	Powdered crystal	360	505	<<0.1
		280	455	1.25;0.14
		310	475	1.15;0.10
Tl(I)	Crystal	-	None	-
	EPA glass	270	470	2.0;0.2

might occur in certain instances. Perhaps it is such broadening which is responsible for the thermochromism of $Hg_2(NO_3)_2$: Yellow at 300°K, colorless at 77°K. We know of no other non-transition metal nitrate salt which is colored.

D. OTHER SALTS. Observations similar to those on nitrite, acetate and nitrate salts have been made for the following anions:[6] Thiocyanate, cyanate, sulfite and chlorate. The triplet states of these compounds lie at energies greater than 25kK and it is not expected that any of their non-transition metal salts should exhibit color because of triplet enhancement.

III. THE COLORS OF POST-TRANSITION METAL SALTS

It has been shown that the color of the post-transition metal nitrite salts is due to the spin-orbitally enhanced triplet ← singlet transition of the nitrite ion. It is now our intention to extend this conclusion, in a speculative way, to other inorganic salts. We note first that the occurrence of color among the post-transition metal salts of colorless anions is quite common (Table 4). In Table 4, the salts of Ag(I) are used for illustration; however, color is equally prevalent among the salts of Pb(II), Tl(I) and Hg(I).

Pitzer and Hildebrand suggested[7] that the color of a salt formed from colorless ions is a measure of the covalent character of the bond between the ions. Donahue and Shand,[8] noting that the sum of the ionic radii for silver(I) and oxygen is 2.46 Å and that the sum of the covalent radii is 2.19 Å, pointed out that the available data for silver salts (see Table 4) are at most only in rough accord with this suggestion. At any rate, the discussion by

TABLE 4: Color, Metal-Nearest Neighbor Distance and Position of First Singlet ← Singlet Electronic Transitions of the Silver Salts of Some Hydrated Anions

Compound	Ag-Nearest Atom Distance (Å)	Color	$S_1 \leftarrow S_0$ Energy of Hydrated Anion (mμ)
$AgClO_3$[a]	2.51	colorless	190
Ag_2SO_4	2.34	colorless	<200
Ag_2MoO_4	2.42	bright-yellow	210
$KAgCO_3$	2.42	colorless	210
Ag_3PO_4	2.34	yellow	<200
Ag_3AsO_4	2.34	red	<200
Ag_2CO_3	2.30	yellow	210
$AgNO_2$	2.04	yellow	355
$AgClO_2$	2.20	greenish-yellow	290
$Ag_2N_2O_2$	----	yellow	248
$AgNO_3$	----	colorless	300
Ag_2SO_3	----	colorless	<200

[a]In the first seven salts, the atom nearest to the cation is oxygen. For these salts, data is from: Walter Hückel, Structural Chemistry of Inorganic Compounds (Elsevier Publishing Co., 1951), Vol. 2, p. 577 and references contained therein.

[b]J. A. A. Ketelaar, Z. Krist. 95, 383 (1936).

[c]R. Curti, V. Riganti and S. Locchi, Acta Cryst. 10, 687 (1957).

Pitzer-Hildebrand does not indicate whether the color is due to "new" absorption bands or merely due to shifts of the allowed transitions of the anion. Phillips and Williams[9] attribute the colors of the oxyanion salts to absorption-band shifts which are induced by the cation because of its supposed ability to polarize the anion. Such shifts do occur, of course, but in order to account for the color of silver phosphate, say, a red-shift of at least 25kK ($\sim$ 3 eV) is required. It appears very likely, therefore, that such shifts are not the only important factor and that the enhancement of forbidden transitions by spin-orbit coupling is, at least, equally important. Such enhancement should depend upon covalent character in such a way as to validate the Pitzer-Hildebrand suggestion; however, spin-orbital coupling also depends upon the manner of mixing of the atomic orbitals on the cation with the molecular orbitals of the anion, and this mixing depends not only on the distance of separation but also on the geometry of the adduct and on a number of other subtle features.

In view of the above, it is interesting that we predict the following colors for Ag(I) salts: chlorate--colorless; carbonate--colorless or slightly yellow; nitrite--yellow; nitrate--colorless; chlorate--colorless. These predictions, based as they are on our knowledge of triplet states of the anions, are in remarkable accord with the data of Table 4. The silver salts of acetate, benzoate, thiocyanate and cyanate ions are also predicted to be colorless—which they are. We have also investigated salts of chlorous acid; unfortunately, these salts do not luminesce and chlorous acid is sufficiently acidic that it does not tend to associate significantly with counter-ions. Nonetheless, even though we have not been able to locate the triplet state of the ClO_2^- entity, our experiments do indicate that the color of these salts is the result of both triplet ← singlet enhancement and slight singlet ← singlet redshifting operating in combination. None of the other anions of Table 4 have as yet been subjected to experimental test.

REFERENCES

1. H. J. Maria, A. Wahlborg and S. P. McGlynn, J. Chem. Phys. (in press).
2. H. J. Maria, A. T. Armstrong and S. P. McGlynn, J. Chem. Phys. 48, 4694 (1968).
3. V. L. Levshin and V. N. Rebane, Optics and Spectroscopy, Suppl. 1, Eng. Ed., 44 (1966).
4. K. Osada, J. Phys. Soc. Japan, 12, 1420 (1957).
5. K. Osada, J. Chem. Phys. 30, 1363 (1959).
6. J. McDonald and A. Wahlborg (unpublished data).
7. K. S. Pitzer and J. H. Hildebrand, J. Am. Chem. Soc. 63, 2472 (1941).
8. J. Donahue and W. Shand, J. Am. Chem. Soc. 69, 222 (1947).
9. C. S. G. Phillips and R. J. P. Williams in Inorganic Chemistry (Oxford University Press, 1966), Vol. 2, p. 498.

RARE EARTH IONS AS PROBES FOR EXCITED MOLECULES IN AQUEOUS SOLUTION

A. A. Lamola and J. Eisinger

Bell Telephone Laboratories, Incorporated
Murray Hill, New Jersey

INTRODUCTION

Unfortunately, neither DNA nor any of its constituent nucleotides exhibit an observable luminescence in water solution (pH 7) at room temperature.[1] The little that is known about the lifetimes of the triplet states of the pyrimidine nucleotides under these conditions indicates that the lifetimes are too short for study by conventional flash photolysis techniques.[2,3] Although many valid conclusions can be drawn about the electronic relaxation processes in nucleic acids at room temperature by extrapolation of low temperature emission studies, in many instances such extrapolation is dangerous. It is, of course, very important for understanding the photochemistry and photobiology of DNA to obtain precise information about the excited states of nucleic acids under "biological conditions." To this end we considered indirect methods involving energy transfer to quenchers whose excited states we could monitor in fluid water solution and were led the rare earth ions Eu^{3+} and Tb^{3+} as appropriate quenchers.

The chlorides of Eu^{3+} and Tb^{3+} are quite soluble in water and exhibit characteristic and easily monitored "line" emissions in the visible[4] which is not quenched by the normal amount of oxygen present.[5] Furthermore, it has already been shown that emission from the solvated ions can be sensitized by energy transfer from the triplet states of organic molecules in acetic acid,[6] in methanol,[7] and in water.[8] Finally, the rare earth ions seem to be relatively photostable and exhibit only weak and narrow absorption bands in the visible and near ultraviolet regions so that it is very easy to avoid direct excitations of the ions in mixtures with organic donors. However, little is known about how the rates of excitation transfer from triplet state donors to the rare earth ions depend upon the triplet energy and structure of the donor. The possible complication of the chelating abilities of the ions has not been fully evaluated. There is the possibility of interaction of the ions with excited singlet molecules. And finally the possibility that the lanthanide ions are heavy atoms capable of inducing intersystem crossing needs investigation.

We report here some early observations concerning some of the questions raised above and present some preliminary results from our studies which are aimed at developing the Eu^{3+} and Tb^{3+} ions as probes for electronically excited molecules in water solution.

RESULTS

TRIPLET TRANSFER. Heller and Wasserman first

demonstrated triplet excitation transfer from organic molecules to Eu^{3+} and Tb^{3+} in glacial acetic acid.[6] They showed that the transfer is of the collisional type but did not measure any transfer rates. Wagner has estimated that triplet transfer from valerophenone to Eu^{3+} and Tb^{3+} in methanol solution is slower than the diffusion-controlled rate by one to two order of magnitude.[7] Heller has used triplet sensitizers to excited Eu^{3+} and Tb^{3+} in water solution but did not determine the transfer rates.[8]

We have used the aromatic carbonyl compound acetophenone as a test triplet donor, primarily because it has a totally efficient intersystem crossing[9] and is therefore a convenient standard for the triplet population. The chlorides of Eu^{3+} and Tb^{3+} were prepared from the oxides.

The simplest mechanism which involves interaction of the lanthanide ions with only the triplet state of the donor is described by the relationship shown in Eq. (1) where Φ_f is the quantum yield of ion emission, β is the efficiency of ion emission once the available ^5D levels have been populated, Φ_{ISC} is the intersystem crossing yield of the donor, τ_T is the lifetime of the donor triplet state, k_q is the bimolecular rate constant for the excitation transfer and $[L^{3+}]$ is the ion concentration.

$$\frac{\beta}{\Phi_f} = \frac{1}{\Phi_{ISC}}\left(1 + \frac{1}{\tau_T k_q [L^{3+}]}\right) \qquad (1)$$

In Fig. 1 are shown plots of I^{-1} vs $[Eu^{3+}]^{-1}$ for acetophenone as donor in H_2O and in D_2O where I is the Eu^{3+} emission intensity monitored at 590 nm ($^5D \rightarrow {}^7F_1$) in arbitrary units. The excitation wavelength was 280 nm where the samples (∿ 1 mm path) were optically thick in acetophenone (0.01 M). The samples were not deoxygenated and the pH was near 7. Both curves in Fig. 1 are

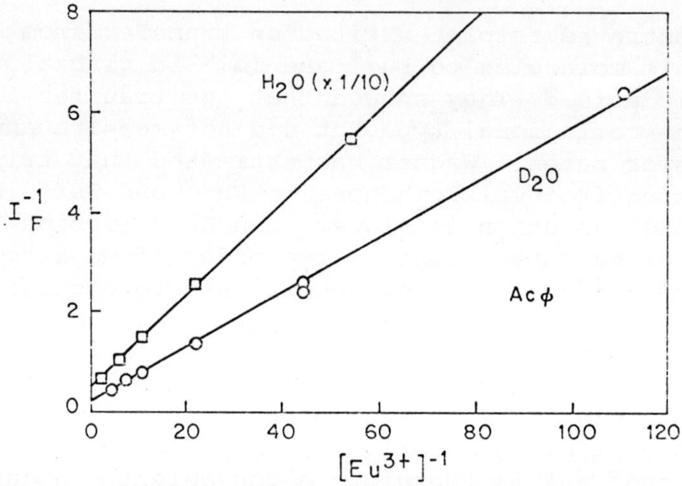

Figure 1 The reciprocal intensity (arbitrary units) of sensitized Eu^{3+} emission as a function of the reciprocal of the Eu^{3+} concentration (M^{-1}) for acetophenone as the donor in H_2O and in D_2O.

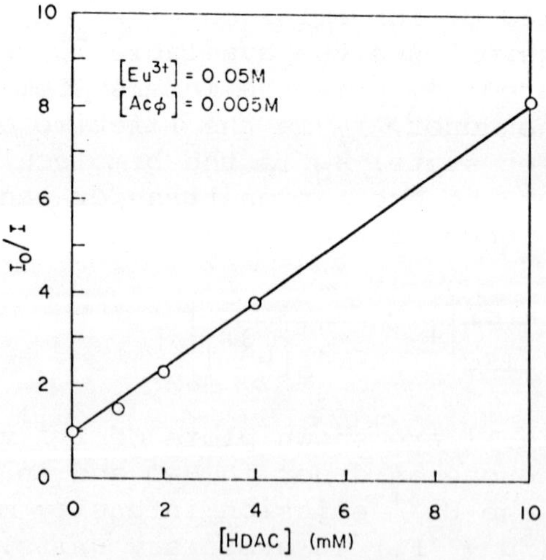

Figure 2 A Stern-Volmer plot for the quenching of the acetophenone sensitized emission of Eu^{3+} by (2,4-hexadienyl) trimethylammonium chloride.

good straight lines. The ratio of the intercepts to the slopes gives $k_q\tau_T$ values of 2 for D_2O and 5 for H_2O. The large difference in intensities of Eu^{3+} emission on going from D_2O to H_2O is due to the solvent isotope effect on the efficiency of the Eu^{3+} emission.[4,5]

τ_T for acetophenone or for any other suitable triplet donor in water are not known so that these results cannot be used to determine k_q directly. An indirect method of obtaining an estimate of k_q is provided by measuring the competition between the quenching rates of Eu^{3+} and a diene quencher whose quenching rate is expected to be diffusion limited.

The Eu^{3+} emission from solutions of acetophenone (0.005 M) in D_2O containing a constant amount of Eu^{3+} (0.05 M) and various amounts of the water soluble diene

$$CH_3CH=CH-CH=CH-CH_2N^+(CH_3)_3Cl^-$$

(2,4-hexadienyl) trimethylammonium chloride[10] (HDAC) was measured and the results plotted according to Stern-Volmer kinetics (Fig. 2). The slope of the resulting straight line gives $kq_{(HDAC)}\tau_T$ as 720 where $kq_{(HDAC)}$ is the bimolecular rate constant for quenching of the acetophenone triplet by HDAC and τ_T is the lifetime of triplet acetophenone in D_2O in the presence of 0.05 M Eu^{3+}. Making the reasonable assumption that $kq_{(HDAC)}$ is equal to the diffusion-controlled rate constant $\sim 5 \times 10^9$ l M^{-1} s^{-1} and using the $k_q\tau$ value mentioned above we calculate that k_q, the rate constant for energy transfer from triplet acetophenone to Eu^{3+} in D_2O, is 1.3×10^7 l M^{-1} s^{-1} and the lifetime of the acetophenone triplet in aerated D_2O is 1.5×10^{-7} sec.

The low value we estimate for k_q for Eu^{3+} in water ($\sim$ 400 times smaller than the diffusion-controlled rate constant) agrees with the findings of Wagner for methanol as solvent.[7]

FLUORESCENCE QUENCHING. Tryptophan fluoresces in water solution at room temperature. The fluorescence lifetimes are 4.5×10^{-9} sec in H_2O and 8.5×10^{-9} sec in D_2O.[11] We found that Eu^{3+} quenches tryptophan fluorescence at the diffusion-controlled rate, as can be seen by the Stern-Volmer plots shown in Fig. 3. The quenching rate constant obtained from the slopes of the plots is $\sim 5 \times 10^9$ l M^{-1} s^{-1}. Curiously, no concomitant Eu^{3+} emission was observed. However, tryptophan does sensitize Tb^{3+} emission and Tb^{3+} quenches tryptophan fluorescence. We have not performed quantitative experiments with Tb^{3+} as yet so that we do not know whether or not the quenching and sensitization are related.

THYMIDYLIC ACID. Figure 4 shows a plot of β/Φ_f vs $[Eu^{3+}]^{-1}$ (see Eq. (1)) for sensitization of Eu^{3+} emission in D_2O (pD $\sim$ 6) by thymidylic acid (TMP). Intensity values were transformed into quantum yields by using the limiting intensity obtained with acetophenone as the donor as the standard. The curve can be interpreted in terms of a model which includes energy transfer from both the triplet and excited singlet states of the donor. The expected large lifetime difference between the excited singlet and triplet states leads to two limits in the kinetics. The low Eu^{3+} concentration or triplet limit is given by Eq. (1). At high concentrations where interaction with the singlet state dominates the relationship of Eq. (2) applies.

$$\frac{\beta}{\Phi_f} = 1 + \frac{1}{\tau_s k_q' [L^{3+}]} \qquad (2)$$

In Eq. (2), τ_s is the lifetime of the donor excited singlet state and k_q' is the bimolecular rate constant for sensitization of the ion emission by the donor.

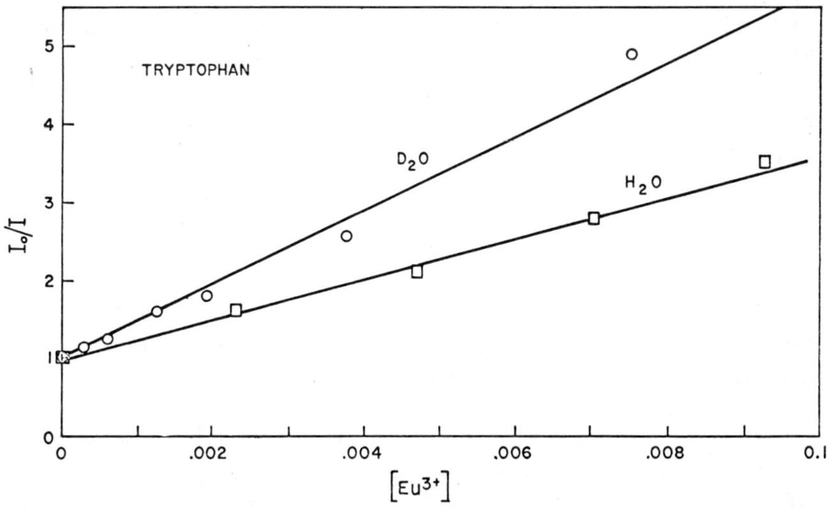

Figure 3 Stern-Volmer plot of the quenching of tryptophan fluorescence by Eu^{3+}.

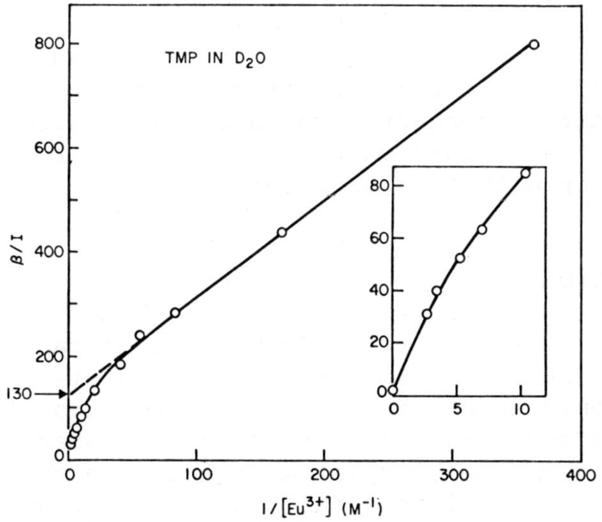

Figure 4 A plot of β/Φ_f against $[Eu^{3+}]^{-1}$ for TMP sensitized Eu^{3+} emission in D_2O.

Extrapolation of the linear portion of the TMP curve at low [Eu^{3+}], the triplet region, to infinite [Eu^{3+}] gives Φ_{ISC} according to our model. The value obtained 0.008 is in agreement with the estimate of Johns and co-workers which was based upon the kinetics[3] for the photodimerization via the triplet state of the TMP in water.

Similar curves were obtained using guanidylic acid and orotic acid as donors.

WAVELENGTH DEPENDENCE OF Φ_{ISC} FOR OROTIC ACID. We measured the relative yields of sensitized Eu^{3+} emission with orotic acid as the donor in D_2O (pD 2.5) as a function of the wavelength of the exciting light. The Eu^{3+} concentration was such that interaction with the excited singlet state of orotic acid was negligible. The results are shown in Fig. 5 along with the relative quantum yields for orotic acid photodimer production in H_2O at room temperature as measured by Whillans and Johns.[12] They have shown that the photodimerization of orotic acid in water solution proceeds by way of the triplet state and have proposed that the intersystem crossing is the wavelength dependent step in the mechanism. Our results using Eu^{3+} as a triplet probe are in full agreement with this proposal.

DISCUSSION

Potentially the rare earth ions can quench excited states by a number of mechanisms including electronic energy transfer, electron transfer, complex formation, and induction of intersystem crossing by the heavy atom effect. In the cases we have examined thus far, it seems certain that Eu^{3+} quenches the triplet donors by the energy transfer mechanism. The low value we found for the transfer rate constant 1.3×10^7 l M^{-1} s^{-1}

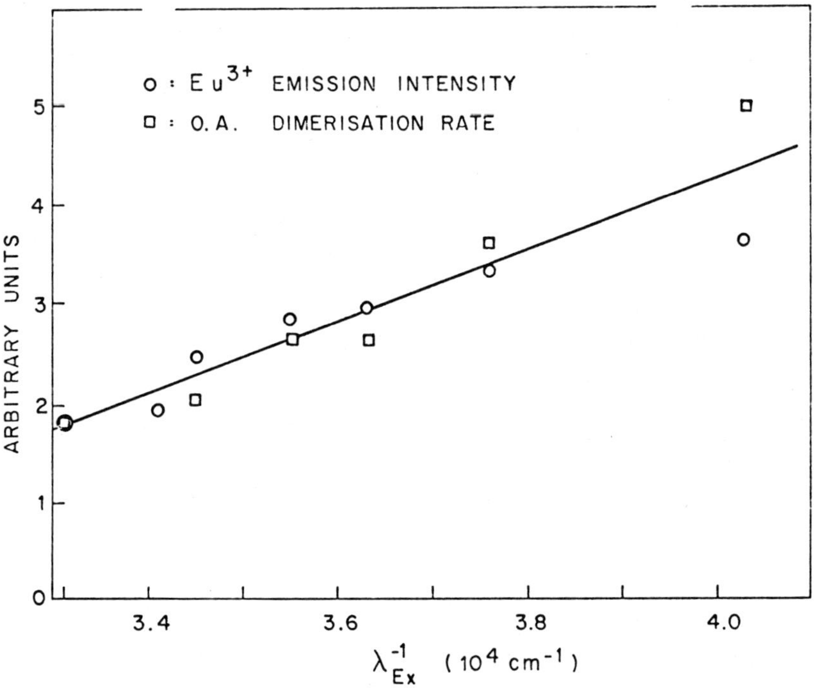

Figure 5 Relative yield of the orotic acid sensitized Eu^{3+} emission as a function of the exciting wavelength; relative yield of orotic acid photodimers as a function of the exciting wavelength (from Reference 12).

using acetophenone as the donor agrees with the findings of Wagner. The reason for this low value is not known. Perhaps the small spectral overlap is responsible or the tightly bound solvent shell may be interfering with close approach of the donor. Some particular matching of the donor excitation energy or spectrum may be required for fast transfer. At any rate, it is certainly not safe at this time to assume that the k_q value of 1.3×10^7 l M^{-1} s^{-1} found for acetophenone as the donor can be applied to other donors. It is interesting that using this value we calculate the lifetime of the TMP triplet in water to be 5×10^{-6} sec, a reasonable value.

A result of importance to the understanding of the photochemistry of nucleic acids at room temperature comes from a comparison of the intersystem crossing yields of thymidylic and guanadylic acids (GMP). It has been shown that at low temperature in a polar glass TMP has a negligible intersystem crossing yield while that of GMP is about 15%.[1] It now appears that in aqueous solution at room temperature this relationship is reversed, Φ_{ISC} being about 0.01 for TMP and of the order of 10^{-4} for GMP.

Much more investigation is necessary before definite conclusions can be drawn about the mode(s) of interaction of Eu^{3+} and Tb^{3+} with excited singlet molecules. One interesting possibility for the case of TMP is that Eu^{3+} induces intersystem crossing of the singlet to the triplet which is followed by triplet energy transfer to the Eu^{3+}. This is kinetically indistinguishable from energy transfer directly from the excited singlet state. It is again interesting to note that assuming a diffusion-controlled rate (which we found for tryptophan) for the interaction between Eu^{3+} and the TMP excited singlet state, the lifetime of the TMP singlet state is calculated to be 10^{-11} sec which agrees well with estimates made from other data.[1,2]

Although many questions are left unanswered, our results to date do indicate that the rare earth ions will be useful probes for excited molecules in polar solvents and especially important for water.

REFERENCES

1. M. Gueron, J. Eisinger and R. G. Shulman, J. Chem. Phys. 47, 4077 (1967); J. Eisinger, Photochem. Photobiol. (in press).
2. A. A. Lamola, Photochem. Photobiol. (in press).
3. C. L. Greenstock, et al., Biochem. Biophys. Res. Comm. 27, 431 (1967).
4. J. L. Kropp and M. W. Windsor, J. Chem. Phys. 39, 2769 (1963).
5. J. L. Kropp and M. W. Windsor, J. Chem. Phys. 42, 1599 (1965).
6. A. Heller and E. Wasserman, J. Chem. Phys. 42, 949 (1965).
7. P. Wagner (private communication).
8. A. Heller, Proceedings of the Fifth Rare Earth Research Conference, Air Force Office for Scientific Research, 1965, p. 77.
9. A. A. Lamola, J. Chem. Phys. 47, 4810 (1967).
10. The synthesis of HDAC will be reported later; A. A. Lamola and D. Patel (unpublished work).
11. W. E. Blumberg, J. Eisinger and G. Navon, Biophys. J. Soc. Abstracts 8, A106 (1968).
12. D. W. Whillans and H. E. Johns, Biophysical Journal 8, (Society Abstracts) A83 (1968).

EXPERIMENTAL INVESTIGATIONS OF COMPOUNDS EXHIBITING ANOMALOUS EMISSION

J. A. Poole andR. C. Dhingra

Department of Chemistry
Temple University of the Commonwealth
System of Higher Education
Philadelphia, Pennsylvania 19122

INTRODUCTION

By definition, fluorescence is the radiation emitted spontaneously in a transition between states of like multiplicity.[1,2] Concerning the singlet manifold, such radiative trnasitions have generally been observed to originate from the lowest excited singlet state (S_1) due to rapid non-radiative processes (viz., internal conversions and/or intersystem crossings, vibrational relaxation, chemical transformations, and energy transfer mechanisms) which compete with photon emission from higher excited singlet states. Kasha summarized the evidence in the empirical rule: "The emitting level of a given multiplicity is the lowest excited level of that multiplicity."[3] Thus, fluorescence corresponding to transitions other than $S_1 \rightarrow S_o$ is considered anomalous.

The first authentic exception to Kasha's rule

was discovered by Beer and Longuet-Higgins[4] who showed that the emission from the non-alternant hydrocarbon azulene could only be interpreted as an $S_2 \rightarrow S_o$ transition. Their original observations were confirmed by Viswanath and Kasha.[5] The work of Sidman and McClure[6] established that the naphthalene sensitized emission of azulene also originated from the second excited singlet state and their vibrational analysis was later confirmed by Ruzevich.[7] In the paper by Viswanath and Kasha[5] some simple alkyl substituted azulenes (viz., 2,4,8-trimethylazulene; 2,4,5-trimethylazulene; and 1,4-dimethyl-7-isopropylazulene (guaiazulene)) were also characterized as exhibiting anomalous fluorescence. In 1967, Hiebronner, et al. reported[8] that 2-phenylazulene, 1,3-dibromoazulene, and the three isomeric benzazulenes behaved anomalously in their emissive properties (the cases of benz[f]azulene and 1,3-dibromoazulene are in accord with our own observations.)

It has been stated[9,10,11] that azulene, in the gaseous phase, emits anomalously from the second excited singlet level. However, these statements are based on the original work of Hunt and Ross[12] who did not observe any fluorescence from gaseous azulene under optical excitation. The emission referred to in References (9), (10), and (11) was observed by Hunt and Ross only when gaseous azulene was excited by a radiofrequency oscillator, or Tesla coil, producing a rearrangement to naphthalene, and then to a brown, unidentified substance. The spectrum, they go on to state, consists of a strong continuum, and the fluorescence emitted by azulene and naphthalene has superimposed on it the emission from CO, CN, etc. Thus, the gas phase $S_2 \rightarrow S_o$ fluorescence of azulene, if any, deserves further investigation.

Here it should be mentioned that Rentzepis,[13] in a double photon experiment, has observed both the $S_1 \rightarrow S_o$ and the $T_1 \rightarrow S_o$ emission of azulene, the 0-0 band of the latter emission being at

11,900 A, which is in good agreement with the theoretical predictions of Pariser.[14]

Eaton and Leermakers[15] have investigated the following compounds: 3,5-dimethylcyclopenta[ef]-heptalene; 1,3-diacetylazulene; 4,6,8-trimethyl-1,3-diacetylazulene; and 1,4-dimethyl-7-isopropyl-azulene (guaiazulene). They have observed anomalous emissive behavior except in the case of the first mentioned compound where an initial $S_2 \rightarrow S_o$ observation could not be reproduced.

RESULTS AND DISCUSSION

Our own investigations have been confined to molecular systems whose spectral and/or structural resemblance to azulene suggested that a similar $S_2 \rightarrow S_1$ radiationless prohibition was efficient enough to allow $S_2 \rightarrow S_o$ radiative competition.

The first series of compounds to be observed[16] were the following pericondensed hydrocarbons: 3,5-dimethylcyclopenta[ef]heptalene; 3,5-dimethyl-8-phenylcyclohepta[cd]pentalene; and 4-methylpantaleno[2,1,6-def]heptalene. The structure and spectra of these compounds is illustrated in Fig. (1), where they are arranged in the above order from top to bottom. The results indicate that in all cases the emission originates from an excited singlet state above S_1. For further details concerning these results, including oscillator strengths, lifetimes, and comparisons with theoretically predicted levels, the reader is referred to Reference (16). The spectral properties of naphth[2,1,8-cde]azulene shown in Fig. (2) are interesting, and it is instructive to compare the spectra with that of the compound shown at the bottom of Fig. (1). Note that here also, anomalous emission is observed.[17]

We also investigated the absorptive and emissive properties of certain 1-substituted azulenes, viz., 1-trifluoroacetylazulene, 1-nitro-

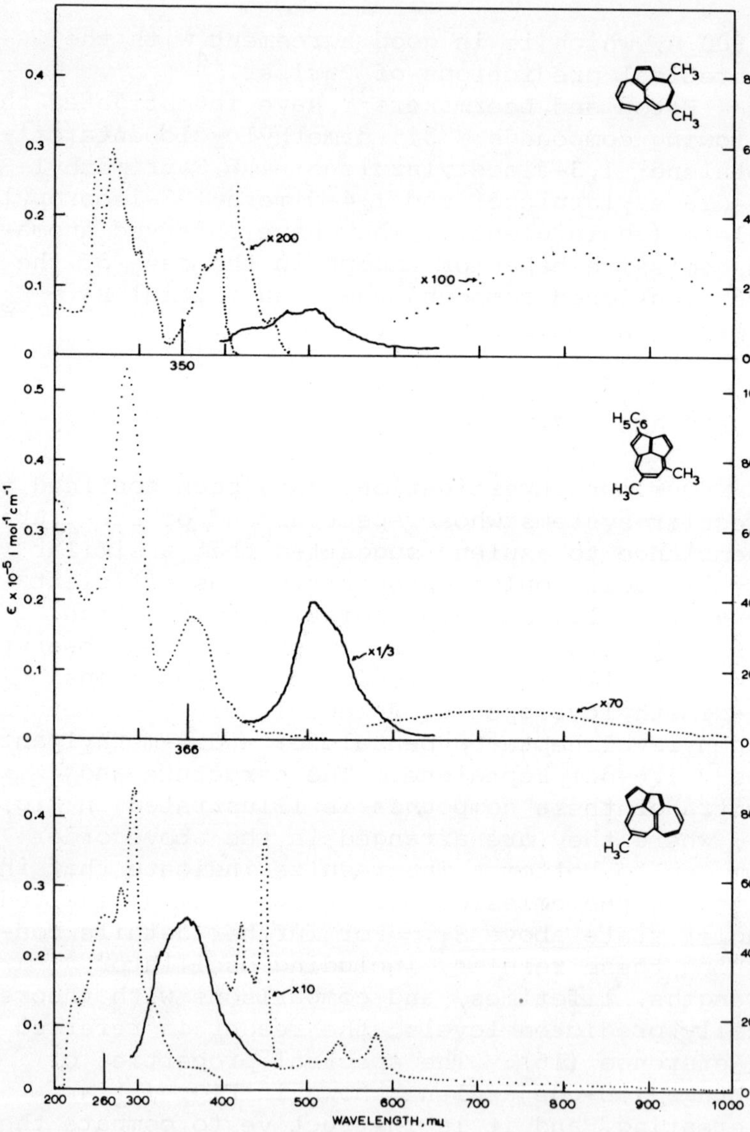

Figure 1 Absorption (···), and emission (——) spectra of "Hafner's hydrocarbons" taken in fluid solution at room temperature, with cyclohexane (for absorption) and methylcyclohexane (for emission) as solvents.

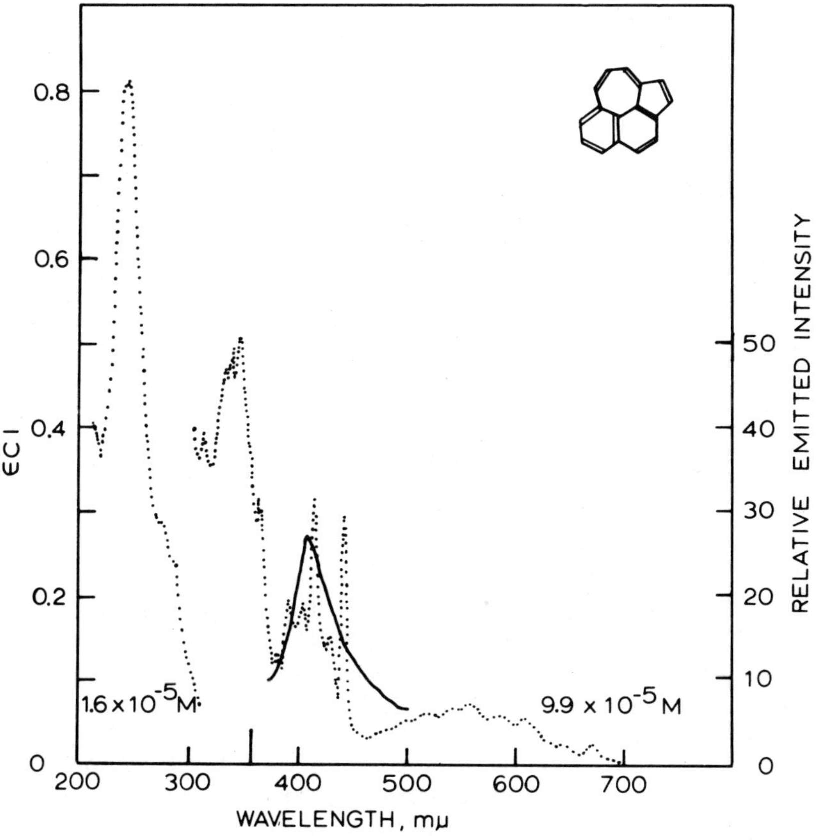

Figure 2 Absorption (···), and emission (——) spectra of naphth[2,1,8-cde]azulene taken in fluid solution at room temperature with cyclohexane (for absorption) and methylcyclohexane (for emission) as solvents.

azulene, and 1-azuloic acid.[18] These results are illustrated in Fig. (3) where it can be seen that the anomalous behavior in emission is strikingly conserved. Here, it appears that the emission originates from an excited state above S_2.

Although the emissive behavior of a number of derivatives of azulene, as well as compounds showing spectral and structural resemblances to azulene, have been investigated, no structural modifications were successful in eliminating the fluorescence anomaly. While inquiring into the extent of modification of the basic ring resonance required for elimination of the anomaly, we studied the properties of the protonated species, both in absorption and in emission.[17]

The results of protonation of azulene and certain 1-substituted azulenes have been reported in the literature.[19-22] Briefly, the results are as follows: reversible, monoprotonation occurs with azulene at the 1-position. For 1-trifluoroacetylazulene and 1-nitroazulene, the aci-compound is produced by oxygen protonation, the conjugate acid carrying the acidic proton on the nitro, or trifluoroacetyl group rather than on the carbon atom at the 3-position. The case of 1-azuloic acid is uncertain, and it is not clear how much protonation occurs at the 3-position. These results concern the species immediately formed in concentrated acid; in certain cases other tautomeric forms are produced after some time has elapsed.

Our investigations of the spectral properties of the protonated species are illustrated in Figs. (4), (5), (6), which illustrations are to be compared with Figs. (1), (2), and (3), respectively, for comparisons with the unprotonated molecules. It is clear that only 4-methylpentaleno-[2,1,6-def]heptalene and pentaleno[2,1,8-def]-heptalene emit anomalously after protonation.

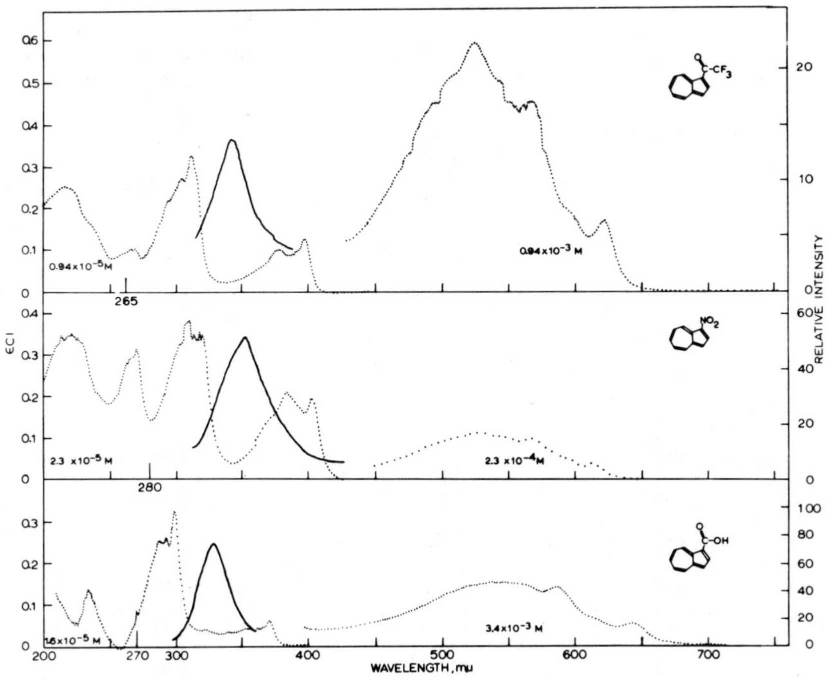

Figure 3 Absorption (···), and emission (——) spectra of certain 1-substituted azulenes, taken in fluid solution at room temperature with cyclohexane (for absorption) and methylcyclohexane (for emission) as solvents.

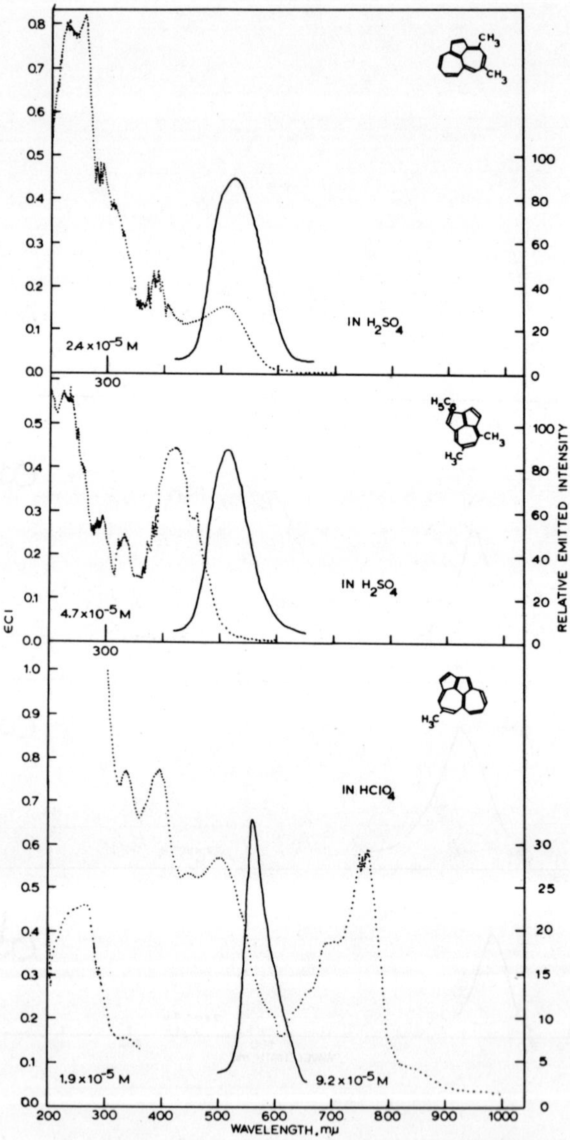

Figure 4 Absorption (···), and emission (——) spectra of protonated Hafner's hydrocarbons taken in fluid solution at room temperature with 60% sulfuric acid, or 70% perchloric acid as solvents.

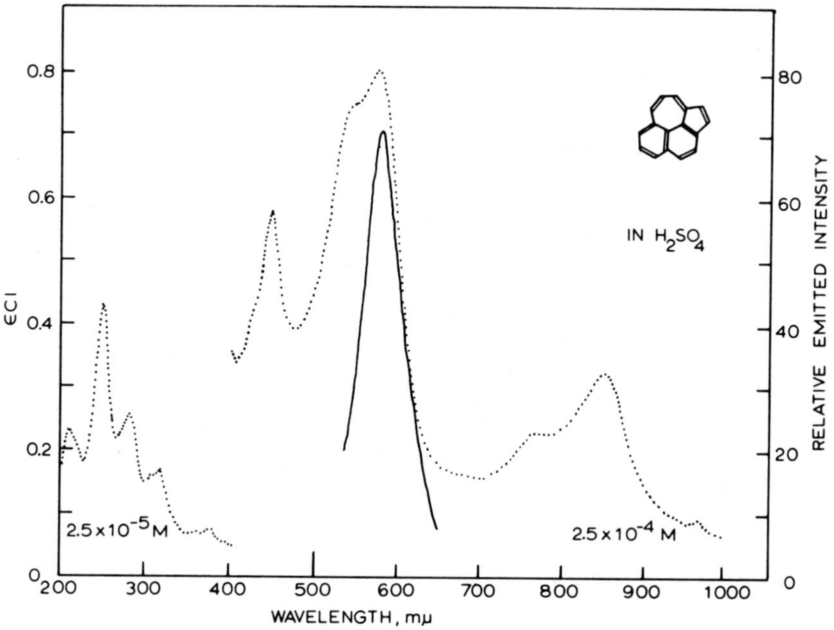

Figure 5 Absorption (···), and emission (——) spectra of protonated naphth[2,1,8-cde] azulene taken in fluid solution at room temperature with 60% sulfuric acid as solvent.

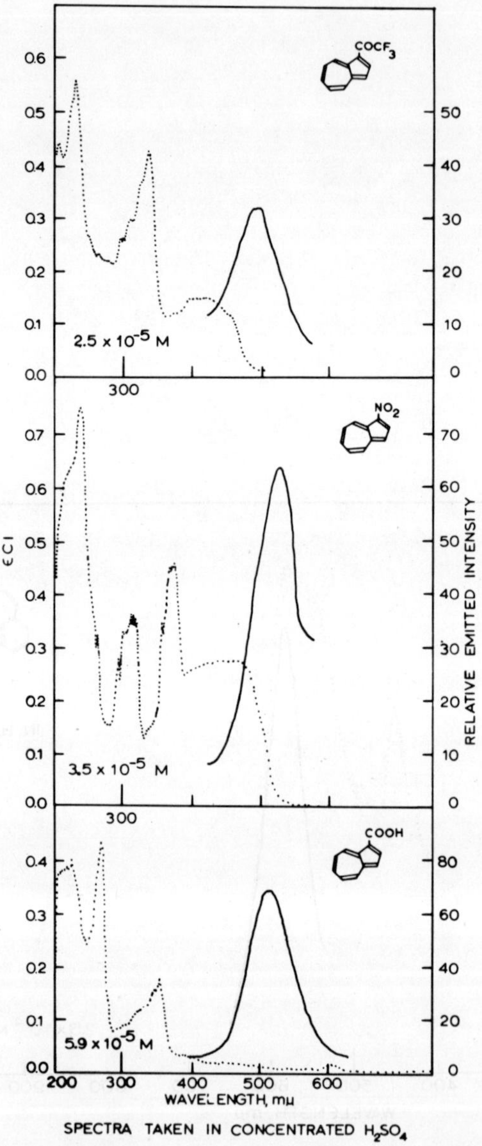

Figure 6 Absorption (···), and emission (——) spectra of certain protonated 1-substituted azulenes taken in fluid solution at room temperature with 60% sulfuric acid as solvent.

If one examines the data on the S_2-S_1 energy gap for the alternant (benzenoid) hydrocarbons compiled by Platt and co-workers[23] the small gap for naphthalene seems typical. For the anomalously fluorescent non-alternants and substituted azulenes the corresponding gap for azulene, which is large, seems to be typical. In the case of the protonated species, such correlations seem to be less general.

Generally, internal conversion between the lowest excited singlet state and the ground state is an inefficient process.[24-27] For the higher excited singlet states of most large polyatomic molecules, lifetimes are shorter by at least three or four powers of ten when compared to the lifetime of the first excited singlet state. Thus internal conversions and vibrational deactivation result in a rapid population of S_1. For the cases of the anomalously emitting molecules discussed in this paper, this cascade process ends at S_2. This phenomenon has been considered previously in connection with azulene.[4,6,28-32] The anomalous emission may be interpreted as arising from the large electronic energy separation between the first and second excited singlet states. The small vibrational coupling between these states decreases the probability of non-radiative internal conversion to S_1 and thus concomitantly increases the probability of fluorescence from S_2. The absence of a measureable amount of $S_1 \rightarrow S_o$ normal fluorescence or $T_1 \rightarrow S_o$ phosphorescence must be due to efficient $S_1 \rightarrow$ triplet intersystem crossings followed by non-radiative transitions to S_o.

The results quoted in this paper offer evidence that the phenomenon of "anomalous" emission appears to be more general and further investigations of this phenomenon will be of interest in deciding whether the description of the process offered above is a generality.

EXPERIMENTAL

Most of the experimental details can be found in References (16), (17), and (18). The compounds indicated in Figs. (1) and (2) were chromatogrammed and recrystallized samples. All other compounds were three times recrystallized from fluorometric grade methylcyclohexane and sublimed in vacuum. All absorption spectra were recorded with a Cary Model 14 Recording Spectrophotometer in fluid solution at room temperature ($23.5 \pm 1^{o}C$) with spectrograde cyclohexane or 60% sulfuric acid as solvent, except otherwise noted. Emission spectra were taken at room temperature using fluorometric grade methylcyclohexane as solvent. The spectra were recorded using an Aminco-Bowman Spectrophotofluorometer, a Baird Atomic Fluorispec SF1, or a Spex 1700-II Spectrometer-Spectrograph. No attempt was made to exclude dissolved oxygen, and all solutions were prepared just prior to recording the emission or absorption spectra. It was generally observed that the ions exhibited more intense luminescence than the corresponding non-protonated species. In all Figures, the exciting line is indicated, in each case, by a short vertical line in the short wavelength region of the spectrum. In all cases, the $S_1 \rightarrow S_o$ normal fluorescence was sought for but not observed. For the compounds indicated in Fig. (1), the search was carried to 1100 mu., whereas for all others, the limit was 700 mu.

ACKNOWLEDGEMENTS

The authors are greatly indebted to Professor K. Hafner, Institut fur Organishe Chemie, Technische Hochschule, Darmstadt, for the generous gift of samples of the compounds shown in Figs. (1), (2), and (3). We also wish to thank Professor A. G. Anderson, Jr., Department of Chemistry, University of Washington, for the gift of a sample of 1-nitroazulene, and Professor P. D. Gardner, Department of Chemistry, University of Utah, for the gift of a sample of naphth[2,1,8-cde]azulene. We owe Dr. G. Litwack and Mr. J. Rosenberg, Fels Research Institute, Temple University, thanks for their assistance in connection with the use of an Aminco-Bowman Spectrophotofluorometer. Finally, one of us (JAP) acknowledges the E. I. duPont de Nemours Co. for a 1967 Summer Research Grant during which some of this research was performed.

REFERENCES

1. G. N. Lewis and M. Kasha, J. Amer. Chem. Soc. 66, 2109 (1944).
2. J. N. Pitts, F. Wilkinson and G. S. Hammond, "The Vocabulary of Photochemistry," in Advances in Photochemistry, W. A. Noyes, Jr., G. S. Hammond and J. N. Pitts, Jr., Eds. (Interscience Pub., New York, 1963), Vol. 1, P. 16.
3. M. Kasha, Disc. Faraday Soc., No. 9, 14 (1950).
4. M. Beer and H. C. Longuet-Higgins, J. Chem. Phys., 23, 1390 (1955).
5. G. Viswanath and M. Kasha, J. Chem. Phys. 24, 574 (1956).
6. J. W. Sidman andD. S. McClure, J. Chem. Phys. 24, 757 (1956).
7. Z. S. Ruzevich, Optika i Spektroskopiya 15, 357 (1963), Engl translation, Optics and Spectroscopy, 15, 191 (1963).
8. G. Binsch, E. Heilbronner, R. Jankow, and D. Schmidt, Chem. Phys. Letters 1, 135 (1967).
9. P. Seybold and M. Gouterman, Chem. Revs. 65, 413 (1965).
10. H. Sponer, Radiation Res. Suppl. 1, 558 (1959).
11. H. Sponer, Chemical Abstracts 51, 12667i (1957).
12. R. Hunt and I. G. Ross, Z. Naturforsch, 11a 1043 (1956).
13. P. M. Rentzepis, 155th National Meeting, American Chemical Society, San Francisco, 1968, Abstract No. 91.
14. R. Pariser, J. Chem. Phys. 25, 1112 (1956).
15. D. F. Eaton, "The Fluorescence of Azulene Systems," B.A. thesis (private communication), Wesleyan University, Middletown, Conn., 1968.
16. R. C. Dhingra and J. A. Poole, J. Chem. Phys. 48, (1968).
17. R. C. Chingra and J. A. Poole, J. Phys. Chem. (submitted for publication).
18. R. C. Dhingra and J. A. Poole, Chem. Phys. Letters 2, (1968).

19. S. S. Danyluk and W. G. Schneider, J. Amer. Chem. Soc. 82, 997 (1960).
20. D. Meuche and E. Heilbronner, Helv. Chim. Acta 45, 1965 (1962).
21. J. Schulze and F. A. Long, J. Amer. Chem. Soc. 86, 322 (1964).
22. W. Meier, D. Meuche and E. Heilbronner, Helv. Chim. Acta 45, 2628 (1962).
23. J. R. Platt, et al., Systematics of the Electronic Spectra of Conjugated Molecules (J. Wiley, New York, 1964).
24. J. Franck and H. Sponer, J. Chem. Phys. 25, 172 (1956).
25. H. Ishikawa and W. A. Noyes, Jr., J. Chem. Phys. 37, 583 (1962).
26. E. C. Lim, J. Chem. Phys. 36, 3497 (1962).
27. S. K. Lower and M. A. El-Sayed, Chem. Rev. 66, 199 (1966).
28. R. Hunt and I. G. Ross, J. Mol. Spectry. 9, 50 (1962).
29. R. Hunt, et al., Aust. J. Chem. 15, 591 (1962).
30. G. W. Robinson and R. P. Frosch, J. Chem. Phys. 38, 1187 (1963).
31. N. J. Turro, Molecular Photochemistry (W. A. Benjamin, Inc., New York, 1965), p. 61.
32. D. M. Hercules, "Theory of Luminescence Processes," in Fluorescence and Phosphorescence Analysis, D. M. Hercules, Ed. (Interscience, 1966), p. 20.

LUMINESCENCE OF CORANNULENE

J. F. Verdieck and W. A. Jankowski

Department of Chemistry
University of Michigan
Ann Arbor, Michigan

The interesting hydrocarbon, corannulene, has recently been synthesized by Barth and Lawton.[1] The planar projection for this compound is shown in Figure (1A). If corannulene existed in this form the pentagonal angles force the benzene inner angles on the pentagon to take on values of 126° rather than 120°. This considerable strain is avoided in the bowl-shaped structure of Figure (1C), a structure confirmed by the X-ray studies of Hanson and Nordman.[2] The middle structure of Figure (1), the polar form, is an attractive contributor in that it yields an inner and outer ring system each of which satisfy the Huckel 4n + 2 rule. Thus corannulene is a non-planar, non-alternate hydrocarbon, yet retains appreciable aromatic character as evidenced by chemical behavior.[1]

The absorption spectrum of corannulene is shown in Figure (2). The two prominent bands are the broad structureless band peaking at 286 nm and the well resolved system of three peaks around 250 nm. This spectrum was obtained on a Cary 14 with a solution of 3 x 10^{-5} M corannulene in ethanol. It might be expected that corannulene would resemble rather closely in spectral properties the similar compound coronene. However, neither in form or

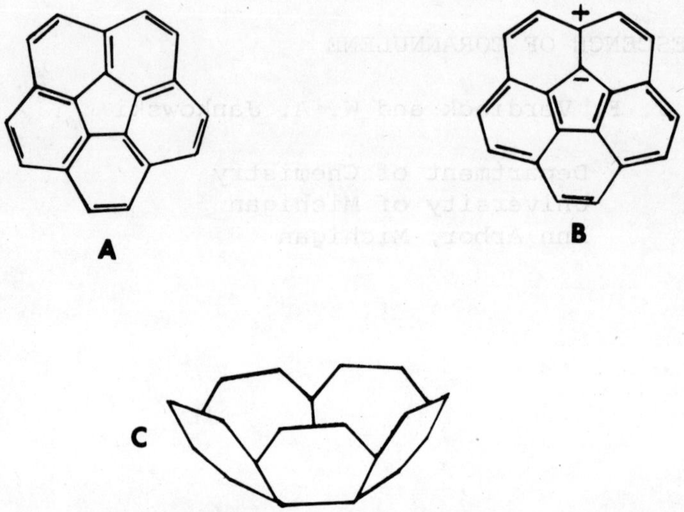

Figure 1 Corannulene: (A) planar projection; (B) polar resonance form; (C) 3-d representation.

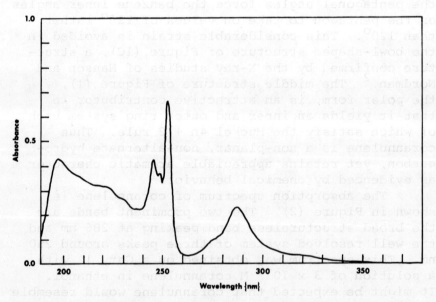

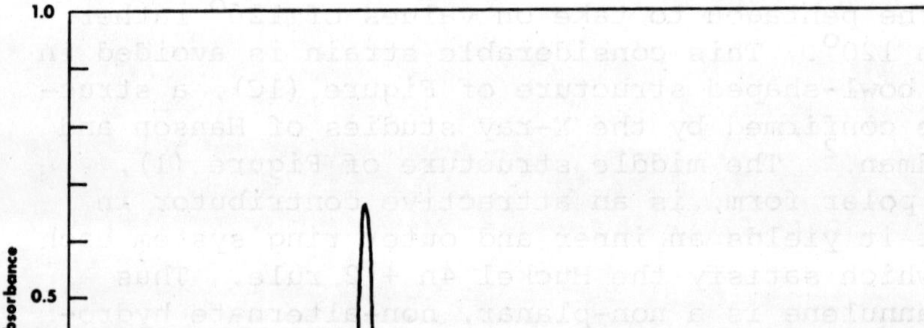

Figure 2 Absorption spectrum of corannulene: 3 x 10^{-5} M in ethanol.

spectral position are the spectra similar. Rather, the corannulene spectrum is much closer to that of hexihelicene and 3,4;5,6-dibenzophenanthrene, in form and wavelength position. The resemblance is not sufficient to assign Platt notation labels to the bands, however.[3]

Corannulene has C_{5v} symmetry as might be expected and is proven by the X-ray study.[2] This symmetry is retained in the radical anion as demonstrated by the ESR studies.[4] According to the irreducible representations of point group C_{5v} the Huckel molecular orbitals can be ordered as shown in Figure (3).[5] The first excited states, in this simple approximation, have symmetries E_1 and E_2. Transitions from the ground state to E_1 are allowed and x,y polarized whereas transitions to E_2 are forbidden. Both are degenerate, of course, and difficult to correlate with the Platt states; hence, our earlier reluctance to do so.

Fluorescence and phosphorescence spectra in ethanol and I_2M_3 (isopentane and methylcyclohexane, 2:3 by volume) were excited by a 200 W Osram HBO mercury arc. Excitation into the first band at 2990 Å was selected by a Jarrell-Ash 1/4 meter monochromator and $NiSO_4$-$CoSO_4$ filter. Emission from the 1 cm square Spectrosil sample cell was focussed into a 1 meter Jarrell-Ash monochromator and detected with an EMI 6256S photomultiplier. Cooling was provided by a dewar of unknown quartz which passed 3000 Å, but absorbed appreciable 2537 Å radiation. All samples were degassed thoroughly according to standard methods. Polarization of incident and emitted beams was obtained and analyzed through the use of Polacoat filters. These polarizers suffer from low transmission (30%), but do not require critical alignment of collimated beam.

Some representative spectra are shown in Figures (4) through (7). These are uncorrected for spectrometer and photomultiplier response. Although there is considerably more vibrational structure in the luminescence spectra than in the

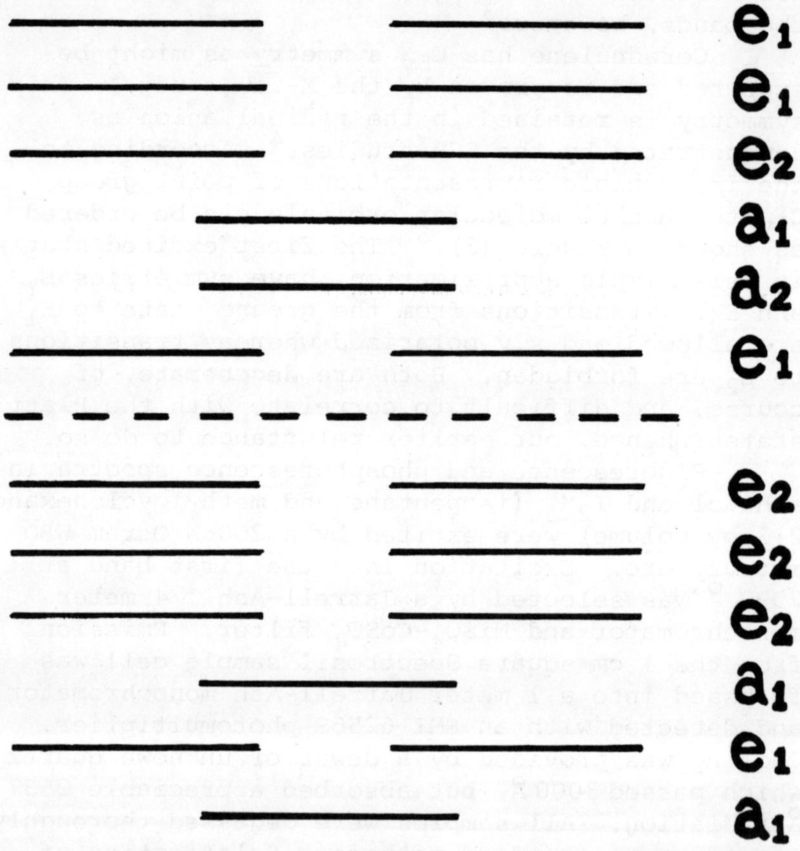

Figure 3 Ordering of molecular orbitals according to the irreducible representation of point group C_{5v}.

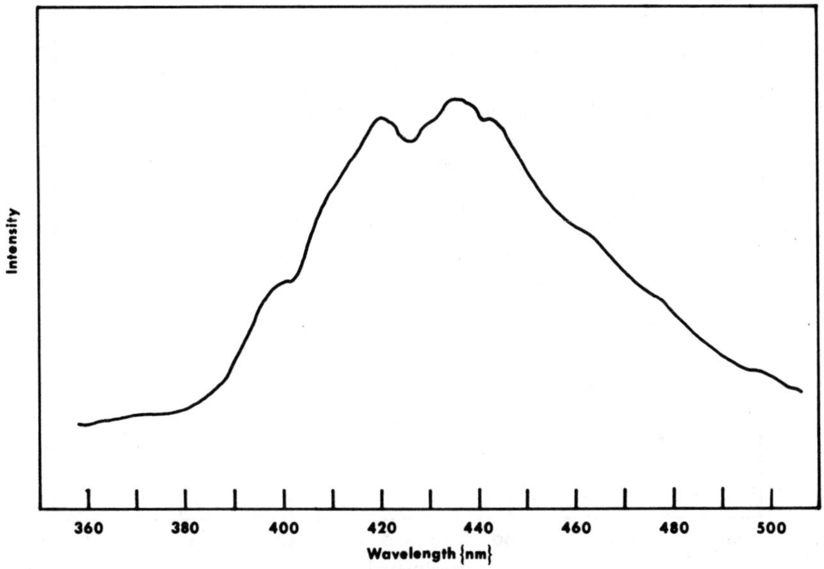

Figure 4 Room-temperature fluorescence spectrum of corannulene in ethanol.

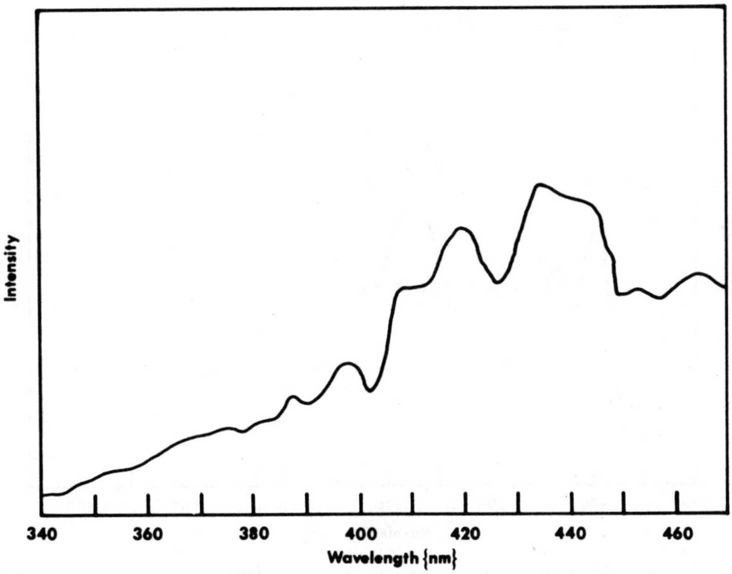

Figure 5 Fluorescence spectrum of corannulene in ethanol at 77°K.

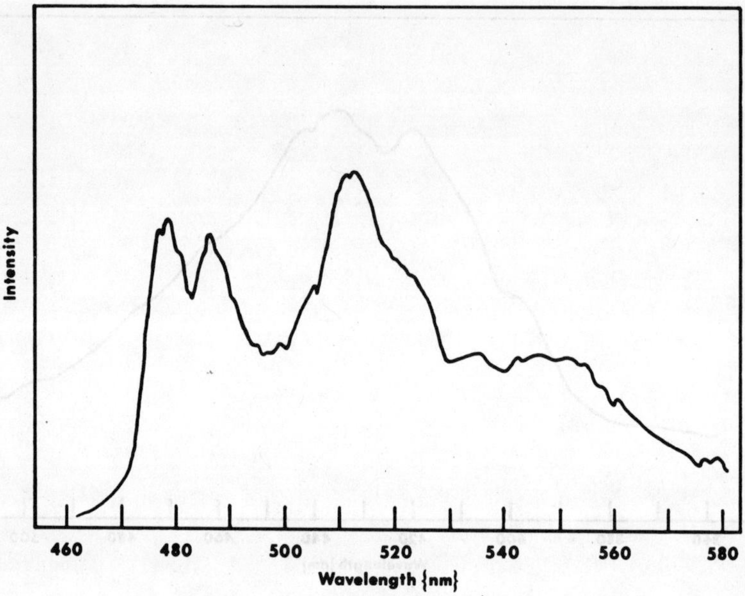

Figure 6 Phosphorescence spectrum of corannulene in ethanol at 77°K.

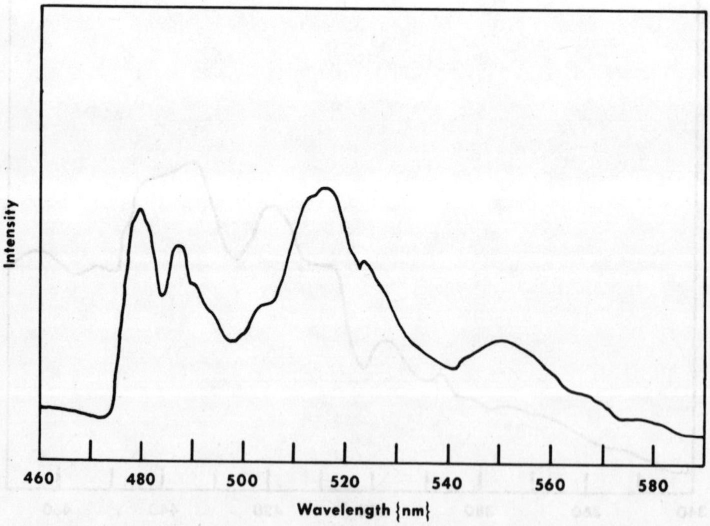

Figure 7 Phosphorescence spectrum of corannulene at 77°K in an isopentane-methylcyclohexane solution (2:3 by volume.)

absorption spectrum, no attempt was made to analyze or identify vibrational spacings. We felt that our resolution was not good enough and as no infrared or Raman data was available there was no basis for comparison. We do note a slight red shift in going from the alcohol solutions to the I_2M_3 solutions, especially noticeable in the 77°K fluorescence spectra. This may result from the polar nature of the molecule. It is opposite to the solvent shift obtained for $\pi-\pi^*$ transitions in planar aromatic hydrocarbons.

The polarization factor for both fluorescence and phosphorescence is negative for the excitation employed, ranging from about -0.1 to -0.2. This simply indicates that we are exciting into a vibronic band, which is already known. A detailed, structured polarization factor, including corrections after the classic study of Azumi and McGlynn[6] was not carried out because of variations in intensity from run to run arising from our dewar transmission changing because of snow. The correction factor should not be large for our large diameter dewar and square cell. Improvements in our system now in progress hopefully will allow us to obtain detailed polarization. Polarization for excitation into the band system at 2500 Å could not be obtained because of the dewar absorption.

The phosphorescent lifetime, measured on fastest chart speed, is 2.6 sec. The phosphorescent yield is about 5 times the fluorescent yield estimated from the relative intensities.

The nature of the excited states of corannulene has not been elucidated by our studies. Efforts toward improving our signal-to-noise ratio in order to obtain resolved polarization factors are in progress. These studies will include excitation spectra, and high resolution absorption spectra in addition to the luminescence spectra.

The authors are indebted to the Petroleum Research Fund of the American Chemical Society and the National Science Foundation for support of this research.

REFERENCES

1. W. E. Barth and R. G. Lawton, J. Amer. Chem. Soc., 88, 380 (1966).
2. J. Hanson and C. Nordman (private communication).
3. J. Janata et al., J. Amer. Chem. Soc., 89, 3056 (1967).
4. O. E. Weigang, Jr., J. A. Turner and P. A. Trovard, J. Chem. Phys., 45, 1126 (1966).
5. L. Salem, The Molecular Orbital Theory of Conjugated Systems (W. A. Benjamin, Inc., New York, 1966).
6. T. Azumi and S. P. McGlynn, J. Chem. Phys., 37, 2413 (1962).

EMISSION OF LIQUID BENZENE: COMPARISON OF 1849 Å AND 2537 Å EXCITATION*

Craig Lawson, Fumio Hirayama and Sanford Lipsky

Department of Chemistry
University of Minnesota
Minneapolis, Minnesota

I. INTRODUCTION

The efficiency of internal conversion, $\beta(\lambda_n)$, from an upper electronic state S_n to the lowest excited state S_1 is defined as the primary quantum yield for production of S_1 for excitation at wavelength λ_n. The usual technique for determining $\beta(\lambda_n)$ is to study the dependence on exciting wavelength of the S_1 fluorescence quantum yield, $\phi_f(\lambda_n)$.[1] The fundamental assumption made here is that $\phi_f(\lambda_n)$ is proportional to $\beta(\lambda_n)$. The ratio $\beta_f(\lambda_n) = \phi_f(\lambda_n)/\phi_f(\lambda_1)$ is then taken equal to $\beta(\lambda_n)$. In the case of the liquid aromatics a more sensitive technique for determination of $\beta(\lambda_n)$ is to utilize the ability of S_1 to sensitize the fluorescence of

*This work was supported by the U. S. Atomic Energy Commission COO-913-26.

a suitable solute. This technique, however, involves an additional assumption, namely that the transfer process occurs exclusively from S_1. The ratio $\beta_t(\lambda_n) = \phi_t(\lambda_n)/\phi_t(\lambda_1)$, where $\phi_t(\lambda)$ is the transfer quantum yield for excitation at wavelength λ, is now taken equal to $\beta(\lambda_n)$.

Preliminary measurements by Braun[2] indicated that for excitation to S_3, β_t is ca. 25% greater than β_f for a 2 x 10^{-3} M solution of p-terphenyl in benzene. More recently, Laor and Weinreb[3] have reported that β_t increases with increasing solute concentration (0.2 - 3 g/l of PPO in benzene) and have interpreted this as evidence for energy transfer from S_3.

In this paper we present our results on the dependence on solute concentration of both β_f and β_t and demonstrate that all concentration effects can be consistently explained while retaining the assumption that the $S_n \rightarrow S_1$ internal conversion is much more rapid than bimolecular reactions of S_n with solute. The concentration dependence is shown to derive from the failure of the fundamental assumption that $\phi_f(\lambda_n)$ and $\phi_t(\lambda_n)$ are proportional to $\beta(\lambda_n)$.

II. EXPERIMENTAL

The exciting system consisted of a Hg resonance lamp and a 0.4 meter McPherson Model 235 monochromator. The analyzing system consisted of a 0.3 meter McPherson Model 218 monochromator (operated at a band pass of 13A), a dry ice cooled EMI 6256S photomultiplier and Keithley Model 417 picoammeter. Appropriate Suprasil quartz lens systems were used to focus the incident beam onto the front face (Suprasil I quartz) of the sample cell and to collect and focus the emission from the same face into the analyzing system. The axes of the exciting and analyzing systems made a 45° angle. The intensity of the exciting light was monitored by a degassed solution of 5 g/l PPO in cyclohexane.

Matheson Coleman and Bell benzene (spectroquality), toluene (fluorometric grade), p-xylene and cyclohexane (spectroquality) were further purified by distillation. Pilot PPO (scintillation grade), Eastman CCl_4 (spectrograde), Linde O_2 (research grade) and Linde high purity dry nitrogen were used without further purification.

III. RESULTS AND DISCUSSION

Emission spectra of liquid benzene for excitation at 2537A ($S_1 \leftarrow S_o$) and 1849A ($S_3 \leftarrow S_o$) are presented in Fig. 1. The two spectra are normalized to the same intensity at 2870A. Due to the much smaller penetration depth of the 1849A light, reabsorption is sufficiently reduced to permit an analysis of the short wavelength edge of the spectrum (See Fig. 1b). Two new features appear not previously observed for $S_1 \leftarrow S_o$ excitation. The shoulder at 2646A is attributed to the "hot" transition from the S_1 state containing one quantum of the ν_{18} (e_{2g}) vibration to the vibrationless ground state. The shoulder is found to lie at 1170 $\pm$ 50 cm^{-1} to higher energies of the peak at 2731A whereas in the vapor the corresponding separation is 1127 cm^{-1}. Additionally we have found the shoulder in the same relative position in dilute solutions of a wide variety of solvents. The shoulder at 2684A is attributed to the 0-0 transition. It is separated by 530 cm^{-1} from the 2646A shoulder and 640 cm^{-1} from the 2731A peak. These separations are, within our uncertainties, in reasonable agreement with the corresponding vapor separations of 521 cm^{-1} and 606 cm^{-1}. The corresponding 0-0 absorptive transition (the Ham band) has been seen recently in liquid benzene by Koyanagi.[4] Additionally we find this emission shoulder in all solvents in which the Ham band has

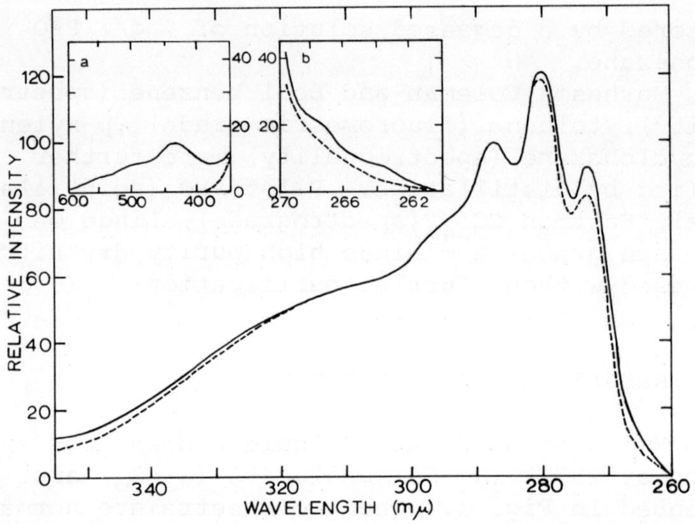

Figure 1 Emission Spectra of Benzene Excited at 1849 Å (solid line) and 2537 Å (dashed line).

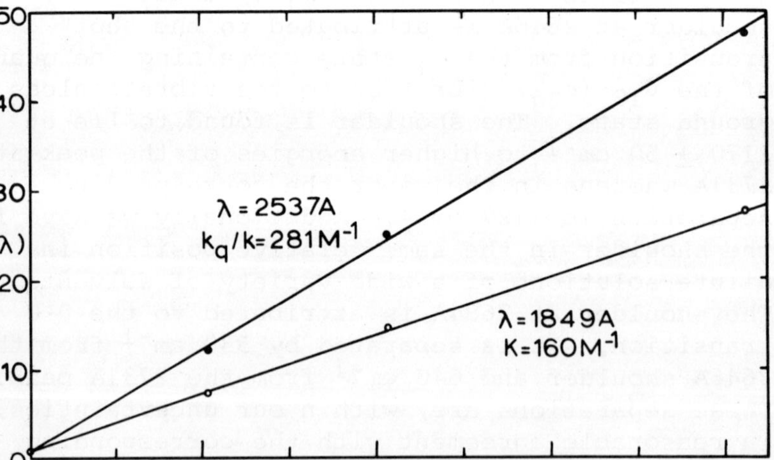

Figure 2 CCl_4 Quenching of Benzene Fluorescence Excited at 2537 Å and 1849 Å.

been reported (e.g. methanol, isopropyl alcohol, ether, acetonitrile, etc.) and to be absent in all solvents in which the Ham band is absent (e.g. hexane, cyclohexane, isooctane, decalin, etc.). Aside from these two features, and a slight enhancement of the 2731A and 2800A peaks for 1849A excitation (caused by reduced penetration depth), the two spectra are very similar from 2700A to 3600A. This spectral region covers both the monomer and excimer emissions of benzene and the implication then is that internal conversion from S_3 to S_1 is very rapid as compared to the direct formation of excimer from S_3.

Beyond 3500A and extending to about 6100A a new emission appears for 1849A excitation (See Fig. 1a). The significance of this emission is discussed below.

In Table I are presented the effects of O_2, CCl_4 and PPO on the benzene emission yield for 1849A and 2537A excitation. In the absence of quencher, $\beta_f(\lambda_3) = 0.22$ and approaches for all quenchers, at sufficiently high concentration, the value 0.37-0.39. For convenience in the following discussion we define $\beta_o = \lim_{c_q \to \infty} \beta_f(\lambda 3) = 0.38$ and define a function $F(c_q)$ such that

$$\beta_f(\lambda_3) = \beta_o F(c_q) \tag{1}$$

The dependence of $F(c_q)$ on c_q is most simply determined from the observation that both $\phi_f(\lambda_3)$ and $\phi_f(\lambda_1)$ satisfy the Stern-Volmer equation in their dependence on c_q (see Fig. 2). From this and the definition of $\beta_f(\lambda_3) = \phi_f(\lambda_3)/\phi_f(\lambda_1)$ it follows that

$$\frac{\phi_f^o(\lambda_3)}{\phi_f(\lambda_3)} = \frac{F(0)}{F(c_q)}(1 + \frac{k_q c_q}{k}) = 1 + Kc_q \tag{2}$$

TABLE I: Effect of Added Quenchers on $\phi_f(\lambda)$[a] at λ_1 = 2537 Å and λ_3 = 1849 Å

CCl_4

c_q(M)	$\phi_f^{-1}(\lambda_1)$	$\phi_f^{-1}(\lambda_3)$	$\beta_f(\lambda_3)$	$F(c_q)$
0.0000	1.00	1.00	0.22	0.58
0.0415	12.2	7.62	0.35	0.92
0.0830	24.6	14.7	0.36	0.96
0.165	47.7	29.9	0.37	0.98

O_2

c_q(M)	$\phi_f^{-1}(\lambda_1)$	$\phi_f^{-1}(\lambda_3)$	$\beta_f(\lambda_3)$	$F(c_q)$
0.0000	1.00	1.00	0.22	0.58
0.0014[b]	2.86	2.20	0.30	0.79
0.0070[c]	12.3	7.25	0.37	0.98

PPO

c_q(M)	$\phi_f^{-1}(\lambda_1)$	$\phi_f^{-1}(\lambda_3)$	$\beta_f(\lambda_3)$	$F(c_q)$
0.0000	1.00	1.00	0.22	0.58
0.0010	1.81	1.54	0.26	0.69
0.0050	5.06	3.20	0.35	0.92
0.0100	8.02	4.56	0.39	1.02

a Normalized to 1.00 in absence of quencher.
b Air equilibrated.
c O_2 saturated (at 1 atm).

where k_q is the rate constant for quenching of S_1, k is the rate constant for all other decay processes of S_1 and K is a constant independent of c_q. Since, by definition, $F(c_q)$ is required to approach unity at high c_q, it follows from Eq. (2) that

$$F(c_q) = \frac{k + k_q c_q}{A + k_q c_q} \tag{3}$$

where $A = k/F(0)$ and is independent of c_q. Since $F(c_q) \leq 1$, it is possible to define a positive parameter k_x such that $A = k + k_x$. Substitution of Eq. (3) into Eq. (1) gives

$$\phi_f(\lambda_3) = \frac{\beta_o k_f}{k + k_x + k_q c_q} \tag{4}$$

where k_f is the rate constant for radiative decay of S_1, i.e.

$$\phi_f(\lambda_1) = \frac{k_f}{k + k_q c_q} \tag{5}$$

The form of Eq. (4) suggests that $\phi_f(\lambda_3)$ is the product of the probability for $S_3 \rightarrow S_1$ internal conversion and the probability for emission from S_1. The parameter β_o is most plausibly identified with the internal conversion efficiency $\beta(\lambda_3)$ so that $k_f/(k + k_x + k_q c_q)$ must be the S_1 emission probability for excitation at 1849A. However, Eq. (5) demands that for excitation at 2537A the S_1 emission probability be simply $k_f/(k + k_q c_q)$. This apparent inconsistency is most simply resolved by assuming that under 1849A excitation conditions a photochemical product "X" is present at sufficiently high concentrations so as to additionally quench S_1. Thus k_x is interpreted to be the rate constant for this quenching times the concentration of X.

This interpretation is also consistent with the results of energy transfer studies. The intensity of benzene sensitized PPO emission has been studied over a 70 fold range of PPO concentration ($c = 5.46 \times 10^{-4}$ to 3.64×10^{-2} M). The energy transfer quantum yield is obtained from comparison of the sensitized emission with that directly excited by 3130A light.

The transfer quantum yield for $\lambda = 2537$ may be written as

$$\phi_t(\lambda_1) = \frac{k_t c}{k + k_q c_q + k_t c} = \frac{\alpha c}{1 + \alpha c} \qquad (6)$$

where k_t is the rate constant for energy transfer. If our interpretation of the quenching results is correct we would therefore expect that for $\lambda =$ 1849A

$$\phi_t(\lambda_3) = \frac{\beta_o k_t c}{k + k_x + k_q c_q + k_t c}$$

$$= \frac{\beta_o F(c_q)\alpha c}{1 + F(c_q)\alpha c} \qquad (7)$$

Thus a plot of $\phi_t^{-1}(\lambda_3)$ versus c^{-1} is expected to be linear with intercept of β_o^{-1} and ratio of intercept to slope of $F(c_q)\alpha$. Similarly, a plot of $\phi_t^{-1}(\lambda_1)$ versus c^{-1} is expected to be linear with intercept of 1.00 and ratio of intercept to slope of α. Fig. 3 shows such plots for air equilibrated solutions of PPO in benzene. The results of these measurements and similar measurements on nitrogenated solutions are summarized in Table 2. The agreement of β_o and $F(c_q)$ obtained via sensitization and quenching measurements is well within our expected experimental uncertainty (compare with columns 4 and 5 in Table I).

From Eqs. (6) and (7) it follows that

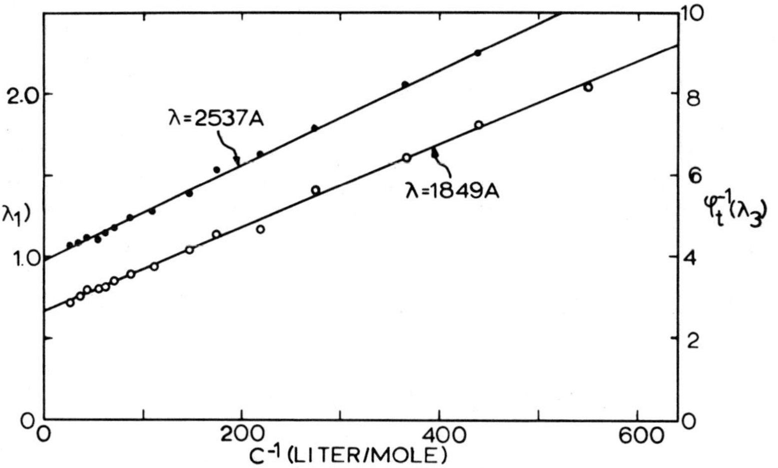

Figure 3 Energy Transfer from Benzene to PPO in Air-equilibrated Solutions.

TABLE II: Values of $\beta(\lambda_3)$, $F(c_q)$ and α from Energy Transfer Measurements in Benzene and PPO Solutions

	degassed ($c_q = 0$)		air-equilibrated ($c_q = 0.0014$ M)	
$\beta_o{}^a = \beta(\lambda_3)$	0.38		0.38	
$\alpha F(c_q)^a$	635	l/m	261	l/m
α^b	1134	l/m	335	l/m
$F(c_q)$	0.56		0.78	

a From plot of $\phi_t{}^{-1}(\lambda_3)$ versus c^{-1} (Eq. 7).
b From plot of $\phi_t{}^{-1}(\lambda_1)$ versus c^{-1} (Eq. 6).

$$\beta_t(\lambda_3) = \frac{\beta_o F(c_q)\left[1 + \alpha c\right]}{1 + F(c_q)\alpha c} \qquad (8)$$

so that $\beta_t(\lambda_3)\to\beta_o$ as $c\to\infty$ or $c_q\to\infty$. Equation (8) satisfactorily explains the concentration dependence of $\beta_t(\lambda_3)$ observed earlier by Laor and Weinreb.[3]

Since the absorption coefficient of benzene at 1849A is ca. 10^3 times larger than at 2537A, photolytic products will be present at much higher local concentrations for the short wavelength excitation. On this basis we would predict $F \simeq 1$ were it possible to generate the S_3 state of benzene more homogeneously. With gamma ray excitation this condition is approximately achieved since the majority of the Compton recoil electrons are sufficiently energetic to excite preferentially the optically allowed S_3 state. Accordingly it is not surprising that energy transfer constants, α, obtained with gamma ray (or fast electron) excitation are reported to be in good agreement with the same constants obtained using 2537A light as excitation source.[5-8] Additionally, we have found that F increases on dilution of benzene (regardless of the nature of the solvent) and also with use of exciting wavelengths less strongly absorbed than 1849A (e.g. the 2144A Cd line).

The nature of X remains uncertain. Although the emission spectrum of benzene liquid shows the presence of some product that is made evident when excitation is at 1839A, it is not certain that this emitting species is to be identified with X. There may be, of course, many products.

The photochemistry of liquid benzene excited at 2537A has been extensively investigated.[9-11] Low yields of fulvene and benzvalene have been reported. The emission spectra of these products are not known nor is there any information available on the efficiency with which they quench excited benzene. In order to identify X, we have therefore repeated these earlier photochemical experiments at 2537A. In carefully degassed solutions we have so far obtained evidence for three products. The absorption spectrum of one of these products identifies it as fulvene. The fulvene does not fluoresce and we have verified that it quenches excited benzene with a quenching constant of about 400 l/m. Our quantum yield for fulvene production is 0.012, in good agreement with the value of 0.01 obtained by Angus et al.[9] This quantum yield and quenching constant can be shown to be adequate to explain the magnitude of $F(c_q)$ under our excitation conditions at 1849A. We are therefore inclined to identify X with fulvene. Since we have found no effect on $F(c_q)$ for a 100 fold variation in the intensity of exciting light, it is required that fulvene be destroyed on reaction with excited benzene and further that the rate of removal of fulvene via the quenching reaction be much more rapid than diffusion of fulvene out of the illumination volume. The quenching reaction of fulvene with benzene is currently being studied.

Two other products have been found. One of these products is present exclusively as a residue after vacuum distillation of the photolyzed benzene, the other is found predominantly in the distillate (with the fulvene). Neither product has been identified although their emission and absorption spectra have been obtained and will be reported elsewhere. However we have verified that a superposition of their emission spectra can account for the long wavelength emission spectrum we observe for 1849A excitation (see Fig. 1a).

Our procedure now for obtaining reliable values for the internal conversion efficiency, $\beta(\lambda_3)$, is to first saturate the system with O_2 (which generally gives an adequately high concentration of quencher to guarantee $F(c_q) \simeq 1$) and then to measure $\beta_f(\lambda_3)$. In this way we have obtained for toluene and p-xylene the values $\beta(\lambda_3) = 0.68 \pm 0.03$ and 0.95 ± 0.04 respectively.

A more complete report of this work including its extension to the effect of solvent on $\beta(\lambda_n)$ will be presented elsewhere.

REFERENCES

1. C. L. Braun, S. Kato and S. Lipsky, J. Chem. Phys. 39, 1645 (1963).
2. C. L. Braun, Ph.D. Dissertation, University of Minnesota, 1963.
3. U. Laor and A. Weinreb, J. Chem. Phys. 43, 1565 (1965).
4. M. Koyanagi, J. Mol. Spect. 25, 273 (1968).
5. S. Lipsky and M. Burton, J. Chem. Phys. 31, 1221 (1959).
6. S. Lipsky, W. P. Helman and J. F. Merklin, Luminescence of Organic and Inorganic Materials, Kallmann and Spruch, Ed. (John Wiley and Sons, New York, 1962), p. 86.
7. I. B. Berlman, Luminescence of Organic and Inorganic Materials, Kallmann and Spruch, Ed. (John Wiley and Sons, New York, 1962), p. 62.
8. M. Burton, M. A. Dillon, C. R. Mullin and R. Rein, J. Chem. Phys. 41, 2236 (1964).
9. H. J. F. Angus, J. M. Blair and D. Bryce-Smith, J. Chem. Soc, 2003 (1960).
10. L. Kaplan and K. E. Wiltzbach, J. Amer. Chem. Soc, 89, 1031 (1967).
11. H. R. Ward and J. S. Wishnok, J. Amer. Chem. Soc. 90, 1085 (1968).

ROTATIONAL DIFFUSION COEFFICIENTS AND TIME DEPENDENT FLUORESCENCE DEPCLARIZATION

Terence Tao

Department of Chemistry
Columbia University
New York, New York 10027

I. INTRODUCTION

Typically, we work with systems such as a fluorescent dye complexes with a macromolecule. At room temperature and in aqueous solution, the macromolecule can undergo slow Brownian rotational motion, such that the fluorescence of the complexed dye is only partially depolarized. In contrast, when the dye molecules are uncomplexed and are free to rotate rapidly, the fluorescence will be completely depolarized. In the other extreme, if the dye molecules are held rigidly in a solid matrix, say, then the fluorescence polarization will attain a certain maximum intrinsic value. If we now excite a system such as ours with a pulse of linearly polarized light, and then follow the fluorescence polarization as a function of time, then at small times after the excitation, the macromolecules would hardly have had a chance to rotate, such that the polarization is close to that maximum value, as in the case when the dye molecules are rigidly held. At large times, however, much reorientation would have taken place, such that the polarization would drop to a value approaching zero. In essence what we do here is to introduce a certain amount of anisotropy into an otherwise isotropic medium; this anisotropy arises from the fact that linearly polarized light preferentially photoselects those molecules whose transition dipoles are oriented near the polarization axis; this anisotropy tends to get destroyed as reorientation takes place, and we follow this transition from an anisotropic state of affairs to an isotropic one by monitoring the fluorescence polarization as a function of time.

The time dependence of the fluorescence polarization therefore must be related to the rotational mobility of the macromolecules. The rotational properties of a body are completely characterized by its rotational diffusion coefficients; and the rotational diffusion coefficients, in turn, tell us something about the size and the shape of the macromolecule.

This idea, of course, is not new. Francis Perrin[1] in 1934 first formulated this relation between fluorescence polarization and macromolecular structure. Perrin's work, however, pertains only to measurements performed with steady state excitation. Here, we extend Perrin's work to describe the time dependence of the process, and it's clear that the full time dependence of the phenomenon potentially yields more information than the time averaged measurements.

II. THEORY

To be more quantitative, one should want to write down an expression for the fluorescence polarization as a function of time, and the diffusion coefficients. The experimental conditions are defined in the usual fashion: Let x, y, and z be a space fixed coordinate system in the laboratory. Let the sample be placed at the origin. Let the excitation travel along the x-axis, polarized along the z-axis. The fluorescence, polarized parallel to the z-axis ($I_{\parallel}$), and perpendicular to the z-axis ($I_{\perp}$), is observed along the y-axis. The fluorescence polarization is defined as the quantity:

$$r(t) = \frac{I_{\parallel}(t) - I_{\perp}(t)}{I_{\parallel}(t) + 2I_{\perp}(t)} \tag{1}$$

It has been shown that the fluorescence polarization as defined above is proportional to a correlation function:[2]

$$r(t) = \frac{2}{5}\langle P_2\{\hat{\mu}(o)\cdot\hat{\mu}(t)\}\rangle \tag{2}$$

where $\hat{\mu}$ is a unit vector in the direction of a dye molecule's transition dipole. The correlation function $\langle P_2\{\hat{\mu}(o)\cdot\hat{\mu}(t)\}\rangle$ can be computed when the Brownian rotational diffusion model is invoked. For a spherical body of volume V in a medium of η viscosity , the following well known result is obtained:[3]

$$r(t) = \frac{2}{5}e^{-6Dt} \tag{3}$$

where the diffusion coefficient D is given by the Einstein equation

$$6D = \frac{kT}{V\eta} \tag{4}$$

Expectedly, the expressions become more complicated when we treat a completely asymmetric body. The problem of Brownian rotational diffusion of an asymmetric body had been examined by Favro.[4]

After a certain amount of mathematical manipulation with Favro's results, one gets the following expression for the fluorescence polarization:

$$r(t) = \frac{2}{5}P_2(\cos\lambda)\Big[3\frac{\mu_1^2\mu_2^2}{\mu^4}\exp-3(D_3 + D)t + 3\frac{\mu_1^2\mu_3^2}{\mu^4}\exp-3(D_2 + D)t + 3\frac{\mu_2^2\mu_3^2}{\mu^4}\exp-3(D_3 + D)t + \frac{3}{4}(B + A)\exp-(6D - 2\Delta)t + \frac{3}{4}(B - A)\exp-(6D + 2\Delta)t\Big] \quad (5)$$

Where

$$D = \frac{1}{3}(D_1 + D_2 + D_3)$$

$$\Delta = (D_1^2 + D_2^2 + D_3^2 - D_1D_2 - D_1D_3 - D_2D_3)^{\frac{1}{2}}$$

$$A = \frac{D_1}{\Delta}\left(\frac{\mu_1^4 + 2\mu_2^2\mu_3^2}{\mu^4}\right) + \frac{D_2}{\Delta}\left(\frac{\mu_2^4 + \mu_1^2\mu_3^2}{\mu^4}\right) + \frac{D_3}{\Delta}\left(\frac{\mu_3^4 + 2\mu_1^2\mu_2^2}{\mu^4}\right) - \frac{D}{\Delta}$$

$$B = \frac{\mu_1^4 + \mu_2^4 + \mu_3^4}{\mu^4} - \frac{1}{3}$$

Here, μ_1, μ_2, μ_3 are the components of the transition dipole with respect to the principal diffusion axes; D_1, D_2, D_3 are the three diffusion coefficients for rotation about the three principal diffusion axes. The factor $P_2(\cos\lambda)$, Legendre Polynomial of order 2, is included here to take into account of the possibility that the absorption dipole may not be parallel to the emission dipole, but make an angle λ with respect to each other.

Various simplifications are possible for expression (5). If we assume, for example, that the dye is attached to random sites on the macromolecule, then only three exponentials with equal amplitudes remain:

$$r(t) = \frac{2}{15}P_2(\cos\lambda)\{\exp-3(D_1 + D)t + \exp-3(D_2 + D)t + \exp-3(D_3 + D)t\} \tag{6}$$

One may also assume that the macromolecule has an axis of symmetry, in which case, the expression for the polarization becomes:

$$r(t) = \frac{2}{5}P_2(\cos\lambda)\{(\frac{\mu_1^2 - \mu_3^2}{\mu^2})^2 \exp-6D_\perp t + 6\frac{\mu_1^2\mu_3^2}{\mu^4}\exp-(5D_\perp + D_{||})t + 3\frac{\mu_1^4}{\mu^4}\exp-(2D_\perp + 4D_{||})t\} \tag{7}$$

where $D_{||}$ is the diffusion coefficient for rotation about the symmetry axis, and $D_\perp$ is the one for rotation about an axis that is perpendicular to the symmetry axis.

III. EXPERIMENTAL

Experimentally, to measure the time dependence of fluorescence in the nanosecond region, we have used the "Single Photon Counting" technique. This method has the advantage of being able to detect very low photon fluxes. For excitation, we used a discharge by tungsten electrodes in air. This gives us pulses of light about 3.5 nanoseconds wide at half height, with peak wavelengths in the region 320 nm to 380 nm. The system we chose to test this technique with is the dye 1-anilino-8-naphthalene sulfonate (ANS), complexed with the protein apomyoglobin. As Stryer[5] has shown, a strong one to one complex is formed between the dye and the protein. Presumably, the dye goes into the hydrophobic cleft that was vacated by the heme moiety, and therefore must be fairly rigidly held with respect to the protein.

Figure I shows a plot of $I_{||}$ and $I_{\perp}$ as a function of time. We note that $I_{||}$ must decay faster than a single exponential, since reorientation would remove intensity from the parallel component, and build up on the perpendicular component. The natural decay of the complexed dye is a good exponential for over three decades, with a lifetime of 16.4 ± 0.2 nsec. Figure II shows a plot of $I_{||} - I_{\perp}$, which must be the polarization multiplied by the emission decay $e^{-t/5}$. No deviation from a single exponential can be detected, indicating that the dye-protein complex is roughly spherical. From the slope of this plot, one can get a value of the diffusion coefficient D. By adding sucrose to the solution, we can vary the diffusion rate as a function of viscosity η. The results have been plotted in Figure III in the form of the Einstein equation. From the slope of the straight line, one gets the radius of this complex to be 20.6 Å. The X-ray structure of myoglobin, of course, is known; it is roughly spherical, with a radius of 13.3 Å. This difference is actually within our present experimental error. One would expect a slightly larger radius, however, if one takes into account of the solvation shell, which is not picked up by the X-ray measurements. In any case, it appears that the gross structure of the complex does not deviate substantially from that of myoglobin, as optical rotatory dispersion measurements have borne out.

It is perhaps unfortunate that this complex turns out to be spherical, since the time dependent method yield no additional information over the steady state method when the body is spherical. We have also looked at ANS complexed with apohorse radish peroxidase, a protein with a molecular

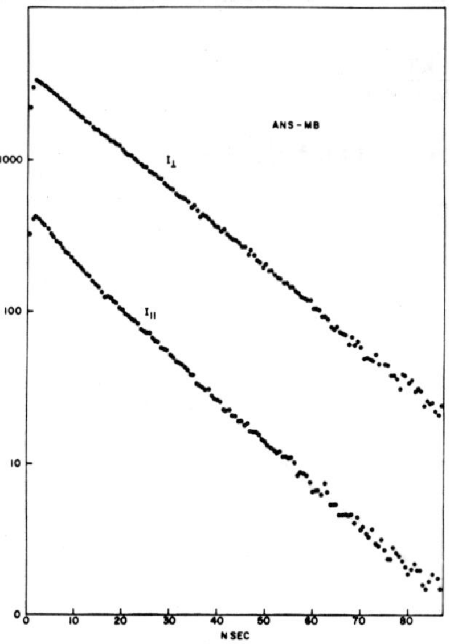

Figure I The parallel and perpendicular components of emission as a function of time.

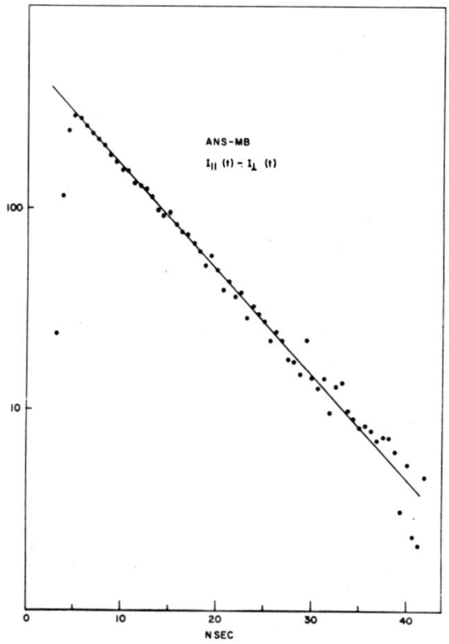

Figure II $I_{||}(t) - I_{\perp}(t) \sim e^{-6Dt}\, e^{-t/\tau}$

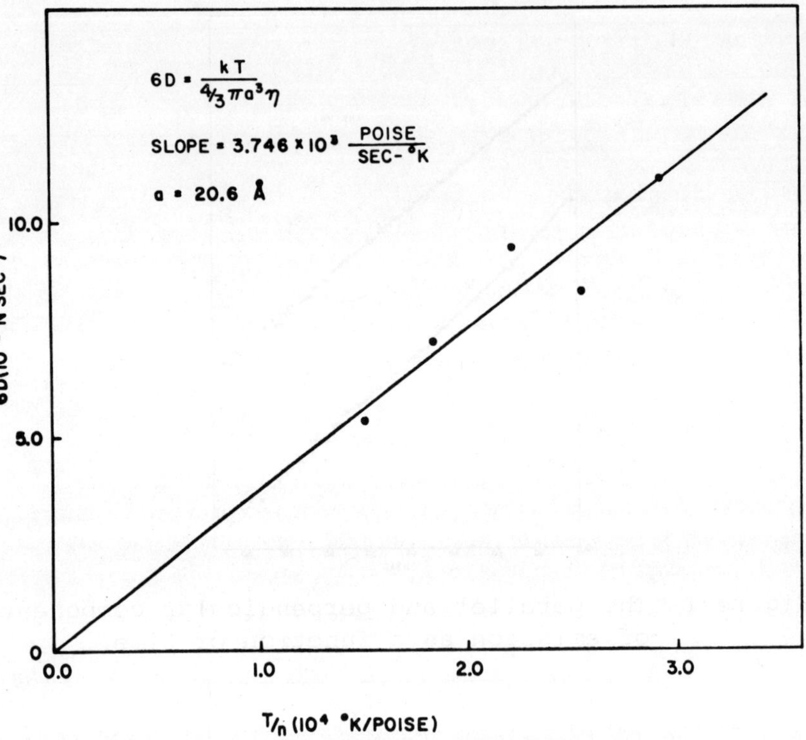

Figure III Plot of the Einstein equation.

weight of 40,000 compared with 17,000 for myoglobin. The results again indicate that the complex is a spherical structure with a radius of 27.4 Å. It is interesting to note here in passing, that the complexed dye in this case has a lifetime of 18 nanoseconds, a value that is even higher than in the case of apomyoglobin. This is an indication that the interior of horse radish peroxidase is even more hydrophobic than that of myoglobin. Recently we began investigating the system ethidium bromide complexed with transfer RNA's. Here, preliminary results do show that we can detect deviation from spherical geometry in these macromolecules. Experiments are also under way to investigate the rotational properties of smaller molecules, such as quinine, in viscous solvents.

IV. SUMMARY

In summary, we have derived general expressions for the time dependence of fluorescence depolarization. We have performed experiments that make use of these expressions to measure rotational diffusion coefficients of macromolecules. Like the steady state fluorescence polarization experiments, these experiments hold much promise for probing structures and sizes of macromolecules. In contrast with the steady state measurements, the time resolved measurements can in principle extract all three diffusion coefficients individually, rather than the harmonic mean of the diffusion coefficients.

ACKNOWLEDGEMENTS

I am indebted to Professor Richard Bersohn for his guidance and encouragement throughout this work. I would like to thank Mr. Robert Dichter for his work on horse radish peroxidase.

The support by the National Institutes of Health under Grant CA-07712 is also gratefully acknowledged.

REFERENCES

1. F. Perrin, J. Phys. Radium 5, 497 (1934).
2. R. G. Gordon, J. Chem. Phys. 45, 1643 (1966).
3. See for example, A. Abragam, The Principles of Nuclear Magnetism (Oxford University Press, London, 1961), p. 299.
4. L. Dale Favro, Phys. Rev. 119, 53 (1960).
5. L. Stryer, J. Mol. Biol. 13, 482 (1965).

FLUORESCENCE AND SINGLET ENERGY TRANSFER FROM AMINOPYRIDINES

A. C. Testa, A. Weisstuch and J. Hennessy

Department of Chemistry
St. John's University
Jamaica, New York 11432

INTRODUCTION

Recently, we reported that the fluorescence of 2-, 3-, and 4-aminopyridines (AMP) are very solvent dependent.[1] The 2- and 3-isomers have low fluorescence yields of 0.07 and 0.02, respectively, in cyclohexane; however, the quantum yields increase with solvent polarity approaching unity in 0.1 N sulfuric acid. In contrast to this behavior 4-AMP does not fluoresce in acid solutions and only very weakly in cyclohexane ($\phi_f < 10^{-3}$). It is well known that pyridine and pyridinium ion are non-fluorescent.[2] The results suggested that the lowest singlet state of 2- and 3-AMP is π,π^* in all solvents with the possible exception of cyclohexane. In contrast 4-AMP has a low lying n,π^* state and a second excited singlet which has a large charge transfer contribution.[3] Studies of tautomerism involving the amino and imino forms of these molecules have shown that the amino form is the only important species.[4]

In view of the trend in the fluorescence quantum yield for these compounds, i.e., $\Phi_f(2-) > \Phi_f(3-), > \Phi_f(4-)$, it appears that proximity effects may be important. In the present work we have investigated the fluorescence of the following diaminopyridines (DAP): 2,3-; 2,6; 3,4-, to further test the effect of the amino group on the ring nitrogen. In addition results from fluorescence quenching and sensitization experiments with 2- and 3-AMP are presented.

EXPERIMENTAL

MATERIALS. Diaminopyridines (2,3-; 2,6-; and 3,4-) obtained from Aldrich Chemical Co. were purified as follows: 2,3-DAP was recrystallized twice from benzene; 2,6-DAP was recrystallized from benzene and then *n*-hexane; 3,4-DAP was recrystallized twice from 1:1 ethanol/*n*-hexane and white crystals were obtained by adding excess *n*-hexane and cooling in an ice bath. All samples were dried in a vacuum desiccator. The physical and spectroscopic properties of these samples agreed with the literature.[5-8] The purification of the 2-, 3-, and 4-AMP has been described elsewhere.[1] Biacetyl obtained from Matheson, Coleman and Bell was vacuum distilled and the middle fraction collected and found to contain < 0.2% impurities. A sample of zone refined biacetyl was also used with no significant difference in behavior.

Spectrograde solvents and reagent grade chemicals were used as received. Harleco fluorimetric grade HCl and NaOH were used for acid and base solutions.

APPARATUS. All fluorescence data were obtained at room temperature with 285 mμ excitation employing an interference filter (10 mμ half band width) from Thin Films Products, Cambridge, Massachusetts. Other details have been presented elsewhere.[1] Quantum yields were determined relative to a value of 0.09 for d,l-tryptophan at pH 6.5.[9] The accuracy of fluorescence quantum yields is ± 50%, however, relative yields are reliable to ± 10%.

RESULTS

(a) FLUORESCENCE OF DIAMINOPYRIDINES. The fluorescence data presented in Table I suggest the importance of the proximity of the amine group to the ring nitrogen as a significant factor in determining the fluorescence of these molecules. It is evident from the results that the fluorescence quantum yield for DAP decreases in the following manner: 2,6- > 2,3- > 3,4-. This trend agrees with our previous study of the mono-aminopyridines where the fluorescence quantum yield decreases as follows: 2- > 3- > 4-.[1] Although pyridine and pyridinium ion exhibit no fluorescence, the aminopyridines, particularly the 2-, 3- and 2,6-isomers, have quantum yields approaching unity in 0.1 N H_2SO_4. The fluorescence yields for 3,4-DAP are very low in all solvents studied relative to the 2,3- and 2,6-isomers.

The data for 2,3- and 2,6-DAP are consistent with the assignment of a π,π^* lowest singlet

TABLE I: Absorption and Fluorescence Characteristics of Diaminopyridines. Excitation at 285 mμ.

	2,3-Diamino (pK_a = 7.00)					2,6-Diamino (pK_a = 7.10)					3,4-Diamino (pK_a = 9.14)				
Solvent	(abs) λ_{max}	ϵ_{max}	(fl) λ_{max}	ϕ_f^a	0-0[b] band cm^{-1}	(abs) λ_{max}	ϵ_{max}	(fl) λ_{max}	ϕ_f	0-0 band cm^{-1}	(abs) λ_{max}	ϵ_{max}	(fl) λ_{max}	ϕ_f	0-0 band cm^{-1}
Cyclohexane	298	-	356	0.12	31,000	300	-	339	0.31	31.650	285	-	340	0.007	32,300
Ethyl Ether	305	5000	369	0.28	30,000	305	6870	345	0.46	31.000	289	-	344	0.05	31,900
Acetonitrile	306	5430	370	0.54	29,900	305	6980	348	0.83	30,900	290	2800	348	0.08	31,550
Ethanol	309	5660	374	0.82	29,400	309	7190	355	0.34	30.300	291	3700	352	0.12	31,000
Water	304	5350	378	0.59	29,250	311	5680	362	0.88	29.100	286	5360	369	0.002	30,550
0.1 N HCl (monocation)	318	7205	395	0.13	28.350	331	11,600	389	1.30	28.300					
0.01 N HCl											286	7600	368	0.002	31,200
0.1 N H_2SO_4 (monocation)	317	6970	395	0.13	28,350	331	12,100	388	1.21	28,300					
0.01 N H_2SO_4											286	7540	369	0.003	30,500
10 N HCl (dication)	309	5870	379	0.01	29,750	332	9050	391	0.86	28.300	263	12,270	NF	0.000	-
10 N H_2SO_4											262	10,750	390	0.004	-
0.001 N NaOH (neutral form)	-	-	382	0.54	-	-	-	361	0.66	-	-	-	360	0.01	-
0.1 N NaOH	302	5285	379	0.27	29,800	304	6450	359	0.48	30.300	284	3720	357	0.009	31,550

[a] Fluorescence yields are normalized to a value of 0.09 for d,l-tryptophan at pH 6.5. See Ref. 9.
[b] 0-0 bands determined from mirror image plots.

similar to that for 2- and 3-AMP. In all cases the wavelength maxima for absorption and fluorescence shift to higher wavelengths with increasing solvent polarity. Similar effects have been observed for p-aminoacetophenone where the n,π^* and π,π^* levels lie close together, and the latter is lowest lying in polar solvents.[10]

3,4-DAP appears to be exceptional as has been observed with 4-AMP, with respect to exhibiting low fluorescence yields in all solvents and also when protonated. These two compounds exhibit their largest yields in ethanol, which may be due to hydrogen bonding between the ring nitrogen and the hydrogen atom of the alcohol. Ermolaev[11] has demonstrated this effect with the quinoline molecule where hydrogen bonding slows down the intersystem crossing rate constant while concomitantly increasing the fluorescence yield. Although 3,4-DAP fluoresces in 10 N H_2SO_4, the lack of fluorescence in 10 N HCl is due to chloride ion quenching, which has been shown for the monoaminopyridines.[1]

In view of the possibility of excited state dissociation in these molecules, it follows that the fluorescence spectrum of the monocation (protonation at the ring nitrogen) is generated in 0.1 N HCl and the fluorescence of the neutral molecule is obtained in 0.1 N NaOH. The excited state pK's were determined from the shift in the 0-0 bands together with the Förster cycle,[12,13] i.e.,

$$pK - pK^* = hc(\Delta\tilde{\nu})/2.303\ kT$$

where pK and pK^* are the equilibrium constants for acid dissociation in the ground and excited states, respectively, and $\Delta\tilde{\nu}$ is the frequency shift in cm^{-1} of the cation minus the neutral form of the molecule. It can be seen from Table II that in all cases the amino-pyridines are weaker acids in the excited state. It has been shown that heterocyclic nitrogens are more basic in the excited state relative to the ground state.[14]

TABLE II: pK_a and pK_a^* values for aminopyridines (Acid dissociation of ring nitrogen)

	pK_a [8,15]	pK_a^*
2-aminopyridine	6.86	8.95
3-aminopyridine	5.98	11.2
4-aminopyridine	9.17	-
2,3-diaminopyridine	7.00	10.0
2,6-diaminopyridine	7.10	11.3
3,4-diaminopyridine	9.14	11.6

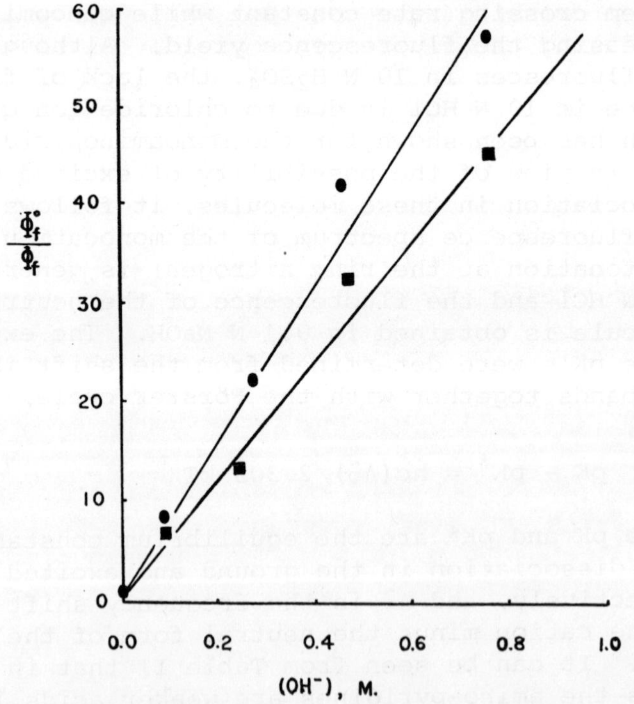

Figure 1 Stern-Volmer fluorescence quenching of 2(●)- and 3(■)-aminopyridine with hydroxide ion.

(b) FLUORESCENCE QUENCHING OF AMINOPYRIDINES. In the course of our investigations with aminopyridines we observed fluorescence quenching of 2- and 3-AMP by halide and hydroxide ions. Quenching data obtained in NaOH are presented in Fig. 1, which exhibits the linear behavior of a Stern-Volmer relationship. The slopes of 61 and 81 M^{-1} for 2- and 3-AMP, respectively, suggest no significant difference in the singlet of the two molecules. The quenching by hydroxide ion appears to involve a rapid proton transfer in the excited state between OH^- and the amine of the excited molecule.[1]

The quenching efficiency arising from halide ions decrease in the order NaI > NaBr > NaCl, which can be interpreted in terms of an external heavy atom effect.[16] Another possibility is to impose a charge transfer complex with the halide ion as a donor and the excited molecule as acceptor, i.e.,

$$(AMP)^{*1} + X^- \rightleftharpoons (\overline{AMP}\ldots\overset{+}{X})^* \rightarrow AMP + X^-$$

Similar effects have been suggested in the fluorescence quenching of dyes with halide ions[17] and in the fluorescence quenching of molecules in different hydrocarbon solvents, depending upon the electron-donating ability of the latter.[18] This interpretation is also consistent with the electron affinities of the halogens I < Br < Cl.

The results for the Stern-Volmer quenching of 2- and 3-AMP with NaBr in the concentration range 1-10 m mole/lit indicate slopes of 161 and 286 M^{-1}, respectively. These values are larger than those from the hydroxide ion quenching experiments, which suggest a different quenching mechanism for the two cases considered.

(c) SENSITIZED FLUORESCENCE OF BIACETYL. The method of sensitized fluorescence developed by Dubois et. al.[19-21] was used to perform quenching experiments with biacetyl as acceptor (A) and 2-, 3-, and 4-aminopyridine as donors (D). It was observed that only 2-AMP sensitized the fluorescence of biacetyl while 3- and 4-AMP do not. Experiments also indicated sensitization with 2,3-DAP, but these results were complicated by photochemistry.

The Stern-Volmer fluorescence quenching of 2-AMP in cyclohexane solutions with increasing concentration of biacetyl is presented in Fig. 2 where F_D^o and F_D represent fluorescence intensities of 2-AMP in the absence of and presence of biacetyl, respectively. The fluorescence quenching of 2-AMP was followed at its fluorescence wavelength maximum, 332 mμ. The slope of the line is 63 M^{-1}, which coupled with an assumed diffusion controlled quenching process ($k_q = 7 \times 10^9$ M^{-1} sec^{-1}) predicts the singlet lifetime of 2-AMP to be 1×10^{-8} sec.

The results presented in Fig. 3 for the sensitized fluorescence of biacetyl with 2-AMP were obtained with the monochromator set at 465 mμ, the fluorescence wavelength maximum of biacetyl. The enhancement of biacetyl fluorescence by 2-AMP is illustrated by plotting F_A/F_A^o vs. concentration of added donor, where F_A is the fluorescence intensity with donor and F_A^o is the fluorescence intensity of biacetyl without donor.

In order to relate the data to measureable parameters of the molecules, the inverse slopes from Fig. 3, $d(2\text{-AMP})/d(F_A/F_A^o)$, in the limit as (2-AMP) → 0 were plotted vs. concentration of biacetyl. These results are presented in Fig. 4 from which the slope and intercept are related to the lifetime of 2-AMP. The slope of the line in Fig. 4 gives the ratio of extinction coefficients $\varepsilon_A/\varepsilon_D$, as 3.27×10^{-3} which compares satisfactorily with 4.33×10^{-3} for the experimentally determined values at 285 mμ using conventional absorption spectrophotometry. From the ratio of slope to intercept, the sensitization constant, $k_{et}\tau_D$, where k_{et} is the rate constant for the energy transfer

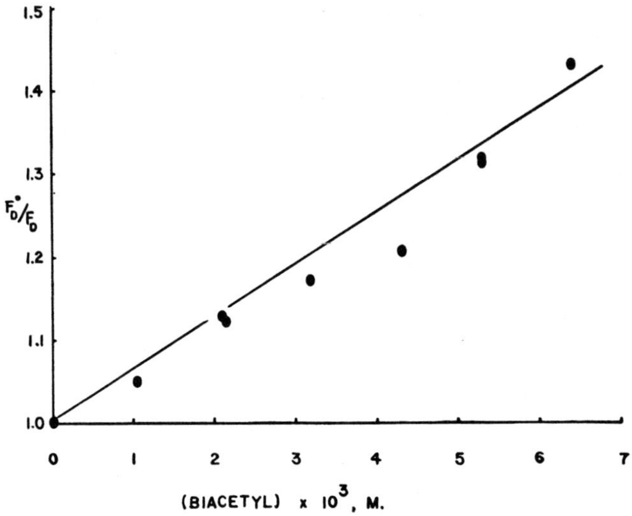

Figure 2 Fluorescence quenching of 2-aminopyridine by biacetyl in aerated solutions of cyclohexane at 25°C. (285 mμ excitation).

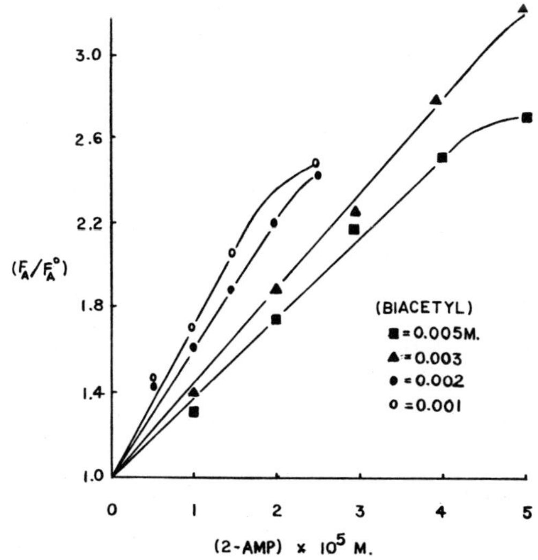

Figure 3 The sensitized fluorescence of biacetyl by 2-aminopyridine in aerated solutions of cyclohexane at 25°C. (285 mμ excitation).

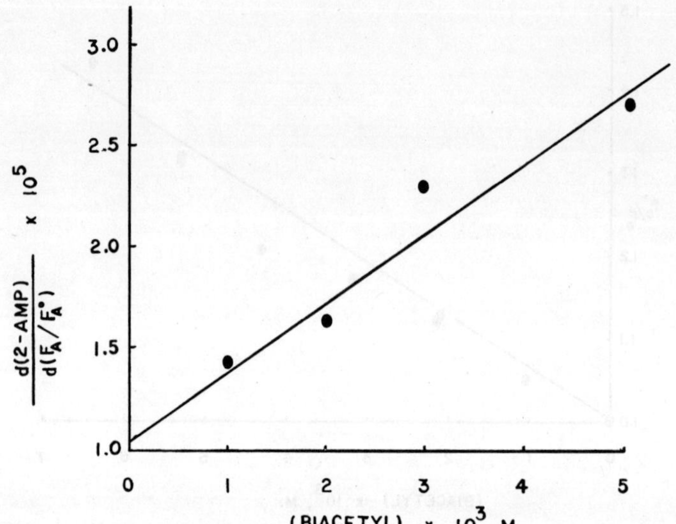

Figure 4 Sensitized fluorescence of biacetyl by 2-aminopyridine. Inverse slopes from Fig. 3 versus biacetyl concentration.

process and τ_D is the lifetime of the donor (2-AMP), was determined to be 327 M^{-1}. Assuming the diffusion controlled rate constant of 7 x 10^9 M^{-1} sec^{-1} for cyclohexane solutions, the lifetime of the 2-AMP singlet was determined to be 4 x 10^{-8} sec.

DISCUSSION

The fluorescence characteristics of the aminopyridines are very solvent dependent and can be quenched by halide and hydroxide ions. The high fluorescence yields (with the expeption of 4- and 3,4-isomers) suggest low lying π,π^* singlets with negligible contributions from the n,π^* states. The latter however, may be significant in non-polar hydrocarbon solvents. Vapor phase ultraviolet spectra of the aminopyridines reported by Misra[22] indicate separation of n,π^* and π,π^* states with the former lying lowest in 2- and 3-AMP. In _n_-hexane the n,π^* transition of 2-AMP is masked and the π,π^* state is lowest lying. With 3-AMP in _n_-hexane the n,π^* singlet appears as the lowest energy singlet; however, in polar solvents the lowest singlet is π,π^*. The fluorescence data for the mono-aminopyridines and diaminopyridines exhibit this behavior by showing increasing fluorescence yields in polar solvents. This is a predicted behavior since in polar solvents n,π^* singlets move to higher energies while π,π^* move to lower energies. The combined effect can cause an inversion of levels which are close together.[23,24]

The anomalous behavior of 4-AMP and 3,4-DAP in acid is probably due to some prototropic tautomerism in the excited state, which does not occur with the 2-, 3-, 2,3- and 2,6-isomers. The importance of charge transfer in 4-AMP has been reported by Favini et. al.[3] Unfortunately most discussions of tautomerism in aminopyridines refer to ground states, which can be misleading when applied to the interpretation of excited state species.

The quenching and sensitization data for 2-AMP indicate a value of $2 \pm 1 \times 10^{-8}$ sec. for the singlet lifetime. The observation that 2-AMP sensitizes the fluorescence of biacetyl whereas 3-AMP does not is unexpected. The similarity between the two molecules is as follows: (a) the integrated absorptions in cyclohexane are identical within 20%, (b) the overlap areas of the donor fluorescence with biacetyl absorption are equal, and (c) the fluorescence yield of 2- and 3-AMP in cyclohexane solutions have been determined to be 0.07 and 0.02, respectively.

Wilkinson and Dubois have estimated that substances which do not transfer singlet energy to biacetyl have singlet lifetimes $\leq 10^{-10}$ sec.[21] Undoubtedly, the singlet lifetime of 3-AMP is much shorter than 2-AMP, since it is not quenched by biacetyl. In view of the similarities in the spectral characteristics of 2- and 3-AMP an explanation is needed to account for the unexpected short lifetime of 3-AMP relative to 2-AMP. Presumably, if the excited state configuration for the two molecules were different this situation would result in a difference in lifetime. Fluorescence studies of 2- and 3-AMP in sodium halide solutions suggest that the excited state dipole moment maintains the same direction for 2-AMP, but is reversed for 3-AMP.[1] This unfavorable environment for the excited state of 3-AMP may contribute to a shortening of its lifetime. An alternate explanation for the rapid relaxation of 3-AMP is the favorable intersystem crossing from a low-lying n,π^* singlet in non-polar solvents to a π,π^* triplet, according to El-Sayed's rules of intersystem crossing probabilities in heterocyclic molecules.[25] The movement of energy levels with solvents appears to be an important consideration since we observed that the energy transfer for 2-AMP is less efficient in acetonitrile despite a three-fold increase in the fluorescence yield relative to cyclohexane solutions.

An inviting possibility to the luminescence chemist is the ability to predict the fluorescence of molecules. It would appear that molecular orbital theory and π-electron charge densities derived from wavefunctions should be useful in dealing with electronic excitation. It has been shown for example that the distribution of unpaired electron densities in free radicals can be predicted from Hückel MO's.[26] Consequently, an attempt to correlate emission characteristics of molecules using charge densities seems reasonable. In this regard it is fortunate that Kwiatowski has calculated charge densities for 2-, 3-, and 4-AMP in the ground and first excited states.[27] His results show an interesting trend in that 2- and 3-AMP, which fluoresce efficiently in polar solvents, exhibit an increase in charge density at the ring nitrogen upon excitation, whereas 4-AMP, which exhibits very weak or no fluorescence, undergoes a decrease in charge density at the ring nitrogen upon excitation. It would appear then that movement of electron charge towards the heteroatom in the excited state is favorable to the fluorescence of the molecule.

This prediction for the mono-aminopyridines is corroborated by the experimental results for the diaminopyridines, where the fluorescence yield of 2,6- > 2,3- > 3,4-. A precaution in this simple approach, however, is that it may not be applicable to different types of molecules. In addition, the method is complicated by the neglect of non-bonding electrons, which may determine the behavior of the lowest singlet.

In summary the fluorescence of aminopyridines, as a simple heterocyclic system exhibits significant solvent effects related to the interaction of n,π* and π,π* singlets. The proximity of the amine group to the ring nitrogen is an important factor in determining the fluorescence of these compounds.

REFERENCES

1. A. Weisstuch and A. C. Testa, J. Phys. Chem. 72, 1982 (1968).
2. T. Förster, Fluoreszenz Organischer Verbindungen (Vandenhoeck and Ruprecht, Göttingen, Germany, 1951), p. 105.
3. G. Favini, A. Gamba and I. R. Bellobono, Spectrochim. Acta 23A, 89 (1967).
4. A. R. Katritzky and J. M. Lagowski, Advances in Heterocyclic Chemistry, A. R. Katritzky, Ed. (Academic Press, New York, 1963), Vol. I, p. 341.
5. H. Bayzer, Monatsh. Chemie 88, 72 (1957).
6. R. C. DeSelms and H. S. Mosher, J. Am. Chem. Soc. 82, 3762 (1960).
7. J. Barassin and H. Lumbroso, Bull. Soc. Chim. France, 492 (1961).
8. G. B. Barlin, J. Chem. Soc. (London) 2150 (1964).
9. V. G. Shore and A. B. Pardee, Archiv. Biochem. Biophys. 60, 100 (1956).
10. G. Yamaguchi, T. Kakinoki and H. Tsubomura, Bull, Chem. Soc. Japan 40, 526 (1967).
11. V. L. Ermolaev and I. P. Kotlyar, Opt. and Spectry. 9, 183 (1960).
12. T. Förster, Z. Elektrochem. 54, 42 (1950).
13. A. Weller, in Progress in Reaction Kinetics, G. Porter, Ed. (Pergamon Press, New York, 1961), Vol. I, p. 189.
14. A. Weller, Z. Elektrochem. 61, 956 (1957).
15. A. Albert, R. Goldacre and J. Phillips, J. Chem. Soc. (London) 2240 (1948).
16. M. Kasha, Radiation Research, Suppl. 2, 243 (1960).
17. J. Weiss, Trans. Faraday Soc. 35, 48 (1939).
18. D. K. Majumdar and S. Basu, J. Chem. Phys. 33, 1199 (1960).
19. J. T. Dubois and B. Stevens, in Luminescence of Organic and Inorganic Materials, H. P.

Kallmann and G. M. Spruch, Eds. (J. Wiley and Sons, Inc., New York, 1962), p. 115.
20. J. T. Dubois and M. Cox, J. Chem. Phys. 38, 2536 (1963).
21. F. Wilkinson and J. T. Dubois, J. Chem. Phys. 39, 377 (1963).
22. T. N. Misra, Ind. J. Phys. 35, 420 (1961).
23. M. A. El-Sayed and M. Kasha, Spectroch. Acta 15, 758 (1959).
24. E. L. Wehry, in Fluorescence-Theory, Instrumentation and Practice, G. G. Guilbault, Ed. (M. Dekker, Inc., New York, 1967), p. 109.
25. M. A. El-Sayed, J. Chem. Phys. 38, 2834 (1963).
26. A. Carrington, Quart. Rev. 17, 67 (1963).
27. S. Kwiatowski, Acta Phys. Polon. 30, 963 (1966).

LUMINESCENT PROPERTIES OF SENSITIZING DYES ADSORBED TO SILVER HALIDE SUBSTRATES

P. B. Gilman, Jr.

Eastman Kodak Company
Rochester, New York 14650

LUMINESCENCE OF SILVER HALIDES

Before detailed luminescent studies of adsorbed dyes were made, the fluorescent and delayed luminescent properties of both pure powders and zone-refined single crystals of silver halide were studied. The phosphorescent properties of pure powdered silver chloride alone and with treatments that markedly affected the delayed luminescence are shown in Figures 1-6. The qualitative effects are summarized in Figure 7.

It is seen that the phosphorescent emission from silver chloride appears to consist of two bands made up of a long wavelength (520 nm), slow component and a short wavelength (480 nm), fast component. This structure in the luminescent emission is not readily observed from the fluorescence measurements of the pure materials as reported by Randall,[1] Farnell, et al.,[2,3] Vacek,[4] and Smith[5] but a similar type of banding to that reported here was described by Sonoike and Akimoto[6]

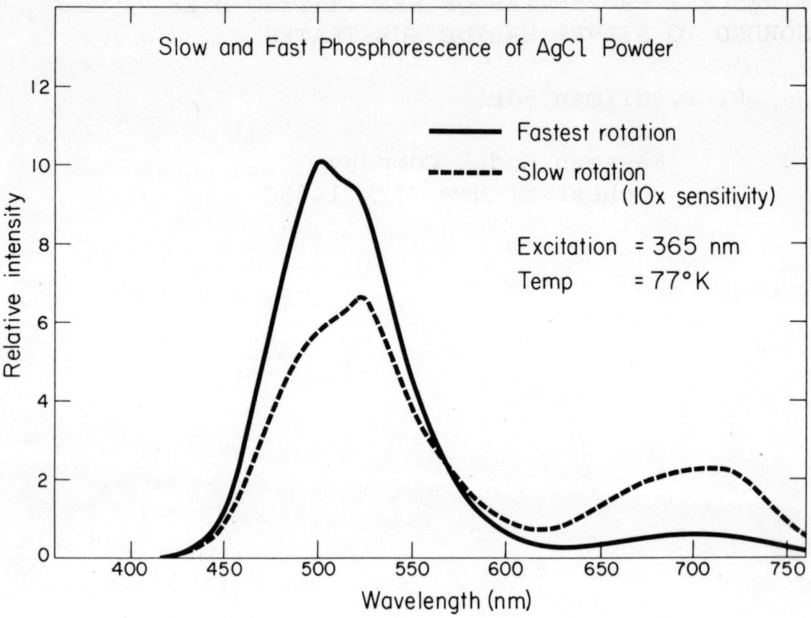

Figure 1

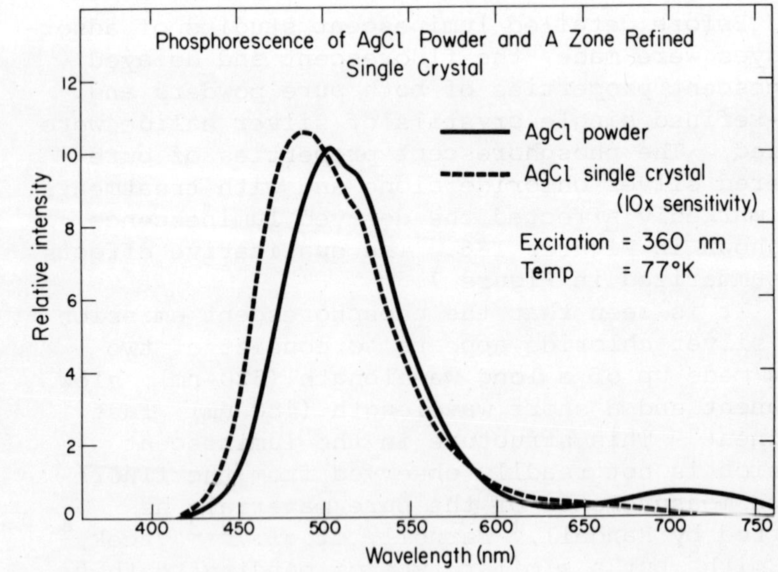

Figure 2

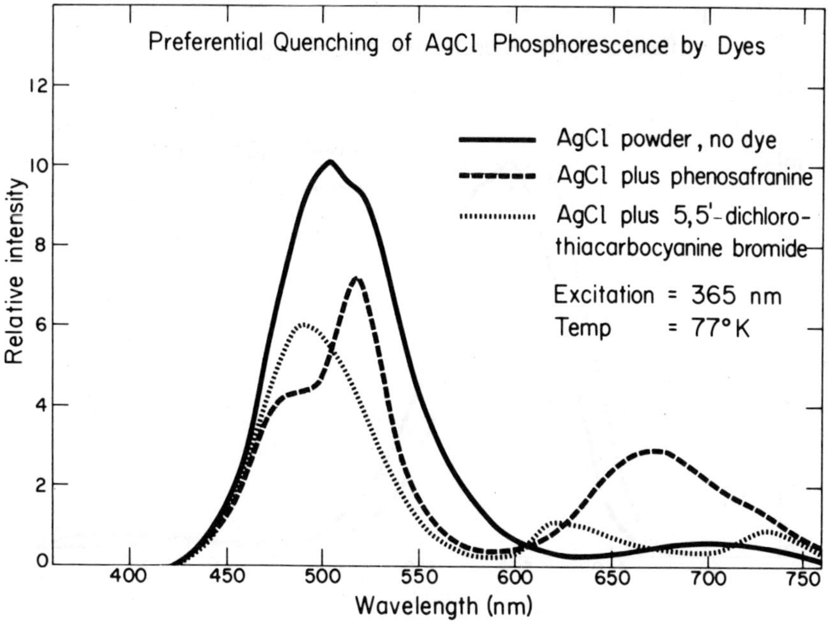

Figure 3

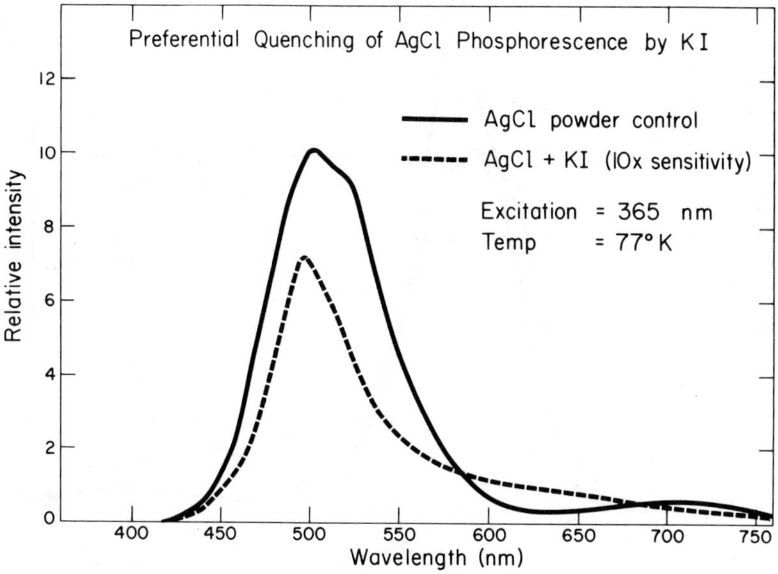

Figure 4

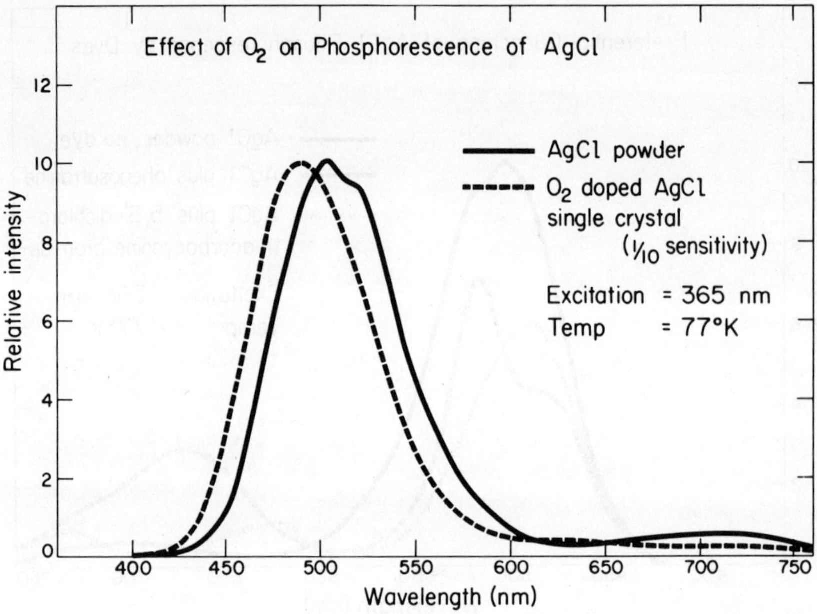

Figure 5

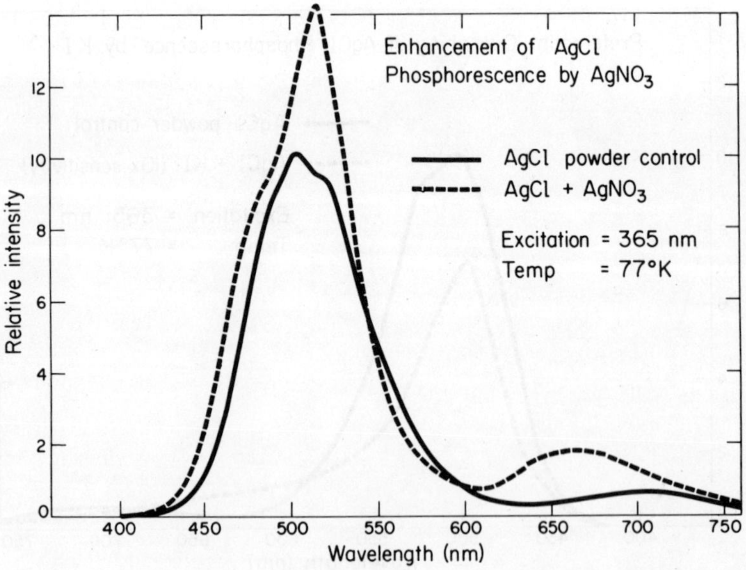

Figure 6

Summary of Factors Influencing Luminescence of Silver Chloride

COMPOUND	Emission (nm) 480	520	
Phenosafranine	↓↓	↓	Competing $e^{\ominus}$ trap
Dichlorothiacarbocyanine	↓	↓↓	Competing ⊕ trap
KI	↓	↓↓	Competing ⊕ trap
$AgNO_3$	↑	↑↑	More $e^{\ominus}$ traps
O_2	↑↑	↑	More ⊕ traps
Zone refine	↓	↓↓	Fewer $e^{\ominus}$ traps

Possible Reactions

$$e^{\ominus}_{mobile} + \oplus_{trapped} \longrightarrow 480\text{ nm} \quad \text{Fast}$$

$$e^{\ominus}_{trapped} + \oplus_{mobile} \longrightarrow 520\text{ nm} \quad \text{Slow}$$

Figure 7

Energy Band Model for Silver Chloride Phosphorescence

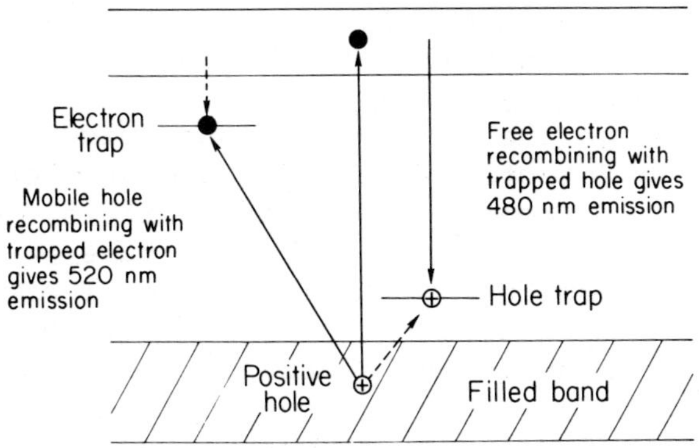

Figure 8

for the fluorescence of impurity doped silver chloride.

The effects shown in Figures 1-6 may be interpreted in terms of the mechanism of latent image formation discussed by Hamilton and Bayer[7] in which two types of recombination events were proposed which competed with the latent image forming step. Recombination of a free electron with a trapped hole and capture of a free hole by a trapped electron are two different recombination events which would occur after exposure to light and be radiative at the liquid nitrogen temperature used for studying these systems. It is therefore proposed that the fast emission at 480 nm is mainly the radiative recombination of free electrons with trapped holes and the slower, 520 nm emission is the radiative recombination of free holes with trapped electrons, as shown in the simple energy level diagram in Figure 8.

FLUORESCENCE OF DYE

In this study, the sensitizing dye, 1,1'-diethyl-2,2'-cyanine chloride, was chosen for investigation mainly because of its well-known ability to exist in two photochemically active states: as discrete molecules in a monomeric condition and in a highly ordered, two-dimensional crystalline state called a J-aggregate, which was first described by Jelley.[8,9]

Although the dye in the monomeric state exhibits no detectable fluorescence at room temperature when an alcoholic solution of it is evaporated on a glass plate, dramatic changes take place in both the absorption spectrum and the fluorescence with the formation of the J-aggregate, which is characterized by a very sharp, new long wavelength absorption band. This aggregate state of the dye exhibits the "resonance fluorescence" first described by Jelley[8,9] and is unique with cyanine dyes.

A comparison of the absorption spectrum and fluorescence of the dye in the *J*-aggregate state at room temperature is shown in Figure 9.

PHOSPHORESCENCE OF DYE

The phosphorescent emissions of the dye, 1,1'-diethyl-2,2'-cyanine chloride, in the monomeric state at liquid nitrogen temperature and excited by radiation of wavelengths 325 and 525 nm, are shown in Figure 10.

The type of phosphorescent emission that occurs is seen to be strongly dependent on the wavelength of excitation. The delayed luminescence produced by the ultraviolet excitation consists of two emissions, one at 565 nm and the other at 640 nm. The delayed emission at 565 nm is similar in shape and position to the fluorescent emission observed for the dye. This emission at 565 nm may best be described as a "delayed fluorescence" and the mechanism by which it arises may be similar to that described by Kern, Dorr, and Scheibe[10] and by Lim and Swenson[11] for solutions of cyanine and other dyes at low temperature.

The delayed fluorescence has been explained as resulting from a photoionization of the dye, followed by recombination of electrons temporarily trapped in the solvent with the dye radical ion to produce an excited singlet state which then radiatively decays with a fluorescent emission.

The longer-wavelength emission at 640 nm is the normal phosphorescence described by West[12] and is due to the radiative transition of electrons in the triplet state to the ground-state singlet.

LUMINESCENCE OF DYE IN A PHOTOGRAPHIC MEDIUM

In an attempt to learn more about the luminescent behavior of 1,1'-diethyl-2,2'-cyanine chloride

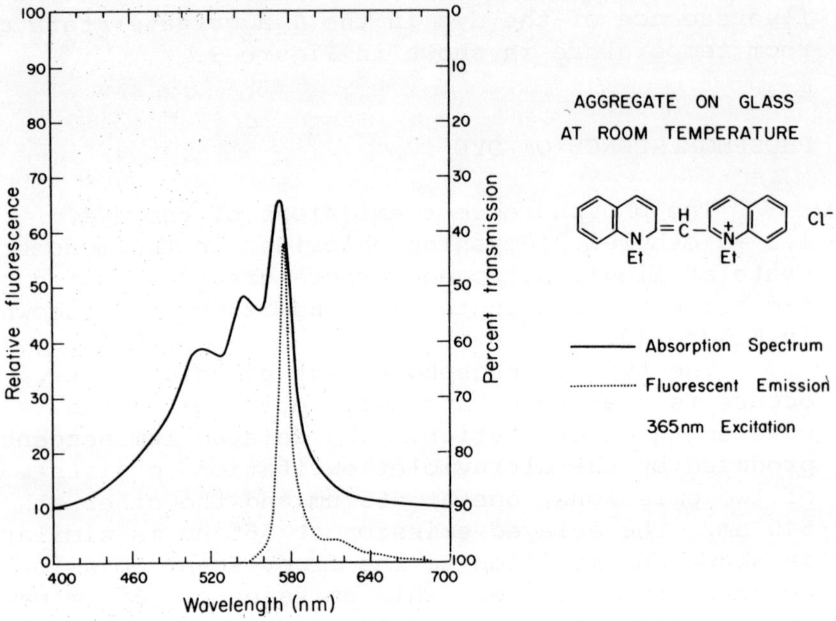

Figure 9

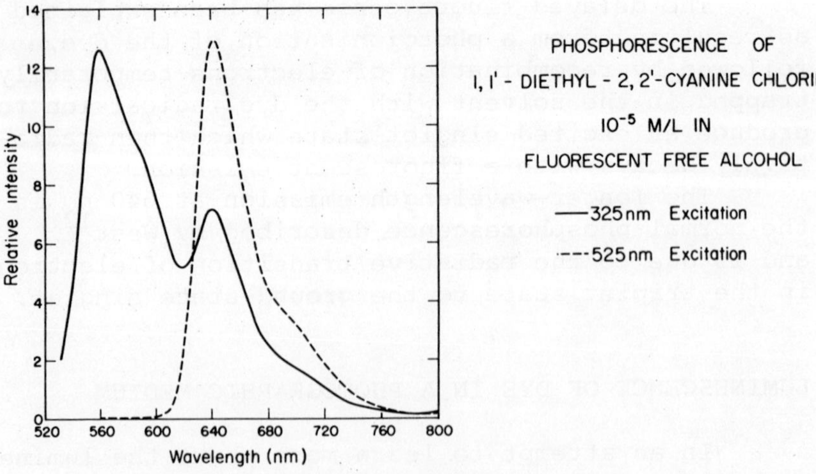

Figure 10

in a photographically active environment, the dye was adsorbed onto powdered samples of silver halides and attempts were made to measure the luminescence of the resulting dyed substrate.

When luminescent measurements of the dye on the powdered samples of AgCl were attempted, the results varied widely depending on the amount of dye adsorbed and the degree of moisture present.

Consistently reproducible results were obtained by adding the dye to a pure, silver chloride-gelatin dispersion and making coatings which allowed a comparison of the photographic, luminescent and spectral absorption properties at many dye levels.

The phosphorescent measurements for representative coatings of this type are shown in Figures 11 and 12.

The most significant result from these measurements is the presence of a strong, new phosphorescent emission at 700 nm associated with high levels of the dye in the *J*-aggregate state. With increased dye coverage, the monomeric emission at 640 nm decreases and the new emission at 700 nm increases.

In an attempt to better understand the nature of this new 700 nm emission, which appeared only when the dye was adsorbed in the *J*-aggregate state on silver halide, further measurements were made to determine its dependence on intensity of excitation and its decay characteristics after excitation.

In considering the origin of the 700 nm emission, it does not seem likely at first that the excited state responsible for the emission is the *J*-band triplet, since the nonadsorbed dye in the *J*-aggregate state itself shows no phosphorescence and one would expect that a "nonemitting" triplet would not emit, whether it was formed optically or by a recombination process.

However, the failure to see phosphorescence in the nonadsorbed *J*-aggregated dye may be due

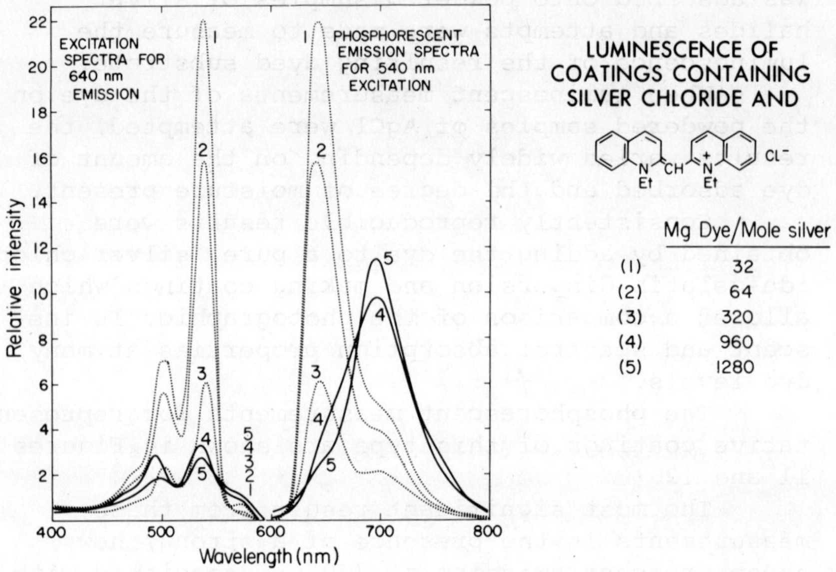

Figure 11

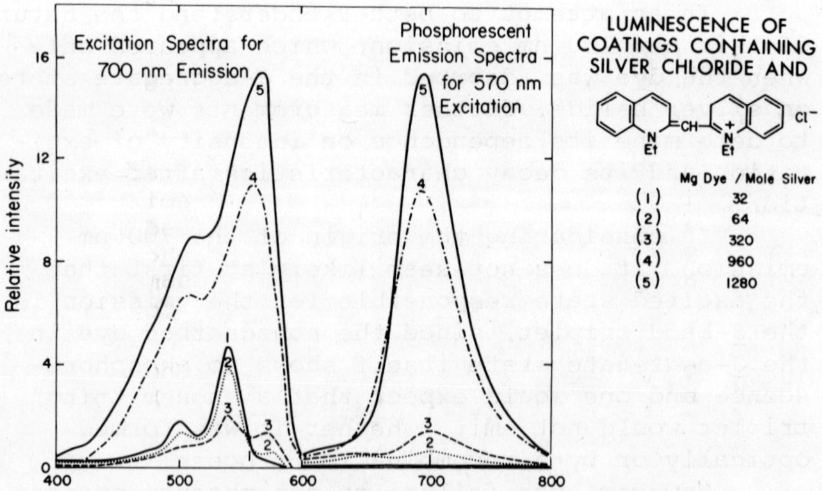

Figure 12

simply to an intrinsically low triplet yield, rather than to a radiationless dissipation of the triplet energy.

This is consistent with the "resonance fluorescence" of the dye in the *J*-aggregate state, and the lack of phosphorescence may be a direct consequence of the highly ordered nature of the dye molecules in the *J*-state. In the nonadsorbed state very rapid electron-hole recombination is possible and only fluorescence from the dye aggregate is observed.

When the dye is adsorbed on a silver halide surface, a strong electronic interaction is known to take place on optical excitation because of the observed spectral sensitizing properties of the dye. It therefore seems reasonable to suggest that, upon excitation with light, electrons from the dye are temporarily freed in the conduction band of the silver halide and after exposure, the electrons and the dye positive holes, trapped in the *J*-aggregate, recombine to produce an excited state which may be a *J*-aggregate triplet. This triplet is then either self-quenched or may radiatively decay with the observed 700 nm emission. The situation is thus:

PROPOSED MECHANISM OF DELAYED LUMINESCENCE AT 700 nm FOR *J*-AGGREGATE ON SILVER CHLORIDE.

(1) $^{1}D_{(J)} + h\nu\,(575\text{ nm}) \xrightarrow{k_1} {}^{1}Dye^{*}_{(J)}$ (singlet)

(2) $^{1}Dye^{*}_{(J)} + AgX \xrightarrow{k_2} Dye^{\oplus}_{(J)} + \ominus$ (conduction band)

(3) $Dye^{\oplus}_{(J)} + \ominus\,(\text{conduction band}) \xrightarrow{k_3}$

$^{3}Dye^{*}_{(J)}$ (triplet)

(4) $^{3}Dye^{*}_{(J)} \xrightarrow{k_4} {}^{1}Dye_{(J)} + h\nu_{(700\text{nm})}$

$$(5)\quad 2\ {}^3\mathrm{Dye}^*_{(J)} \xrightarrow{k_5} 2\ {}^1\mathrm{Dye}_{(J)}$$

Excited singlet molecules of the dye interact with the silver halide grain to produce electrons and the dye positive holes which later recombine in a second-order process to form in high yield an excited J-aggregate triplet which then radiatively decays with an emission peak at 700 nm.

The main assumption upon which this mechanism is based is that reaction (3) is the rate-determining step and that all the other reactions involved are fast compared to the electron-hole recombination step.

SENSITIZED LUMINESCENCE

The J-band recombination luminescence first observed on silver chloride is not restricted to silver chloride and may be observed equally well at the same wavelength when the dye is adsorbed to either silver bromide or silver iodide crystals. In the case of silver iodide it was observed that absorption of light by the adsorbed dye, 1,1'-diethyl-2,2'-cyanine chloride could produce the intrinsic blue-violet luminescence normally associated with absorption of blue light by the silver iodide. This spectral sensitization of the intrinsic luminescence of silver iodide is similar to that reported by Feofilov and Ovsyankin[13] in which the cooperative sensitization of luminescence by dyes in the crystals of HgI_2, PbI_2, AgI, TiCl, and ZnO was reported for fluorescent emissions.

It was observed in these studies that the delayed emission from silver iodide at low temperatures was also spectrally sensitized. The delayed luminescence of silver iodide powder in the absence of adsorbed dye is shown in Figure 13; Figure 14 shows the spectrally sensitized luminescence. The intensity dependence of excitation and the second

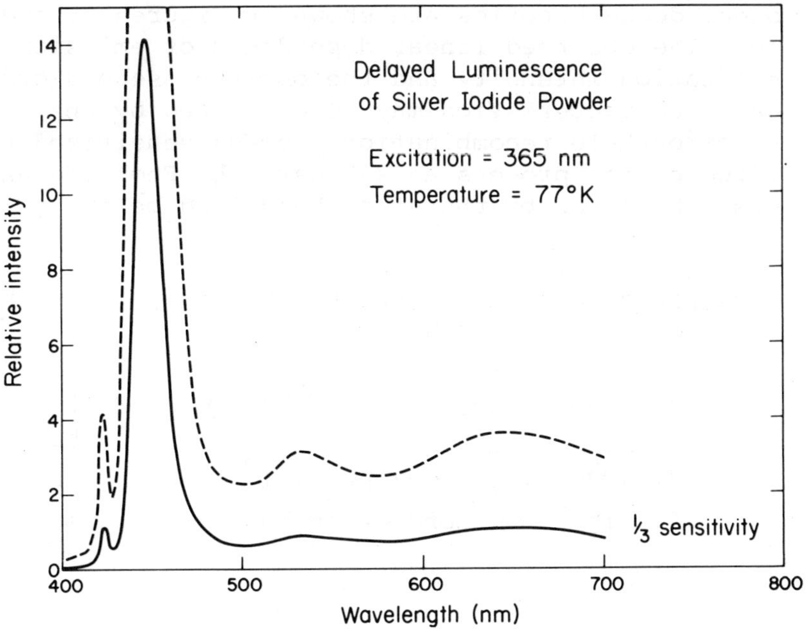

Figure 13

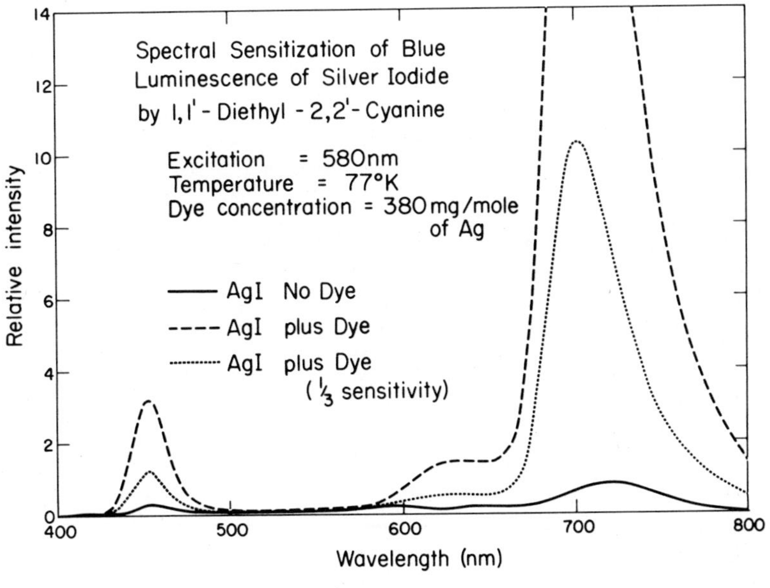

Figure 14

order decay kinetics are shown in Figures 15 and 16. The observed linear dependence of emission on excitation intensity and the observed second order decay characteristics may be explained by an electron-hole recombination process sensitized via a two photon process as suggested by Feofilov and Ovsyankin[13] or by the steps suggested below:

POSSIBLE MECHANISM OF SPECTRALLY SENSITIZED BLUE LUMINESCENCE OF SILVER IODIDE.

1. $\text{Dye} + h\nu \longrightarrow \text{Dye}^*$
2. $\text{Dye}^* + \text{AgI} \longrightarrow \text{Dye}^{\oplus} + \ominus_{\text{conduction band}}$
3. $\text{Dye}^+ + \text{I}_s^- \longrightarrow \text{Dye} + \text{I}_s^o$
4. $\text{I}_s^o + \ominus_{\text{conduction band}} \longrightarrow \text{I}_s^- + h\nu_{455\text{nm}}$

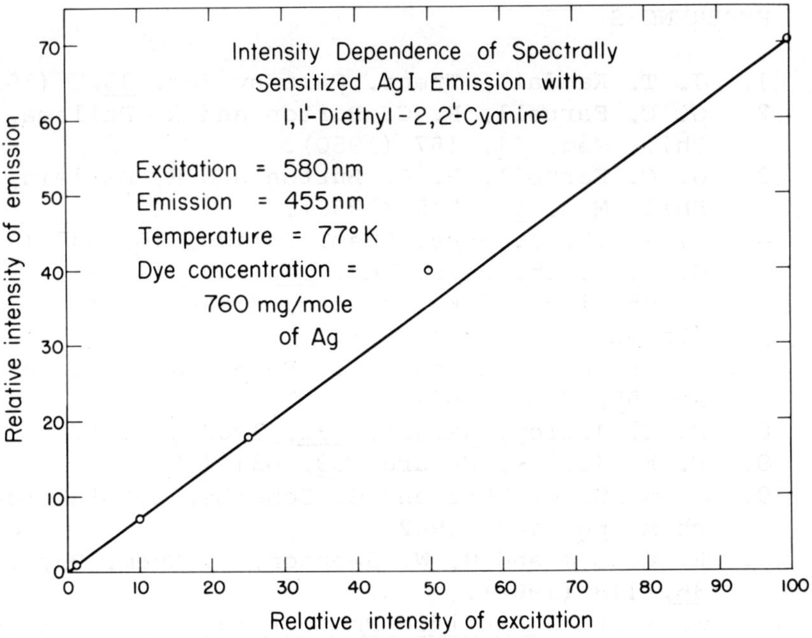

Figure 15

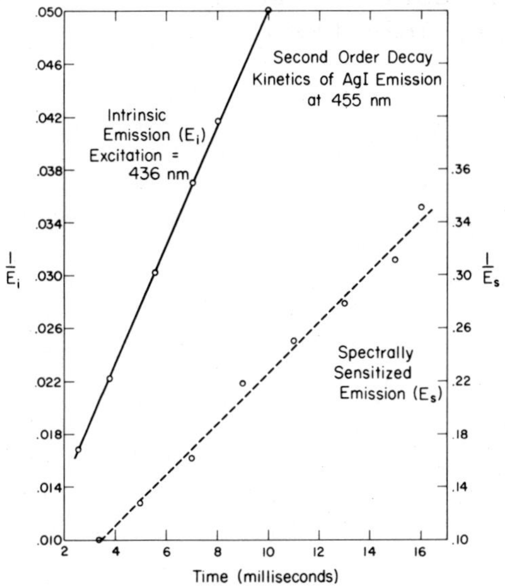

Figure 16

REFERENCES

1. J. T. Randall, Trans. Faraday Soc. 35,2 (1939).
2. G. C. Farnell, P. C. Burton and R. Hallama, Phil. Mag. 41, 157 (1950).
3. G. C. Farnell, P. C. Burton and R. Hallama, Phil. Mag. 41, 545 (1950).
4. K. Vacek, J. Phys. Chem. Solids, 16, 337 (1960).
5. G. C. Smith, Phys. Rev. 140, 221 (1965).
6. S. Sonoike and K. Akimoto, J. Phys. Soc. (Japan) 18, 320 (1963).
7. J. F. Hamilton and B. E. Bayer, J. Opt. Soc. Am. 55, 528 (1965).
8. E. E. Jelley, Nature, 138, 1009 (1936).
9. E. E. Jelley, Nature 139, 631 (1937).
10. J. Kern, F. Dörr and G. Scheibe, Z. Elektrochem. 66, 462 (1962).
11. E. C. Lim and G. W. Swenson, J. Chem. Phys. 36, 118 (1962).
12. W. West, Scientific Photography, H. Sauvenier, Ed. (Macmillan, New York, 1962), Proceedings of the Liege Conference, p. 557.
13. P. P. Feofilov and V. V. Ovsyankin, Appl. Opt. 6, 1828 (1967).

CHEMILUMINESCENCE FROM RADICAL ION RECOMBINATION

Albert Weller*

Max-Planck-Institut für Spektroskopie
Göttingen, Germany

Klaas Zachariasse

Chemisch Laboratorium
der Vrije Universiteit
Amsterdam, Netherlands

INTRODUCTION

Recent fluorescence quenching and fluorescence transformation studies have shown[1] that formation of charge-transfer (CT) complexes in the excited state (exciplex formation) according to

$$ {}^{1}\overset{*}{A} + D \rightarrow {}^{1}(A^{-}D^{+}) \qquad (1a) $$

or

$$ A + {}^{1}\overset{*}{D} \rightarrow {}^{1}(A^{-}D^{+}) \qquad (1d) $$

giving rise to a characteristic broad structureless fluorescence band some 6000 cm^{-1} to the red of the normal emission of the primarily excited species (see bottom part of Fig. 1 and 2) is a phenomenon

*To whom correspondence should be addressed.

which occurs quite generally whenever a suitable electron acceptor, A, and electron donor, D, are combined.

The question, whether the same type of excited CT complexes can also be formed from the (solvated) radical ions A_s^- and D_s^+, has led us to search for chemiluminescent reactions between radical anions of aromatic compounds and Wurster's Blue cations. The latter ones are stable and can easily be obtained through univalent oxidation of tetramethyl-paraphenylenediamine (TMPD).

Flow experiments in which an etheral solution containing radical anions (A_s^-) slowly flowed through a narrow cuvette filled with a powdered mixture of glass (or quartz) and crystalline Wurster's Blue perchlorate were carried out at room temperature as described elsewhere.[2] The chemi-luminescence emitted from the cuvette was measured with the same rapid scanning spectrofluorimeter (5 sec/spectrum) that was used, also, for the fluorescence spectra so that the chemiluminescence could be directly compared with the fluorescence spectra of the parent compounds, A and D, as measured, e.g. after the flow experiment, when the electron transfer reaction

$$A_s^- + D_s^+ \rightarrow A + D \qquad (2)$$

is completed.

The chemiluminescence spectra obtained with the radical anions of the larger aromatic hydrocarbons (like anthracene which as one example of these experiments is listed in Table I) have been shown previously[2] to be identical with the fluorescence spectra of the respective hydrocarbons. No chemiluminescence due to emission from the CT complex could be found in these experiments. At that time it was not quite clear whether the failure to observe CT complex chemiluminescence was due to the low sensitivity of our apparatus in the longwavelength region (around 16,000 cm^{-1})

TABLE I: Energies (in ev) involved in chemiluminescent reactions between radical anions (A^-) and Wurster's Blue cation (D^+). $E(D/D^+) = 0.16$ V (vs. SCE in acetonitrile).

A	$E(D/D^+)-E(A^-/A)$ (in acetonitrile)	Chemiluminescence emitter	$-\Delta F(A_s^-...D_s^+)$	$\Delta E(^3\overset{*}{A})$	$\Delta E(^3\overset{*}{D})$	Excited species produced in the primary process
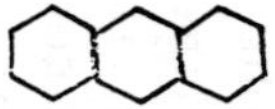	2.12	$^1\overset{*}{A}$	2.32	1.82	2.83	$^3\overset{*}{A}$
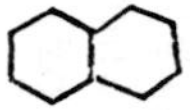	2.72	$^1(A^-D^+)$ $^1\overset{*}{D}$ $^1\overset{*}{A}$	2.92	2.64	2.83	$^3\overset{*}{A}$ $^3\overset{*}{D}$
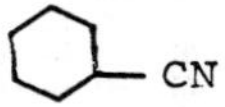	2.50	none	2.70	3.35	2.83	none
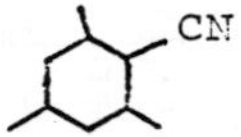	2.74	$^1\overset{*}{D}$	2.94	3.12	2.83	$^3\overset{*}{D}$
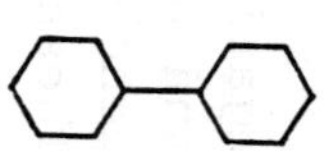	2.81	$(^1(A^-D^+))$ $^1\overset{*}{D}$ $(^1\overset{*}{A})$	3.01	3.01[a]	2.83	$^3\overset{*}{D}$ $(^3\overset{*}{A})$
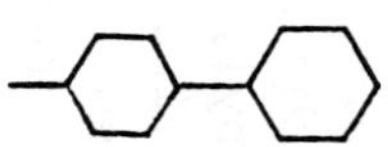	2.87	$^1(A^-D^+)$ $^1\overset{*}{D}$ $^1\overset{*}{A}$	3.07	2.98[a]	2.83	$^3\overset{*}{D}$ $^3\overset{*}{A}$
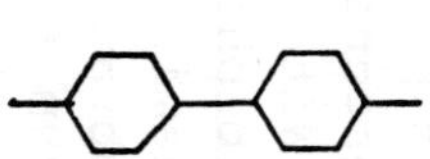	2.93	$^1(A^-D^+)$ $^1\overset{*}{D}$ $^1\overset{*}{A}$	3.13	2.95[a]	2.83	$^3\overset{*}{D}$ $^3\overset{*}{A}$

[a] Energy difference between the presumably planar triplet state and the twisted ground state according to Wagner[4].

where this emission occurs or due to the fact that the excited CT complex was not formed at all in these experiments.

With the aim to decide on this question the chemiluminescence experiments described below have been carried out using smaller aromatic acceptor compounds whose CT complex emission (with TMPD as the donor) occurs around 18,000 cm^{-1}.

RESULTS AND DISCUSSION

Fig. 1 shows the chemiluminescence and fluorescence spectra obtained with naphthalene. Three bands observed in the chemiluminescence spectrum can easily be identified as naphthalene fluorescence ($^1\overset{*}{A}$), TMPD fluorescence ($^1\overset{*}{D}$) and CT complex fluorescence ($^1(A^-D^+)$). The latter two also occur in the fluorescence spectrum of a fairly concentrated solution of naphthalene and TMPD (see bottom part of Fig. 1). The possible occurrence in chemiluminescence experiments of triplet emission as indicated by the dotted curve (phosphorescence spectrum of TMPD) in Fig. 1 has been discussed previously.[2]

No chemiluminescence has been found with benzonitrile negative ion, although a solution containing both, benzonitrile (> 0.01 M) and TMPD shows TMPD as well as CT complex fluorescence.

The chemiluminescence spectrum obtained with 2,4,6-trimethyl-benzonitrile negative ion (cf. Fig. 2) consists only of one band, the fluorescence of TMPD ($^1\overset{*}{D}$), whereas the fluorescence spectrum of a solution of TMPD and 2,4,6-trimethyl-benzonitrile (bottom part of Fig. 2) also shows CT complex fluorescence.

With the negative ions of biphenyl, p-methylbiphenyl, and bitolyl (p,p'-dimethylbiphenyl) the chemiluminescence spectra shown in Fig. 3 have been obtained. These consist of three bands with the TMPD fluorescence ($^1\overset{*}{D}$) being the most prominent.

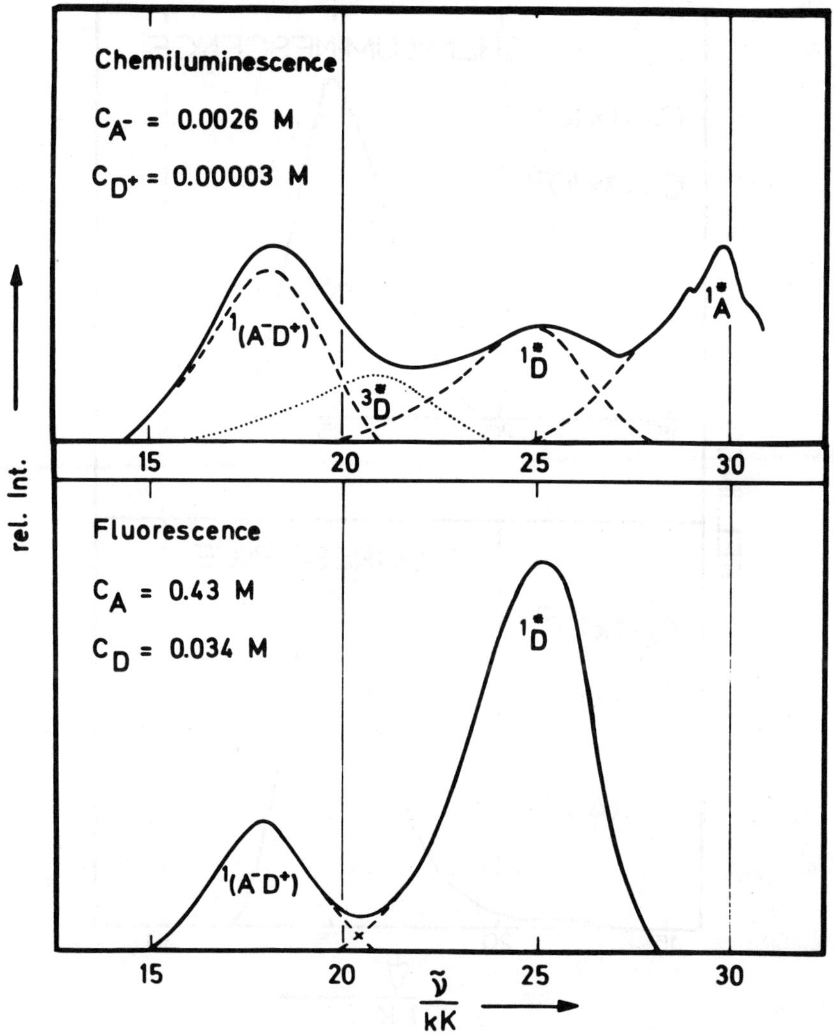

Figure 1 Chemiluminescence spectrum obtained in flow experiment with naphthalene anion (A^-) and Wurster's Blue (D^+) perchlorate in dimethoxyethane at room temperature and fluorescence spectrum of tetramethyl-p-phenylenediamine plus naphthalene in dimethoxyethane at room temperature, excited with λ = 365 nm.

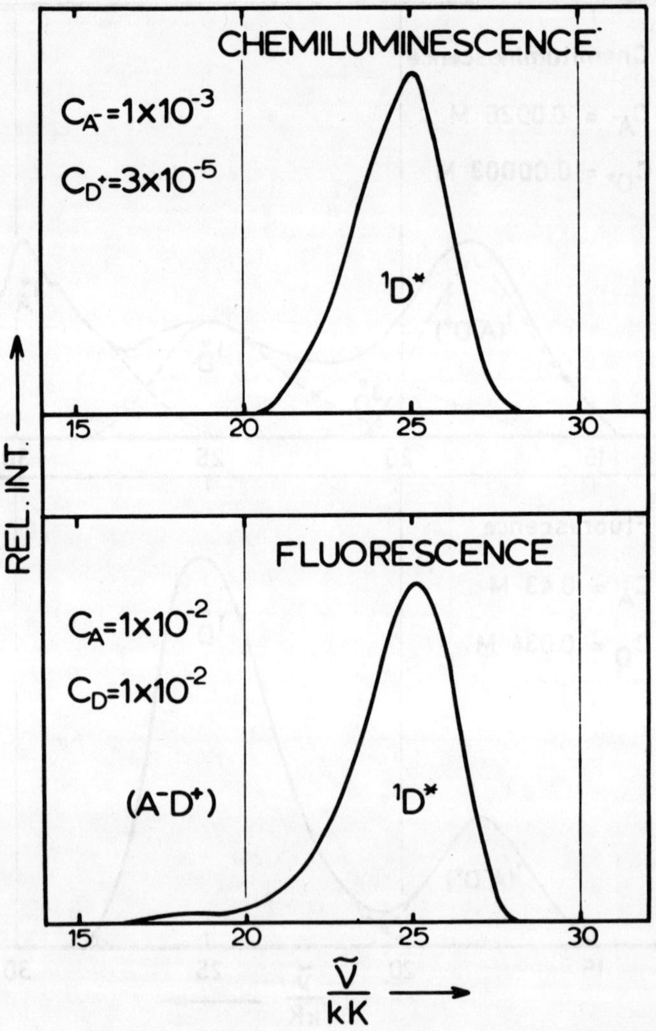

Figure 2 Chemiluminescence spectrum obtained in flow experiment with 2,4,6-trimethylbenzonitrile anion (A^-) and Wurster's Blue (D^+) perchlorate in dimethoxyethane at room temperature and fluorescence spectrum of tetramethyl-p-phenylenediamine plus 2,4,6-trimethylbenzonitrile in dimethoxyethane at room temperature, excited with λ = 313 nm.

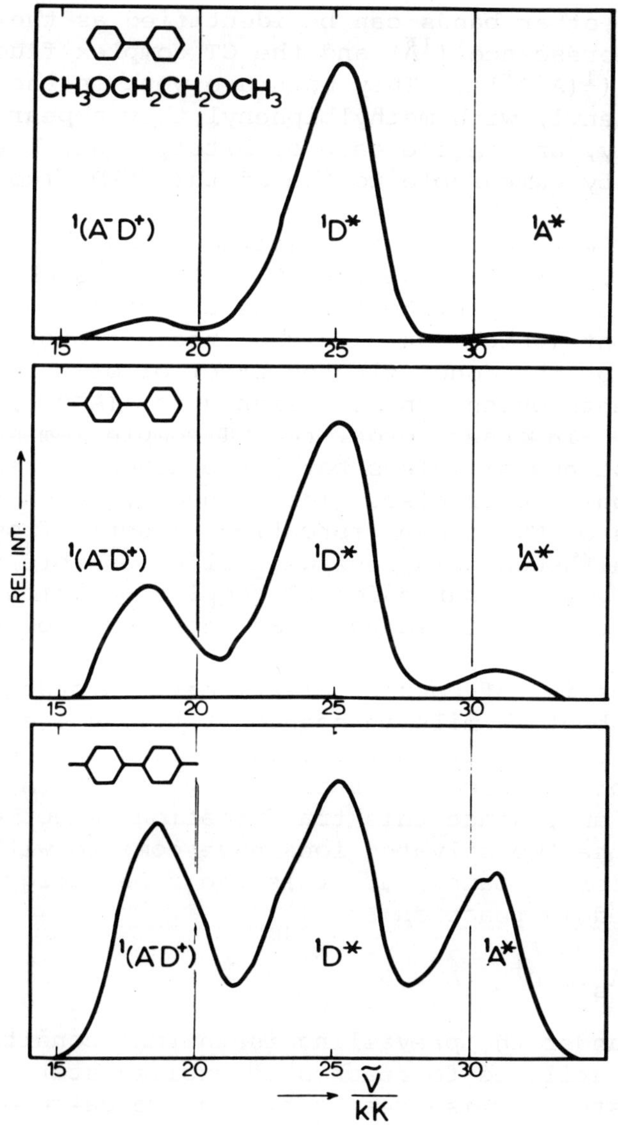

Figure 3 Chemiluminescence spectra obtained in flow experiments with negative ions of biphenyl, p-methylbiphenyl, p,p'-dimethylbiphenyl and Wurster's Blue perchlorate in dimethoxyethane at room temperature.

The two other bands can be identified as the acceptor fluorescence ($^1\overset{*}{A}$) and the CT complex fluorescence ($^1(A^-D^+)$). They both are weak in the case of biphenyl, with methylbiphenyl they appear more strongly, and in the case of bitolyl they have an intensity comparable to the of the TMPD fluorescence.

The results are summarized in column 3 of Table I. It is evident that if there is chemiluminescence its spectrum consists either of one single component (which can be either the acceptor fluorescence or the donor fluorescence) or of three components which can be assigned to $^1(A^-D^+)$, $^1\overset{*}{D}$, and $^1\overset{*}{A}$. In other words, the CT complex emission does not appear unless both, the donor and acceptor emissions appear also. This, indeed, makes the process of CT complex formation directly from the ions, although being energetically possible,[3] very unlikely as a source for CT complex emission observed in chemiluminescence. So there must be another way.

It is, of course, clear that, in order to bring about chemiluminescence at all, the energy stored chemically in the radical ions must be transformed into excitation energy of the A,D system and, since this tranformation cannot occur until the two solvated ions have come to within encounter distance, a, it is the free energy involved in reaction (3)

$$A_s^- \ldots D_s^+ \rightleftarrows A \ldots D \qquad (3)$$

which under the prevailing isothermal conditions can be utilized to reach some excited state of the A,D system. This free energy can be calculated according to

$$-\Delta F(A_s^- \ldots D_s^+) = E(D/D^+) - E(A^-/A) + \Delta\Delta F(\mathrm{solv}) - (e_o^2/\varepsilon a) \qquad (4)$$

from the redox potentials of the D/D^+ and A^-/A couples which have been measured in acetonitrile (cf. column 2 of Table I). The difference of the free solvation energies in acetonitrile ($\varepsilon = 37.5$) and dimethoxyethane ($\varepsilon = 6.8$) can be calculated with the aid of Born's equation:

$$\Delta\Delta F(\text{solv}) = \frac{e_o^2}{2}\left(\frac{1}{r_+} + \frac{1}{r_-}\right)\left(\frac{1}{6.8} - \frac{1}{37.5}\right) \qquad (5)$$

which gives with $r_+ \approx r_- = 3.1 \pm 0.4$ Å

$$\Delta\Delta F(\text{solv}) = 0.56 \pm 0.06 \text{ ev}$$

For the last term in equation (4) one obtains with the encounter distance $\alpha = 6 \pm 1$ Å

$$(e_o^2/6.8a) = 0.36 \pm 0.06 \text{ ev}$$

The energy values thus calculated and listed in column 4 of Table I are throughout considerably smaller than the singlet excitation energies of the acceptor and donor molecules involved. However, with respect to the triplet excitation energies $E(^3\overset{*}{A})$ and $E(^3\overset{*}{D})$ one finds that whenever it is energetically possible in the electron transfer process between the radical ions to produce A and/or D in their triplet states (cf. last column of Table I) the corresponding molecular fluorescencies, evidently brought about by triplet-triplet annihilation, appear in chemiluminescence. The simultaneous occurrence of CT complex fluorescence in the chemiluminescence experiments with naphthalene and the biphenyls can now be rationalized in terms of a mixed triplet-triplet annihilation process

$$^3\overset{*}{A} + {}^3\overset{*}{D} \rightarrow {}^1(A^-D^+) \qquad (6)$$

This interpretation of the experimental results implies that electron transfer between the radical ions to produce molecules in their triplet and/or ground states can and, evidently, does occur without intermediate formation of a CT complex and at a center to center distance which is larger than that for triplet energy transfer because otherwise only the lowest triplet state would result in the case of naphthalene and the biphenyls.

ACKNOWLEDGEMENT

This work, supported by the Netherlands Organization for the Advancement of Pure Research (Z.W.O), was carried out under the auspices of the Netherlands Foundation for Chemical Research (S.O.N.).

REFERENCES

1. See paper of H. Beens and A. Weller (this volume p. 203) and literature cited therein.
2. A. Weller and K. Zachariasse, J. Chem. Phys. 46, 4984 (1967).
3. H. Knibbe, D. Rehm, and A. Weller, Ber. Bunsenges. Phys. Chem. 72, 257 (1968).
4. P. J. Wagner, J. A. C. S. 89, 2820 (1967).

REFERENCES

1. See paper of D. Rehm and A. Weller (this volume p. 205) and literature cited therein.
2. A. Weller and K. Zachariasse, J. Chem. Phys. 46, 4984 (1967).
3. H. Knibbe, D. Rehm, and A. Weller, Ber. Bunsenges. Physik. Chem. 72, 257 (1968).
4. P. J. Wagner, J. A. C. S. 89, 2820 (1967).

NOMENCLATURE

The following definitions, suggested by J. B. Birks, were accepted unanimously by the conference members.

An EXCIPLEX is an electronically excited atomic or molecular complex of definite stoichiometry, which is dissociated in its electronic ground state.

This definition includes the entities described previously as

- <u>exciplexes</u> (Lumry, Birks)
- <u>mixed excimers</u> (Birks, Hochstrasser, Ferguson)
- <u>heteropolar excimers</u> and <u>hetero-excimers</u> (Mataga)
- <u>intramolecular mixed excimers</u> (Hirayama, Eisinger)

It does not include excited molecules which interact with an unspecified number of solvent molecules (Eisinger). An exciplex may or may not be luminescent.

An EXCIMER is an exciplex between identical atoms or molecules.

AUTHOR INDEX